MACHINE DEVICES AND INSTRUMENTATION

Mechanical
Electromechanical
Hydraulic
Thermal
Pneumatic
Pyrotechnic
Photoelectric
Optical

Edited by
NICHOLAS P. CHIRONIS

ASSOCIATE EDITOR, *Product Engineering*

McGRAW-HILL BOOK COMPANY
New York   San Francisco   Toronto   London   Sydney

MACHINE DEVICES AND INSTRUMENTATION

10785

234567890HD721069876

PREFACE

This book is a unique compilation of mechanical, electrical, hydraulic, pneumatic, optical, thermal, and photoelectric devices and arrangements for providing a wide variety of functions and motions in automatic machines and instruments.

Modern systems no longer rely entirely on ingenious mechanisms to perform a job. Such mechanisms are frequently too slow and bulky, and not sufficiently precise. But when they are teamed up with new-generation gadgetry, such as transducers, sensors, potentiometers, limit switches, magnetic devices, counters, automatic control clutches, and vacuum pickups, they can perform jobs that were unheard of not too many years ago.

Thus, the book is chock-full of illustrations and clear-cut descriptions showing how to arrange such systems and components for

Feeding	Reciprocating	Flow controlling
Sorting	Chucking	Automatic stopping
Transporting	Clamping	Speed varying
Actuating	Vending	Speed measuring
Flipping	Measuring	Acceleration measuring
Tensioning	Metering	Pumping
Counting	Timing	Switching
Indexing	Force amplifying	Film advancing

The book also contains a section on modern linkage-design techniques with many time-saving charts and formulas for the design of slider cranks, power linkages, power cams, snap-action toggles, gear mechanisms, geneva mechanisms, cardioid drives, and others.

This wealth of material has been drawn largely from *Product Engineering* and has been thoroughly compiled and indexed for speedy location of items by type or application.

Nicholas P. Chironis

CONTENTS

1
FEEDING, SORTING, AND TRANSPORTING MECHANISMS

Your latest group of mechanisms to
Sort, feed, or weigh

Sooner or later, you may be faced with the need
to design such devices for your plant. These 19
selections are easily modified to suit your product

NICHOLAS P. CHIRONIS, Associate Editor

ORIENTING DEVICES

Orienting short, tubular parts

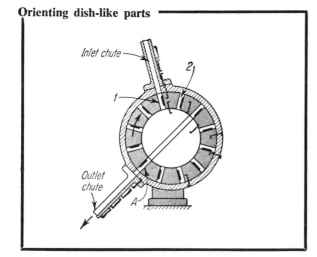

Here's a common problem: Parts come in either open-end or closed-end first; you need a device which will orient all the parts so they feed out facing the same way. In (A), when a part comes in open-end first, it is pivoted by the swinging lever so that the open end is up. When it comes in closed-end first, the part brushes away the lever to keel over head-first. Fig B and C show a simpler arrangement with pin in place of lever.

Orienting dish-like parts

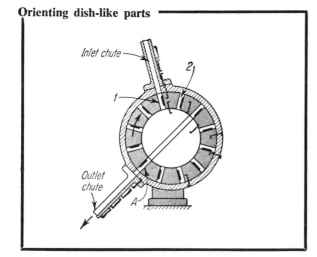

Orienting pointed-end parts

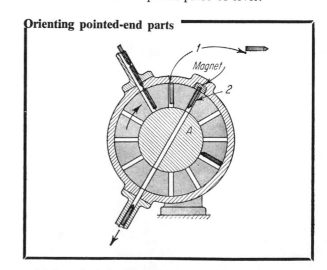

Part with open-end facing to the right (part 1) falls on to a matching projection as the indexing wheel begins to rotate clockwise. The projection retains the part for 230 deg to point *A* where it falls away from the projection to slide down the outlet chute, open-end up. An incoming part facing the other way (2) is not retained by the projection, hence slides *through* the indexing wheel so that it, too, passes through the outlet with the open-end up.

Main principle here is that the built-in magnet cannot hold on to a part as it passes by if the part has its pointed end facing the magnet. Such a correctly oriented part (part 1) will fall through the chute as the wheel indexes to a stop. An incorrectly oriented part (part 2) is briefly held by the magnet until the indexing wheel continues on past the magnet position. The wheel and the core with the slot must be made of nonmagnetic material.

Orienting U-shaped parts

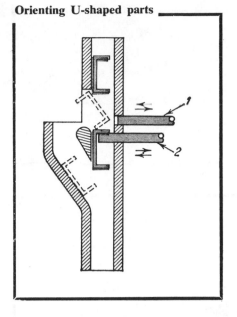

Key to this device is two pins which reciprocate one after another in the horizontal direction. The parts come down the chute with the bottom of the U facing either to the right or left. All pieces first strike and rest on pin 2. Pin 1 now moves into the passage way, and if the bottom of the U is facing to the right, the pin would kick over the part as shown by the dotted lines. If on the other hand the bottom of the U had been to the left, motion of pin 1 would have no effect, and as pin 2 withdrew to the right, the part would be allowed to pass down through the main chute.

Orienting cone-shaped parts

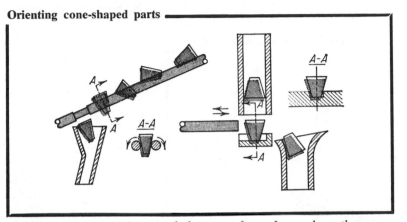

Regardless of which end of the cone faces forward as the cones slide down the cylindrical rods, the fact that both rods rotate in opposite directions causes the cones to assume the position shown in section A-A (left). When the cones reach the thinned-down section of the rods, they fall down into the chute as illustrated.

In the second method of orienting cone-shaped parts (right), if the part comes down small end first, it will fit into the recess. The reciprocating rod, moving to the right, will then kick the cone over into the exit chute. But if the cone comes down with its large end first, it sits on top of the plate (instead of inside the recess), and the rod merely pushes it into the chute without turning it over.

Orienting stepped-disk parts

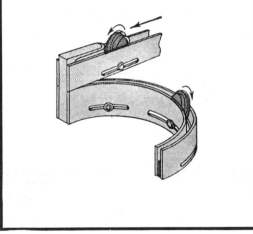

Parts rolling down the top rail to the left drop to the next rail which has a circular segment. The parts, therefore, continue to roll on in the original direction but their faces have now been rotated 180 deg. The idea of dropping one level may seem over simplified, but it avoids the use of camming devices which is the more common way of accomplishing this job.

SIMPLE FEEDING DEVICES

Feeding a fixed number of parts

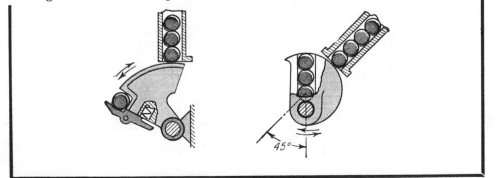

The oscillating sector picks up the desired number of parts, left diagram, and feeds them by pivoting the required number of degrees. The device for oscillating the sector must be able to produce dwells at both ends of the stroke to allow sufficient time for the parts to fall in and out of the sector.

The circular parts feed down the chute by gravity, and are separated by the reciprocating rod. The parts first roll to station 3 during the downward stroke of the reciprocator, then to station 1 during the upward stroke; hence the time span between parts is almost equivalent to the time it takes for the reciprocator to make one complete oscillation.

The device in (B) is similar to the one in (A), except that the reciprocator is replaced by an oscillating member.

One-by-one separating device

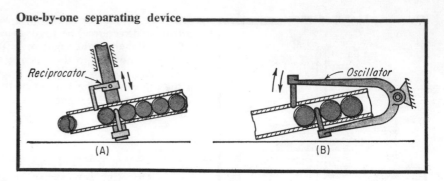

(A)   (B)

Mixing different parts together

Two counter rotating wheels form a simple device for alternating the feed of two different workpieces.

Pausing until actuated

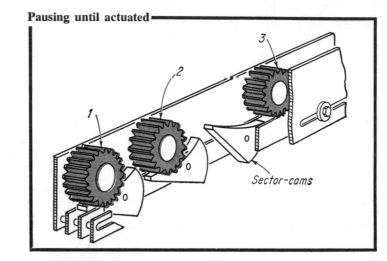

Each gear in this device is held up by a pivotable cam sector until the gear ahead of it moves forward. Thus, gear 3, rolling down the chute, kicks down its sector cam but is held up by the previous cam. When gear 1 is picked off (either manually, or mechanically), its sector cam pivots clockwise because of its own weight. This permits gear 2 to move into the place of gear 1—and frees cam 2 to pivot clockwise. Thus, all gears in the row move forward one station.

SORTING DEVICES

In the simple device (A) the balls run down two inclined and slightly divergent rails. The smallest balls, therefore, will fall into the left chamber, the medium-size ones into the middle-size chamber, and the largest ones into the right chamber.

In the more complicated arrangement (B) the balls come down the hopper and must pass a gate which also acts as a latch for the trapdoor. The proper-size balls pass through without touching (actuating) the gate. Larger balls, however, brush against the gate which releases the catch on the bottom of the trapdoor, and fall through into the special trough for the rejects.

Sorting balls according to size

(A)   (B)

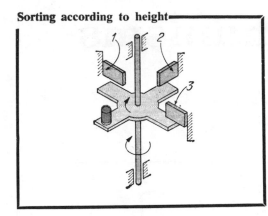

This is a simple device in which an assembly worker can place the workpiece on a slowly rotating cross-platform. Bars 1, 2, and 3 have been set at decreasing heights beginning with the highest bar (bar 1), and the lowest bar (bar 3). The workpiece is therefore knocked off the platform at either station 1, 2, or 3 depending on its height.

WEIGHT-REGULATING ARRANGEMENTS

By varying the vibration amplitudes

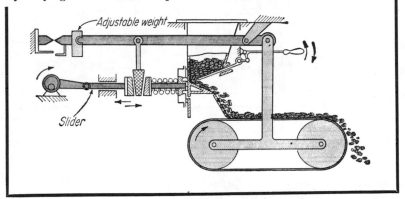

The material in the hopper is fed to a conveyor by means of vibration actuated by the reciprocating slider. The pulsating force of the slider passes through the rubber wedge and on to the actuating rod. The amplitude of this force can be varied by moving the wedge up or down. This is done automatically by making the conveyor pivot around a central point. As the conveyor becomes overloaded, it pivots clockwise to raise the wedge which reduces the amplitudes—and the feed rate of the material.

Further adjustments in feed rate can be made by shifting the adjustable weight or by changing the speed of the conveyor belt.

By linkage arrangement

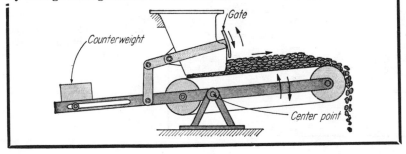

The loose material comes down the hopper and is fed to the right by the conveyor system which can pivot about the center point. The frame of the conveyor system also actuates the hopper gate, so that if the material on the belt exceeds the required amount the conveyor pivots clockwise and closes the gate. The position of the counterweight on a frame determines the feed rate of the system.

By electric-eye and balancer

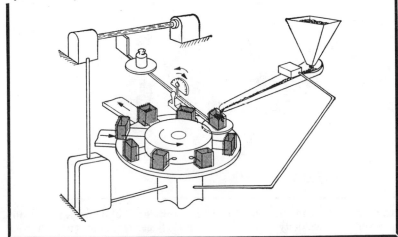

The indexing table automatically comes to a stop at the feed station. As the material drops into the container, its weight pivots the screen upward to cut off the operation of the photocell relay. This in turn shuts the feed gate. Reactuation of the indexing table can be automatic after a time interval, or by the cutoff phase of the electric eye.

EDITOR'S NOTE: The above material is based on the book *"Mechanism,"* by C. H. Kohevnikov, published in Russian, Moscow, 1965. For other foreign mechanisms, see the book **Mechanisms, Linkages and Mechanical Controls**, McGraw-Hill Book Co, 1965; $9.75

More selections of
Machinery mechanisms

Clamping and cutting device

Pressing the foot pedal of this ingenious device down causes the top knife and the clamp to move downward. However, when the clamp presses on to the material it (and link *EDO*) will not be able to move any further, Link *AC* will now begin to pivot around point *B*. This draws up the lower knife to begin the cutting action.

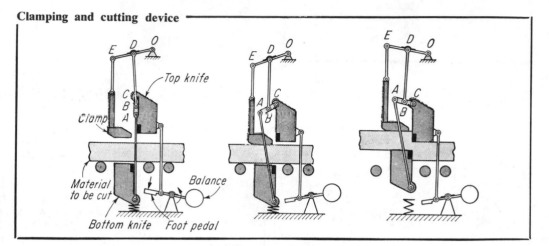

Four-bar cutter devices

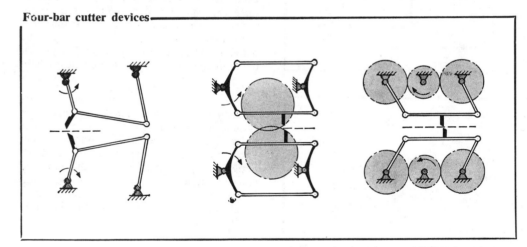

These three arrangements provide a very stable, strong cutting action by coupling two sets of links to obtain a four-bar arrangement.

Parallel cutter mechanisms

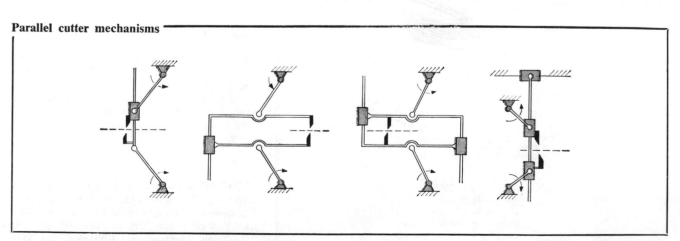

The cutting edges of the knives in the four arrangements move parallel to each other, and also remain vertical at all times to cut the material while the material is in motion. The two cranks are rotated with constant velocity by means of a 1:1 gear system (not shown) which also feeds the material through the mechanism.

Curved-motion cutter

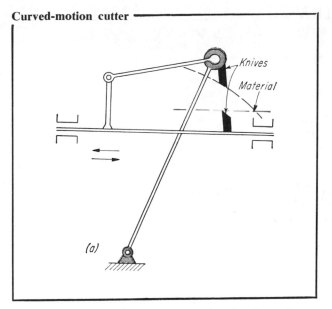

(a)

The material is cut while in motion by the reciprocating action of the horizontal bar. As the bar with the bottom knife moves to the right, the top knife will arc downward to perform the cutting operation.

Vertical cutter motion

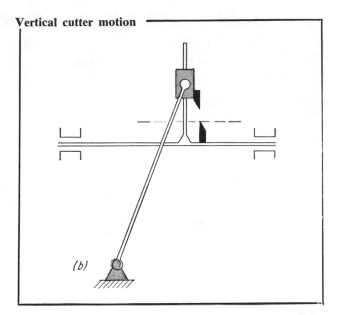

(b)

The top knife in this arrangement remains parallel to the bottom knife at all times during cutting to provide a true scissor-like action, but friction in the sliding member can limit the cutting force.

Slicing mechanism

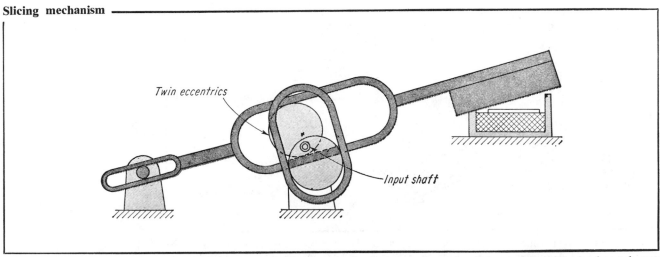

Slicing motion is obtained from the synchronized effort of two eccentric disks. The two looped rings actuated by the disks are welded together. In the position shown, the bottom eccentric disk provides the horizontal cutting movement and the top disk the up-and-down force necessary for the cutting.

Web-cutting mechanism

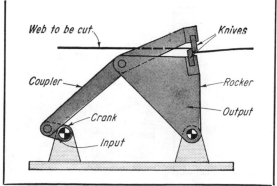

This four-bar linkage with an extended coupler can cut a web on the run at high speeds. The four-bar linkage is proportioned to provide a knife velocity during the cutting operation equal to the linear velocity of the web.

The mechanism can turn over a flat piece by driving two four-bar linkages from one double crank. The two flippers are actually extensions of the fourth members of the four-bar linkages. Link proportions are selected so that both flippers come up the same time to meet at a line slightly off the vertical to transfer the piece from one flipper to the other by the momentum of the piece.

Turn over device

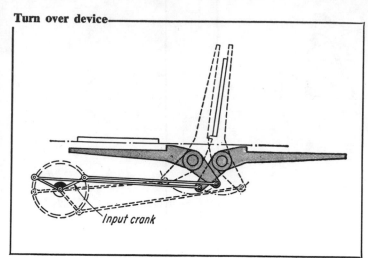

Input crank

Upside-down flipper

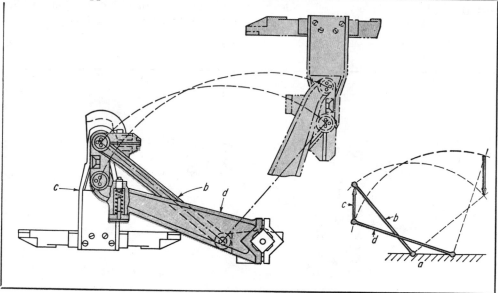

This is actually a four-bar linkage (links *a, b, c, d*) in which the part that is to be turned over is the coupler *c* of the linkage. For the proportions shown, the 180-deg rotation of link *c* is accomplished during 90-deg rotation of the input link.

SPECIAL-FUNCTION DEVICES

Vibrating mechanism

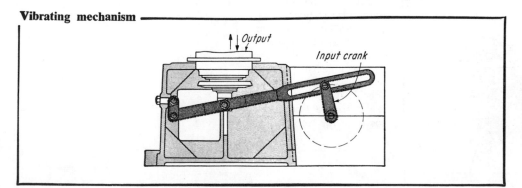

Output

Input crank

As the input crank rotates, the slotted link, which is fastened to the frame with the aid of an intermediate link, oscillates to vibrate the output table up and down.

Computing mechanism for sine function

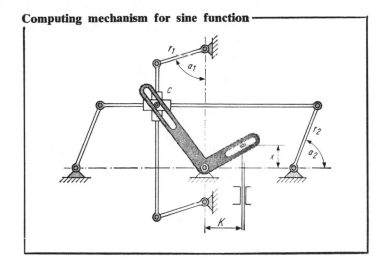

This device makes use of two four-bar linkages which restrain a block but permit it to slide along the linkage rods. The block causes the L shaped link to pivot which, in turn, raises or lowers the vertical rod. For any desired input rotation of a_1, and a_2, the device will solve the equation

$$x = K \frac{\sin a_1}{\sin a_2}$$

where K is a constant put into the device by locating the output rod an appropriate distance.

Grinding wheel dresser

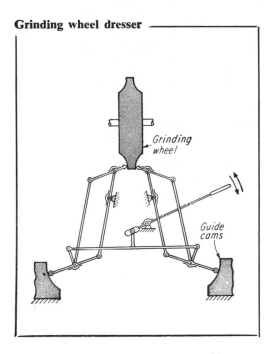

Two pantographs follow fixed guide cams to produce the desired curves at the dressing wheel. The cams are easily changed to produce different contours.

Walking-link drive

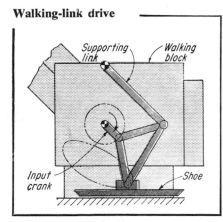

This is actually a four-bar linkage with a triangular extension which supports a shoe which can pivot. The crank and supporting link are connected to a block which is moved forward by the linkage. The drive motor can be inside the block and powered by flexible cables. Used in earth-moving equipment.

If you want to design a fork truck or tractor that won't bog down in soft earth, or new vehicle to explore the moon, take a look at an old idea: walking plates.

In England, Lansing Bagnall, Ltd has just designed and patented what it claims is the first application of this type of mechanism to a moving vehicle. In this case, the vehicle is a fork lift truck. The mechanism (see diagrams) consists of a pair of plates mounted between the front and rear wheels of a truck. The plates, attached to a crankpin, are mounted so that normally they do not interfere with operation of the wheels. But, when they are brought into play, they can be pushed down so the wheels are lifted from the ground and a walking motion is created. They can also be used to assist the wheels when needed, since power can be applied to either system, or to both.

In the US, one of the latest systems for lunar locomotion, proposed by J. D. Mc-Kenney of Space-General Corp at the last ARS meeting, is a remarkably similar arrangment, the plates in this case being attached to jointed legs (see sketch).

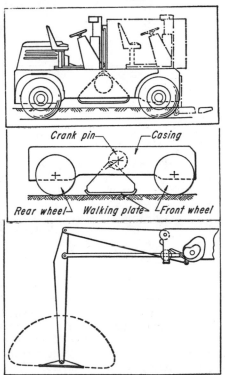

THE appeal of cycloidal mechanisms is that they can easily be tailored to provide one of these three common motion requirements:

- **Intermittent motion**—with either short or long dwells
- **Rotary motion with progressive oscillation**—where the output undergoes a cycloidal motion during which the forward motion is greater than the return motion
- **Rotary-to-linear motion with a dwell period**

All the cycloidal mechanisms covered in this article are geared; this results in compact positive devices capable of operating at relatively high speeds with little backlash or "slop." The mechanisms can also be classified into three groups:

Hypocycloid—where the points tracing the cycloidal curves are located on an external gear rolling inside an internal ring gear. This ring gear is usually stationary and fixed to the frame.

Epicycloid—where the tracing points are on an external gear which rolls in another external (stationary) gear

Pericycloid—where the tracing points are located on an internal gear which rolls on a stationary external gear.

Basic hypocycloid curves

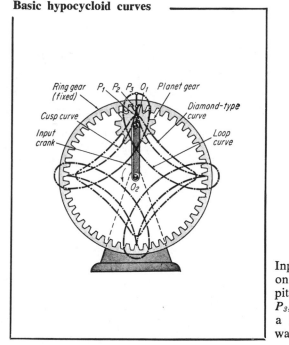

Double-dwell mechanism

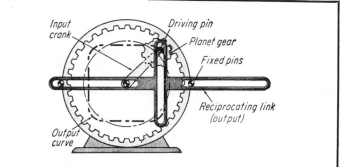

Coupling the output pin to a slotted member produces a prolonged dwell in each of the extreme positions. This is another application of the diamond-type hypocycloidal curve.

Input drives a planet in mesh with a stationary ring gear. Point P_1 on the planet gear describes a diamond-shape curve, point P_2 on the pitch line of the planet describes the familiar cusp curve, and point P_3, which is on an extension rod fixed to the planet gear, describes a loop-type curve. In one application, an end miller located at P_1 was employed in production for machining a diamond-shape profile.

Long-dwell geneva drive

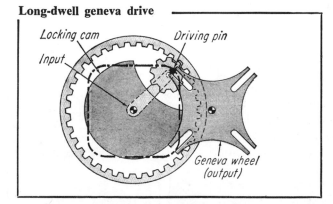

As with standard four-station genevas, each rotation of the input indexes the slotted geneva 90 deg. By employing a pin fastened to the planet gear to obtain a rectangular-shape cycloidal curve, a smoother indexing motion is obtained because the driving pin moves on a noncircular path.

Internal-geneva drive

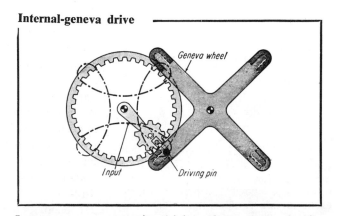

Loop-type curve permits driving pin to enter slot in a direction that is radially outward from the center, and then loop over to rapidly index the cross member. As with the previous geneva, the output rotates 90 deg, then goes into a long dwell period during each 270-deg rotation of the input.

Cycloidal motion is becoming popular for mechanisms in feeders and automatic machines.

Cycloidal parallelogram

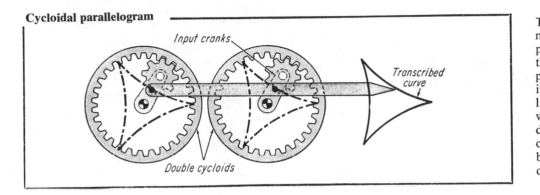

Input cranks

Transcribed curve

Double cycloids

Two identical hypocycloid mechanisms guide the point of the bar along the triangularly shaped path. They are useful also in cases where there is limited space in the area where the curve must be described. Such double-cycloid mechanisms can be designed to produce other types of curves.

Short-dwell rotary

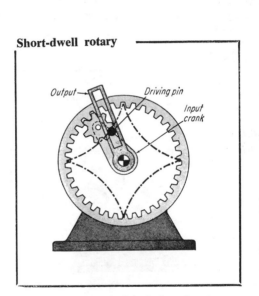

Output *Driving pin*

Input crank

Here the pitch circle of the planet gear is exactly one-quarter that of the ring gear. A pin on the planet will cause the slotted output member to have four instantaneous dwells for each revolution of the input shaft.

Cycloidal rocker

P''' *P*

Input crank

Approximately an arc of a circle

P'' *P'*

Rocker (output)

Rocker displacement, deg

90   180   270   360

Dwell period

P   P'   P''   P'''   P

Input rotation, deg

The curvature of the cusp is approximately that of an arc of a circle. Hence the rocker comes to a long dwell at the right extreme position while point P moves to P'. There is then a quick return from P' to P'', with a momentary dwell at the end of this phase. The rocker then undergoes a slight oscillation from point P'' to P''', as shown in the displacement diagram.

Rectangular-motion drive

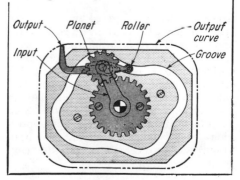

Output *Planet* *Roller* *Output curve*

Input *Groove*

For producing closed curves consisting of several sections of straight lines. Rectangular-shaped curve is shown, but the device is capable of producing many sided curves. The output member is eccentrically mounted on a planet gear and simultaneously guided by the roller which runs in a stationary cam groove.

PREBEN W. JENSEN, Mechanism Consultant

Cycloidal reciprocator

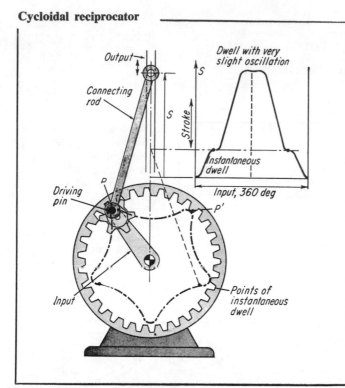

Portion of curve, *P-P'*, produces the long dwell (as in previous mechanism), but the five-lobe cycloidal curve avoids a marked oscillation at the end of the stroke. There are also two points of instantaneous dwell where the curve is perpendicular to the connecting rod.

By making the pitch diameter of the planet equal to half that of the ring gear, every point on the planet gear (such as points P_2 and P_3) will describe elliptical curves which get flatter as the points are selected closer to the pitch circle. Point P_1, at the center of the planet, describes a circle; point P_4 at the pitch circle describes a straight line. When a cutting tool is placed at P_3, it will cut almost-flat sections from round stock, as when machining a bolt. The other two sides of the bolt can be cut by rotating the bolt, or the cutting device, 90 deg. (Reference: H. Zeile, *Unrund- und Mehrkantdrehen*, VDI-Berichte, Nr. 77, 1965.)

Adjustable harmonic drive

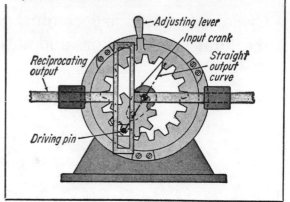

By making the planet-gear half that of the internal gear, a straight-line output curve is produced by the driving pin which is fastened to the planet gear. The pin engages the slotted member to cause the output to reciprocate back and forth with harmonic (sinusoidal) motion. The position of the fixed ring gear can be changed by adjusting the lever, which in turn rotates the straight-line output-curve. When the curve is horizontal, the stroke is at a maximum; when the curve is vertical, the stroke is zero.

Elliptical-motion drive

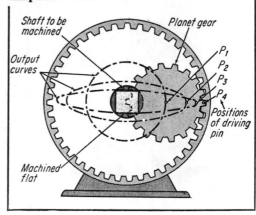

EPICYCLOID MECHANISMS

Epicycloid reciprocator

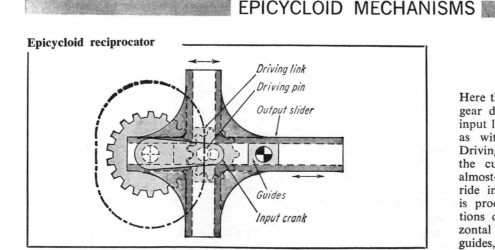

Here the sun gear is fixed and the planet gear driven around it by means of the input link. There is no internal ring gear as with the hypocycloid mechanisms. Driving pin *P* on the planet describes the curve shown which contains two almost-flat portions. By having the pin ride in the slotted yoke, a short dwell is produced at both the extreme positions of the output member. The horizontal slots in the yoke ride the end-guides, as shown.

Progressive oscillating drive

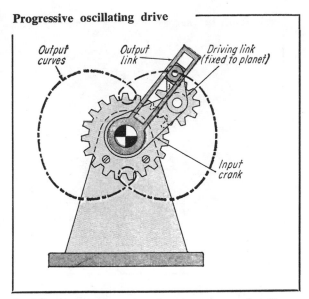

By fixing a crank to the planet gear, a point *P* can be made to describe the double loop curve illustrated. The slotted output crank oscillates briefly at the vertical portions.

Parallel-guidance mechanisms

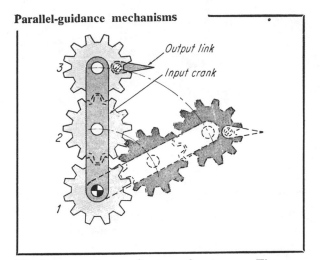

The input crank contains two planet gears. The center sun-gear is fixed as in the previous epicycloid mechanisms. By making the three gears equal in diameter and having gear *2* serve as an idler, any member fixed to gear *3* will remain parallel to its previous positions throughout the rotation of the input ring crank.

INTERMITTENT-MOTION MECHANISMS

Dual-track geneva

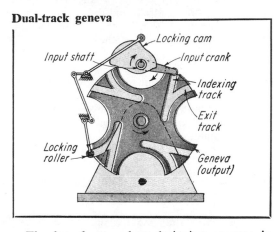

The key factor when designing genevas is to have the input roller enter and leave the geneva slots tangentially (as the crank rapidly indexes the output). This is accomplished in the novel device above by employing two tracks. The roller enters one track, indexes the geneva 90 deg (in a four-stage geneva), and then automatically follows the exit slot to leave the geneva. (Make a model to see how nicely it indexes.)

Purpose of the associate linkage mechanism is to lock the geneva when it is not indexing. In the position shown, the locking roller is just about to exit from the geneva.

The output in this simple device is prevented from turning in either direction—unless actuated by the input motion. In operation, the drive lever indexes the output disk by bearing on the pin. The escapement is cammed out of the way during indexing because the slot in the input disk is in the position to permit the escapement tip to enter into it. But as the lever leaves the pin, the input disk forces the escapement tip out of its slot and into the notch to lock output in both directions.

Internal-groove geneva

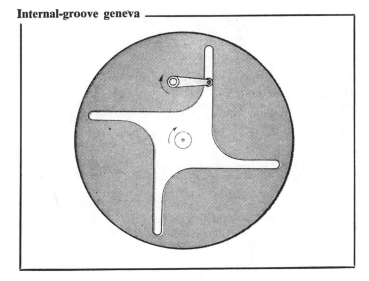

This arrangement again permits the roller to exit and enter the driving slots tangentially. In the position shown, the driving roller has just completed indexing the geneva and is about to coast for 90 deg as it goes around the curve. (During this time a separate locking device may be necessary to prevent an external torque from reversing the geneva.)

Controlled-output escapement

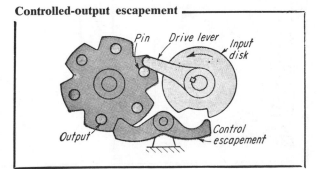

Oscillating-output geneva

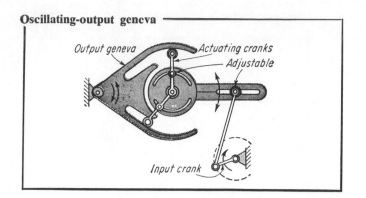

Three adjustable output-links provide a wide variety of oscillating motions. The input crank oscillates the central member which has an adjustable slot to vary the stroke. The oscillation is transferred to the two actuating rollers, which alternately enter the geneva slots to index it, first in one direction and then another. Additional variation in output motion can be obtained by adjusting the angular positions of the output cranks.

Plunger-actuated indexer

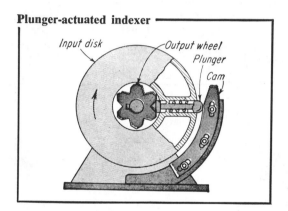

Single tooth indexer

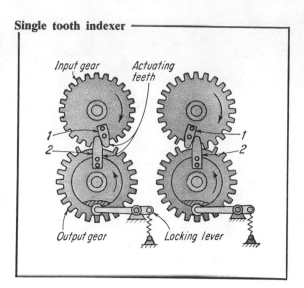

Key factor in this device is the use of an input gear which is smaller than the output gear—hence it can complete its circuit faster than the output when both are in mesh. In the left diagram, the actuating tooth of the input, tooth 1, strikes that of the output, tooth 2, to roll both gears into mesh. After one circuit of the input (right diagram), tooth 1 is now ahead of tooth 2, the gears go out of mesh, and the output comes to a stop (kept in position by the bottom locking detent) for almost 360 deg of the input.

Here the output rotates only when the plunger, which is normally kept in the outer position by means of its spring, is cammed into the toothed wheel attached to the output. Hence, for every revolution of the input disk, the output is driven approximately 60 deg, and then comes to a stop for the remaining 300 deg.

ROTARY TO RECIPROCATING DEVICES

Track-switching scotch yoke

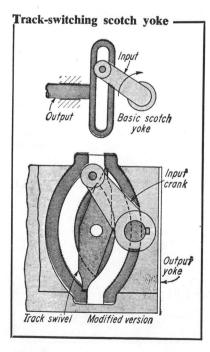

In a typical scotch yoke, the motion of the rotating input crank is translated into the reciprocating motion of the yoke. But this provides only an instantaneous dwell at each end. To obtain sought for long dwells, the left slot (in the modified version) is made curved with a radius equal to that of the input crank radius. This causes a 90-deg dwell at the left end of the stroke. For the right end, the crank pushes aside the springloaded track swivel as it comes around the bend and is shunted into the second track to provide also a 90-deg dwell at the right end.

In-line reciprocator

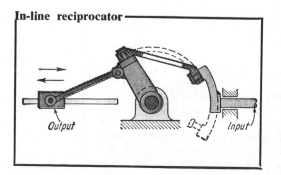

This is a simple way of converting rotary motion to reciprocating motion in which both input and output shafts are in line with each other. The right half of the device is the well known three-dimensional reciprocator. Rotating the input crank causes its link to oscillate. A second, connecting link then converts it into the desired in-line motion.

VARYING-SPEED DEVICES

Elliptical-gear planetary

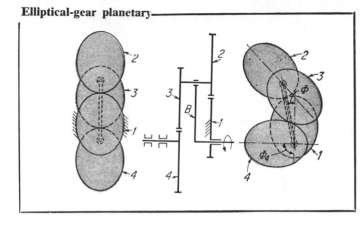

By employing elliptical gears instead of the usual circular gears, a planetary drive is obtained which can provide extra-large variations in the angular speed output.

This is a normal parallel-gear speed reducer, but with cam actuation to provide a desired variation in the output speed. If the center of the idler shaft were stationary, the output motion would be uniform, but the cam attached to the idler shaft gives the shaft an oscillating motion which varies the final output motion.

Cammed-gear speed variator

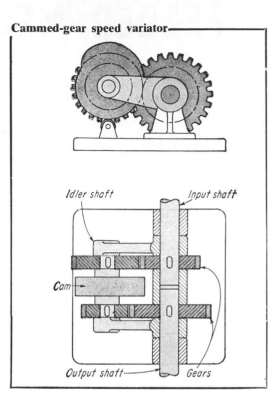

ADJUSTABLE-SPEED DRIVES

Output of this novel device is varied infinitely by changing the distance that the balls will operate from the main shaft line. The unit employs multiple disks, free to rotate on a common shaft, except for the extreme left and right disks which are keyed to the input and output shafts respectively. Every second disk carries three uniformly spaced balls which can be shifted closer to or away from the center by means of the adjustment lever. When disk 1 rotates the first group of balls, disk 3 will rotate slower because of the different radii, r_{x1} and r_{x2}. Disk 3 will then drive disk 5, and disk 5 will drive disk 7, all with the same speed ratios, thus compounding the ratios to get the final speed reduction.

The effective radii can be calculated from

$$r_{1x} = R_x - \tfrac{1}{2} D \cos \psi$$
$$r_{2x} = R_x + \tfrac{1}{2} D \cos \psi$$

where R_x is the distance from the shaft center to the ball center, D is the diameter of the ball, and ψ is one half the cone angle.

Multicone drive

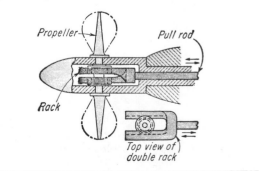

Shifting the controlled rod linearly twists the propellers around on the common axis by means of the rack and gear arrangement. Note the use of a double rack, one above and on either side of the other to obtain an *opposing* twisting motion required for propellers.

Adjustable-pitch device

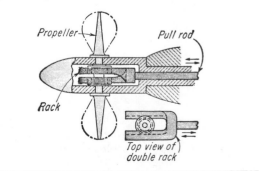

FEEDER MECHANISMS—types

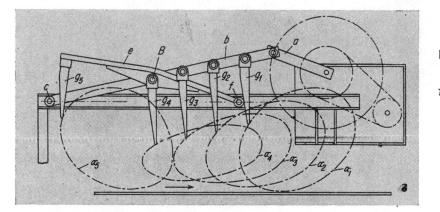

H SCHAEDLER and G MARX
Institute for Fundamental Research
Brunswick, Germany
Translated by F R Erskine Crossley, Yale University

*How to perform systematic analysis of individual
motions and translate them into mechanisms—the basic
steps for precise design of feeder mechanisms.*

Feeding parts into a continuous or piece-processing machine involves many complex motions. First step in a systematic analysis is to catalog the motions, determine the minimum actual time duration, and coordinate complementary motions. Second step is to translate these motions into hardware.

Feeder mechanisms can be classified according to type and stage of the process, Fig 1. This diagram is divided vertically, between continuous and piece-processing; and horizontally into four process stages. Continuous-flow material can be granular, bulk, fluid, or continuous strip. Furthermore, the production process can change the form of the material from continuous-flow to piece-processing or vice versa as shown by dotted lines in the chart.

Generally, mechanisms are more complex in the piece-processing operation, although some continuous-flow operations require auxiliary mechanisms for feeding or removal. In sheetmetal processing, auxiliary mechanisms may be needed on fixed or adjustable universal strip-metal presses, special-purpose self-actuating presses, or shearing, bending and forming machines. Mechanisms for continuously advancing strip and sheetmetal combine feeding, advancing and removal; and employ cams, tongs or grippers, or rolling clamps.

By contrast, a piece-processing mechanism performs these functions:

• Hopper loading, which requires supplying and introducing the material.
• Arranging, separating, turning, shaking, and directing.
• Holding with means for charging or removing from the machine.
• Transferring product to the next machine.

Small parts can be advanced by gripping jaw or turntable carriers with cam, geneva or gear drives; by compressed-air-actuated feed mechanism; by sliding track or plunger; or by a pushing mechanism.

Preliminary handling functions

In a continuous-flow process, the handling functions that precede actual processing largely consist of continuously withdrawing material from a steady source of supply, and feeding it into the process at a predetermined rate. Mechanisms for such functions are relatively simple, as shown in (A) of Fig 2.

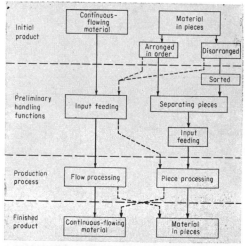

1 FEEDER-MECHANISM REQUIREMENTS
here are classified according to type of
material and processing stage.

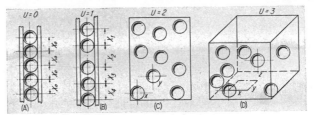

3 DEGREES OF DISORDER of spherical parts depend on number of dimensions required to specify the position.

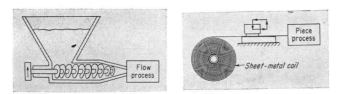

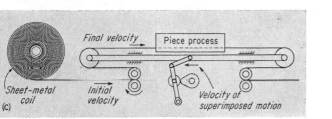

(A)   (B)

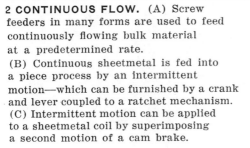

2 CONTINUOUS FLOW. (A) Screw feeders in many forms are used to feed continuously flowing bulk material at a predetermined rate.
(B) Continuous sheetmetal is fed into a piece process by an intermittent motion—which can be furnished by a crank and lever coupled to a ratchet mechanism.
(C) Intermittent motion can be applied to a sheetmetal coil by superimposing a second motion of a cam brake.

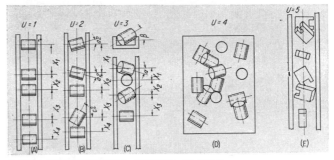

4 FOR CYLINDRICAL PARTS, degrees of disorder depend on number of dimensions and angles required to specify the position. Similarly, in (E) degrees of disorder of odd-shape parts depends on number of dimensions and angles, and their relation to a reference plane.

A continuous-flow process feeding into a piece process, Fig 2(B), sometimes requires intermittent motion, as in stamping presses, sewing machines and film projectors. Another example of continuous material feeding into a piece process is shown in Fig 2(C) where a secondary motion by a cam is superimposed on the uniform initial velocity of the sheetmetal coil in such a way that the final velocity of the sheet is zero.

In the piece process, degree of difficulty required to produce some orderly arrangement of the pieces can be defined in terms of parameter U, or the "degree of disorder" of the individual pieces. For example, if uniform spherical pieces fit a grooved guide, then the distance between them is nominally zero. This is sufficient to determine their relative positions; thus $U = 0$ as at (A) in Fig 3. However, if the balls are to be spaced at different intervals, as in (B), one dimension becomes necessary to determine their positions, and $U = 1$. To establish positions of the balls in contact with a given plane, two coordinates are needed as in (C), and $U = 2$. But to establish a systematic order of the balls within the space of a container, three dimensions are required as in (D); here $U = 3$.

Handling cylindrical pieces is somewhat more complicated than handling spherical pieces. Fig 4(A) shows that $U = 1$ when only one dimensional factor is required to establish the positions. When one dimensional factor and one angular factor are required, $U = 2$, as in (B). When one dimensional factor and two angular factors are required, $U = 3$, as in (C). To establish positions of the cylinders in contact with a given plane, two coordinates and two angular factors are required, which makes $U = 4$ as in

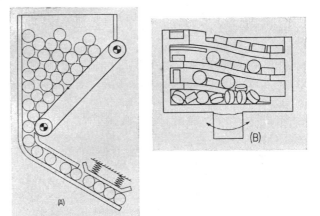

5 MAGAZINE LOADING OF PARTS can be done a number of ways. In (A) gravity-fed balls are slowed down by a spring-actuated device. In (B) a vibrating or oscillating drum elevates parts that fall on grooves specially designed to fit the parts.

(D). To establish a position for the cylinders in space, the value of U increases to 5. The degree of disorder of odd-shape objects, as in (E), is also 5 since their position is determined by two geometric axes and by the surface planes of the object.

Mechanisms for preliminary handling

Three general methods of sorting and arranging, independent of the degree of disorder are: continuous sorting, sorting into groups, arranging by individual separation.

Continuous sorting sets in order a group of disordered parts steadily yet not in any exactly predictable time, Fig 5. When sorting into groups a few disordered parts are

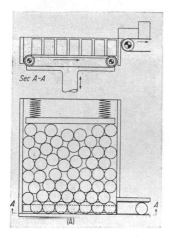

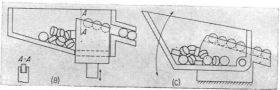

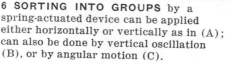

6 SORTING INTO GROUPS by a spring-actuated device can be applied either horizontally or vertically as in (A); can also be done by vertical oscillation (B), or by angular motion (C).

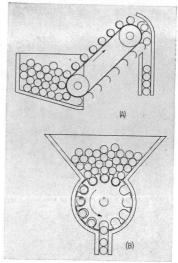

7 ARRANGING BY SEPARATING: (A) by a belt conveyor with specially fitted cogs; (B) by rotating grooves.

separated and forced into a desired orderly position, Fig 6. To arrange by individual separation, a single piece is selected from a disordered quantity, and taken off in a constrained manner as shown by the several varieties in Fig 7.

Mechanisms for input and removal

Mechanisms for control and positioning the part involve two principal factors:

- Space limitations surrounding the machine entrance.
- Accessibility of the mechanism to the central working position of the machine.

Also, the number of free or forced movements must be considered. Free or gravity movements require mechanisms to control their direction and velocity, but forced movements require mechanisms that actuate as well as guide the movements, and more complexity adds to cost. However, mechanisms that actuate forced movements are positive, and therefore more reliable.

Removal of parts from a processing position requires fewer movements, and consequently less-complex mechanisms. Primarily, this is a transfer operation, in which the parts are forced out, or fall out of the machine. Fig 8 shows an arrangement for simultaneous input and removal from a machine. The tubelike workpiece b rolls out of the feed magazine a into a recess in the slider c. It is then advanced into the work station by the forward stroke of the slide, and carried into the machine by a ramrod (not shown). At the same time a previously finished part rolls down the inclined surface of the slider, and on the next stroke is pushed into the transfer channel.

An arrangement that uses complex forced movements for feeding and gravity movements for removal of parts is shown in Fig 9. Three power cylinders a, b, c connected to an adjustable bell crank are used to generate the forced movements required to feed sheetmetal into a machine. Removal by gravity occurs after the part has been directed by forced movements into the desired direction.

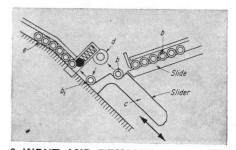

8 INPUT AND REMOVAL OF PARTS can sometimes be done with a single mechanism. In this unit, slider c simultaneously pushes incoming part b and outgoing part b_1.

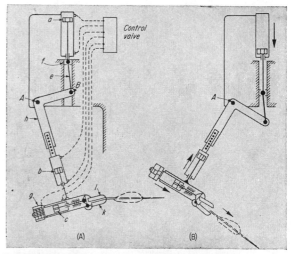

9 ADJUSTABLE BELL CRANK pivoted at A provides the angular motion while 3 air cylinders with a central control valve provide the linear motion. Counterbalancing is provided by adjustable weights g.

FEEDER MECHANISMS —
applications

H SCHAEDLER and G MARX

Institute for Fundamental Research, Brunswick, Germany
Translated by F R Erskine Crossley, Yale University

Knowing the basic hoppers, feeders, and conveyors will be helpful in developing new feeder combinations.

1 . . . EIGHT SPIRAL-SHELF HOPPERS

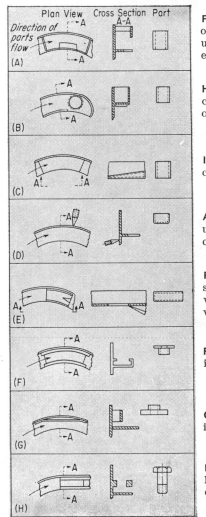

RAILED SHELF with a cutout carries only those cylindrical parts that remain upright. Those that fall horizontal are ejected through the cutout.

HOLE IN SHELF ejects those cylindrical parts that are upright, lets horizontal ones pass.

INCLINED SECTION on shelf turns cylinders into upright position.

AIR JET will pass cup-like pieces in the upright position, and eject them in any other position.

RECTANGULAR HOLE in shelf with spear will catch long U-shape cylinders with open end in front, and let fall those with open end in rear.

FLANGED SHELF carries T-shape cylinders in upright position only.

CHORD SECTION on the shelf carries inverted T-shape cylinders only.

NECK IN SHELF passes bolts with heads up or down, ejects bolts aligned otherwise.

2 . . . OTHER

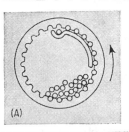

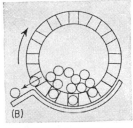

DRUM HOPPERS. Cylindrical parts are spaced for any suitable interval (A) and injected to the machine by a ramrod. Spherical parts are spaced in a drum hopper with holes (B) and gravity-fed into machine. U-shape parts are handled by hooks on the outside of the drum (C).

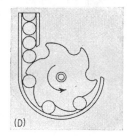

Choosing the right design for feed hoppers and mechanisms requires intuitive experience as well as straightforward analysis of motions. Parts in a supply hopper normally have random motion; the problem is to design the feed mechanism so that it accepts only those parts that are positioned properly, and rejects the rest until they fall into place. Often the feeder will help guide the parts.

Fig 1 shows eight rotating or vibrating spiral-shelf hoppers of this type. Successful operation of any of these mechanisms depends on how well the "bugs" are excluded —such as improper clearances for the parts, wear of parts and feed mechanisms, dirt, lubrication, and operating abuse. Parts that are ejected on one trial must be directed to fall back into the hopper for succeeding trials.

Hoppers and discharge mechanisms can assume many different forms and combinations (Fig 2 shows typical examples).

After parts have been arranged, the method for introducing them into the machine must be determined. Generalized methods in Fig 3 can be helpful in synthesizing the actual feeders.

TYPICAL FEEDERS

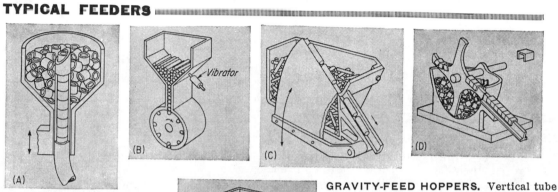

GRAVITY-FEED HOPPERS. Vertical tube (A) oscillates up and down to entrain cylindrical parts. Rotary drum with slots (B) entrains cylinders. Cylinders fall on track (C) as it oscillates. U-shape parts are picked up by rotating track (D). U-shape parts are picked up by drum and placed on vibrating track (E). Combination paddle wheel and track (F) directs grooved washers into sequence.

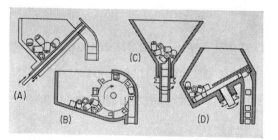

VARIETY OF HOPPERS for the same part: Oscillating piston and tube (A) elevate and arranges the disordered parts. Rotary pickup (B) performs the same task. Rotary vertical tube (C), or inclined rotary plate (D) use gravity feed.

◄ **STAR FEEDERS** (D) for spherical or cylindrical parts can be made with dwell periods.

3 . . . SIX WAYS TO FEED ALIGNED PARTS

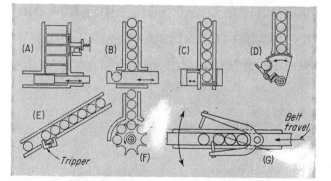

RECIPROCATING LINEAR MOTION is used for feeding parts in (A), (B) and (C). Angular motion combines with a gravity slide to deliver balls in (D) and (E). Star feeder (F) with or without dwell periods, feeds parts in round-table fashion. Belt conveyor with an angular motion device (G) separates individual cylinders.

FEEDER MECHANISMS—
angular motions

*How to use four-bar linkages to
generate continuous or intermittant angular motions
required by feeder mechanisms.*

H SCHAEDLER AND G MARX
*Institute for Fundamental Research
Brunswick, Germany*
Translated by F R Erskine Crossley, Yale University

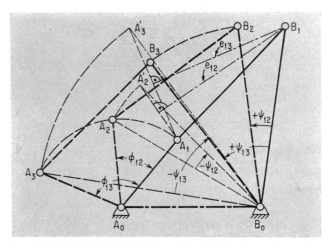

1 . . . **FOUR-BAR LINKAGE** synchronizes 2 angular movements, ϕ_{12} and ϕ_{13}, with ψ_{12} and ψ_{13}.

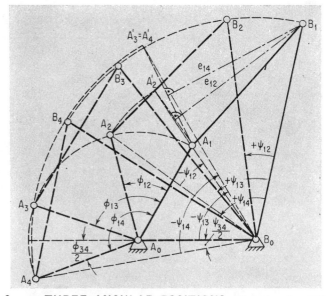

2 . . . **THREE ANGULAR POSITIONS,** ϕ_{12}, ϕ_{13}, ϕ_{14}, are synchronized by four-bar linkage here with ψ_{12}, ψ_{13}, and ψ_{14}.

In feeder mechanisms it is often necessary to synchronize two sets of angular motions. A four-bar linkage offers one way. For example, in Fig 1 two angular motions, ϕ_{12} and ϕ_{13}, must synchronize with two others, ψ_{12} and ψ_{13}, about the given pivot points A_o and B_o and the given crank length A_oA. This means that crank length B_oB must be of such length that the resulting four-bar linkage will coordinate angular motions ϕ_{12} and ϕ_{13} with ψ_{12} and ψ_{13}. Procedure is:

1. Obtain point A'_2 by revolving A_2 about B_o through angle $-\psi_{12}$ but in the opposite direction.

2. Obtain point A'_3 similarly by revolving A_3 about B_o through angle $-\psi_{13}$.

3. Draw lines $A_1A'_2$ and $A_1A'_3$ and the perpendicular bisectors of the lines which intersect at desired point B_1.

4. The quadrilateral $A_oA_1B_1B_o$ represents the four-bar linkage that will produce the required relationship between the angles ϕ_{12}, ϕ_{13}, and ψ_{12}, ψ_{13}.

Three angles with four relative positions can be synchronized in a similar way. In Fig 2 it is desired to synchronize angles ϕ_{12}, ϕ_{13}, and ϕ_{14} with corresponding angles ψ_{12}, ψ_{13}, and ψ_{14}, using freely chosen pivot points A_o and B_o. In this case crank length A_oA as well as B_oB is to be determined, and the procedure is:

1. Locate pivot points A_o and B_o on a line that bisects angle $A_3A_oA_4$, the length A_oB_o being arbitrary.

2. Measure off $\frac{1}{2}$ of angle $B_3B_oB_4$ and with this angle draw B_oA_4 which establishes crank length A_oA at intersection of A_oA_4. This also establishes points A_3, A_2 and A_1.

3. With B_o as center and B_oA_4 as radius mark off angles $-\psi_{14}$, $-\psi_{13}$, $-\psi_{12}$, the negative sign indicating they are in opposite sense to ψ_{14}, ψ_{13} and ψ_{12}. This establishes points A'_2, A'_3 and A'_4, but here A'_3 and A'_4 coincide because of symmetry of A_3 and A_4 about A_oB_o.

4. Draw lines $A_1A'_2$ and $A_1A'_4$, and the perpendicular bisectors of these lines, which intersect at the desired point B_1.

5. The quadrilateral $A_oA_1B_oB_1$ represents the four-bar linkage that will produce the required relationship between the angles ϕ_{12}, ϕ_{13}, ϕ_{14} and ψ_{12}, ψ_{13}, ψ_{14}.

The illustrations show how these angles must be coordinated within the given space. In Fig 3(A) input angles of crank must be coordinated with output angles of forked escapement. In (B) input angles of crank are coordinated with output angles of tilting hopper. In (C) input angles of crank are coordinated with output angles of segment. In (D) a box on a conveyor is tilted 90° by output crank, which is actuated by input crank through coupler. Other mechanisms shown similarly coordinate input and output angles—some have dwell periods between the cycles, others give linear output with dwell periods.

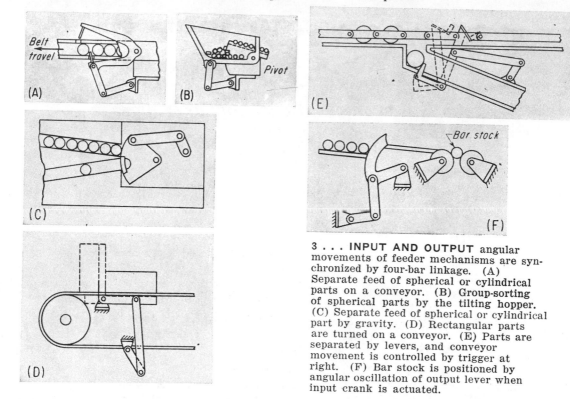

3 . . . INPUT AND OUTPUT angular movements of feeder mechanisms are synchronized by four-bar linkage. (A) Separate feed of spherical or cylindrical parts on a conveyor. (B) Group-sorting of spherical parts by the tilting hopper. (C) Separate feed of spherical or cylindrical part by gravity. (D) Rectangular parts are turned on a conveyor. (E) Parts are separated by levers, and conveyor movement is controlled by trigger at right. (F) Bar stock is positioned by angular oscillation of output lever when input crank is actuated.

FEEDER MECHANISMS—
curvilinear motions

Four-bar linkages can be combined into 6, 8 or more linkages for the feeder mechanisms in film cameras, automatic lathes, farm machinery, and torch cutters.

KURT HAIN
Institute for Fundamental Research
Brunswick, Germany

When feeder mechanisms require complex curvilinear motions, it may be necessary to use compound linkages of more than four links. However, four-bar linkages can be synthesized to produce curvilinear motions of various degrees of complexity, and all possibilities of four-bar linkages should be considered before complex types.

For example, a camera film-advancing mechanism, Fig 1, has a simple four-bar linkage with coupler point d which generates a curvilinear and straight-line motion a resembling a "D". Another more complex curvilinear motion, Fig 2, is also generated by a coupler point E of a four-bar linkage which controls an automatic profile cutter. Four-bar linkages can be used to generate a number of curvilinear motions as in Fig 3. Here the points of the coupler prongs, g_1, g_2, and g_3 on coupler b, and g_4 and g_5 on coupler e, are chosen in such a way that their motions result in the desired progressive feeding of straw into a press (manufactured by Gebr. Welger, Wolfenbuttel, Germany).

A similar feeding and elevating device (designed by Moertl in Germany) is shown in Fig 4. The rotating drive crank a moves coupler b and swinging lever c, which actuates the guiding arm f through the link e. The bar h carries the prone fingers g_1 through g_7. They generate coupler curves a_1 through a_7.

As another practical example, consider the torch-cutting machine in Fig 5(A) which is designed to cut sheetmetal along a curvilinear path a. Here the points A_0 and B_0 are fixed in the machine and the lever A_0A_1 is of adjustable length to suit different curvilinear paths a desired.

The length B_0B_1 is also fixed. The problem is to find the length of the levers A_1B_1 and E_1B_1 in the four-bar linkage to give the desired path a which is to be traced by the coupler point E on which the cutting torch is mounted.

The graphical solution for this problem as shown in (B) requires selection of the points A_1 and E_1 in such manner that the distances A_1E_1 to A_8E_8 are equal and the points

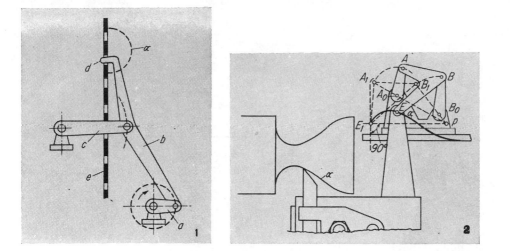

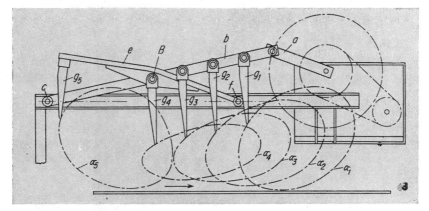

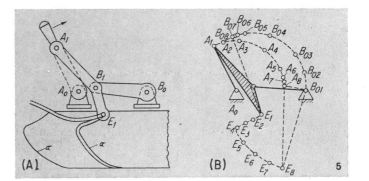

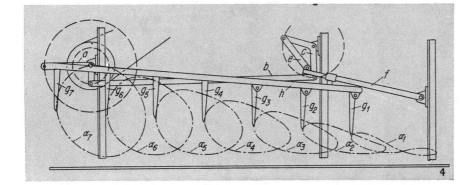

E_1 to E_8 lie on the desired coupler curved α. In this case only the points E_4 to E_8 represent the desired profile to be cut. The correct selection of points A_1 and E_1 depends upon making the following triangles congruent:

$$\Delta E_2 A_2 B_{01} = \Delta E_1 A_1 B_{02}$$
$$\Delta E_3 A_3 B_{01} = \Delta E_1 A_1 B_{03}$$
$$\Delta E_8 A_8 B_{01} = \Delta E_1 A_1 B_{08}$$

and so on until $E_8 A_8 B_{01} = E_1 A_1 B_{00}$. At the same time all points A_1 to A_8 must lie on the arc having A_0 as center, and all the points B_{01} to B_{08} must lie on the arc having B_1 as center.

Synthesis of an 8-bar linkage

Let us now design a linkage with 8 precision points, as shown in Fig 6. In this mechanism the curvilinear motion of one 4-bar linkage is coordinated with angular oscillation of a second four-bar linkage. The first four-bar linkage consists of AA_0BB_0 with coupler point E which

text continued, next page

generates γ with 8 precision points E_1 through E_8 and drives a second four-bar linkage HH_0GG_0. Coupler point F generates curve δ with precision points F_1 through F_8. The coupler points F_2, F_4, F_6, F_8 are coincident, because straight links GG_0 and GH are in line with one another in these coupler positions. This is what permits HH_0 to oscillate despite the continuous motion of the coupler point F. The coupler points F_1 coincident with F_5, and F_3 coincident with F_7, have been chosen in such a way that F_1 is the center of a circle k_1 and F_3 is the center of a circle k_3. These circles are tangent to coupler curve γ at E_1, and E_5, E_3, and E_7; and they indicate the limiting positions of the second four-bar linkage HH_0GG_0.

The limiting angular oscillation of HH_0, which is one of the requirements of this mechanism, is represented by positions H_0H_1 and H_0H_3. It oscillates four times for each revolution of the input crank AA_0, and the positions H_1 to H_8 correspond to input crank positions A_1 to A_8.

Synthesis of a compound linkage with dwell periods and coordinated intermittent motion is shown in Fig 7. The four-bar linkage AA_0BB_0 generates an approximately triangular curve with coupler point E, with six precision points E_1 through E_6. A linkage to do this is not unusual and can be readily proportioned from known methods of four-bar linkage synthesis. However, the linkage incorporates dwell periods which are used to produce coordinated intermittent motion by means of a second four-bar linkage FF_0HB_0. Here the tangent arc k_{12}, k_{34} and k_{56} are drawn with EF as radius from centers F_{12}, F_{34} and F_{56}, and these centers establish the circle with F_0 as the center and pivot point for the second four-bar linkage. Each tangent arc causes a dwell of the link FF_0, while AA_0 rotates continuously. Thus the link FF_0, with three rest periods in one revolution, can produce intermittent curvilinear motion in the second four-bar linkage FF_0HB_0. In laying out the center F_0 it must be so selected that the angle EFF_0 deviates only slightly from 90° because this will minimize the required torque that is to be applied at E. The length of B_0H can be made to suit, and the rest periods at H_{34}, H_{12} and H_{56} will correspond to crank angles ϕ_{34}, ϕ_{12} and ϕ_{56}.

A compound linkage can also produce a 360° oscillating motion with a dwell period as in Fig 8. The two four-bar linkages are AA_0BB_0 and BB_0FF_0, and the output coupler curve γ is traversed only through segment E_1E_2. The oscillating motion is produced by lever HH_0 connected to the coupler point by EH. The fixed point H_0 is located within the loop of the coupler curve γ. The dwell occurs at point H_3 which is the center of circular arc k tangent to the coupler curve γ during the desired dwell period, and in this case the dwell is made to occur in the middle of the 360° oscillation. The coincident positions H_1 and H_2 indicate the limiting positions of the link HH_0, and correspond to the positions E_1 and E_2 of the coupler point.

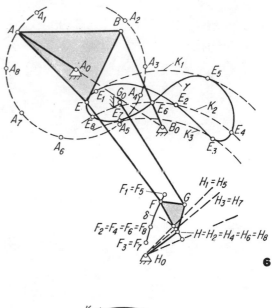

6

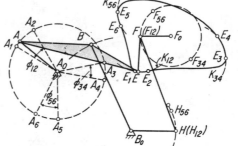

7

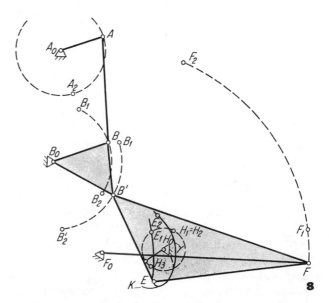

8

HOW LABELING MACHINES WORK

Fingers, suction and glue-pads are some of the ways these machines
perform high-speed sleight of hand with stacks of cut paper labels.

J A CUCKSON

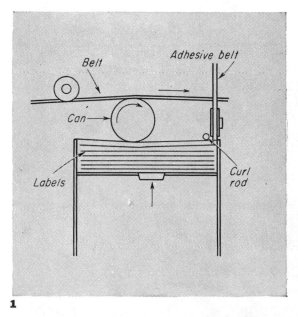

1

There are two ways to put a label on a package. One way is to coat the package with glue so that it picks up the label as flypaper does a fly. The other way is to coat the label with glue and stick it on like a postage stamp.

Flypaper feed

Can-labeling machines label 600 to 750 cans per hour this way. Fig 1 shows how a belt rolls a can streaked with glue over the pile of labels. As it rolls, the can wraps itself in a label. The adhesive belt smears glue on the end of the label to keep it from lifting up.

Labeling boxes is more complex, because boxes won't roll. The machine in Fig 2 uses three stations for the job. A roller puts glue on a rubber pad, which transfers the glue to the package at station I. At station II, a cross-slide presses a stack of labels against the package. When the slide pulls back, it leaves a label behind. Another rubber pad at station III presses the label more firmly to the package.

(continued next page)

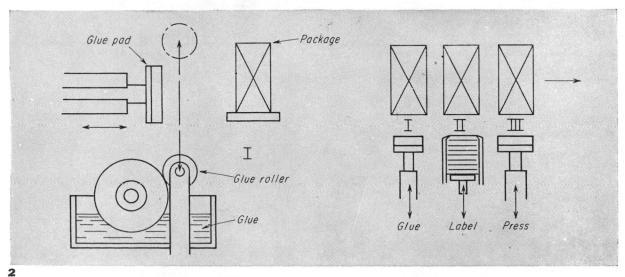

2

Postage-stamp method

Labels may, indeed, be like postage stamps—preglued so they only have to be moistened. Other labels have pressure-sensitive adhesives, or thermoplastic backing that sticks when it is heated.

However, the machine in Fig 3 puts wet glue on the label just before it goes on the package. A roller spreads glue on each face of the octagonal drum. When the glued face reaches the bottom, it picks a label off the pile that pops up to meet it. At the top of rotation, fingers snatch the label off the drum.

One disadvantage of feeding labels off the top of the pile is the need for a mechanism like a counterweighted piston to keep the stack rising. A stack that deals from the bottom slides down by its own weight. Another advantage of bottom feed is that an operator can replenish the pile without stopping the machine.

Instead of a drum, some machines use a picker (Fig 4). The picker is a plate with a slot big enough for the package to fit through. After picking a label, the picker lowers down over the package and lays on the label.

Suction pickup and transfer

Suction heads can pick up labels dry. In Fig 5 the suction head pulls down one corner of the label, and the

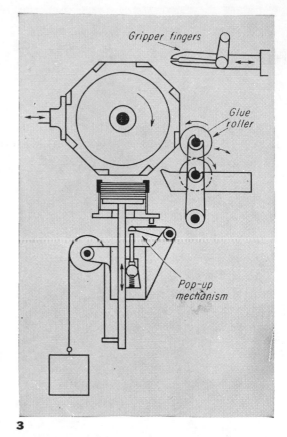

3

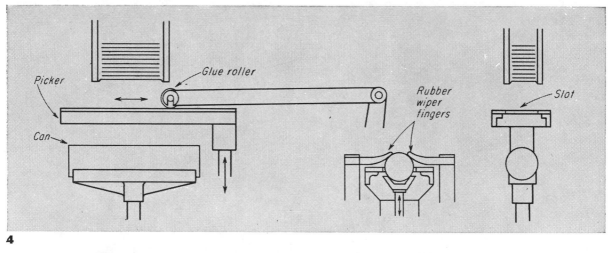

4

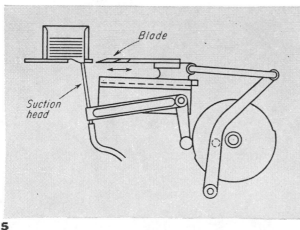

5

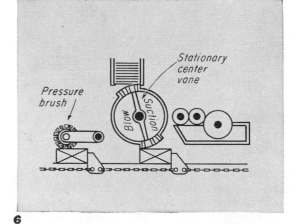

6

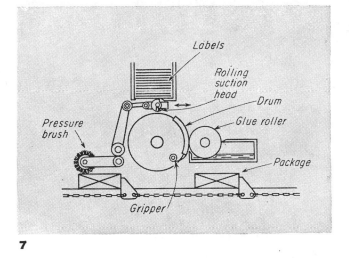

7

blade slides across and peels it off the bottom of the pile, at the same time pushing up the hopper. With suction holes in the bottom, the blade can carry away the label on the return stroke.

The cylinder in Fig 6 both inhales and exhales. Suction picks up the label and holds it for gluing. When the holes rotate to the other side of the center vane, air blows out of them to apply the label.

Friction feed

Between two sheets of smooth, dry paper there is less friction than between the paper and a rubber roller. Needles (Fig 8), which pierce the first five or six sheets on the bottom of the pile, ensure only one sheet leaves at a time. The rubber feed roller pushes the labels into the forwarding rollers.

The machine in Fig 9 uses a combination of suction nozzle and friction. In sequence, the suction nozzle pulls down the end of the label, and then a moving roller moves in against a fixed rotating roller, which pushes the label on its way.

Making labels stick

The last step is to press on the label after it is in place to make sure it sticks. The machine in Fig 2 uses direct pressure at station III. Because each package must stop momentarily under the rubber pad, the machine can run only so fast. Moving the pad in a D-shape path and never stopping the package beats the speed limit that stop-start motion imposes. During the straight-line part of the cycle the pad follows the moving package and presses on the label.

Direct-pressure pads can cover only 140° of a cylinder. Substitute methods are wiper fingers (Fig 4) or rollers arranged to cradle the cylinder.

Flat packages ride on belts under roller brushes, (Fig 6) or, for higher pressures, between roller.

Troubles

Three things commonly cause labels to stick together in the magazine: (1) Edges locked together during cutting. (2) Embossing made by print. (3) Ink that dried after the

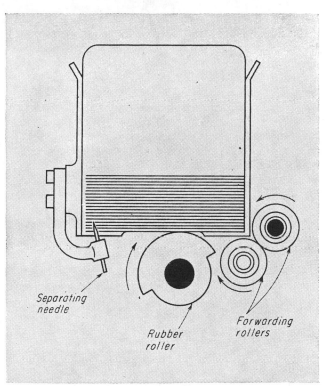

8

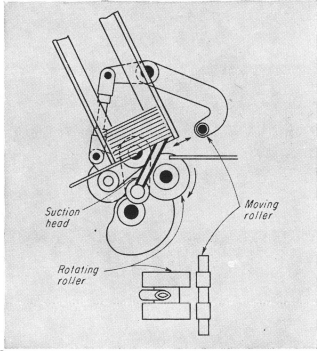

9

labels were stacked. Bending, twisting or riffling will loosen the sheets.

With needles, the grain of the paper must be in the direction of feed so that the tear is clean.

REFERENCE:
"Devices for Feeding Small Cut Sheets," by J. A. Cuckson. Published in *Mechanical World*, Nov '60, pp 454-8.

7 *BASIC SELECTORS*

Hoppers, feeding single parts to an assembly
station, speed up many operations. Reviewed here
are some devices that may not be familiar
to all design engineers.

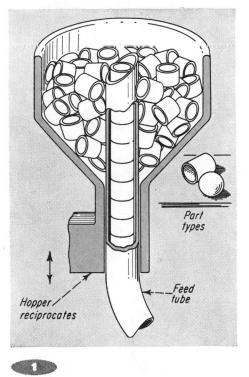

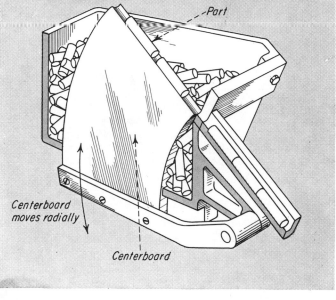

Reciprocating feed . . .
for spheres or short cylinders is perhaps the
simplest feed mechanism. Either the hopper
or the tube reciprocates. The hopper must be
be kept topped-up with parts unless the tube
can be adjusted to the parts level.

Centerboard selector . . .
is similar to reciprocating feed. The centerboard top can be milled
to various section shapes to pick up moderately complex parts. It
works best, however, with cylinders too long to be fed with the
reciprocating hopper. Feed can be continuous or as required.

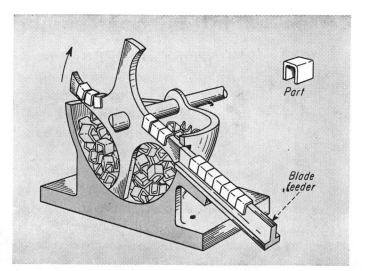

Rotary centerblades . . .
catch small U-shaped parts effectively if their legs are not
too long. Parts must also be resilient enough to resist permanent set from displacement forces as blades cut through
pile of parts. Feed is usually continuous.

for PARTS

PETER C. NOY *Manufacturing Engineer*

Canadian General Electric Co., Ltd., Barrie, Ont.

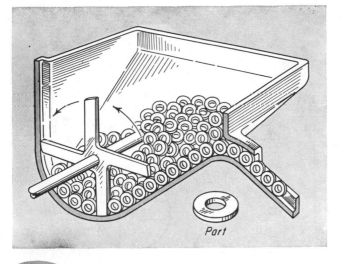

4

Paddle wheel . . .
is effective for disk-shaped parts if they are stable enough. Thin, weak parts would bend and jam. Such designs must be avoided if possible—especially if automatic assembly methods will be employed.

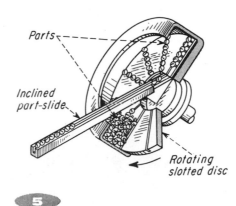

5

Rotary screw-feed . . .
handles screws, headed pins, shouldered shafts and similar parts. In most hopper feeds, random selection of chance-orientated parts necessitates further machinery if parts must be fed in only one specific position. Here, however, all screws are fed in the same orientation (except for slot position) without separate machinery.

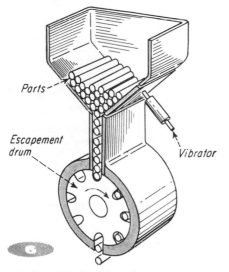

6

Long-cylinder feeder . . .
is a variation of the first two hoppers. If the cylinders have similar ends, the part can be fed without pre-positioning, thus assisting automatic assembly (PE—Mar. 31, '58, p. 124.) A cylinder with differently shaped ends requires extra machinery to orientate the part before it can be assembled.

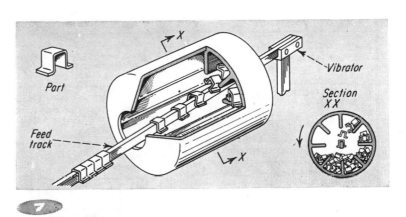

7

Barrel hopper . . .
is most useful if parts tend to tangle. The parts drop free of the rotating-barrel sides. By chance selection some of them fall onto the vibrating rack and are fed out of the barrel. Parts should be stiff enough to resist excessive bending because the tumbling action can subject parts to relatively severe loads. The tumbling sometimes helps to remove sharp burrs.

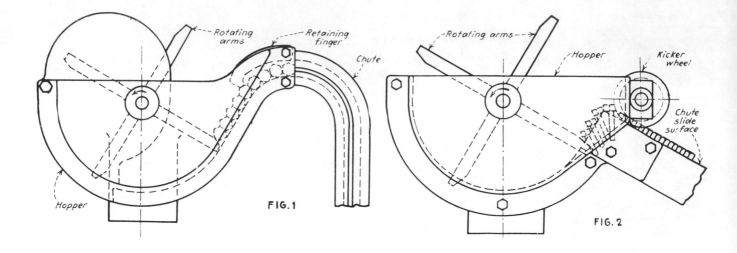

Hoppers for Feeding

W. E. SUMMERHILL

Designs of stationary hoppers with rotating arms and disks, reciprocating and oscillating blades, and those wherein the hopper rotates angularly or is automatically tilted

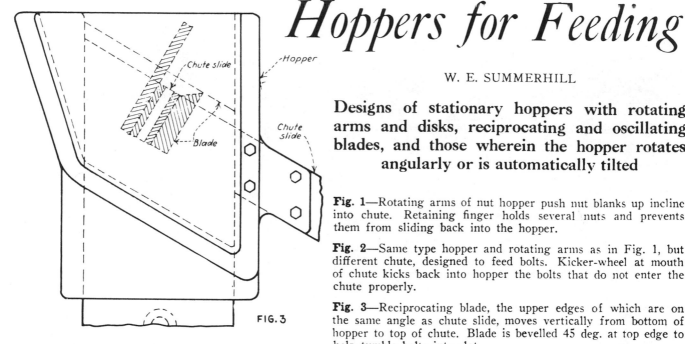

Fig. 1—Rotating arms of nut hopper push nut blanks up incline into chute. Retaining finger holds several nuts and prevents them from sliding back into the hopper.

Fig. 2—Same type hopper and rotating arms as in Fig. 1, but different chute, designed to feed bolts. Kicker-wheel at mouth of chute kicks back into hopper the bolts that do not enter the chute properly.

Fig. 3—Reciprocating blade, the upper edges of which are on the same angle as chute slide, moves vertically from bottom of hopper to top of chute. Blade is bevelled 45 deg. at top edge to help tumble bolts into slot.

Fig. 4—Hopper used for feeding shell-like pieces into tube conveyor. A reciprocating plunger picks up work at lower end of stroke and deposits it in snap-fingers at end of conveyor tube.

Fig. 5—Hopper is adjustable for feeding various lengths and diameters of plain round stock, the pieces falling into chute by

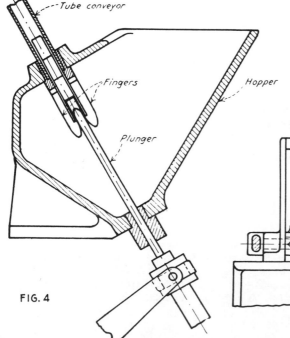

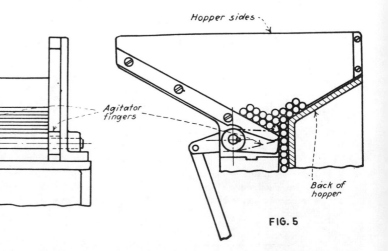

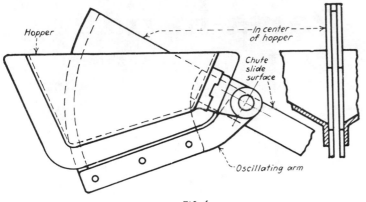

FIG. 6

Work Automatically

gravity. Agitator finger at either end of work prevents bridging or wedging of blanks over chute opening.

Fig. 6—An oscillating arm carries the blade through the center of the bolt hopper and at the top of its stroke forms a continuation of the bolt chute. Sides of hopper are inclined toward center to feed bolts into blade at low position in hopper. One blade is used for each diameter of stock handled, tapered spacers in hopper being adjustable to accommodate varying widths of blade.

Fig. 7—Tilting hopper for small rivets and screws in which the work falls into slot at bottom center of the hopper which is tilted to same angle as chute.

Fig. 8—Rotating hopper set at angle is slotted at lower face to feed into the chute small cup shaped objects, as shown at *A*, positioning them with their open end up. Should cups enter chute open end down they will drop through selector slot in chute thereby allowing only those correctly positioned to proceed to assembly point.

Fig. 9—Vertical rotating disk hopper for feeding shouldered pieces to chute. By adjusting hardened dog-point screws it is possible to feed pieces with difference of only 0.010 in. on the diameter.

Fig. 10—Another type of vertical rotating disk hopper for feeding hollow cylindrical pieces having blind hole. Prongs are milled on periphery of disk which prevent work being fed open end up into chute.

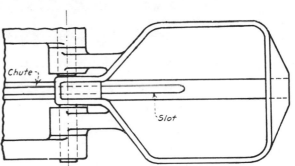

FIG. 7

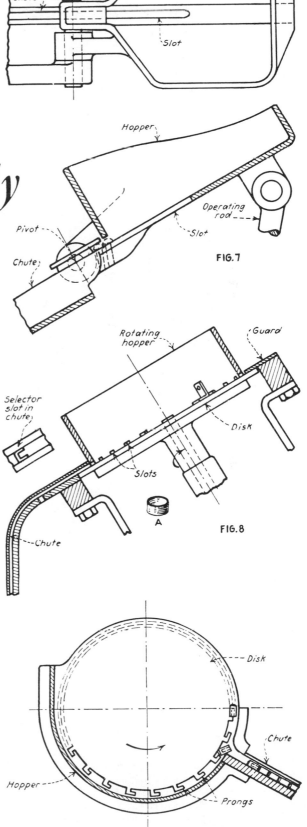

FIG. 8

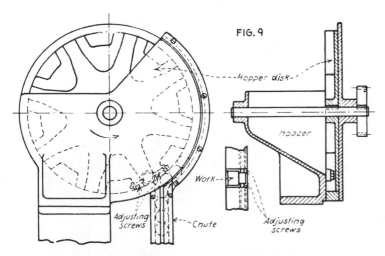

FIG. 9

FIG. 10

From Japan: Parts handling

These drawings of devices for feeding special shapes, labels, rivets, glass tubes, etc, are copied from the originals (with **Product Engineering** annotations) exactly as we received them

SHIGENOBU ARICHIKA, Director, Matsushita Electrical Industrial Co, Ltd

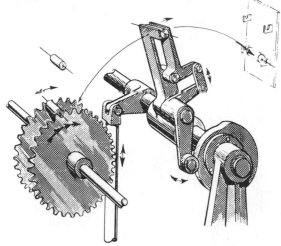

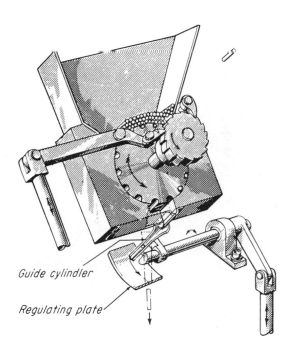

Guide cylindler

Regulating plate

2 FEEDING ELECTRONIC COMPONENTS. Condensers, for example, are delivered by a pair of intermittently rotating disks with notched circumferences. Then a pick-up arm lifts the condenser and carries it to the required position by the action of a cam and follower.

1 GRAVITY FEED FOR RODS. Single rods of a given length are transferred from the hopper to the lower guide-cylinder by means of an intermittently rotating disk with notched circumference. The guide cylinder, moved by a lever, delivers the rod when the outlet moves free of the regulating plate.

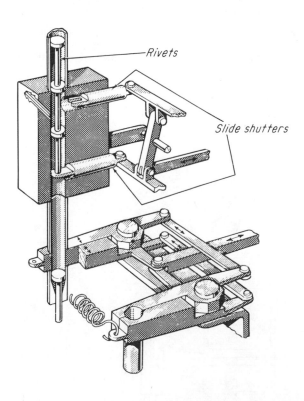

Rivets

Slide shutters

4 FEEDING HEADED RIVETS. Headed rivets, correctly oriented, are supplied from a parts-feeder in a given direction. They are dropped, one by one, by the relative movement of a pair of slide shutters. Then the rivet falls through a guide cylinder to a clamp. Clamp pairs drop two rivets into corresponding holes.

mechanisms

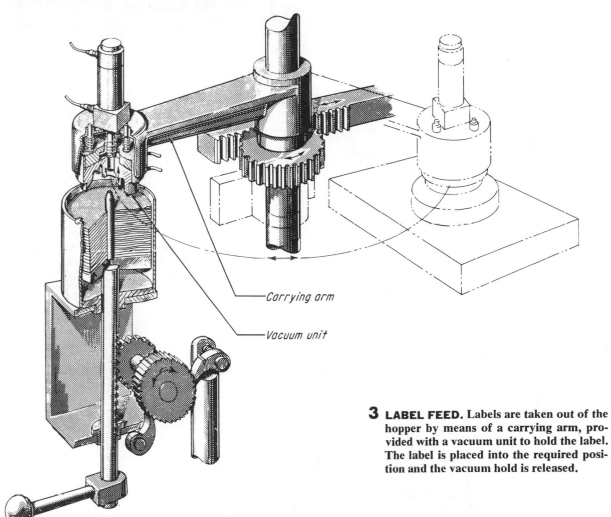

Carrying arm

Vacuum unit

3 **LABEL FEED.** Labels are taken out of the hopper by means of a carrying arm, provided with a vacuum unit to hold the label. The label is placed into the required position and the vacuum hold is released.

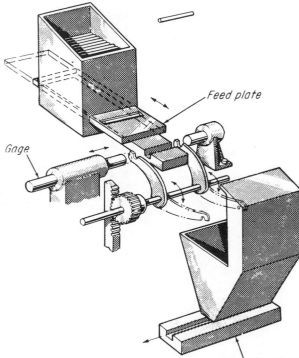

Feed plate

Gage

Vibrating stand

5 **HORIZONTAL FEED FOR FIXED-LENGTH RODS.** Single rods of a given length are brought from the hopper to the slot of a fixed plate by means of a moving plate. After gaging in the notched portion of the fixed plate, the rod is moved to the shoot by means of a lever, and is taken out from the shoot by a vibrating table.

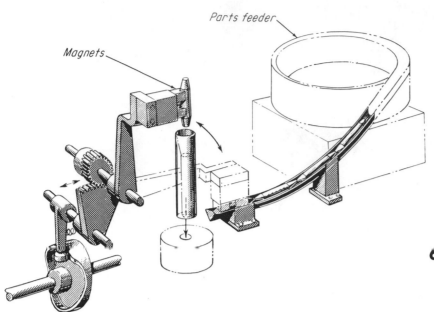

Parts feeder

Magnets

6 **PIN INSERTER.** Pins, supplied from the parts-feeder, are raised to the vertical position by means of a magnet arm. The pin drops through a guide cylinder when the magnetic hold is turned off.

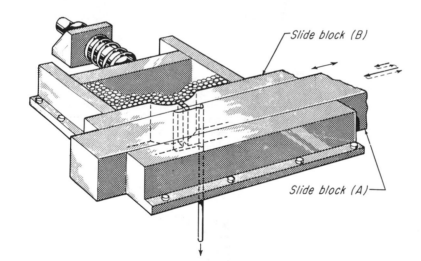

Slide block (B)

Slide block (A)

8 **VERTICAL FEED FOR WIRES.** Wires of fixed length are stacked vertically as illustrated. They are taken out, one by one, as blocks A and B are slid by means of cam and lever (not shown) while the wires are pressed into the hopper by a spring.

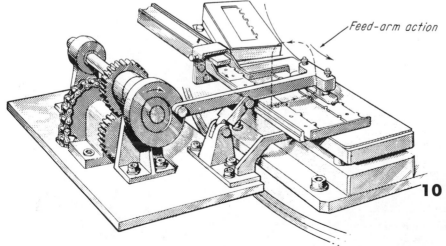

Feed-arm action

10 **LATERAL FEED FOR PLAIN STRIPS.** Strips supplied from the parts-feeder are put into the required position, one by one, by an arm that is part of a D-drive linkage.

7 **CUTOFF AND TRANSFER DEVICE FOR GLASS TUBES.** Rotating glass tube has its upper portion held by a chuck (not shown). The moment the cutter sections it to a given length, the mandrel comes down and a spring member (not shown) drops the tube on the chute.

9 **FEEDING SPECIAL-SHAPED PARTS.** Parts of such special shapes as shown are taken out, one by one, in a given direction, and then moved into the corresponding indents on transfer platforms.

11 **VERTICAL FEED FOR RODS.** Rods supplied from the parts-feeder are fed vertically by means of a directing drum and a pushing bar. The rod is then drawn away by a chucking lever.

12 Ideas

WILLIAM SCHWARTZ
Consulting Engineer, New York, New York

Materials and Shapes	1	2	3	4	5	6	7	8	9	10	11	12
Round and Flat	X				X	X	X		X	X	X	X
Long Cylinders			X	X		X	X	X		X		
Cubes				X				X	X	X		X
Irregular Shapes		X		X		X						X
Symmetrical Parts having Projections			X	X		X	X	X	X			X
Spheres	X				X				X			X
Fragile or Brittle	X		X				X			X		X
Soft	X				X	X	X	X	X	X	X	X
Nesting or Tangling		X		X		X		X				
Delivery Rate over 100 parts per minute	X	X		X	X	X	X	X				X
Delivery Rate under 100 parts per minute			X					X		X	X	X
Multiple Stream Delivery	X				X			X				X

Best Applications of Designs Illustrated: The selections noted above can only be a rough guide to designers. Where several mechanism could handle a given type the simplest designs have been noted; special considerations must be weighed in all cases.

SMALL PARTS, FASTENINGS, AND PACKAGE COMPONENTS are usually brought to processing and assembly operations in random heaps. Where these operations are to be mechanical, the parts must each be separated from their pile, oriented into the correct position, and fed in proper numbers and timing. Several firms manufacture ingeniously contrived hoppers applicable to many of these feeding, sorting, and counting operations, but except in the case of standard screws, nuts, washers, caps, and parts approximating them in shape, modification or a special design is usually necessary. Ten designs by the author are

1. Pierced Drum Feeding, Sorting, and Counting Hopper

A drum driven by a ring gear and supported on idler rolls has stationary troughs fitted into the ends which hold the supply of parts. One line of holes around the drum, closely spaced, will remove a stream of parts when they drop onto a slide at the exit point. A stationary external guard keep parts from falling through except at the discharge point, and an internal guard lining the upper half keeps parts not discharged from falling back. The drum is slightly thicker than the height of the part, a bearing cap in the illustration. The drum revolves slowly enough so the supply of parts does not tumble, but rides in the bottom. A pair of slides projecting far enough into the chute to pick up an upturned rim but clearing those turned down, will remove improperly oriented pieces. These may be dumped into a bucket at the end of the slides, or into a hopper equipped with a conveyor to return them to the feeding troughs. A counting roll fitted with spokes projecting up through slots in the delivery slide, will hold parts on the slide until needed. The slide will fill back to the drum, and

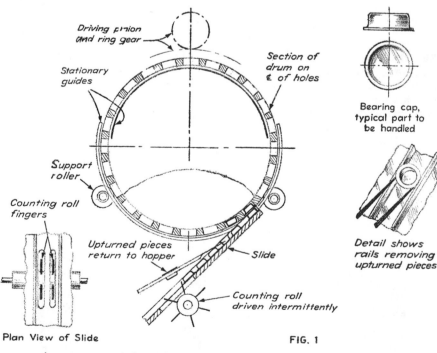

Plan View of Slide

FIG. 1

successive parts carried to this point by the drum will pass over the last piece on the slide, remaining in their hole in the drum until they pass the drum delivery point again and find it unoccupied. Dividing the counting roll into the proper number of segments, and rotating it through part of one revolution will count pieces as required by different applications.

for design of feeding, sorting and counting mechanisms

illustrated and are presented as a guide to the designer faced with this type of problem. Two other designs, interesting examples of devices now being made and sold as standard equipment by well known companies, have been included to broaden the scope and utility of the article. These 12 designs should solve a big percentage of industry's feeding, sorting, and counting problems. However, they are not presented as the definitive work on this subject. Variations are of course infinite; each part must be handled as a special case, but the development work involved is made increasingly worthwhile by rising labor costs and the distaste, even of unskilled labor, for monotony. The

recommendations checked in the accompanying table will furnish a rough guide to designers. Where several selections can handle a given type of material or component the simplest design should be chosen, and must be modified to meet the special requirements of the particular job. Quantities of pieces to be sorted, space requirements, speeds required, and other such factors will also enter into the selection of these mechanisms. Full-scale models must be built and thoroughly proven before these mechanisms can be placed in production, but their construction is not too expensive because wood, plastics, and sheet metal can be used for many parts.

2. Reciprocating Wiper Feeding and Sorting Device

A clip angle with unequal legs is to be chute-fed. The parallel wiper bars K-K move between the end rails B and C, positioned by the rods L-L and driven by the crank N. As they reach the right end of travel, projecting bar G strikes the pivoting gate H, which swings to pass a few parts down the chute from the hopper. The timing is such that they fall between K-K. The spring J keeps the gate closed unless struck, and feed can be regulated by lowering or raising G. As the wiper bars move to the left, the mass of parts is piled against the right hand one, and as it pushes them over the slot in the table between belts E and F, some will drop one flange into the slot. These are carried outwards by the belts, and restrained from falling through by the guides M-M. Clearance between the bottom of the wiper blades and the table is such that the wipers pass over parts falling into the slot. If only one line of clips is needed, belt E dumps its load into a bucket below the delivery end pulley. Belt F is also carrying parts, but half will have their long leg lying across its top surface. A

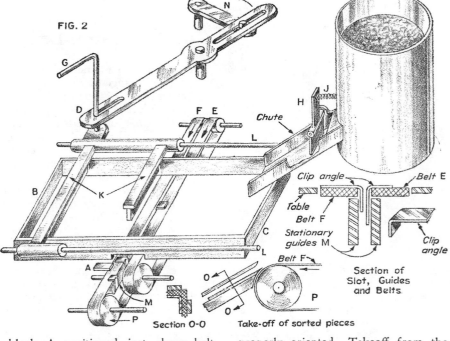

FIG. 2

Section of Slot, Guides and Belts

Section O-O

Take-off of sorted pieces

block A positioned just above belt F and projecting inwards just far enough to be struck by the long leg of the clip but not by the short one, will knock off any clips which are im-

properly oriented. Takeoff from the belt to a chute is shown in Section O-O, where a knifedge angle will pick clips off the belt.

(continued on next page)

3. Sorting Mechanism for Tube-Fed Long Parts

This device, shown end-sorting studs so that all studs enter the funnel with the stud end down, has the advantage that all parts continue in one stream; synchronization of the shaft drive with other equipment can time or count the discharge. The spider has at the end of each arm a cup with an OD equal to that of the part and an ID slightly larger than the small end. While the shaft is making a quarter turn, the edge of the rubber cam projects into the tube, holding the next piece from falling until one of the cutouts appears. Timing is adjusted so that a piece hits the cup just after it is aligned with the tube center-line. If the stub end of the part is down, it will rest across the rim of the cup. After the dwell period of the intermittent-drive the spider moves again, and the cup jerks out from under the stud, the stud falling into the

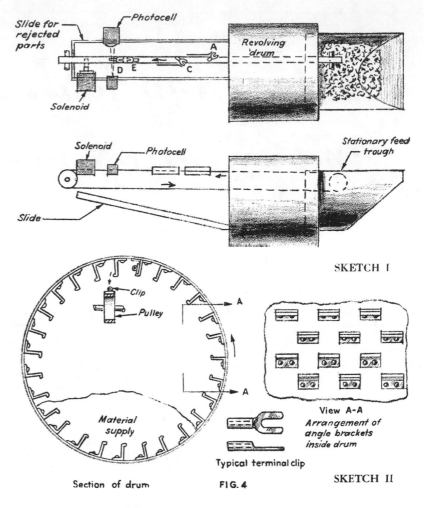

SKETCH I

SKETCH II

Typical terminal clip

View A-A
Arrangement of angle brackets inside drum

Section of drum   FIG. 4

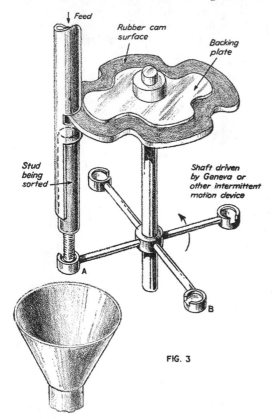

FIG. 3

funnel below, the stub end still down. When a part drops small end down, the small end will drop into the cup. The arm starting to move, the end is held by the cup, and it moves away from the tube, which is split here so that the upper end slides along it. When the cup reaches some position between A and B the top end is no longer supported, and it drops. When the stub end is below the level of the cup the small end slides off the rim, and the piece drops stub end down.

4. Drum-and-Belt Feeding, Sorting Hopper

The drum is end-fed from a fixed trough, and is lined with angle brackets staggered in arrangement and having small lips. The brackets are just large enough to hold one piece, though in operation others will cling. As the terminal clips illustrated ride into the upper right quadrant of sketch II, most parts not securely resting on the brackets will fall. The belt is so placed that parts tipping out of the brackets above will fall onto it; many will of course bounce off if the drop is too great or the belt too resilient. The belt carries the clips past the fixed guides A and B, which either line them up with the belt or push them off. The photocell light is interrupted by the high part of the clip, (the wire ferrule) which, with a suitable time delay circuit corresponding to the time of belt travel from the cell to the solenoid, energizes the solenoid. The solenoid plunger extends and retracts quickly; if the clip is turned like D on sketch I, the plunger hits nothing, but if it is turned opposite like E, the forked part of the clip is in the way and the solenoid plunger knocks the clip off the belt. A trough below the belt slopes down, carrying rejected clips back into the drum. If this feature is unnecessary, the lips on the angle brackets inside the drum may be omitted, and the belt located just above the center and near the right side of the drum. In the case of the clips illustrated, the proportions and speed of the drum and belt may be adjusted so that only pieces falling to the belt with their flat sides down will remain on it. This type of hopper is adaptable to a very wide variety of parts which tangle, nest, or have wires attached. When the drum and belt are properly proportioned a rain of parts strikes the belt in such numbers that even though a small percentage are properly oriented the output is large.

5. Turntable Hopper

Any solid part which will easily orient itself into a round hole and which is not too thin may be handled by this design. The square hopper has a rubber boot around its outlet, which ends just above the turntable. Radial lines of holes in the turntable pick up pieces as they pass under the boot, and a few others besides will lock into the edge of a hole and be pulled out of the boot. These latter are removed by the stationary fence. After passing under the fence, a filled line of holes passes to the discharge sector opposite the hopper, where a dropping gate occupies a slot in the stationary plate under the turntable. Obviously all the holes in a line may not be filled, and it would not be desirable to dump these. A line of microswitches, supported slightly above the turntable, have rollers with "feel" for the piece, which must project slightly above the turntable surface. These switches are normally open circuit, and are wired in series. If all of an entire line of holes is filled, they will all close simultaneously, energizing the solenoid which pulls out the dropping gate. A belt is illustrated carrying off the discharge, but a tube or chute might be located under each hole at the discharge station. Another electrical device can energize the solenoid only when discharge is desired in synchronization with another piece of equipment; the holes will remain filled until the dropping gate empties them.

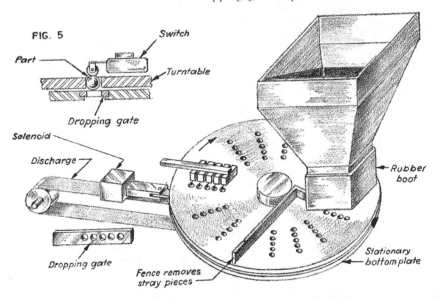

FIG. 5

Switch
Part
Turntable
Dropping gate
Solenoid
Discharge
Rubber boot
Dropping gate
Fence removes stray pieces
Stationary bottom plate

FIG. 6

Drive shaft

6. Non-clogging Stationary Hopper

Stationary hoppers handling granular materials can be equipped with electrical or mechanical vibrators to prevent clogging, but objects having a major dimension more than twice their minor dimension will clog unless the discharge opening is made several times their length. One positive anti-clogging device is the belt illustrated. The cleats are staggered in arrangement, wide enough so that the entire length of the discharge opening is frequently cleared, but too small and narrow to support a piece lifted out of the top of the material heap. The hopper may drop parts to a belt below, or be tilted so that the discharge opening is parallel to a sloping chute. When almost empty this type of hopper increases its rate of discharge, but the flow is quite constant from full to about one quarter full.

7. Coin Changer Feeding Mechanism

In this device, applicable only to round, flat objects, the tube is stationary. The funnel reciprocates, driving the tube end through the material heap; at each downward stroke one or more parts will be passed through the slot in the top of the tube. Lubricant on the OD of the tube will dirty and contaminate the pieces handled. If this is objectionable the bearing bushing must be dry, but lengthening it will extend its useful life. Parts which are too heavy will batter the end of the tube, and burrs will reduce the number fed into it. The clearance between the OD of the piece and the ID of the tube may be sufficient so the design can be applied to parts not too uniform in size.

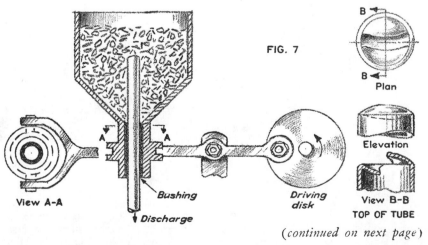

FIG. 7

View A-A
Bushing
Discharge
Driving disk
Plan
Elevation
View B-B
TOP OF TUBE

(continued on next page)

8. Bar-sided Drum Hopper

This design can be used in the random discharge version (shown in sketch I) for parts which tangle, since pieces not discharged are thrown back into the heap at the bottom. Sketch II shows the arrangement of the bars; the outer guide ends at the discharge slide or belt, with the bar at the discharge point sloping at the same angle as the slide.

Sketch III shows how the design can be adapted to discharge more than one stream of material by dividing the openings with separators, but parts which tangle would clog the openings. Cylindrical objects can be discharged at a timed rate or synchronized with other mechanisms according to the operation of the gate solenoid.

Looking at sketch II upside down, the bottom pair of bars at the centerline will be seen to form a funnel shape between surfaces A and B, which facilitates the parts dropping onto surface C, on which they ride in the lower half of the drum. An inner guide may be fitted into the upper half of the drum, in which case the spaces between the bars will remain filled until each slot passes discharge point and finds the gate open.

9. Power Screwdriver Hopper

One of the oldest and most popular feeding and sorting devices, this design has been adapted to a variety of symmetrically shaped parts. The wedge-shaped blocks fastened to the rotating ring are spaced so as to permit the part to fall between them when they pass under the supply stored inside the cover. The baffle plate inside the rotating ring is stationary, being attached to the fixed central shaft which also supports the discharge track. This baffle plate keeps the 50 caliber bullet cores illustrated from falling inwards until they are carried up to the end of the track. The selector guard attached

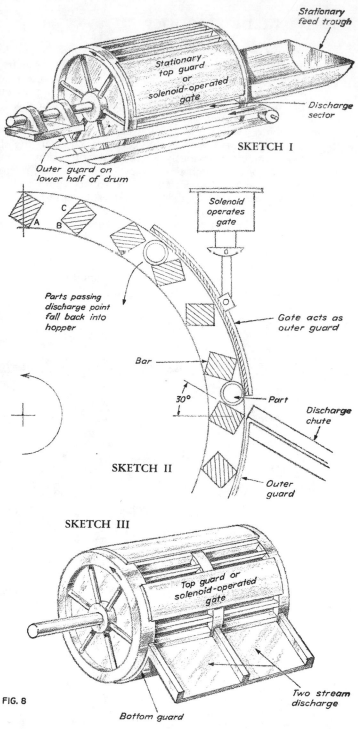

Stationary feed trough

Stationary top guard or solenoid-operated gate

Discharge sector

SKETCH I

Outer guard on lower half of drum

Solenoid operates gate

Parts passing discharge point fall back into hopper

Gate acts as outer guard

Bar

30°

Part

Discharge chute

SKETCH II

Outer guard

SKETCH III

Top guard or solenoid-operated gate

FIG. 8

Bottom guard

Two stream discharge

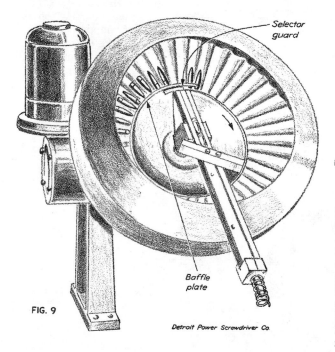

Selector guard

Baffle plate

FIG. 9

Detroit Power Screwdriver Co.

to the baffle plate allows bullet cores oriented point first to pass into the track, but rejects those having their blunt end down. For parts which are bulky and which must be fed at a high rate this hopper must be equipped with an auxiliary device to dump batches of parts inside the cover every few minutes, since the cover cannot hold a very large supply. This hopper is usually driven by a constant speed motor, a feed limiting device or escapement being used to regulate the discharge. Feeds as high as 300 parts per minute can be obtained, but light plastic or sheet metal objects must be discharged at a much lower rate.

10. Squirrel Cage Feeding and Sorting Hopper

Rubber parts are difficult to sort because of their high coefficient of friction and resilience. These rubber casters, pressed into the bottom of small electrical appliances, could not be handled in any device dropping them even a short distance, and their center of gravity is such that orientation by movement would be difficult. However, lying in the outer cover of this hopper, they are tumbled until each piece happens to orient itself with the shank down. A slot passes under them, and they drop into it when other pieces permit. As the hopper turns clockwise, the caster lying with its shank in the slot between two wedges is carried into the upper left quadrant, where the inner guard keeps it from falling out. The inner guard ends at top center, where the chute picks up whatever pieces are in each slot and removes them. The weight of the piece is taken at

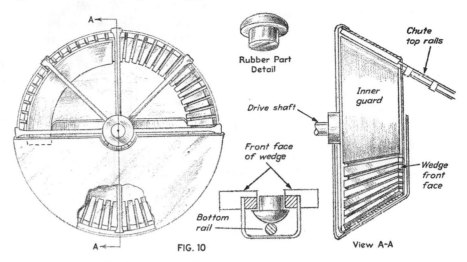

FIG. 10

point contact with the bottom rail, the top rails being stabilizers. This type of chute is best for rubber and other high-friction materials because it is open for clearing jams, has little fric-

tional resistance to movement, and is easy to fabricate. It will handle cubes, long cylinders and other shapes, and is especially good for material that have a high coefficient of friction.

11. Piston Hopper

Materials too fragile to be tumbled or agitated can be fed from this design. The chute angle should be approximately equal to the angle of repose of the material. The drive pinion may be driven by a variable speed motor and gear train, or the screw feed replaced by a hydraulic cylinder. A surprisingly constant flow of material can be maintained, but additional regulation by adjustment of the pivoting gate is difficult unless accompanied by control of the piston feed.

12. Vibratory Bowl Feeder

In this design a bowl is placed above a vibrator and shaken at 60 cycles by an AC solenoid. The center of the dish remains relatively motionless, since the direction of vibration is normal to a radius. Vibration sets up forces which drive parts to the periphery of the bowl, where a spiral track guides them up to the rim of the bowl. The base containing the vibrator is a standard unit, but the shape of the bowl and track are determined by the objects to be handled. Rate of feed is controlled by a rheostat which varies the amplitude of vibration; it is not normally necessary to vary the frequency. Multiple streams of parts can be discharged by making the helical track of multiple pitch like a screw thread. Gates, fences, air blows, or variations in the shape of the track at one point can discharge pieces which are improperly oriented. With proper design and regulation the discharge can be blocked awaiting the needs of the associated equipment, or the vibrator can be turned on and off by counting devices.

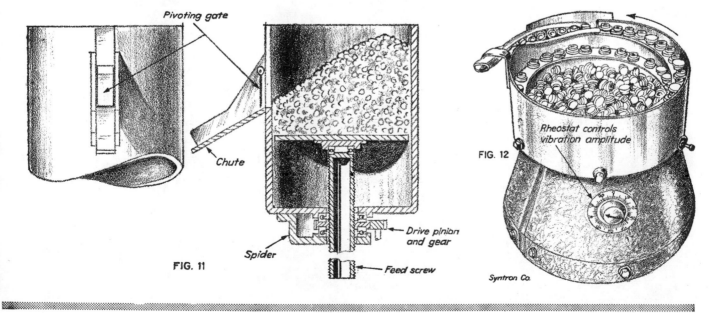

FIG. 11

FIG. 12

Syntron Co.

AUTOMATIC FEED MECHANISMS

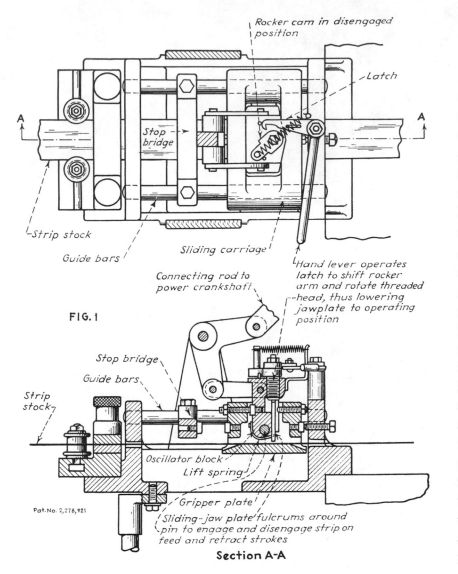

Rocker cam in disengaged position

Latch

A ————— A

Stop bridge

Strip stock

Guide bars

Sliding carriage

Hand lever operates latch to shift rocker arm and rotate threaded head, thus lowering jawplate to operating position

FIG. 1

Connecting rod to power crankshaft

Stop bridge

Guide bars

Strip stock

Oscillator block

Lift spring

Pat.No. 2,278,921

Gripper plate

Sliding-jaw plate fulcrums around pin to engage and disengage strip on feed and retract strokes

Section A-A

Design of feed mechanisms for automatic or semi-automatic machines depends largely upon such factors as size, shape, and character of materials or parts being fed into a machine, and upon the type of operations to be performed. Feed mechanisms may be merely conveyors, may give positive guidance in many instances, or may include tight holding devices if the parts are subjected to processing operations while being fed through a machine. One of the functions of feed mechanism is to extract single pieces from a stack or unassorted supply of stock or, if the stock is a continuous strip of steel, roll of paper, long bar, and the like, to maintain intermittent motion between processing operations. All of these conditions are illustrated in the accompanying feed mechanisms.

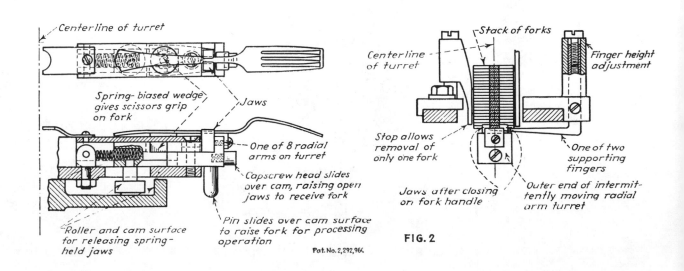

Centerline of turret

Spring-biased wedge gives scissors grip on fork

Jaws

One of 8 radial arms on turret

Capscrew head slides over cam, raising open jaws to receive fork

Roller and cam surface for releasing spring-held jaws

Pin slides over cam surface to raise fork for processing operation

Pat.No. 2,292,966

Stack of forks

Centerline of turret

Finger height adjustment

Stop allows removal of only one fork

Jaws after closing on fork handle

One of two supporting fingers

Outer end of intermittently moving radial arm turret

FIG. 2

FOR VARIOUS MATERIALS

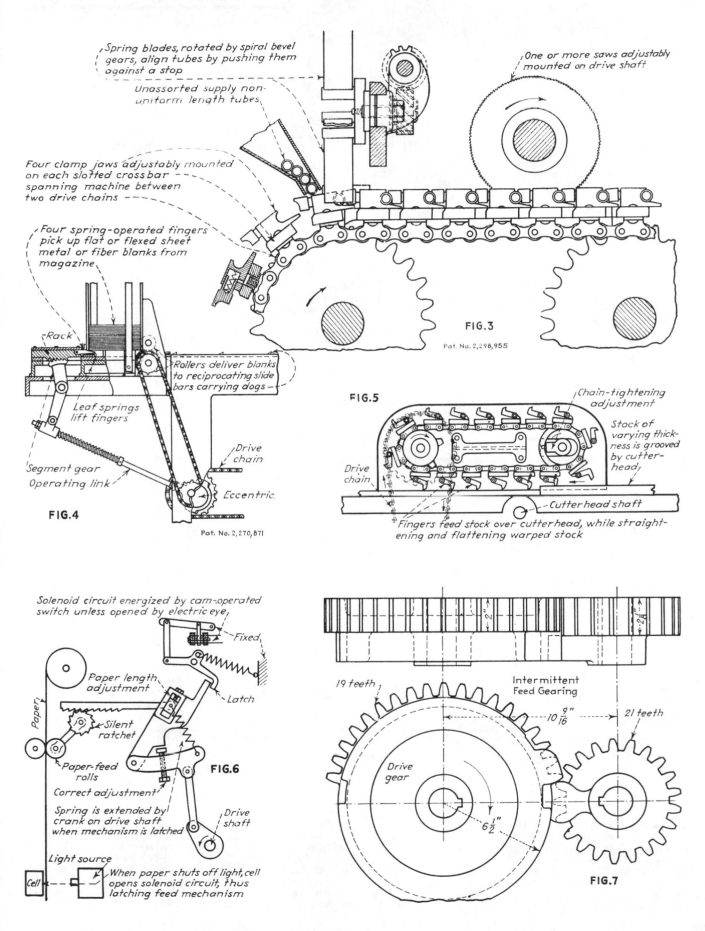

Spring blades, rotated by spiral bevel gears, align tubes by pushing them against a stop

Unassorted supply non-uniform length tubes

One or more saws adjustably mounted on drive shaft

Four clamp jaws adjustably mounted on each slotted crossbar spanning machine between two drive chains

Four spring-operated fingers pick up flat or flexed sheet metal or fiber blanks from magazine

FIG. 3

Pat. No. 2,298,955

Rack

Rollers deliver blanks to reciprocating slide bars carrying dogs

FIG. 5

Chain-tightening adjustment

Stock of varying thickness is grooved by cutterhead

Leaf springs lift fingers

Drive chain

Drive chain

Segment gear
Operating link

Eccentric

Cutterhead shaft

Fingers feed stock over cutterhead, while straightening and flattening warped stock

FIG. 4

Pat. No. 2,270,871

Solenoid circuit energized by cam-operated switch unless opened by electric eye

Fixed

Paper length adjustment

Latch

Paper

Silent ratchet

Paper-feed rolls

Correct adjustment

FIG. 6

Spring is extended by crank on drive shaft when mechanism is latched

Drive shaft

Light source

Cell

When paper shuts off light, cell opens solenoid circuit, thus latching feed mechanism

19 teeth

Intermittent Feed Gearing

21 teeth

$10\frac{9}{16}$"

Drive gear

$6\frac{1}{2}$"

FIG. 7

Linkages for

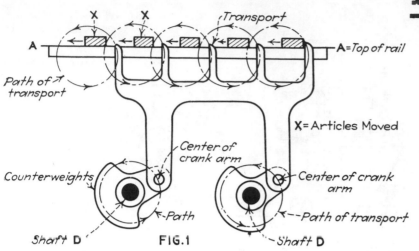

Fig. 1—In this design a rotary action is used. The shafts *D* rotate in unison and also support the main moving member. The shafts are carried in the frame of the machine and may be connected by either a link motion, a chain and sprocket, or by an intermediate idler gear between two equal gears keyed on the shafts. The rail *A-A* is fixed rigidly on the machine. A pressure or friction plate may be used to hold the material against the top of the rail and prevent any movement during the period of rest.

TRANSPORT mechanisms are generally used for moving material. The motion, although unindirectional, gives an intermittent advancement of the material being conveyed. The essential characteristic of such a motion is that all points in the main moving members follow similar and equal paths. This is necessary in order that the members may be subdivided into sections with projecting portions. The purpose of the projections is to push the articles during the forward motion of the material being transported. The transport returns by a different path from that which it follows in its advancement, and the material is left undisturbed until the next cycle begins. During this period of rest while the transport is returning to

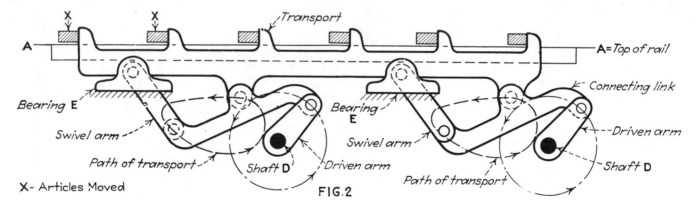

Fig. 2—Here is shown a simple form of link motion which imparts a somewhat "egg-shaped" motion to the transport. The forward stroke is almost a straight line. The transport is carried on the connecting links. As in design in Fig. 1, the shafts *D* are driven in unison and are supported in the frame of the machine. Bearings *E* are also supported by the frame of the machine and the rail *A-A* is fixed. The details of operation can be understood readily from the figure.

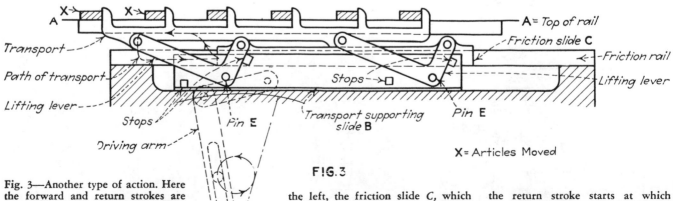

Fig. 3—Another type of action. Here the forward and return strokes are accomplished by a suitable mechanism, while the raising and lowering is imparted by a friction slide. Thus it can be seen from a study of the figure that as the transport supporting slide *B* starts to move to the left, the friction slide *C*, which rests on the friction rail, tends to remain at rest. As a result, the lifting lever starts to turn in a clockwise direction. This motion raises the transport which remains in its raised position against stops until the return stroke starts at which time the reverse action begins. An adjustment should be provided for the amount of friction between the slide and its rail. It can readily be seen that this motion imparts a long straight path to the transport.

Transport Mechanisms

F. R. ZIMMERMAN

The designs shown here represent a summary of typical constructions for obtaining intermittent advancement. Although they are specifically for conveying material, these same mechanisms might be adopted for other purposes

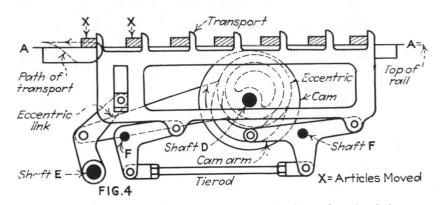

Fig. 4—Here is illustrated an action such that the forward motion is imparted by an eccentric while the raising and lowering of the transport is accomplished by means of a cam. The shafts, F, E and D are located by the frame of the machine. Special bell cranks support the transport and are interconnected by means of a tierod.

its starting position, various operations may be progressively performed.

Selection of the particular type of transport mechanism best suited to any case depends to some degree on the arrangement which may be obtained for the driving means and also the path desired. A slight amount of overtravel is always required in order that the projection on the transport can clear the material when going into position for the advancing stroke.

The designs illustrated here have been selected from numerous sources and are typical of the simplest solutions of such problems. The paths, as indicated in these illustrations, can be varied by changes in the cams, levers and associated parts. Usually the customary cut-and-try method should be used to obtain the best solution.

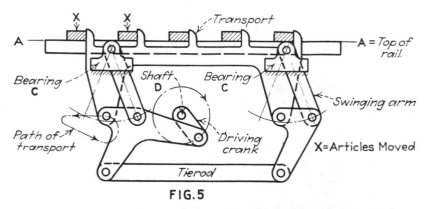

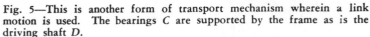

Fig. 5—This is another form of transport mechanism wherein a link motion is used. The bearings C are supported by the frame as is the driving shaft D.

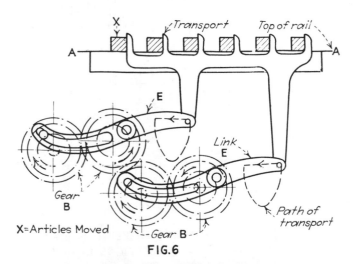

Fig. 6—An arrangement of interconnected gears of equal diameters which will impart a transport motion to a mechanism, the gear and link mechanism imparting both the forward motion and the raising and lowering. The gear shafts are supported in the frame of the machine.

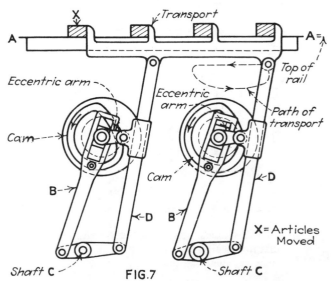

Fig. 7—In this transport mechanism the forward and return strokes are accomplished by the eccentric arms while the vertical motion is performed by the cams.

How to collect and stack

When you're called upon to design a way to collect die stampings as they come from the press, do your shopping here for ideas

FEDERICO STRASSER, Executive Engineer, Duplicon Company Inc, Westboro, Mass

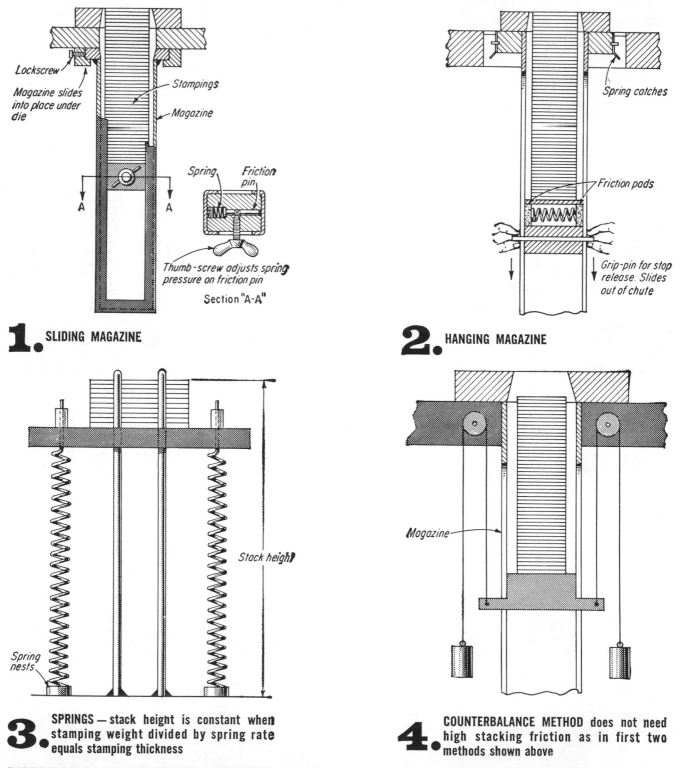

Lockscrew

Magazine slides into place under die

Stampings

Magazine

Spring   Friction pin

Thumb-screw adjusts spring pressure on friction pin

Section "A-A"

Spring catches

Friction pads

Grip-pin for stop release. Slides out of chute

1. SLIDING MAGAZINE

2. HANGING MAGAZINE

Stack height

Spring nests

Magazine

3. SPRINGS — stack height is constant when stamping weight divided by spring rate equals stamping thickness

4. COUNTERBALANCE METHOD does not need high stacking friction as in first two methods shown above

DIRECT STACKING WITH BACK PRESSURE. FRICTION DRAGS, SPRINGS, AND COUNTERBALANCE WEIGHTS PROVIDE BACK PRESSURE TO ALLOW SMOOTH STACKING IN FIRST FOUR METHODS

die stampings

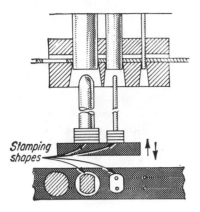

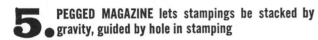

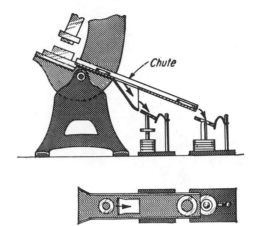

5. PEGGED MAGAZINE lets stampings be stacked by gravity, guided by hole in stamping

6. CHUTED STACKING WITH PEGGED MAGAZINE "sieves" stampings from two-stage die

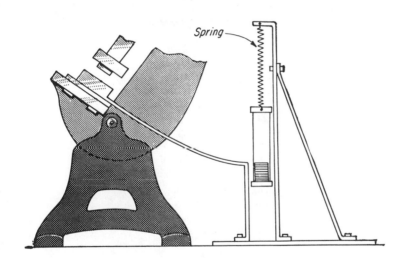

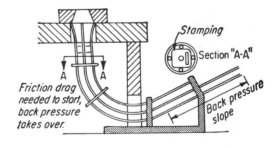

7. CHUTED STACKING WITH SPRING-SUSPENDED MAGAZINE

8. RODS FORM CHUTE

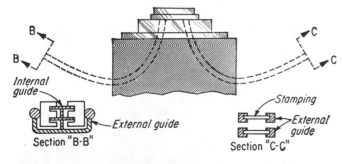

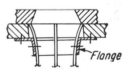

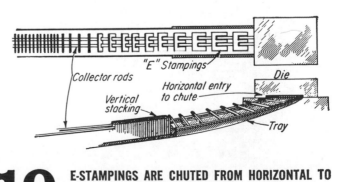

9. SPECIAL SHAPES ARE CHUTED IN CORRECT ORIENTATION

10. E-STAMPINGS ARE CHUTED FROM HORIZONTAL TO VERTICAL STACKING ON RODS

CONVEYORS may be divided into two classes: those that are a part of a machine used in processing a product and those that are used to move products, which are in various stages of fabrication, from one worker to another or from one part of a plant to another. For the most part the accompanying group of conveyors are of the first class and are elements of machines taking part in processing various articles. Both continuous and intermittently moving equipment are illustrated.

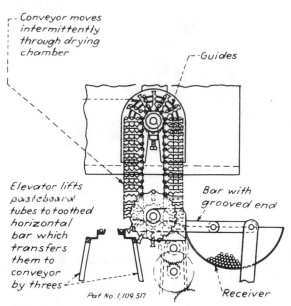

Conveyor moves intermittently through drying chamber

Guides

Elevator lifts pasteboard tubes to toothed horizontal bar which transfers them to conveyor by threes

Bar with grooved end

Receiver

Pat. No. 1,109,517

FIG. 1 – *Intermittently moving grooved bar links convey pasteboard tubes through drying chamber*

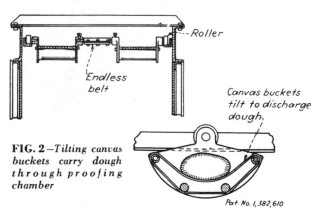

Roller

Endless belt

Canvas buckets tilt to discharge dough

FIG. 2 – *Tilting canvas buckets carry dough through proofing chamber*

Pat. No. 1,382,610

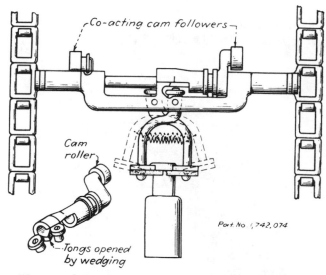

Co-acting cam followers

Cam roller

Tongs opened by wedging

Pat. No. 1,742,074

FIG. 3 – *Co-acting cams in paths of follower rollers open and close tongs over bottle necks by wedging action*

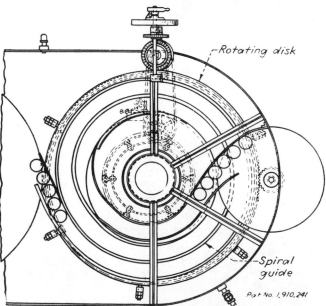

Horizontal sprocket at end of plating tank

Driving gear

Chain

Hanger slides on copper cathode bar

Article suspended in plating batch

Pat. No. 2,142,829

FIG. 4 – *Chain-driven conveyor hooks move articles through plating bath*

Rotating disk

Spiral guide

Pat. No. 1,910,241

FIG. 5 – *Rotating disk carries food cans in spiral path between stationary guides for pre-sealing heat-treatment*

PRODUCTION MACHINES—I

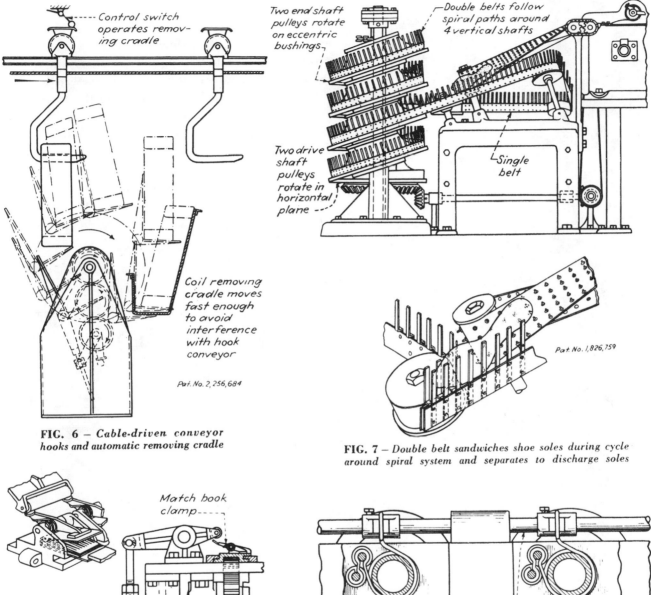

Control switch operates removing cradle

Coil removing cradle moves fast enough to avoid interference with hook conveyor

Pat. No. 2,256,684

FIG. 6 – *Cable-driven conveyor hooks and automatic removing cradle*

Two end shaft pulleys rotate on eccentric bushings

Double belts follow spiral paths around 4 vertical shafts

Two drive shaft pulleys rotate in horizontal plane

Single belt

Pat. No. 1,826,759

FIG. 7 – *Double belt sandwiches shoe soles during cycle around spiral system and separates to discharge soles*

Match book clamp

Drive sprocket

Carrier links driven intermittently by sprocket wheel engaging teeth on under sides of carrier links

Pat. No. 2,141,581

FIG. 8 – *Matchbook carrier links with holding clips are moved intermittently by sprockets*

Bottle support bar

Release bar

Bottle release spring

Link of conveyor chain

Sprocket

Pat. No. 2,258,717

FIG. 9 – *One of several possible types of bottle clips with release bars for automatic operation*

Holding clips on
ends of radial
pins

Drive
shaft

This group of conveyor mechanisms includes principles varying considerably among themselves. Each has been applied in many ways, which are dependent upon the characteristics of the article handled. In addition to the methods shown in this and the previous group, other conveyors have employed vibration, reciprocated jerking motion, suction and magnetic holders, forming carriers, and other principles and mechanisms requiring more space than is here available for adequate explanation.

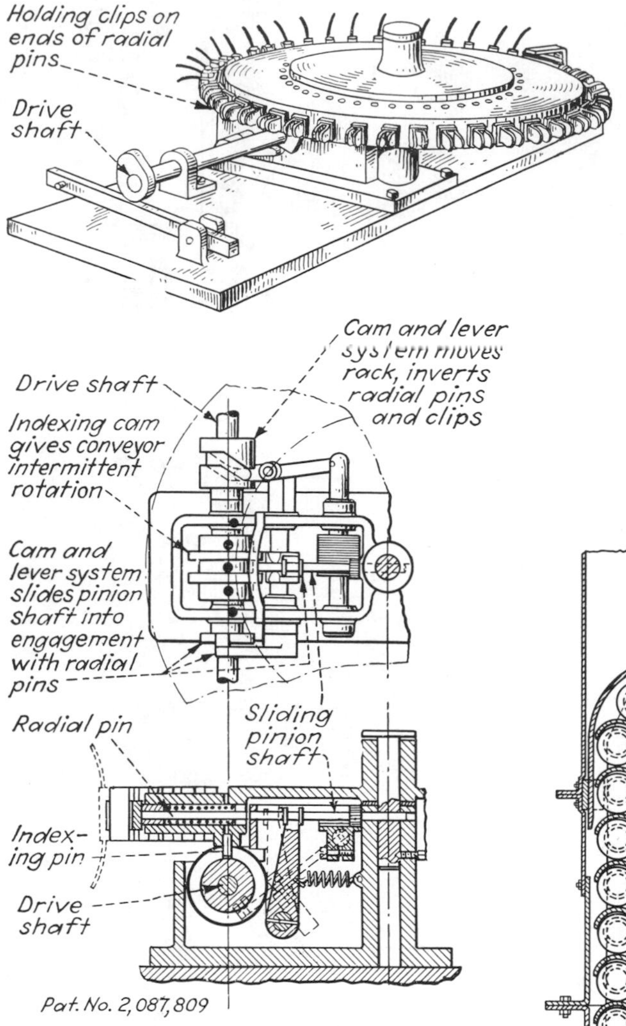

Drive shaft

Cam and lever system moves rack, inverts radial pins and clips

Indexing cam gives conveyor intermittent rotation

Cam and lever system slides pinion shaft into engagement with radial pins

Radial pin

Sliding pinion shaft

Index-ing pin

Drive shaft

Pat. No. 2,087,809

Fig. 1—Intermittent rotary conveyor inverts electrical condensers, to be sealed at both ends, by engaging radial pins to which holding clips are attached

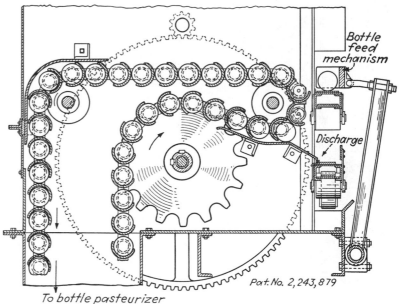

Bottle feed mechanism

Discharge

To bottle pasteurizer

Pat. No. 2,243,879

Conveyor belts on sides and bottom

Tapering guides shape paper sacks

Paper sacks

Pat. No. 1,998,287

Conveyor Detail

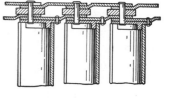

Fig. 2 — Pasteurizer **carrier** links lock bottles in place **on** straightways

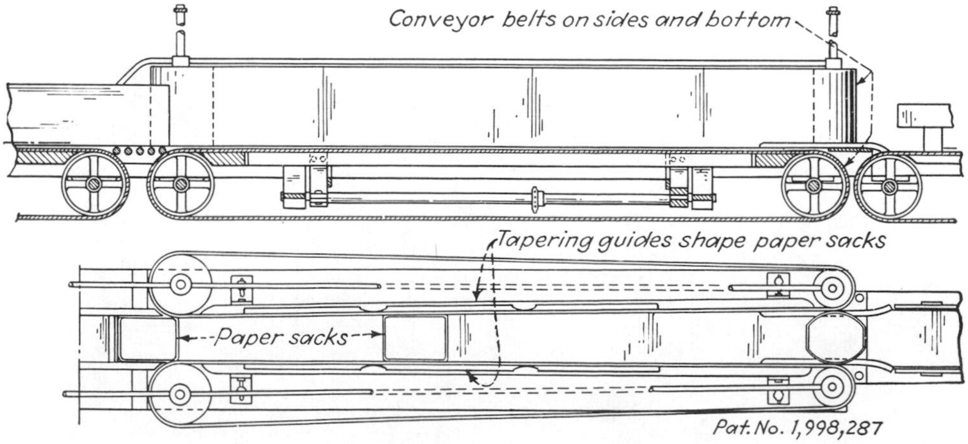

Fig. 3 — Wedging action **of** side belts shapes paper sacks for wrapping and packing

PRODUCTION MACHINES—II

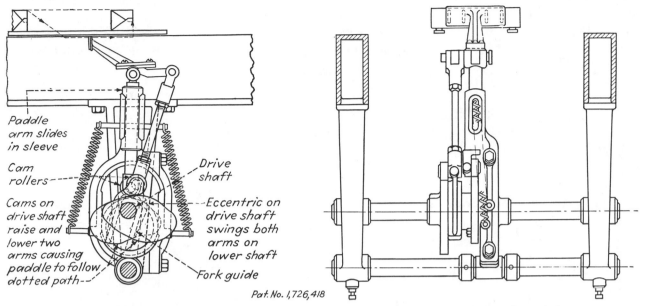

Paddle arm slides in sleeve

Cam rollers

Cams on drive shaft raise and lower two arms causing paddle to follow dotted path

Drive shaft

Eccentric on drive shaft swings both arms on lower shaft

Fork guide

Pat. No. 1,726,418

Fig. 4—Reciprocating pusher plate is activated by eccentric disk and two cams on drive shaft

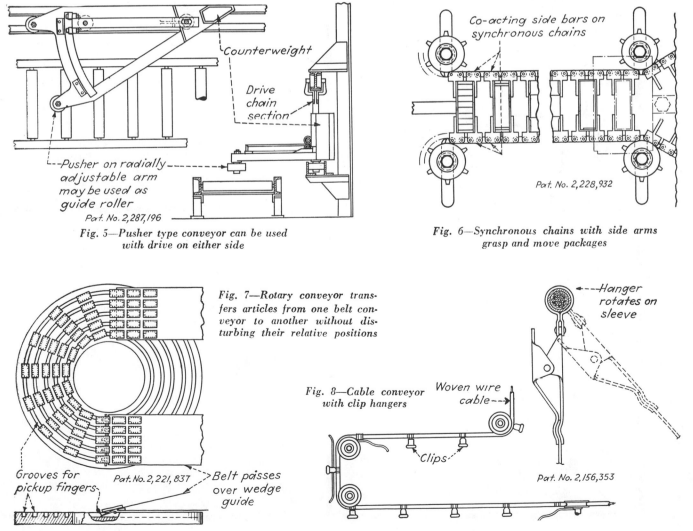

Counterweight

Drive chain section

Pusher on radially adjustable arm may be used as guide roller

Pat. No. 2,287,196

Fig. 5—Pusher type conveyor can be used with drive on either side

Co-acting side bars on synchronous chains

Pat. No. 2,228,932

Fig. 6—Synchronous chains with side arms grasp and move packages

Fig. 7—Rotary conveyor transfers articles from one belt conveyor to another without disturbing their relative positions

Hanger rotates on sleeve

Fig. 8—Cable conveyor with clip hangers

Woven wire cable

Clips

Grooves for pickup fingers

Pat. No. 2,221,837

Belt passes over wedge guide

Pat. No. 2,156,353

EIGHT PAPER-FEED MECHANISMS

In a world of reports, forms and memos, a prime need is to keep paper moving. Here are some ways that do the job for single sheets or continuous strip.

FRANK WILLIAM WOOD JR, president, Advanced Designs Inc, Vienna, Va

VERNAL HUFFINES, Lofstrand Corp, Rockville, Md

SINGLE-SHEET FEEDERS

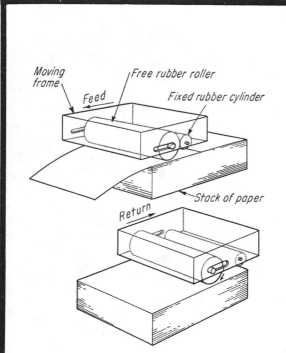

1

FREE ROLLER rides in slot. During feed it jams against the fixed cylinder and grips top sheet of paper. Return motion of frame transfers free roller to opposite end of slot, where it's free to roll back over paper.

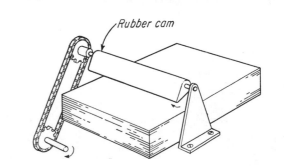

2

RUBBER PADS on rotating cylinder kick out one sheet per pad every revolution. Constant-force spring under paper-holder maintains proper clearance between paper and cylinder. Spacing of pads and the cylinder speed determine feed rate.

3

RUBBER CAM feeds one sheet each revolution. Constant-force spring under paper table keeps correct clearance. By correct timing, two or more cams in a stack will deliver different sheets in sequence. As with all single-sheet feeders, paper must be smooth enough to slide off pile.

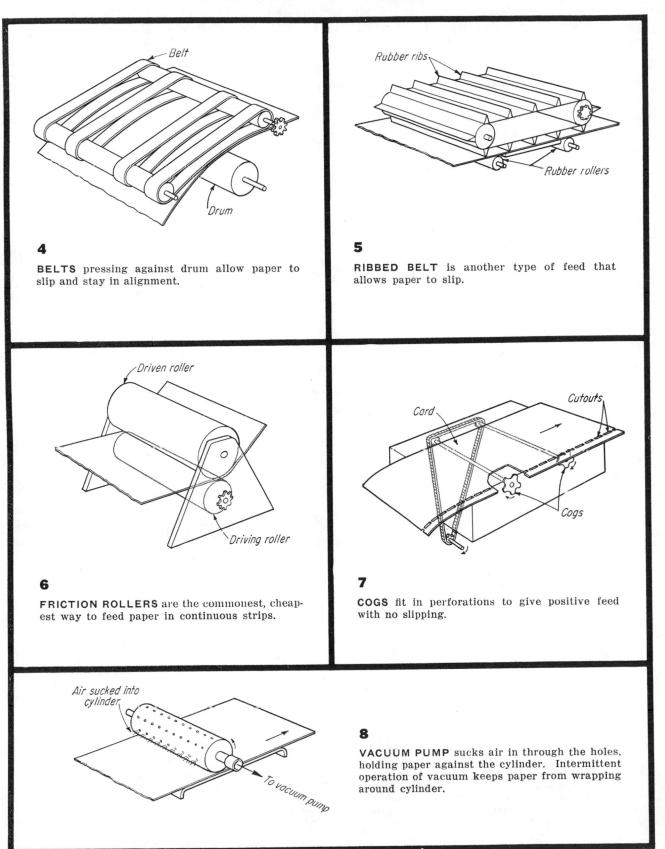

4

BELTS pressing against drum allow paper to slip and stay in alignment.

5

RIBBED BELT is another type of feed that allows paper to slip.

6

FRICTION ROLLERS are the commonest, cheapest way to feed paper in continuous strips.

7

COGS fit in perforations to give positive feed with no slipping.

8

VACUUM PUMP sucks air in through the holes, holding paper against the cylinder. Intermittent operation of vacuum keeps paper from wrapping around cylinder.

Traversing Mechanisms Used

The seven mechanisms shown below are used on different types of yarn and coil winding machines. Their fundamentals, however, may be applicable to other machines which require

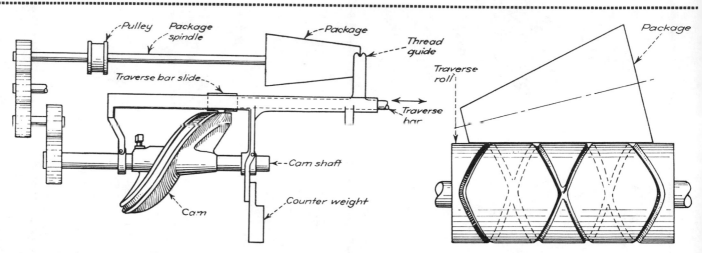

FIG. 1. Package is mounted on belt driven shaft on this precision type winding mechanism. Cam shaft imparts reciprocating motion to traverse bar by means of cam roll that runs in cam groove. Gears determine speed ratio between cam and package. Thread guide is attached to traverse bar. Counterweight keeps thread guide against package.

FIG. 2. Package is friction-driven from traverse roll. Yarn is drawn from the supply source by traverse roll and is transferred to package from the continuous groove in the roll. Different winds are obtained by varying the grooved path.

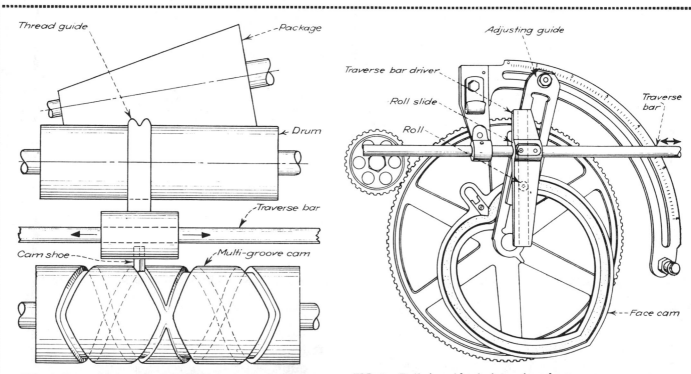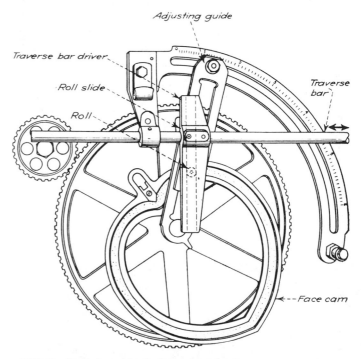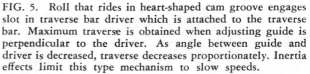

FIG. 4. Drum drives package by friction. Pointed cam shoe which pivots in the bottom side of the thread guide assembly rides in cam grooves and produces reciprocating motion of the thread guide assembly on the traverse bar. Plastic cams have proved quite satisfactory even with fast traverse speeds. Interchangeable cams permit a wide variety of winds.

FIG. 5. Roll that rides in heart-shaped cam groove engages slot in traverse bar driver which is attached to the traverse bar. Maximum traverse is obtained when adjusting guide is perpendicular to the driver. As angle between guide and driver is decreased, traverse decreases proportionately. Inertia effects limit this type mechanism to slow speeds.

on Winding Machines

E. R. SWANSON
Universal Winding Company

similar changes of motion. Except for the lead screw as used, for example on lathes, these seven represent the operating principles of all well-known, mechanical types of traversing devices.

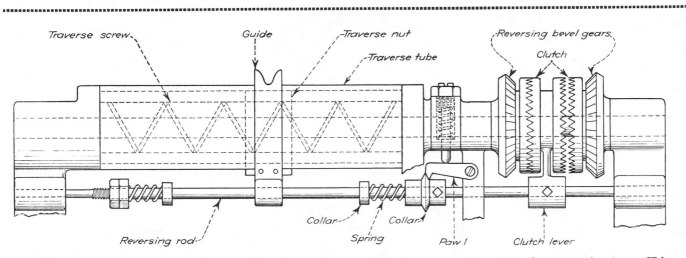

FIG. 3. Reversing bevel gears which are driven by a common bevel gear, drive the shaft carrying the traverse screw. Traverse nut mates with this screw and is connected to the yarn guide. Guide slides along the reversing rod. When nut reaches end of its travel, the thread guide compresses the spring that actuates the pawl and the reversing lever. This engages the clutch that rotates the traverse screw in the opposite direction. As indicated by the large pitch on the screw, this mechanism is limited to low speeds, but permits longer lengths of traverse than most of the others shown.

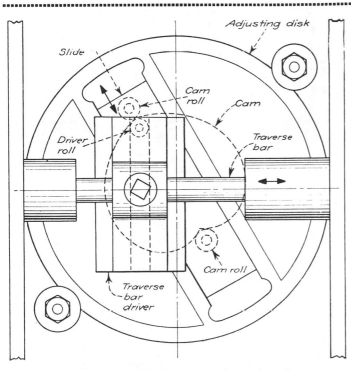

FIG. 6. Two cam rolls that engage heart shaped cam are attached to the slide. Slide has a driver roll that engages a slot in the traverse bar driver. Maximum traverse (to capacity of cam) occurs when adjusting disk is set so slide is parallel to traverse bar. As angle between traverse bar and slide increases, traverse decreases. At 90 deg traverse is zero.

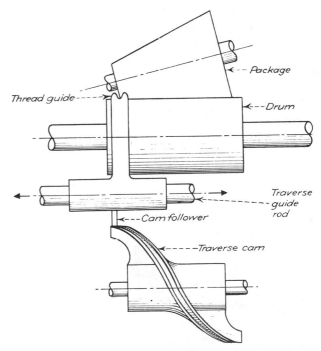
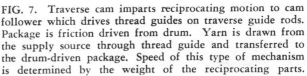

FIG. 7. Traverse cam imparts reciprocating motion to cam follower which drives thread guides on traverse guide rods. Package is friction driven from drum. Yarn is drawn from the supply source through thread guide and transferred to the drum-driven package. Speed of this type of mechanism is determined by the weight of the reciprocating parts.

55

ADHESIVE APPLICATORS FOR

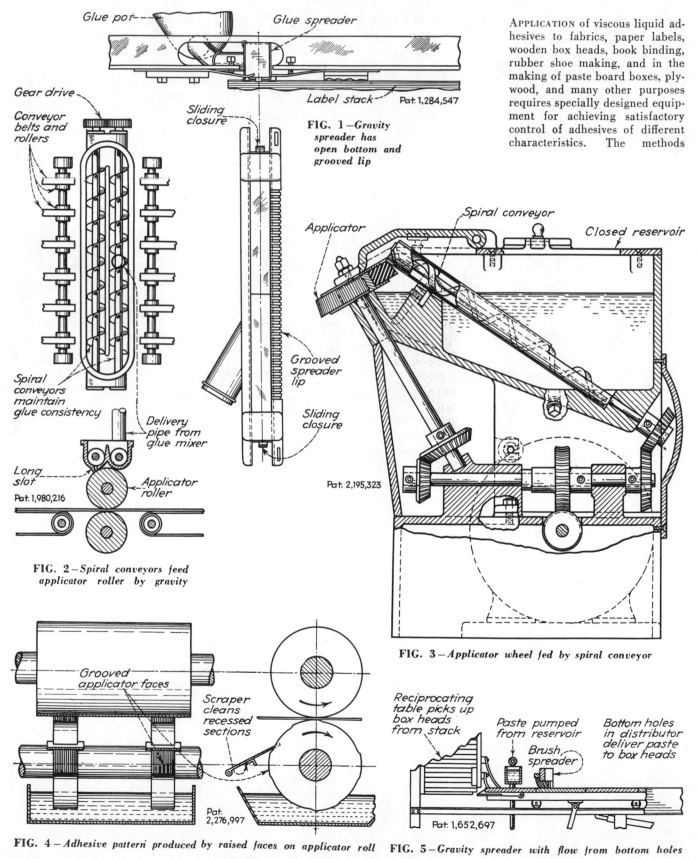

Glue pot

Glue spreader

FIG. 1 – *Gravity spreader has open bottom and grooved lip*

Label stack   Pat. 1,284,547

APPLICATION of viscous liquid adhesives to fabrics, paper labels, wooden box heads, book binding, rubber shoe making, and in the making of paste board boxes, plywood, and many other purposes requires specially designed equipment for achieving satisfactory control of adhesives of different characteristics.   The   methods

Gear drive

Conveyor belts and rollers

Sliding closure

Spiral conveyors maintain glue consistency

Delivery pipe from glue mixer

Long slot

Pat. 1,980,216

Applicator roller

FIG. 2 – *Spiral conveyors feed applicator roller by gravity*

Applicator

Grooved spreader lip

Sliding closure

Pat. 2,195,323

Spiral conveyor

Closed reservoir

FIG. 3 – *Applicator wheel fed by spiral conveyor*

Grooved applicator faces

Scraper cleans recessed sections

Pat. 2,276,997

FIG. 4 – *Adhesive pattern produced by raised faces on applicator roll*

Reciprocating table picks up box heads from stack

Paste pumped from reservoir

Brush spreader

Bottom holes in distributor deliver paste to box heads

Pat. 1,652,697

FIG. 5 – *Gravity spreader with flow from bottom holes*

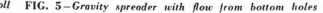

HIGH-SPEED MACHINES – I

shown here have been devised to incorporate the application of adhesives in production machines. Still other methods of application will be presented next month. In many instances these methods may be applicable for applying liquid finishes such as lacquers and paints also.

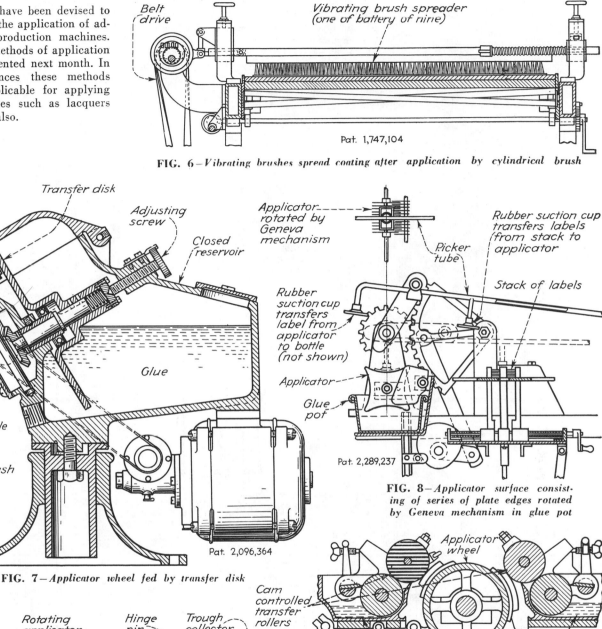

FIG. 6 – *Vibrating brushes spread coating after application by cylindrical brush*

FIG. 7 – *Applicator wheel fed by transfer disk*

FIG. 8 – *Applicator surface consisting of series of plate edges rotated by Geneva mechanism in glue pot*

FIG. 9 – *Rotating applicator disk fed by trough collector on transfer drum*

FIG. 10 – *Cam controlled transfer rollers supply applicator wheel pads with two kinds of adhesive*

ADHESIVE APPLICATORS FOR

METHODS OF APPLYING LIQUID ADHESIVES that are illustrated here are a continuation of the methods given last month. This group includes rotary applicators on movable axes and otherwise movable between adhesive pick-up position and applying position, endless belt applicators, applicators in the form of moving daubers, plates, and the like, reciprocating dies exuding measured quantities of cement, and spray nozzles. All of these mechanisms are used or are applicable on production machines such as for making pasteboard boxes or cartons, pasting labels or envelopes, and making shoes or other products involving the use of liquid adhesives.

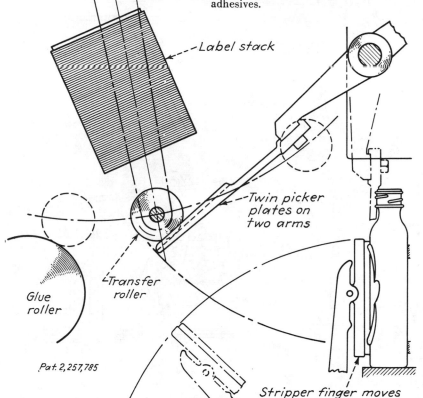

Pat. 2,257,785

FIG. 1 – Bottom label is spread with glue by two abutting glue-coated picker plates, which separate during contact with label stack, then carry label to bottle

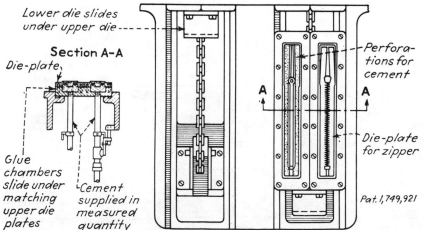

FIG. 2 – Measured quantities of cement are forced through perforations in specially designed upper and lower die plates, which are closed hydraulically over zippers. Lower die only is shown

FIG. 3–Brush applicator is fed through passages between bristle tufts by spring operated plunger

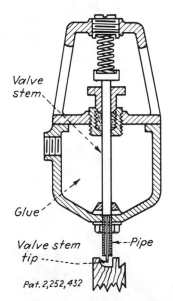

FIG. 4–Shoulder on valve stem in glue chamber retains glue until pressure on tip opens bottom valve

HIGH-SPEED MACHINES – II

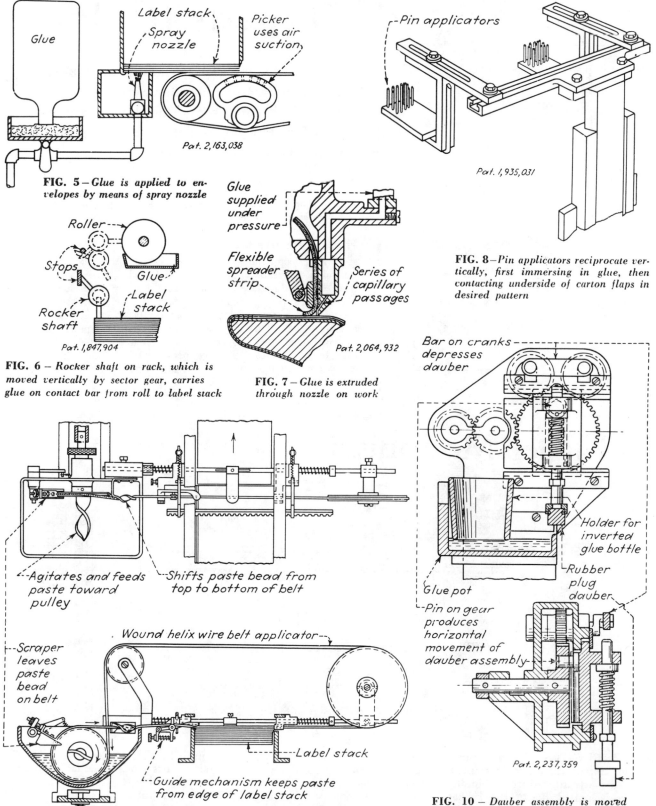

Glue

Label stack

Spray nozzle

Picker uses air suction

Pat. 2,163,038

FIG. 5 – *Glue is applied to envelopes by means of spray nozzle*

Roller

Stops

Glue

Rocker shaft

Label stack

Pat. 1,847,904

FIG. 6 – *Rocker shaft on rack, which is moved vertically by sector gear, carries glue on contact bar from roll to label stack*

Glue supplied under pressure

Flexible spreader strip

Series of capillary passages

Pat. 2,064,932

FIG. 7 – *Glue is extruded through nozzle on work*

Pin applicators

Pat. 1,935,031

FIG. 8 – *Pin applicators reciprocate vertically, first immersing in glue, then contacting underside of carton flaps in desired pattern*

Agitates and feeds paste toward pulley

Shifts paste bead from top to bottom of belt

Scraper leaves paste bead on belt

Wound helix wire belt applicator

Label stack

Guide mechanism keeps paste from edge of label stack

Pat. 2,206,964

FIG. 9 – *Paste belt applicator passes around pulley in pastepot and slides over label stack*

Bar on cranks depresses dauber

Holder for inverted glue bottle

Glue pot

Rubber plug dauber

Pin on gear produces horizontal movement of dauber assembly

Pat. 2,237,359

FIG. 10 – *Dauber assembly is moved horizontally between glue pot and work by eccentric pin on gear. Vertical movements are produced by crank operated bar over dauber shaft*

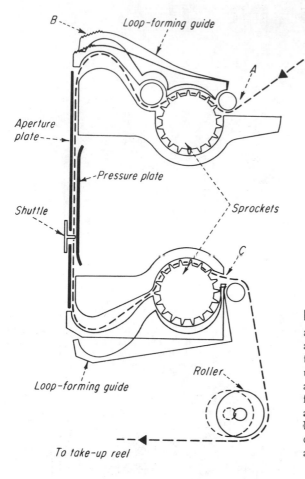

Projector Threads Itself

Film inserted into the mechanism of an 8-mm movie projector is threaded automatically through the shuttle and the drive sprockets. Loop-forming guides determine film path until take-up reel exerts tension.

Designed by Bell & Howell to simplify setting up for home movies, the Auto Load projector threads itself in less than 3 seconds.

Film is inserted . . .

at A after loop-forming guides have been closed. Guides are linked (not shown) so pressure at B will move both of them to the threading position. Top sprocket drives film under roller, through upper loop-forming guide, between aperture and pressure plates, and past shuttle to lower loop-forming guide. Then film is engaged by bottom sprocket and discharged at C. Operator leads film under roller and back to take-up reel. Linkage between roller and guides causes them to move out of threading position when reel absorbs slack and applies tension to film.

Changer Mechanism

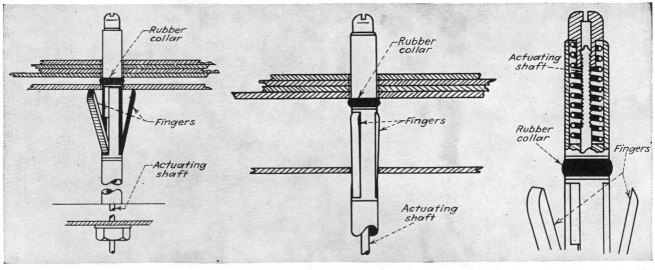

THREE FINGERS in the center spindle support the stack of records. When the actuating shaft within the spindle is pulled down, the rubber collar is compressed. This forces the collar into the stack, separating the bottom record from the rest. Up to this point, the fingers can spread slightly to accommodate the small movement of the bottom record. As the change cycle proceeds, a further downward pull on the actuating shaft retracts the fingers, dropping the record on the turntable. Then, the shaft is released. This spreads the fingers and releases the compression on the collar. This permits the remaining records to rest on the fingers until the start of the next cycle. The shaft acts on the collar through a compensating spring. This spring pre-loads the rubber to assure that wedging will begin the instant the shaft is pulled down—regardless of hole diameter which varies with wear. The Webster-Chicago Corporation of Chicago makes this fast action changer.

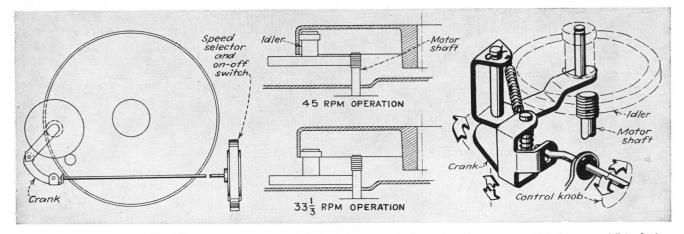

COMPOUND DIAMETER idler converts rotation of the small diameter motor shaft into proper turntable speed. Sketches in center above show idler positions for playing 33⅓ and 45 rpm records. In shifting the idler up and down during speed selection, the idler must be backed away from contact with both motor shaft and turntable before the shift takes place. This is accomplished by the crank motion sketched at the right. An advantage of this arrangement is that idler contacts neither the motor shaft nor the turntable when the crank is in the center position. At this point, the motor switch is open. This design prevents the formation of hollow spots on the rim of the idler's rubber surface while the machine is not in use. These hollow spots introduce noise into the sound system. The control knob used for changing speed also actuates the on-off switch.

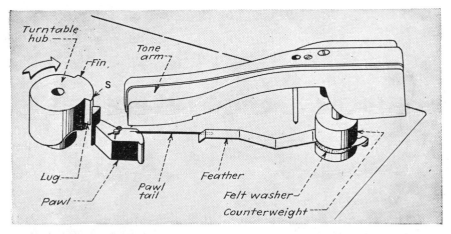

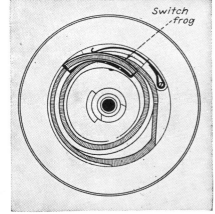

CHANGER MECHANISM responds not to tone arm position but to its rate of travel. As tone arm advances slowly during the playing of a record, the feather moves with it. Connection between tone arm and feather is frictional, through the counterweight pressing against the felt washer. In turn, feather rotates the pawl through the pawl tail. However, the turn table hub carries a cam shaped lug that has a shorter radius at "S" than at "FIN". With each revolution, the lug pushes the pawl and feather back to their original position. Thus, feather has a receding relationship with the tone arm. But when tone arm contacts a velocity groove and advances suddenly, the pawl will engage the lug's driving face. This swings the pawl around, starting the change cycle.

TWO-REVOLUTION CAM that controls changing operations is integral with zinc die cast turntable. When designers considered the many motions involved, they decided that one revolution of the cam would be too rapid for smooth action. The two revolution cam sketched above uses a one-way switch frog at the cross-over point to guide the cam pin.

CAM-PATH is three-dimensional, providing up and down as well as radial motion. When cam depresses the pin on the end of the cam lever, the tone arm is lifted from the record. Then, arm is shifted horizontally away from the turntable, held motionless for a moment and returned to the starting position. A second cam surface is cut into the turntable hub where maximum torque is available for pulling the actuating shaft that compresses the rubber disk.

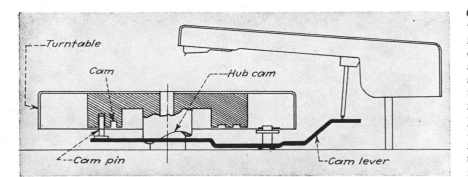

VACUUM PICKUP POSITIONS PILLS

Carrying tablet cores to moving dies, placing cores
accurately in coating granulation, and preventing
formation of tablets without cores

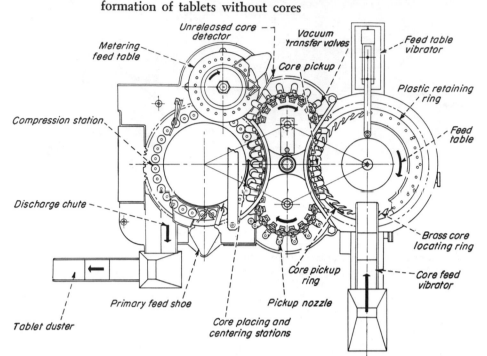

CORES ARE HOPPER FED to a rotating feeder disk through a tablet duster. This disk is vibrated clockwise under a slotted pickup ring which rotates counterclockwise. Each slot in pickup ring holds two cores and lets broken tablets pass through to an area under feeder table. Cores are picked from ring slots, carried to tablet press dies and deposited in dies by vacuum nozzles fastened to a chain driven by press die table. This chain also drives the pickup ring to synchronize motion of ring slots and pickup nozzles. Coating granulation is fed into dies ahead of and after station where vacuum pickup deposits a core in each die. Compressing rolls are at left side of machine. Principal design objectives were to evolve a machine to apply dry coatings at speeds which lowered costs below those of liquid coating techniques and was adapted to positive brand identification.

UNIT APPLIES LABELS FROM STACKS OR ROLLERS

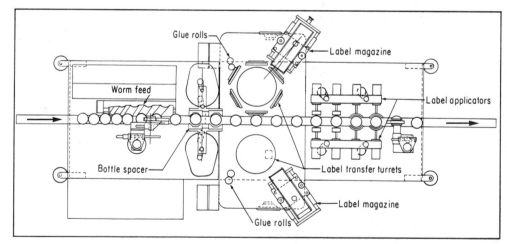

Flow of containers through versatile new labeler is indicated by top-view drawing of machine. Bottle spacers insure that containers remain 7½ in. apart on conveyor. Dual label-transfer turrets allow for simultaneous application of front and back labels.

The new Pony Pacer Labeler—available from New Jersey Machine—is a versatile unit that can use either conventional glue-label application or heat-seal labels in cut or roll form. The device labels front and back of round or odd-shaped containers at speeds of 60 to 160 containers per minute. Containers handled range from 1 in. diameter or thickness to 4¼ in. diameter by 5½ in. wide. Container height can vary from 2 to 14 inches. The unit handles labels ranging from ⅞ to 5½ in. wide and ⅞ to 6½ in. high. The label hopper is designed for labels sub-stantially rectangular in shape, although it can be modified to handle irregular shapes. Provision has been made in design of the unit, according to the manufacturer, to allow labels to be placed at varying heights on the containers

Unit's cut-and-stacked label capacity is 4,500. An electric eye is provided for cutting labels in web-roll form. Model number of the unit is 202-RL-2. *New Jersey Machine Corp., Hoboken, N.J.*

From *Modern Packaging*

2
AUTOMATIC STOP
AND SAFETY MECHANISMS

DEVICES FOR AUTOMATIC DIE OPERATION

EMIL LOEFFEL, Waldwick, N. J.

First step toward automated press operation is development of proper die-protection devices. Many die designers fail to provide such items in the mistaken belief that they are complicated and costly.

Actually, the devices to be described are simple and relatively inexpensive. Some of them have been used exclusively in our plant with satisfying results. Among the most important safety devices is the:

From *American Machinist*

Misfeed Detector

Progressive dies utilize piercing and piloting stations to establish the amount of stock feed per press stroke. Shown in Fig. 1 is a device that is used to protect this kind of die. The misfeed detector is nothing more than a simple push button. The metal cup making contact with the punch holder completes a circuit, Fig. 2, which holds a relay closed, allowing the press to run. Should the stock misfeed, the pilot will contact the stock as the press ram moves down, causing the metal cup to leave the punch holder, breaking the circuit and stopping the press.

This simple protective switch offers reliability, instantaneous action and simplicity of installation. It requires one hole above the probe pilot, slightly larger than the probe pilot head, and an intersecting hole or groove for the insulated wire. The ease of installation and the small space requirements make this switch popular for building protection into existing dies.

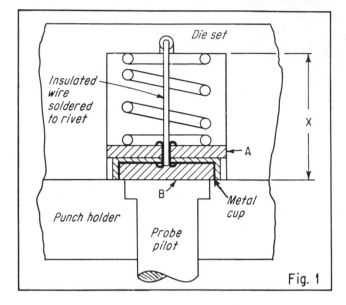

Fig. 1

Design Details

Fiber washer *A* insulates metal cup from spring and guides unit in hole. Fiber washer *B* insulates metal cup from pilot head. Distance *X* should be at least two times the distance the pilot will travel back during a misfeed and hence allow for reasonable spring compression. The spring should be stiff enough to prevent the metal cup from bouncing while running, but not stiff enough to become "solid" during misfeed.

Basic Circuit

An understanding of the basic circuit will enable the designer to design protective devices for many types of dies. The double-pole relay shown at left in Fig. 2 is the heart of the protective system. One set of contacts, held closed by the solenoid, supply current to the solenoid itself. Any break, even a momentary one, in the solenoid circuit—either through operation of the misfeed detector, the stock-buckling relay, or the end-of-stock switch—will cause the solenoid to de-energize, thus releasing both sets of contacts and immediately stopping the press. Once the solenoid contacts open, the solenoid cannot be re-energized by re-establishing the current path through the detectors. The solenoid can be re-energized only by pushing the reset button, and then only if the detectors are in their normal positions. However, the press should not start if the reset

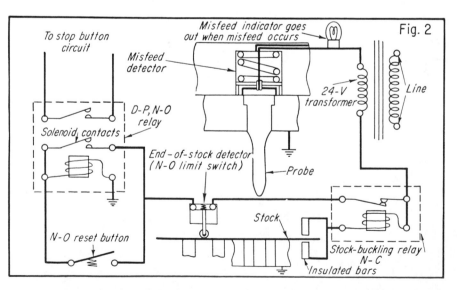

Fig. 2

button is pushed. Accidental starting can be hazardous. Avoid this condition by wiring the protective circuit into the press stop button, if available. In this way the start button must be pushed to restart the press.

The addition of a normal-operation indicator shows when a misfeed has occurred by going out. This feature is helpful when running a bank of presses and it is difficult to hear if a press is actually running.

End-of-Stock Detector

When one man is servicing many presses, an end-of-stock detector is a valuable asset. The device is easy to install, and is independent of the type of die, and can thus be used for all jobs run on the press. As shown in Fig. 2, the detector is a normally open snap-action switch held closed by the stock. The switch is sometimes mounted so as to utilize a small probe which lies on the stock and activates the switch at the end of the coil, as shown in Fig. 3. The normal-operation indicator will go out when the stock has run out and the press has stopped.

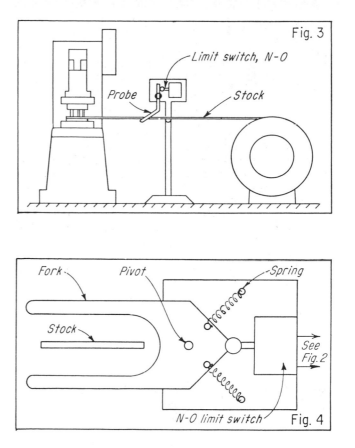

Stock-Buckling Detector

When stock is fed automatically, it is usually better to pull rather than to push the material through a die. In the event that a punch is pulled out or a slug is wedged in the die—or any circumstance prevents the stock from feeding—there is a good chance that the probe pilot will re-enter the same hole, not detect any malfunction, and permit the press to continue to run. Should this occur on a press set up to pull stock through the die, the worst that can happen is that the feeding equipment will slip or a short piece of stock can be ripped from the die. However, if the stock catches in a die equipped with a push feed, the stock can buckle and cause serious damage.

Many dies are fed by pushing because they leave little or no stock to pull on. In order to protect these dies a stock-buckling detector should be used. One design is shown in Fig. 2. If the stock buckles

enough to touch either one of the insulated bars, the press will stop. Shown in Fig. 4 is a method sometimes preferred because it eliminates the use of a relay. The N-O (normally open) limit switch is held in the closed position by the fork.

(continued)

Rules for Designing and Using Protective Devices

Now that we have seen how protective devices can be used, it is reasonable to set down the rules for their design and use:

1. Protective circuits should always be designed as live current-carrying circuits. Thus, if a break in the wiring or a power failure occurs, the press will stop and not continue to run unprotected.

2. Design protective devices to detect malfunctions and to stop the press at the earliest possible moment. Hence, keep the feed pilot and the probe-pilot detector as long as possible without interfering with feeding action.

3. When using protective circuits which have a grounded connection, never use more than 24 volts in the ground circuit.

Avoid using 110 volts in the protective circuit; a 24-v transformer and a relay cost very little as compared to an accident.

4. Protective circuits should be wired into the stop button if available, so that pushing the reset button can never trip the press. The starting button must always be used to initiate starting action.

5. Always provide an air-oil hole for the probe pilot bushing. This hole will prevent unintentional shut-off due to build-up of air or oil.

6. Isolate electronic components of the system from vibration. Use shock mounts or —better yet—mount the components off the press.

7. Make periodic checks to see that the protective system is functioning in the proper manner.

Feed Pilot Used As a Probe

A feed pilot can be used as a misfeed detector, Fig. 5, when stamping stock up to 1/16 in. thick. Scored pilots and pulled pilot bushings are prevented, because the pilot can retract during misfeeds. An added advantage of the method is that on certain dies the stock can be placed right into the feeding equipment and the press started up without the need for hand feeding the stock across the die. This use saves press time and allows a lower-skilled press operator to start new coils. The first few pieces made will be incomplete, but these can be removed without stopping the press, as they come out of the die.

This type of misfeed detector should not be used on stock thicker than 1/16 in., because the pilot cannot position the stock and an unintended shutoff will occur.

Existing progressive dies can be easily protected by giving the feed pilot the dual role of both locating the stock and acting as a probe. For best results the pilot should have a long gradually curved tip.

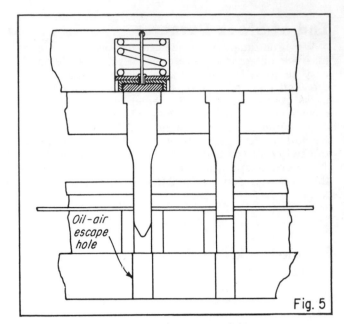

Oil-air escape hole

Fig. 5

Misfeeds Detected by Probe

When the stock is thicker than 1/16 in. and a spring-loaded pilot would not be satisfactory, use the separate probe shown in Fig. 6. The feed pilot, in this case, should be made as long as possible without interfering with feeding of stock. Length A of the probe pilot should be made as long as the feed pilot minus the curved locating tip. With this setup, the feed pilot, not the probe pilot, locates the stock, and a misfeed is detected at the earliest possible moment.

The separate probe pilot method, in most cases, cannot be used to add protection to existing dies. Since experience has proved this method superior to using the feed pilot as a probe, it is recommended that separate probe pilots be used for new tooling.

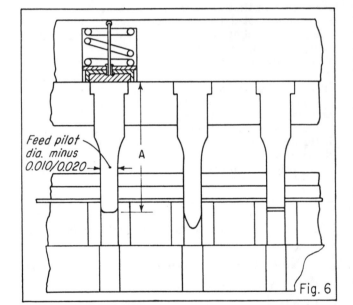

Feed pilot dia. minus 0.010/0.020

A

Fig. 6

Separate Probe Pilot Used in Scrap

Misfeed detection can be extended to probing a hole in the scrap strip, Fig. 7. This method is frequently used to add protection to existing dies. Many dies are made with a solid die block as shown. Application of a separate pilot-misfeed detector into a hardened die block is expensive. However, adding a small die block section is easy and inexpensive. Progressive dies that produce several different items by changing inside diameters are conveniently protected by this method. The added punch plate and die block do not have to be changed to suit the size of hole being punched, because the outside diameter of the blank remains constant.

Dies that produce stampings of irregular outline can be protected by using a round probe which just fits into the opening of the scrap strip. The probe is placed so that it enters the scrap strip after the pilot has registered the stock. Where a round probe would not be practical, a sleeve of the proper shape can be attached to the bottom of the probe.

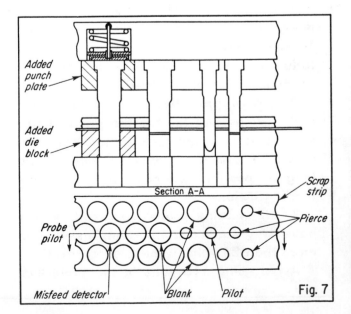

Added punch plate

Added die block

Section A-A

Scrap strip

Pierce

Probe pilot

Misfeed detector

Blank

Pilot

Fig. 7

Insulated Probe Pilot

Fast misfeed detection is provided by the insulated probe, Fig. 8. If the insulated probe comes in contact with the strip, as from a misfeed, the circuit is closed, a solenoid is energized and the normally closed contacts in the latching relay are opened, thus stopping the press. To avoid unnecessary shutdowns the probe diameter A should be made 10 to 20% smaller than the hole in the strip and pilot bushing. Stray metal chips and cocking of the strip might otherwise act to trigger the device.

Under normal operation the wire attached to the probe does not carry any current. However, current is carried during a misfeed when the probe comes in contact with the stock. Should the probe wire break and not come into contact with a grounded surface, the press would continue to run unprotected. But this method offers the advantage that as many probes as desired can be used on the same die with the same relay, each probe affording individual protection.

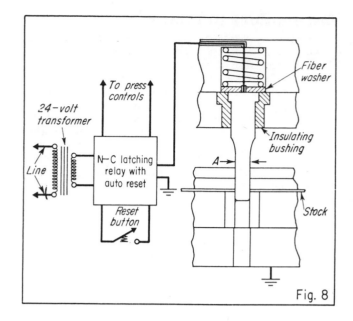

Fig. 8

Snap-Action Misfeed Detector

Here is a popular misfeed detector that uses a manual reset switch, Fig. 9. More space and machine work are required for the device than other methods, but the switch eliminates the relay. This simplifies the electrical part of the system. However, the use of a relay is recommended if the switch is to carry a high voltage. Pushing the manual reset button should not start the press if the switch is properly wired into the stop button.

Adjusting screw should be positioned to trip the switch upon slight movement of the probe pilot, so that a misfeed will be detected as early as possible.

The switch is attached to the bottom die shoe. Sufficient over-travel is built in, to avoid excessive strain on the switch plunger during a misfeed. The probe pilot can be used either as a separate probe pilot or as a feed pilot.

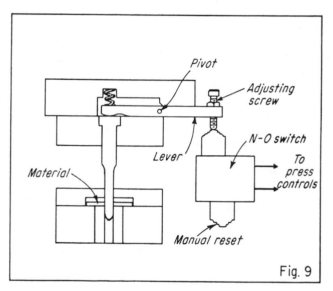

Fig. 9

Cam-Actuated Snap-Action Switch

A cam, instead of a lever, can be used to actuate a snap-action switch, as shown in Fig. 10. A small flat is ground in the pilot to prevent rotation and insure that the cam will always re-enter the cam groove after a misfeed. Make certain that the switch has enough over-travel to prevent damage during misfeeds.

This misfeed detector can also be used as a feed pilot. However, you should remember that the device and its connecting wires move with the press ram and are subject to jolts and possible breakage. If more than 24 volts pass through the switch, a hazardous condition will exist.

When ordinary wires are subjected to constant flexing, they invariably work harden and break. Braided wire has performed satisfactorily and is recommended when flexing is unavoidable.

(continued)

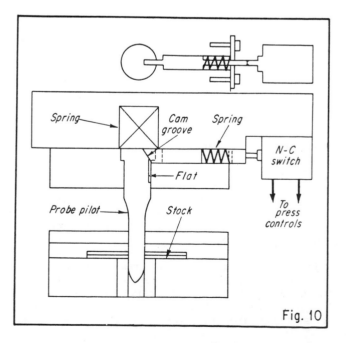

Fig. 10

Missing-Part Detector

Detection of parts missing from the carrier strip is the function of the detector shown in Fig. 11. When progressive dies run at high speeds, many scrap parts can be produced in a very short time, wasting stock, and worse, mixing bad parts with good ones. Difficulty of separation can result in rejection of a large bin of parts because of a small percentage of rejects. However, more important than detecting rejects is the prevention of smash-ups due to the pile-up of missing parts. This switch will detect such a condition and stop the press before damage can occur.

NORMAL OPERATION—As the die closes and the part is in its proper position, the probe will be forced upward, preventing it from activating the switch. The press is allowed to cycle.

ABSENCE OF PART—If a part is missing or not in correct position, the probe will drop, allowing the adjusting screw to activate the switch, stopping the

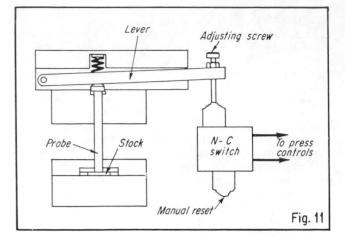

Fig. 11

press. After the malfunction is corrected, the press is made operative by resetting the switch in a normally closed position.

Switch Protects Die

Should the pressure pad of the die shown in Fig. 12 stick or fail to function properly, the press will stop instantly and prevent serious die damage.

NORMAL OPERATION—At bottom stroke the pressure pad is pushed up. Now the cam moves right, where it would activate the switch if the roller were opposite the cam. However, the cam is below the switch roller and the circuit is not opened. As the ram moves upward the spring pin pushes the pressure pad down, and the cam is pushed left before it can strike the switch. Therefore, the press can finish its cycle and begin the next one.

DETECTING A MALFUNCTION—In normal operation the cam is continually moving in and out, both motions taking place beneath the switch. If the pad fails to return to its normal position, the cam will

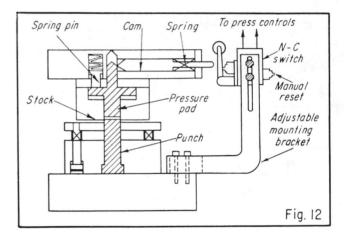

Fig. 12

be held out and will trip the switch as the ram continues upward.

Auxiliary Circuit Protects Dies

Many cut-off dies for heavy stock are built without feed pilots. Because a pilot-protection method cannot be used, another protective method must be employed. Shown in Fig. 13 is a method for protecting a die which cuts off against a stop block.

NORMAL OPERATION—The stock feeds left to right against the insulated stop block, completing the solenoid circuit through the ground connection. The cam then comes into contact with the snap-action switch, opening an alternate supply circuit to the solenoid. As the ram continues down, the cam leaves the snap-action switch, closing the alternate solenoid circuit. The stamping is pushed past the stop-block, opening the solenoid circuit through the ground connection.

MISFEED—The stock does not reach the stop block and cannot complete the solenoid circuit through the ground connection. The cam will then contact the snap-action switch, stopping the press. In essence the cam exposes the press to a shutting-off

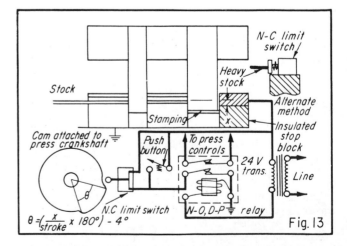

$$\theta = \left(\frac{x}{stroke} \times 180°\right) - 4°$$

Fig. 13

action during the time that the stock should be against the stop block. Should the stock feed up against the stop block and then bounce away the press will stop.

Two Switches in Parallel Protect Dies With Pads and Strippers

Any die that uses a pad or stripper plate can be protected by a circuit that uses two snap-action switches in parallel, Fig. 14. The circuit will stop the press should two parts be stamped or if the pad should stick in its lower position.

NORMAL OPERATION—As press descends, switch No. 1 is closed and current to the solenoid is maintained. Further movement of the ram causes the pad to drop, which then opens switch No. 2. As the ram rises, the pad contacts switch No. 2, closing it. Further movement of the ram causes the spring-loaded finger to leave switch No. 1, opening it. Hence, the switches are alternately opening and closing with a small overlap, so that one switch is always supplying current to solenoid.

DETECTING A MALFUNCTION — Should the pad contain two stampings, switch No. 2 will open before switch No. 1 can close, and the press will stop. During the upstroke if the pad sticks, switch No. 2 will not be closed, switch No. 1 will open, and the press will stop.

The trick in this method is to adjust the overlap to a value which is less than a thickness of stock.

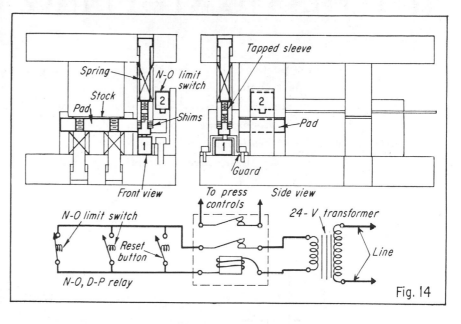

Fig. 14

This adjustment is easily made by placing a piece of stock between the punch and the pad and lowering the ram by hand until the pad just closes switch No. 2. A meter placed across the switch contacts, with the switch wires removed, will indicate when it has been actuated. Enough shim washers are removed from the spring-loaded finger to leave a small gap between the screw and the switch plunger.

A thickness gage is then used to determine the shim washers required to just actuate switch No. 1. The determined thickness of washers plus about 0.010 in. (overlap amount) is added to the spring-loaded finger. The die is now ready to run automatically. The tool should be tested by adding a 0.010 in. plus shim to the pad along with the stock, and tripping the press to see if shut-off occurs.

Cup Switch Protects Compound Dies

A cup switch (see Fig. 1) can be used to protect compound dies. A typical layout is shown in Fig. 15. Because of ejection problems, these dies are particularly vulnerable to breakage. A failure of the knock-out system and a pile-up of stampings can ruin an expensive die and destroy customer good will because of failure to deliver parts on time. This trouble can be avoided by installing the cup switch. Should the knock-out system fail and the stampings pack-up in the die block, the knock-out will push the pin against the insulated cup, breaking the ground connection to the relay circuit (see Fig. 2), immediately stopping the press.

When designing this kind of protection into your compound dies, always make dimension A a minimum of two stock thicknesses. Thus, if the press should make another stroke after shut-off, the die will not hit solid. However, if dimension A is made too large, it will be necessary to shorten the knock-out as the die is ground, in order not to trip the protective device during normal operation.

(continued)

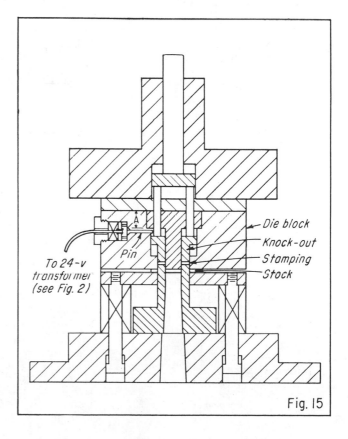

Fig. 15

AUTOMATIC STOPPING MECHANISMS

Many machines, particularly automatically operated production machines, may damage themselves or parts being processed unless they are equipped with devices that stop the machine or cause it to skip an operation when something goes wrong. The accompanying patented mechanisms show principles that can be employed to interrupt normal machine operations: Mechanical, electrical or electronic, hydraulic, pneumatic, or combinations of these means. Endless varieties of each method are in use.

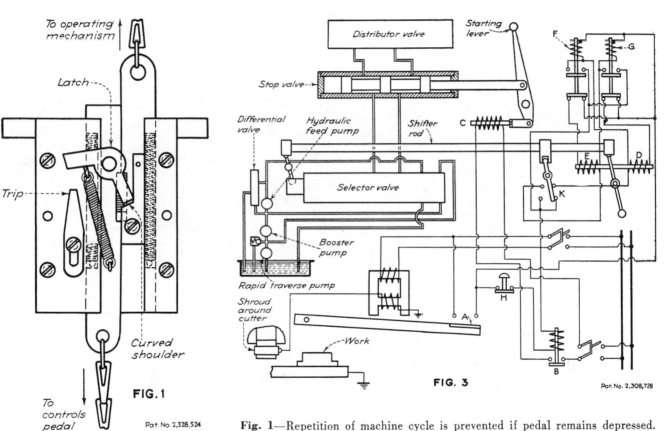

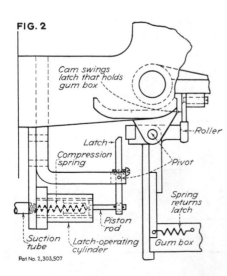

Fig. 1—Repetition of machine cycle is prevented if pedal remains depressed. Latch carried by left slide pushes right slide downward by means of curved shoulder until latch is disengaged by trip member.

Fig. 2—Gumming of suction picker and label carrier when label is not picked up by the suction, is prevented by insufficient suction on latch-operating cylinder, caused by open suction holes on picker. When latch-operating cylinder does not operate, gum box holding latch returns to holding position after cyclic removal by cam and roller, thus preventing gum box and rolls from rocking to make contact with picker face.

Fig. 3—Damage to milling cutter, work or fixtures is prevented by shroud around cutter, which upon contact closes electric circuit through relay, thus closing contact A. This causes contact B to close, thus energizing relay C to operate stop valve, and closes circuit through relay D, thus reversing selector valve by means of shifter rod so that bed travel will reverse on starting. Simultaneously, relay F opens circuit of relay E and closes a holding circuit that was broken by the shifter lever at K. Relay G also closes a holding circuit and opens circuit through relay D. Starting lever, released by push button H, releases contact A and returns circuit to normal. If contact is made with shroud when bed travel is reversed, interchange D and E, and F and G in above sequence of operations.

FOR FAULTY MACHINE OPERATION

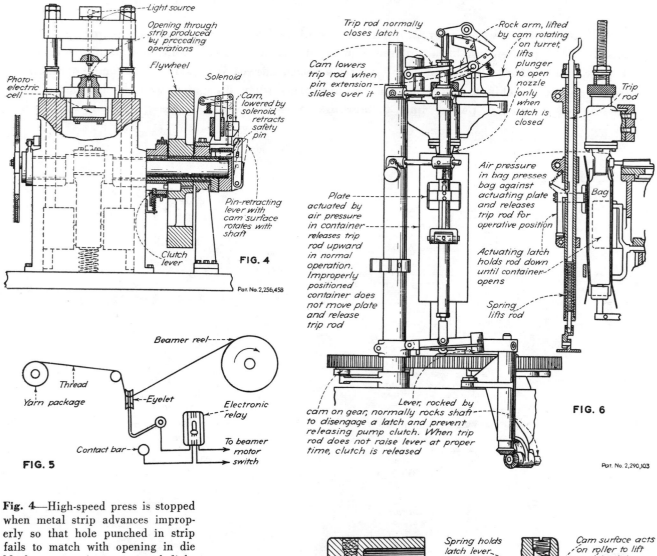

FIG. 4

Light source
Opening through strip produced by preceding operations
Flywheel
Solenoid
Photo-electric cell
Cam, lowered by solenoid, retracts safety pin
Pin-retracting lever with cam surface rotates with shaft
Clutch lever

Pat. No. 2,256,458

Trip rod normally closes latch
Cam lowers trip rod when pin extension slides over it
Rock arm, lifted by cam rotating on turret, lifts plunger to open nozzle only when latch is closed
Trip rod
Plate actuated by air pressure in container releases trip rod upward in normal operation. Improperly positioned container does not move plate and release trip rod
Air pressure in bag presses bag against actuating plate and releases trip rod for operative position
Bag
Actuating latch holds rod down until container opens
Spring lifts rod
Lever, rocked by cam on gear, normally rocks shaft to disengage a latch and prevent releasing pump clutch. When trip rod does not raise lever at proper time, clutch is released

FIG. 6

Pat. No. 2,290,103

Beamer reel
Thread
Yarn package
Eyelet
Electronic relay
Contact bar
To beamer motor switch

FIG. 5

Fig. 4—High-speed press is stopped when metal strip advances improperly so that hole punched in strip fails to match with opening in die block to permit passage of light beam. Intercepted light beam to photo-electric cell results in energizing solenoid and withdrawal of clutch pin.

Fig. 5—Broken thread permits contact bar to drop, thereby closing electronic relay circuit, which operates to stop beamer reeling equipment.

Fig. 6—Nozzle on packaging machine does not open when container is not in proper position.

Fig. 7—Obstruction under explorer foot of wire-stitching machine prevents damage to machine by raising a vertical plunger, which releases a latch lever so that rotary cam raises lever that retains clutch operating plunger.

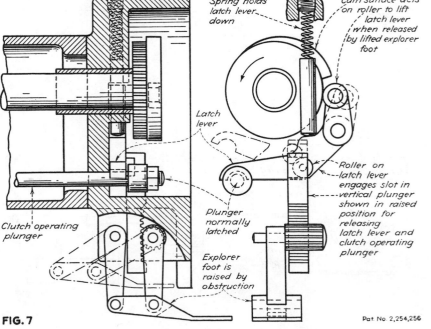

Spring holds latch lever down
Cam surface acts on roller to lift latch lever when released by lifted explorer foot
Latch lever
Roller on latch lever engages slot in vertical plunger shown in raised position for releasing latch lever and clutch operating plunger
Clutch operating plunger
Plunger normally latched
Explorer foot is raised by obstruction

FIG. 7

Pat. No. 2,254,256

Such devices, which prevent automatic machines from damaging themselves or the work passing through them, make use of mechanical, electrical, hydraulic and pneumatic principles. Typical mechanisms illustrated prevent excess speed, misweaving, jamming of toggle press and food canning machines, operation of printing press when the paper web breaks, improper feeding of wrapping paper, and uncoordinated operation of a glass making machine.

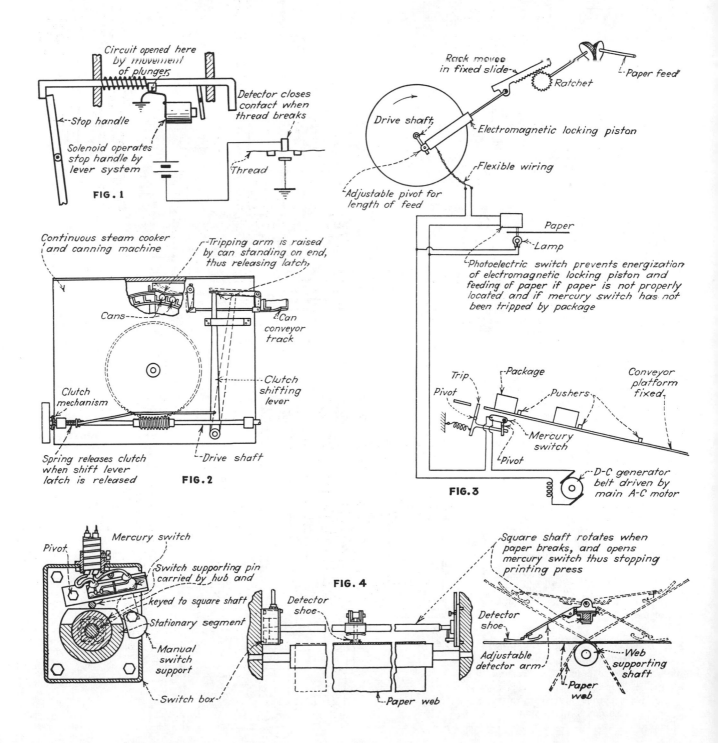

FIG.1

Circuit opened here by movement of plunger
Stop handle
Solenoid operates stop handle by lever system
Detector closes contact when thread breaks
Thread

FIG.2

Continuous steam cooker and canning machine
Tripping arm is raised by can standing on end, thus releasing latch
Cans
Can conveyor track
Clutch shifting lever
Clutch mechanism
Spring releases clutch when shift lever latch is released
Drive shaft

FIG.3

Rack moves in fixed slide
Ratchet
Paper feed
Drive shaft
Electromagnetic locking piston
Adjustable pivot for length of feed
Flexible wiring
Paper
Lamp
Photoelectric switch prevents energization of electromagnetic locking piston and feeding of paper if paper is not properly located and if mercury switch has not been tripped by package
Trip
Pivot
Package
Pushers
Conveyor platform fixed
Mercury switch
Pivot
D-C generator belt driven by main A-C motor

FIG.4

Pivot
Mercury switch
Switch supporting pin carried by hub and keyed to square shaft
Stationary segment
Manual switch support
Switch box
Detector shoe
Paper web
Square shaft rotates when paper breaks, and opens mercury switch thus stopping printing press
Detector shoe
Adjustable detector arm
Web supporting shaft
Paper web

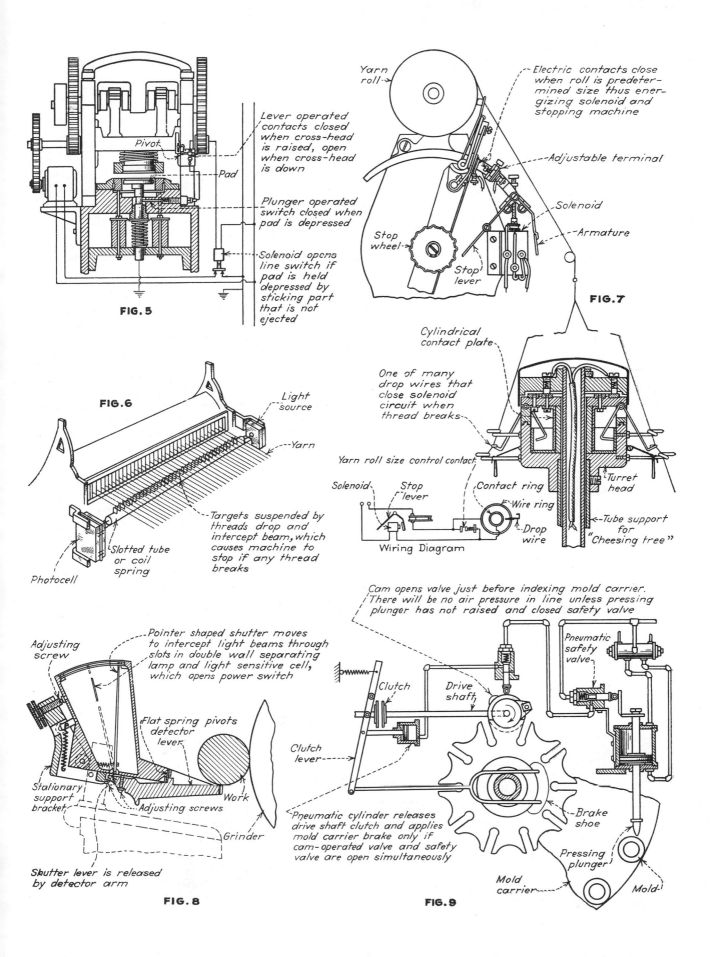

FIG. 5

Pivot

Pad

Lever operated contacts closed when cross-head is raised, open when cross-head is down

Plunger operated switch closed when pad is depressed

Solenoid opens line switch if pad is held depressed by sticking part that is not ejected

Yarn roll

Electric contacts close when roll is predetermined size thus energizing solenoid and stopping machine

Adjustable terminal

Solenoid

Armature

Stop wheel

Stop lever

FIG. 7

FIG. 6

Light source

Yarn

Targets suspended by threads drop and intercept beam, which causes machine to stop if any thread breaks

Slotted tube or coil spring

Photocell

Cylindrical contact plate

One of many drop wires that close solenoid circuit when thread breaks

Yarn roll size control contact

Solenoid

Stop lever

Contact ring

Wire ring

Drop wire

Wiring Diagram

Turret head

Tube support for "Cheesing tree"

Adjusting screw

Pointer shaped shutter moves to intercept light beams through slots in double wall separating lamp and light sensitive cell, which opens power switch

Flat spring pivots detector lever

Stationary support bracket

Adjusting screws

Work

Grinder

Shutter lever is released by detector arm

FIG. 8

Cam opens valve just before indexing mold carrier. There will be no air pressure in line unless pressing plunger has not raised and closed safety valve

Clutch

Drive shaft

Pneumatic safety valve

Clutch lever

Pneumatic cylinder releases drive shaft clutch and applies mold carrier brake only if cam-operated valve and safety valve are open simultaneously

Brake shoe

Pressing plunger

Mold carrier

Mold

FIG. 9

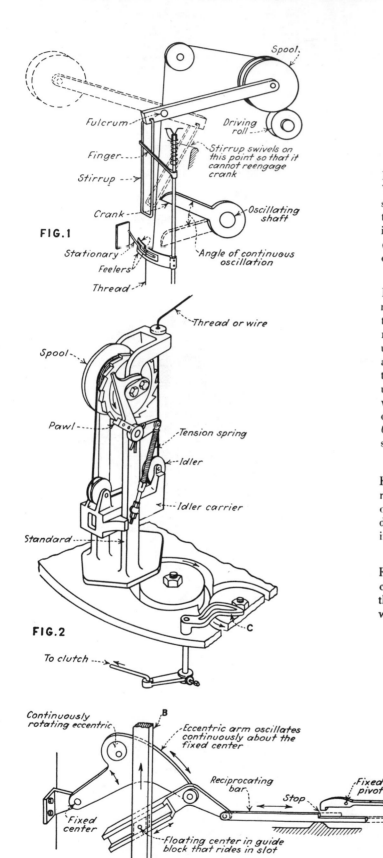

FIG.1

FIG.2

FIG. 1—A mechanism used on the Barber-Colman spooler. When thread breaks the feelers are released and the spiral spring causes the spindle with finger to rotate. Latter throws the stirrup into the path of the oscillating crank, which on its downward stroke throws the spool into the position shown dotted, the stirrup then being thrown out of the path of the oscillating crank.

FIG. 2—Mechanism used with variations on tubular braiding machines. When braiding, tension on the wire or thread lifts the idler carrier which thereby releases the pawl from the ratchet on spool flange and allows the spool to turn and unwind. When machine stops the tension on wire is decreased allowing the idler carrier to fall so that the pawl can engage the ratchet. If wire breaks while the machine is running the unsupported idler carrier falls to the base of the standard and when the standard arrives at the station in the raceway adjacent to the cam C, the lug L on idler carrier strikes the cam C, rotating it far enough to disengage a clutch on the driving shaft, thereby stopping the machine.

FIG. 3—When thread breaks the stop drops and intercepts reciprocating bar. On the next counter-clockwise oscillation of the eccentric arm the bar B is raised. A feature of this design is that it permits the arm B to move up or down independently for a limited distance.

FIG. 4—Schematic diagram of mechanism to cause bobbin changer to operate. If contact arm does not slip on bobbin the lever A will rotate to the position shown. But if contact with bobbin center slips, as it will do if the bobbin is empty,

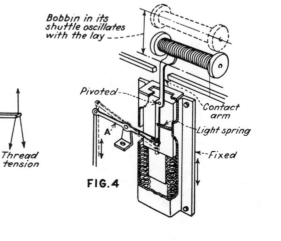

FIG.3

FIG.4

Designs shown here diagrammatically were taken from textile machines, braiding machines and packaging machines. Possible modifications of them to suit other applications will be apparent

lever *A* will not rotate to position indicated by dashed line, thereby causing bobbin changer to come into action.

Fig. 5—Simple type of stop mechanism for limiting the stroke of a reciprocating machine member. Arrows indicate the direction of movements.

Fig. 6—When the predetermined weight of material has been poured on the pan, the movement of the scale beam pushes the latch out of engagement, allowing the paddle wheel to rotate and thus dump the load. The scale beam drops, thereby returning the latch to the holding position and stopping the wheel when the next vane hits the latch.

Fig. 7—In this textile machine any movement that will rotate the stop lever counter-clockwise will bring it in the path of the continuously reciprocating shaft. This will cause the catch lever to be pushed counter-clockwise and the hardened steel stop on the clutch control shaft will be freed. A spiral spring then impels the clutch control shaft to rotate clockwise, which movement throws out the clutch and applies the brake. Initial movement of the stop lever may be caused by the breaking of a thread, a moving dog, or any other means.

Fig. 8—Arrangement used on some package loading machines to stop machine if a package should pass loading station without receiving an insert. Pawl finger *F* has a rocking motion obtained from crankshaft, timed so that it enters the unsealed packages and is stopped against the contents. If the box is not filled the finger enters a considerable distance and the pawl end at bottom engages and holds a ratchet wheel on driving clutch which disengages the machine driving shaft.

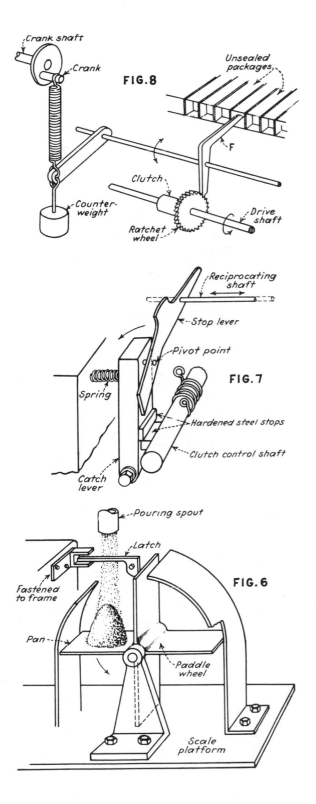

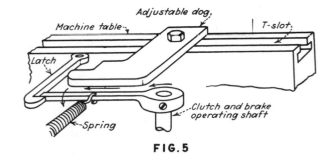

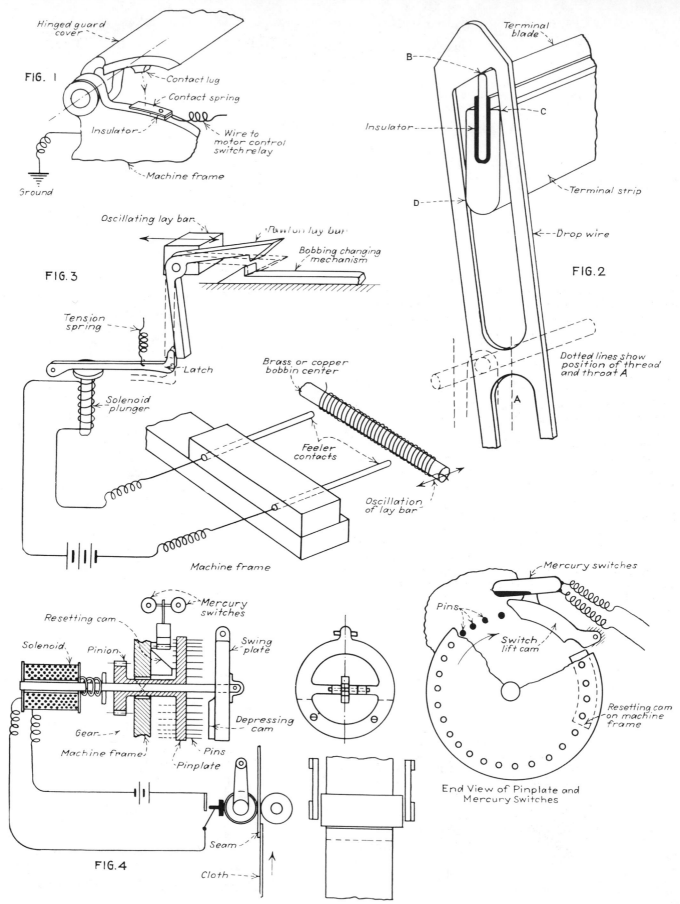

FIG. 1 — Hinged guard cover, Contact lug, Contact spring, Insulator, Wire to motor control switch relay, Machine frame, Ground

FIG. 2 — Terminal blade, B, C, Insulator, D, Terminal strip, Drop wire, Dotted lines show position of thread and throat A, A

FIG. 3 — Oscillating lay bar, Reston lay bar, Bobbing changing mechanism, Tension spring, Latch, Solenoid plunger, Brass or copper bobbin center, Feeler contacts, Oscillation of lay bar, Machine frame

FIG. 4 — Resetting cam, Mercury switches, Solenoid, Pinion, Swing plate, Gear, Depressing cam, Machine frame, Pins, Pinplate, Seam, Cloth, Mercury switches, Pins, Switch lift cam, Resetting cam on machine frame, End View of Pinplate and Mercury Switches

Arrangements and designs diagrammatically illustrated here were taken from packaging machines and textile machines. Modifications of them to perform other operations can be easily devised

Fig. 1—Safety arrangement used on some machines to stop motor when guard cover is lifted. Circuit is complete only when cover is down, in which position contact lug has metal to metal connection with contact spring, completing circuit to relay.

Fig. 2—Electrical 3-point wedging type "warp stop" shown after thread has broken and drop wire has fallen and tilted to close circuit. Dotted lines indicate normal position of drop wire when riding on thread. When thread breaks the drop wire falls and strikes the top of terminal blade at B, the inclined top of the slot causing a wedging effect which tilts drop wire against the terminal strip at C and D intensifying the circuit closing action.

Fig. 3—Bobbin changer. When bobbin is empty the feeders contact the metal bobbin center, completing the circuit through a solenoid which pulls a latch that causes bobbin changing mechanism to operate and put a new bobbin in the shuttle. As long as the solenoid remains deenergized, the pawl on the lay bar will be raised clear of the hook on the bobbin changing mechanism.

Fig. 4—Control for automatic shear. When a seam of two thicknesses of cloth passes between the rolls the swing roller is moved outward and closes a sensitive switch which energizes a solenoid. Action of solenoid pulls in an armature the outer end of which is attached to a hinged ring to which a cam plate is fastened. The cam plate depresses a number of pins in a rotating plate. As the plate rotates the depressed pins lift a hinged cam arm on which are mounted two mercury switches which, when tilted, complete circuits in two motor controls. Fastened on the frame of the machine is a resetting cam for pushing the depressed pins back to their original position. In this arrangement two motors are stopped and reversed until seam has passed through rollers, then stopped and reversed again.

Fig. 5—Electric stop for loom. When thread breaks or slackens the drop wire falls and contact A rides on contact C. The drop wire being supported off center swings so that contact B is pulled against inner terminal strip D completing solenoid circuit.

Fig. 6—Automatic stop for folder or yarder to stop machine always in the same position when a seam in the cloth passes between the rolls. A seam passing between the rolls causes swivel mounted roll to lift slightly. This motion closes contacts in sensitive switch which throws relay in control box, so that the next time the cam closes the limit switch the power of motor with integral magnetic brake is shut off. The brake stops the machine always in the same place.

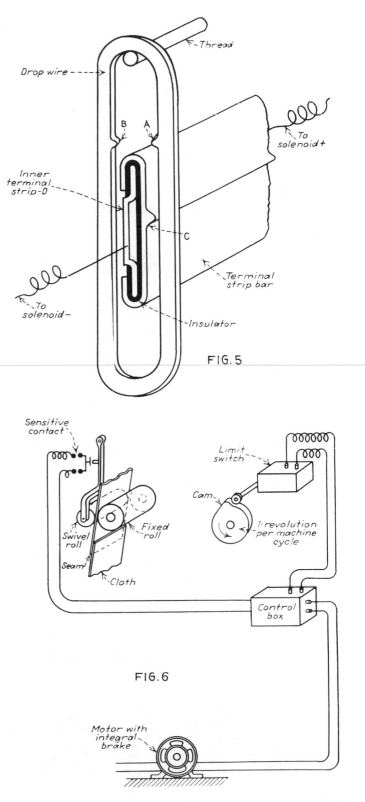

FIG. 5

FIG. 6

the yo-yo despinner...

NEW MECHANISM STOPS SPIN OF ROTATING MASSES

It changes the geometric configuration of a spinning body by letting two small connected masses unwind from it. That's all there is to it—but it can stop a large mass, spinning at high speed, in a fraction of a second.

MERL D CREECH, *professor of mechanical engineering*
RICHARD K FERGIN, *graduate assistant, Physical Science Laboratory*
New Mexico State University
University Park, NM

How can you instantly and inexpensively stop the spin of a high-speed rotating mass—such as a gas turbine rotor—in an emergency? A problem faced in stopping the spin of a space vehicle in flight has brought a solution to this general problem. This answer is a device unofficially dubbed the "yo-yo despinner." It will be installed on the Navy's Hugo III photographic-reconnaissance rocket, scheduled for its first trial shot in the near future. Its job will be to stop the spin of Hugo's payload, allowing high-resolution photos during flight. Tests prove the spin of the space vehicle can be "braked" to dead stop within a fraction of a second.

The device does its job by releasing two small diametrically opposed weights that are connected by cords (actually, Hugo will use flexible metal tapes) to the spinning body, Fig 1. This transfers the total angular momentum of the spinning mass to the two weights—which are automatically jettisoned at the end of the unwinding cycle.

Remarkable features of this device are:

• Once the proper weights and cord length have been selected for the spinning mass, release of the weights will stop the spinning no matter what the initial speed —1 rpm or 100,000 rpm.

• The faster the spin, the quicker will be the stop.

• Braking is smooth—the spinning mass is not jerked to a stop. There is no rebound.

• The device can be designed to cause the spinning mass to reverse its direction of rotation—to a predetermined reverse-spin velocity.

• Tolerances on cord length and weights are fairly liberal to obtain desired results.

HOW IT WORKS

Here's how the yo-yo stops spin: The weights are released and allowed to unwind from the spinning cylindrical section, Fig. 1 (B). Path of the weight relative to the cylinder is a circular involute, from point A to point B. At point B, the cord is tangential to the point of attachment, point P. From point B to point B', the weight follows a circular path, pivoting about point P.

The system can be designed to stop the spin when the weights are at the end of the involute path, B. But the weights must be dropped off when the spin stops, and this is complicated at point B. However, the system can be designed so that spin doesn't stop until the weights are at B' on the circular path; if the cords are retained only by a slot, they will fly free at the right instant— when the weight is in line with OP.

If the weights are not released at the proper time, the tension in the cord would cause the central body to have an angular acceleration in the direction of its initial spin. This acceleration would continue until the cords were fully wound in the opposite direction, at which time the angular velocity of the system would be the same as the initial rate. Following this instant, the small weights would unwind in straight lines tangential to the central cylinder and start a recycling process.

Although the application of this principle is new, the Jet Propulsion Laboratory of California Institute of Technology used a similar method in 1958 for despin of NASA's Pioneer IV. They furnished us their mathematical derivations for our development work; however, our derivations, which are presented here, differ from those of JPL. Ours clearly show that to stop spin, the cord length and size of weights are independent of the initial spin rate.

Two sets of equations have been developed—the first set is for the case where despinning occurs at end of the involute path (tangential release of the weights); the second set is for the case where despinning occurs at end of the circular path (radial release). In addition to the laws of conservation of energy and of momentum, our derivations make use of the relative-velocity theorem. A numerical problem is included to illustrate use of the equations.

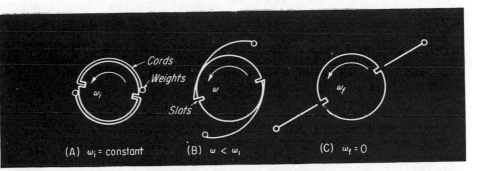

1 . . THREE STAGES OF DESPIN: (A) Spin velocity, ω_1, constant; two weights held in place. (B) Weights have been released and have begun to unwrap; spin velocity has slowed. (C) Spin velocity is zero; weights and cords fly out of slots. Photo shows test model.

SYMBOLS

a = Radius of central-body cylindrical section, ft

m = Point mass and mass of point mass, slugs

R = Length of unwound cord or metal tape, ft

t = Elapsed time from initial start, sec

T = Tension in cord, lb

I = Centroidal mass moment of inertia of central body about spin axis, slug-ft^2

θ = Spin velocity, radians/sec

ψ = ($\beta + \theta - \phi$), additional angle used for solution

ω = θ at $t = 0$ (initial spin velocity), radians/sec

DESIGNING FOR TANGENTIAL RELEASE

Maximum cord tension:

$$T_{max} = \frac{3 I \omega^2}{4} \left[\frac{3 m}{2 (I + 2 ma^2)} \right]^{1/2} \qquad (1)$$

Length of unwound cord:

$$R = a\omega t \qquad (2)$$

Elapsed time to stop the central body:

$$t_{\theta = 0} = \left[\frac{I + 2 ma^2}{2 ma^2 \omega^2} \right]^{1/2} \qquad (3)$$

Required length of cord to unwind tangentially from the cylinder to cause the central body to stop its spin:

$$R_{\theta = 0} = \left[\frac{I + 2 ma^2}{2 m} \right]^{1/2} \qquad (4)$$

Final spin velocity for other cord lengths

$$\theta = \left[\frac{I + 2 ma^2 - 2 mR^2}{I + 2 ma^2 + 2 mR^2} \right] \omega \qquad (5)$$

DESIGNING FOR RADIAL RELEASE

Despin-mechanism design is simplified by allowing the weights to continue their motion until the cords are extended radially outward from the central body. This also allows looser tolerances of the component parts. The equation for the required length of cord to produce zero spin velocity at the end of the circular path has been derived as:

$$R_{\theta = 0} = \left[\frac{I + 2 ma^2}{2 m} \right]^{1/2} - a \qquad (6)$$

This equation shows the same independence of initial spin velocity as does Eq (4). A comparison shows that for radial release, the cord length is reduced by an amount equal to the radius of the central body.

NUMERICAL PROBLEM—INVOLUTE PATH

$m = 2.07$ lb$_m$ = 0.0643 slug (where lb$_m$ is lbmass); M = mass of central body = 40 lb$_m$; K = radius of gyration of central body = 0.219 ft.; $a = 0.279$ ft.; $\omega = 20 \pi$ rad/sec

from which $I = MK^2/g = 0.06$ slug-ft^2

and $\qquad 2 ma^2 = 0.01$ slug-ft^2

CALCULATIONS

Using Eq (1) for maximum cord tension:

$$T_{max} = \frac{(3) (0.06 \text{ slug-ft}^2) (20\pi)^2}{(4) (\text{sec}^2)} \times$$

$$\left[\frac{(3) (0.0643 \text{ slug})}{(2) (0.06 + 0.01) (\text{slug-ft}^2)} \right]^{1/2}$$

$T_{max} = 208.5$ lb force

Using Eq (3) for the elapsed time t for the central body to stop spinning:

$$t_{\theta = 0} = \left[\frac{(0.06 + 0.01) (\text{slug-ft}^2\text{-sec}^2)}{(0.01) (\text{slug-ft}^2) (20 \pi)^2} \right]^{1/2}$$

$= 0.042$ sec

Using Eq (4) for the required length of cord to be unwound tangentially from the cylinder to cause the central-body spin to decrease to zero:

$$R_{\theta} = \left[\frac{0.06 + 0.01}{2 (0.0643)} \right]^{1/2} = 0.739 \text{ ft}$$

AUTOMATIC SAFETY MECHANISMS

T HE most satisfactory automatic guard mechanisms for preventing injury to machine operators are those that have been designed with the machine. When properly designed they (1) do not reduce visibility, (2) do not impede the operator, (3) do not cause painful blows on the operator's hand in avoiding serious injury, (4) are safe with respect to wear in the safety mechanism, (5) are sensitive and instantaneous in operation, and (6) render the machine inoperative if tampered with or removed.

Safety devices range from those that keep both hands occupied with controls away from the work area to guards that completely inclose the work during operation of the machine and prevent operation of the machine unless so protected. The latter might include the "electric eye," which is the activating means of one of the mechanisms illustrated.

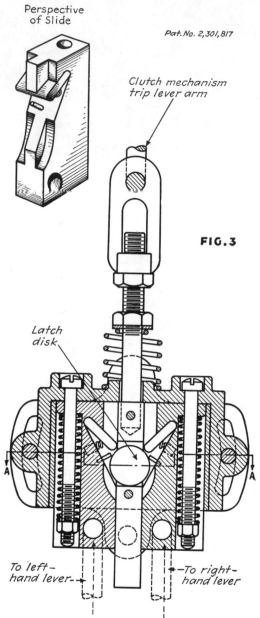

Perspective of Slide

Pat. No. 2,301,817

Clutch mechanism trip lever arm

FIG. 3

Latch disk

To left-hand lever ← ← → To right-hand lever

Unless both slide blocks are moved and engage two latch disks simultaneously, disks are displaced into races of slide block and trip lever arm is not moved

Latch disks

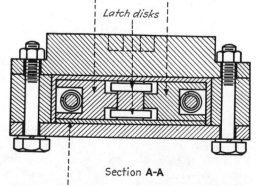

Section A-A

Box assembly slides in stationary housing when slide blocks move together

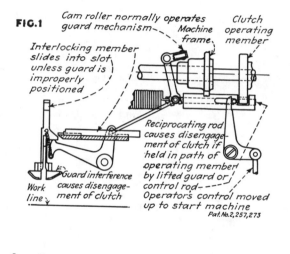

FIG.1

Cam roller normally operates guard mechanism

Machine frame

Clutch operating member

Interlocking member slides into slot unless guard is improperly positioned

Reciprocating rod causes disengagement of clutch if held in path of operating member by lifted guard or control rod

Operator's control moved up to start machine

Pat. No. 2,257,273

Work line

Guard interference causes disengagement of clutch

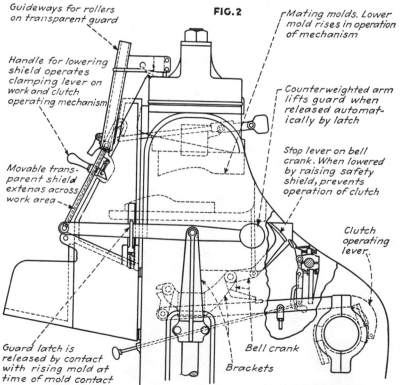

Guideways for rollers on transparent guard

FIG.2

Mating molds. Lower mold rises in operation of mechanism

Handle for lowering shield operates clamping lever on work and clutch operating mechanism

Counterweighted arm lifts guard when released automatically by latch

Stop lever on bell crank. When lowered by raising safety shield, prevents operation of clutch

Movable transparent shield extends across work area

Clutch operating lever

Guard latch is released by contact with rising mold at time of mold contact

Bell crank

Brackets

Pat. No. 2,238,290

FOR OPERATING MACHINES

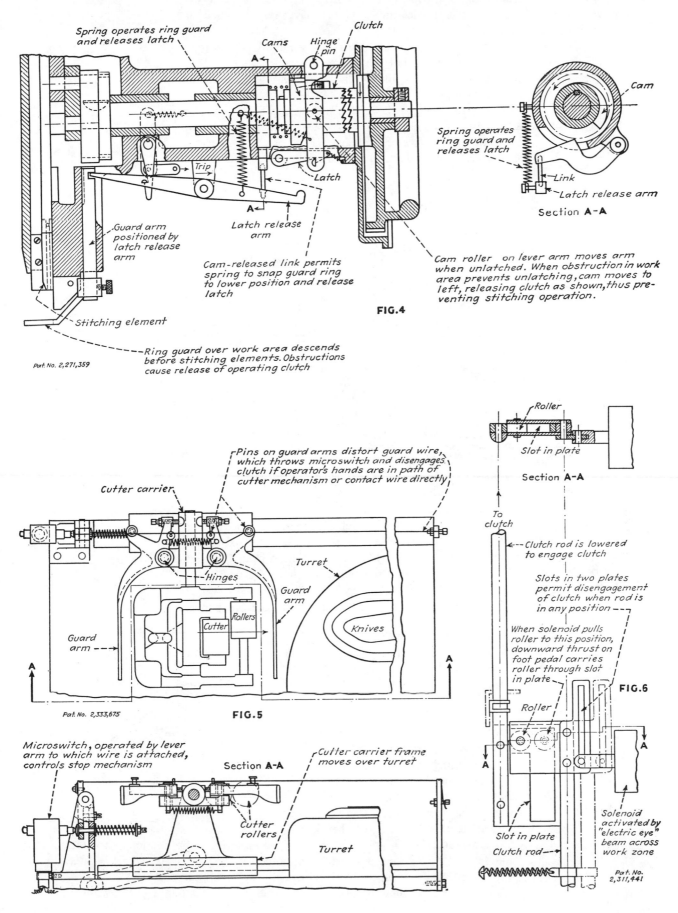

Spring operates ring guard and releases latch

Cams

Hinge pin

Clutch

A

A

Trip

Latch

Latch release arm

Guard arm positioned by latch release arm

Cam-released link permits spring to snap guard ring to lower position and release latch

Stitching element

Ring guard over work area descends before stitching elements. Obstructions cause release of operating clutch

Pat. No. 2,271,359

Spring operates ring guard and releases latch

Cam

Link

Latch release arm

Section A-A

Cam roller on lever arm moves arm when unlatched. When obstruction in work area prevents unlatching, cam moves to left, releasing clutch as shown, thus preventing stitching operation.

FIG.4

Cutter carrier

Pins on guard arms distort guard wire, which throws microswitch and disengages clutch if operator's hands are in path of cutter mechanism or contact wire directly

Hinges

Turret

Guard arm

Guard arm

Cutter

Rollers

Knives

A

A

Pat. No. 2,333,675

FIG.5

Microswitch, operated by lever arm to which wire is attached, controls stop mechanism

Section A-A

Cutter carrier frame moves over turret

Cutter rollers

Turret

Roller

Slot in plate

Section A-A

To clutch

Clutch rod is lowered to engage clutch

Slots in two plates permit disengagement of clutch when rod is in any position

When solenoid pulls roller to this position, downward thrust on foot pedal carries roller through slot in plate

FIG.6

Roller

A

A

Slot in plate

Clutch rod

Solenoid activated by "electric eye" beam across work zone

Pat. No. 2,311,441

NEW SAFETY DEVICES

A mechanical circuit breaker that will trip when the torque on either of the servo-motors connected to it exceeds a predetermined value has been designed at S Smith & Sons (England) Ltd.

The diagram shows how the breaker works. Its key element is the torque switch, with its link and the spring which holds it against the roller bearing unit. This unit, in turn, is attached to an electromagnetic clutch that is fitted to each of the individually controlled servomotors.

The link-and-roller system is so arranged that if the force exerted between the rollers and the spring is too great, the link will be driven back against the spring and will operate the switch, and the clutches of both channels will be disconnected.

The breaker was designed as a safety device for a multiplex autopilot, and it

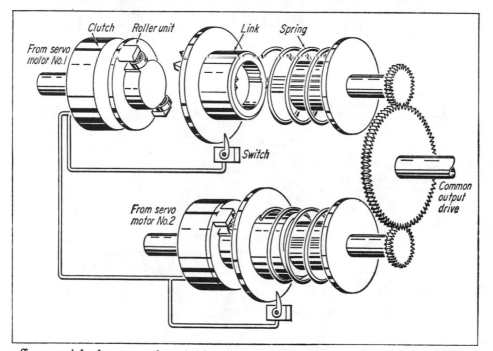

offers special advantages there in that disconnection depends neither on movements of controls nor on changes of attitude. Because it is simply the result of torque opposition, a multiplex autopilot will "fail steady" and no deviation from the glide path will be detected. But Smith's Aviation Div engineers believe the basic idea could be useful in any setup where a fault in one subsystem will introduce a torque another subsystem will oppose to build up sufficient torque to trip the breaker.

A safety-belt locking device that depends on the car, not the passenger, for its response has also been designed in Britain. It's a pendulum-operated, counterweighted device that can be preset to the desired deceleration force and will allow the wearer full freedom of movement until that force is exceeded.

The pendulum (see diagram) swings with the movement of the car, and when that swing exceeds the preset value (as when a car goes around a sharp bend and rolls more than 17 deg, or when it goes

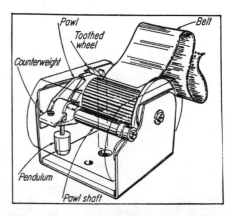

down a gradient with an angle of more than 14 deg), the pendulum rotates the counterweight, engaging pawl with the toothed wheel. Since the wheel is attached to the winding spindle of the belt, this locks the belt in place.

Pendulum and counterweight are adjustable to permit mounting at any angle.

3

LINKAGES, TOGGLES, AND CAMS FOR AUTOMATIC MACHINES

New design curves and equations for
Gear-slider mechanisms

These little-known devices—there are several new ones now—can produce a wide variety of output motions

NICHOLAS P. CHIRONIS, Associate Editor

WHAT is a gear-slider mechanism? In reality, it's little more than a crank-and-slider with two gears meshed in line with the crank (Fig 1). But because one of the gears (planet gear, 3) is prevented from rotating owing to its fixation to the connecting rod, the output is taken from the sun gear, not the slider. This produces a variety of cyclic output motions, depending on the proportions of the members.

In his investigation of the capabilities of the mechanism, Professor Preben Jensen of the University of Bridgeport, Conn nailed down the equations defining its motion and acceleration characteristics—then came up with some variations of his own (Fig 5 through 8). These he believes will outperform the parent type.

Speaking at the ASME Mechanism Conference held at Purdue University,

Jensen illustrated how the output of one of the new devices, Fig 8, can come to dead stop during each cycle, or "progressively oscillate" to new positions around the clock. A machinery designer, therefore, can obtain a variety of intermittent motions out of the arrangement and, by combining two such units, can tailor the dwell period of the mechanism to fit the automatic feed requirements of a machine.

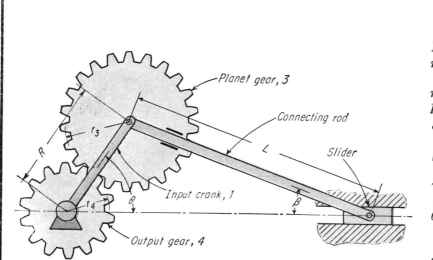

1. Basic gear slider mechanism. It differs from the better known three-gear drive in that a slider is employed to restrict the motion of the planet gear. Note that the output is taken from the gear which is concentric with the input shaft, and not from the slider.

Symbols

L = length of connecting rod, in.
r_3 = radius of gear fixed to connecting rod, in.
r_4 = radius of output gear, in.
R = length of crank, in.
α = angular acceleration of the input crank, rad/sec²
β = connecting rod displacement, deg
γ = output rotation, deg
θ = input rotation, deg
θ_o = crank angle rotation during which the output gear reverses its motion, deg
ϕ = angle through which the output gear rotates back
ω = angular velocity of input crank, rad/sec

Single prime mark denotes angular velocity, rad/sec; double prime marks denote angular acceleration, rad/sec².

The basic form

Input motion is to crank 1; output is from gear 4. As the crank rotates, say counterclockwise, it causes the planet gear 3 to oscillate while following a satellite path around gear 4. This imparts a varying output motion to gear 4 which rotates twice in the counterclockwise direction (when $r_3 = r_4$) for every revolution of the input.

Jensen's equations for angular displacement, velocity, and acceleration of gear 4, when driven at a speed of ω by crank 1, are as follows:

Angular displacement

$$\gamma - \theta + \frac{r_3}{r_4}(\theta + \beta) \qquad (1)$$

where β is computed from the following relationship (see also list of symbols at bottom of previous page):

$$\sin \beta = \frac{R}{L} \sin \theta \qquad (2)$$

Angular velocity

$$\gamma' = \omega + \frac{r_3}{r_4}(\omega + \beta') \qquad (3)$$

where

$$\frac{\beta'}{\omega} = \frac{R}{L} \frac{\cos \theta}{\left[1 - \left(\frac{R}{L}\right)^2 \sin^2 \theta\right]^{1/2}} \qquad (4)$$

Angular acceleration

$$\gamma'' = \alpha + \frac{r_3}{r_4}(\alpha + \beta'') \qquad (5)$$

where

$$\frac{\beta''}{\omega^2} = \frac{R}{L} \frac{\sin \theta \left[\left(\frac{R}{L}\right)^2 - 1\right]}{\left[1 - \left(\frac{R}{L}\right)^2 \sin^2 \theta\right]^{3/2}} \qquad (6)$$

For a constant angular velocity, Eq 5 becomes

$$\gamma'' = \frac{r_3}{r_4} \beta'' \qquad (7)$$

Design charts

The equations were then solved by Prof Jensen for various L/R ratios and positions of the crank angle θ to obtain the design charts in Fig 2, 3, and 4. Thus, for a mechanism with

$$\begin{array}{ll} L = 12 \text{ in.} & r_3 = 2.5 \\ R = 4 \text{ in.} & r_4 = 1.5 \\ \omega = 1000/\text{sec} = \text{rad/sec} \end{array}$$

the output velocity at crank angle $\theta =$

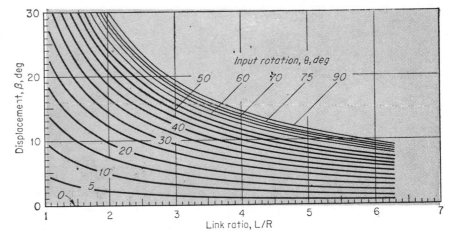

2. Angular displacement diagram for the connecting rod.

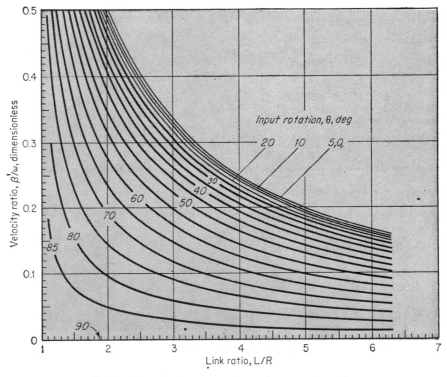

3. Angular velocity curves for various crank angles.

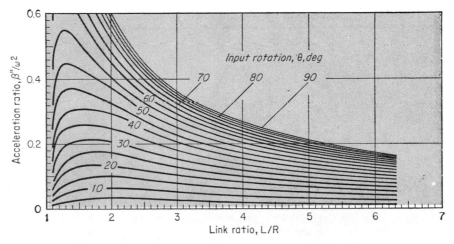

4. Angular acceleration curves for various crank angles.

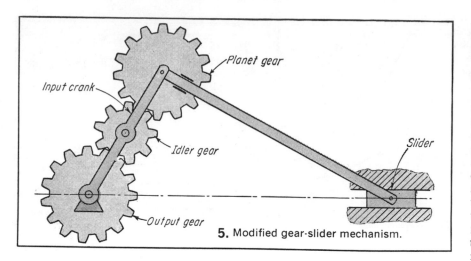

5. Modified gear-slider mechanism.

60 deg can be computed as follows:
$$L/R = 12/4 = 3$$
From Fig 3 $\beta'/\omega = 0.175$
$$\beta' = 0.175 (1000) = 175 \text{ rad/sec}$$
From Eq 3
$$\gamma' = 2960 \text{ rad/sec}$$

Three-gear variation

One interesting variation, Fig 5, is obtained by simply adding an idler, gear 5, to the drive. If gears 3 and 4 are then made equal, the output gear, 4, will then oscillate—and in exactly the same motion as the connecting rod 2.

One use for this linkage, Jensen says, is in machinery where a sleeve is to ride concentrically over an input shaft, and yet must oscillate to provide a reciprocating motion. The shaft can drive the sleeve with this mechanism by making the sleeve part of the output gear.

Internal-gear variations

By replacing one of the external gears of Fig 1 with an internal one, two mechanisms are obtained (Fig 6 and 7) which have wider variable output abilities. But it is the mechanism in Fig 7 that interested Jensen. This could be proportioned to give either a dwell or a progressive oscillation, that is, one in which the output rotates forward, say 360 deg, turns back for 30 deg, moves forward 30 deg, and then proceeds to repeat the cycle by moving forward again for 360 deg.

In this mechanism, the crank drives the large ring gear 3 which is fixed to the connecting rod 2. Output is from gear 4. Jensen derived the following equations:

Output motion

$$\omega_4 = -\left(\frac{L - R - r_4}{Lr_4}\right)R\omega_1 \quad (8)$$

When $r_4 = L - R$, then $\omega_4 = 0$ from Eq 8, and the mechanism is pro-

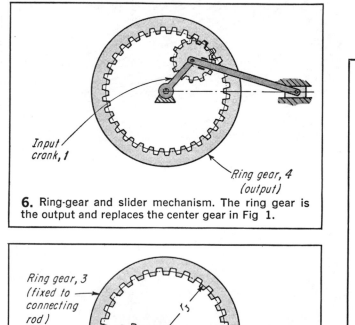

6. Ring-gear and slider mechanism. The ring gear is the output and replaces the center gear in Fig 1.

7. A more practical ring-gear and slider arrangement. Output is now from the smaller gear.

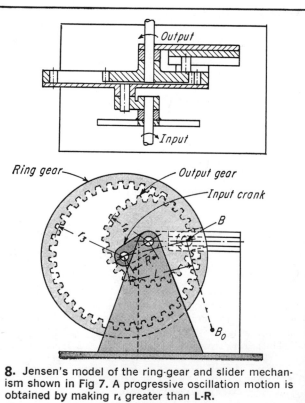

8. Jensen's model of the ring-gear and slider mechanism shown in Fig 7. A progressive oscillation motion is obtained by making r_4 greater than **L-R**.

portioned to give instantaneous dwell. To obtain a progressive oscillation r_4 must be greater than $L - R$, as shown in Jensen's model (Fig 8).

If gear 4 turns back and then starts moving forward again there must be two positions where the motion of gear 4 is zero. These two positions are symmetrical with respect to A_0B. Letting θ_0 = crank angle rotation (of input) during which the output gear reverses its motion, and ϕ = angle through which gear 4 rotates back, then

$$\cos \frac{\theta_o}{2} = \left[\frac{L^2 - R^2}{r_4(2R + r_4)} \right]^{1/2} \quad (9)$$

and

$$\gamma = \theta_o - \frac{r_3}{r_4} (\theta_o - \beta_o) \quad (10)$$

where

$$\sin \beta_o = \frac{R}{L} \sin \frac{\theta_o}{2} \quad (11)$$

Chart for proportioning

The chart in Fig 9 helps proportion the mechanism of Fig 8 to provide a specific type of progressive oscillation.

It is set up for $R = 1$ in. For other values of R, you must convert the chart values for r_4 proportionally, as shown below.

For example, assume that you want the output gear, during each cycle, to rotate back 9.2 deg. Thus $\phi = 9.2$ deg. Also given is $R = 0.75$ in. and $L = 1.5$ in. Thus $L/R = 2$.

From the right side of the chart, go to the ϕ-curve for $L = 2$, then upward to the θ_0-curve for $L = 2$ in. Read $\theta_0 = 82$ deg at the left ordinate.

Now return to the second intersection point and proceed upward to read on the abscissa scale for $L = 2$, a value of $r_4 = 1.5$. Since $R = 0.75$ in., and the chart is for $R = 1$, convert r_4 as follows: $r_4 = 0.75 (1.5) = 1.13$ in.

Thus if the mechanism is built with output gear of radius $r_4 = 1.13$ in., then during 82-deg rotation of the crank, the output gear 4 will go back 9.2 deg. Of course, during the next 83 deg gear 4 will have reversed back to its initial position—and then will keep going forward for the remaining 194 deg of the crank rotation.

Future modifications

The mechanism in Fig 8 is designed to permit easy changing of the output motion from progressive oscillation to instantaneous dwell or non-uniform CW or CCW rotation. This is accomplished by shifting the position of the pin which acts as the sliding piece of the centric slider crank. It is also possible to use an eccentric slider crank, a four-bar linkage, or a sliding-block linkage as the basic mechanism.

Two mechanisms in series will give an output with either a prolonged dwell or two separate dwells. The angle between the separated dwells can be adjusted during the time of operation by interposing a gear differential so that the position of the output shaft of the first mechanism can be changed relative to the position of the input shaft to the second mechanism.

The mechanism can also be improved by introducing an additional link, B-B_0, to guide pin B along a circular arc instead of a linear track. This would result in a slight change for the better in the performance of the mechanism.

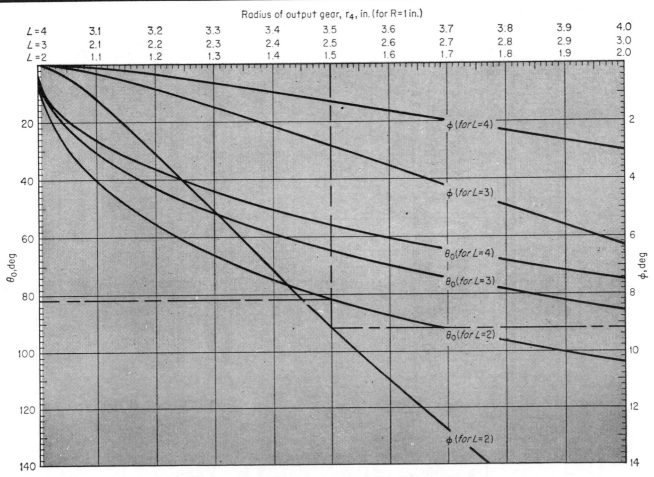

9. Chart for proportioning a ring-gear and slider mechanism.

How to design,

Cycloid gear mechanisms

Cycloidal motion is becoming popular for mechanisms in feeders and automatic machines. Here are arrangements, formulas, and layout methods

PREBEN W. JENSEN, Mechanism Consultant

MOTION EQUATIONS

1. Equations for epicycloid drives

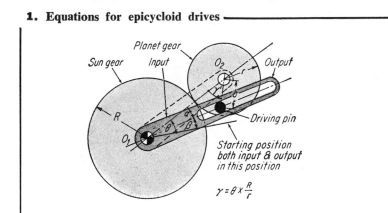

$$\gamma = \theta \times \frac{R}{r}$$

The equations for angular displacement, velocity and acceleration for basic epicyclic drive are given below. (Reference: Schmidt, E. H., "Cycloidal Cranks," *Transactions of the 5th Conference on Mechanisms*, 1958, pp 164-180):

Angular displacement

$$\tan \beta = \frac{(R + r) \sin \theta - b \sin (\theta + \gamma)}{(R + r) \cos \theta - b \cos (\theta + \gamma)} \qquad (1)$$

Angular velocity

$$V = \omega \, \frac{1 + \dfrac{b^2}{r(R + r)} - \left(\dfrac{2r + R}{r}\right)\left(\dfrac{b}{R + r}\right)\left(\cos \dfrac{R}{r}\theta\right)}{1 + \left(\dfrac{b}{R + r}\right)^2 - \left(\dfrac{2b}{R + r}\right)\left(\cos \dfrac{R}{r}\theta\right)} \qquad (2)$$

Angular acceleration

$$A = \omega^2 \, \frac{\left(1 - \dfrac{b^2}{(R + r)^2}\right)\left(\dfrac{R^2}{r^2}\right)\left(\dfrac{b}{R + r}\right)\left(\sin \dfrac{R}{r}\theta\right)}{\left[1 + \dfrac{b^2}{(R + r)^2} - \left(\dfrac{2b}{R + r}\right)\left(\cos \dfrac{R}{r}\theta\right)\right]^2} \qquad (3)$$

Symbols

A = angular acceleration of output, deg/sec²

b = radius of driving pin from center of planet gear

r = pitch radius of planet gear

R = pitch radius of fixed sun gear

V = angular velocity of output, deg/sec

β = angular displacement of output, deg

$\gamma = \theta R/r$

θ = input displacement, deg

ω = angular velocity of input, deg/sec

2. Equations for hypocycloid drives

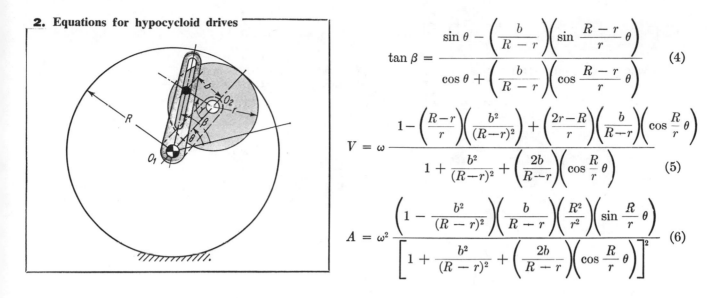

$$\tan \beta = \frac{\sin \theta - \left(\dfrac{b}{R-r}\right)\left(\sin \dfrac{R-r}{r}\theta\right)}{\cos \theta + \left(\dfrac{b}{R-r}\right)\left(\cos \dfrac{R-r}{r}\theta\right)} \quad (4)$$

$$V = \omega \frac{1 - \left(\dfrac{R-r}{r}\right)\left(\dfrac{b^2}{(R-r)^2}\right) + \left(\dfrac{2r-R}{r}\right)\left(\dfrac{b}{R-r}\right)\left(\cos \dfrac{R}{r}\theta\right)}{1 + \dfrac{b^2}{(R-r)^2} + \left(\dfrac{2b}{R-r}\right)\left(\cos \dfrac{R}{r}\theta\right)} \quad (5)$$

$$A = \omega^2 \frac{\left(1 - \dfrac{b^2}{(R-r)^2}\right)\left(\dfrac{b}{R-r}\right)\left(\dfrac{R^2}{r^2}\right)\left(\sin \dfrac{R}{r}\theta\right)}{\left[1 + \dfrac{b^2}{(R-r)^2} + \left(\dfrac{2b}{R-r}\right)\left(\cos \dfrac{R}{r}\theta\right)\right]^2} \quad (6)$$

DESCRIBING APPROXIMATE STRAIGHT LINES

3. Gear rolling on a gear—flatten curves

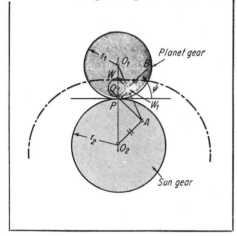

Planet gear

Sun gear

It is frequently desirable to find points on the planet gear that will describe approximately straight lines for portions of the output curve. Such points will yield dwell mechanisms, as shown on pp. 10 to 12. Construction is as follows (shown at left):
1. Draw an arbitrary line PB.
2. Draw its parallel O_2A.
3. Draw its perpendicular PA at P. Locate point A.
4. Draw O_1A. Locate W_1.
5. Draw perpendicular to PW_1 at W_1 to locate W.
6. Draw a circle with PW as the diameter.

All points on this circle describe curves with portions that are approximately straight. This circle is also called the inflection circle because all points describe curves which have a point of inflection at the position illustrated. (Shown is the curve passing through point W.)

4. Gear rolling on a rack—vee curves

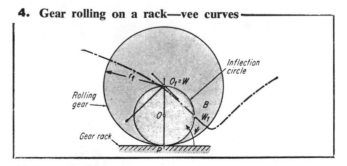

Inflection circle
Rolling gear
Gear rack

This is a special case. Draw a circle with a diameter half that of the gear (diameter O_1P). This is the inflection circle. Any point, such as point W_1, will describe a curve that is almost straight in the vicinity selected. Tangents to the curves will always pass through the center of the gear, O_1 (as shown).

5. Gear rolling inside a gear—zig-zag

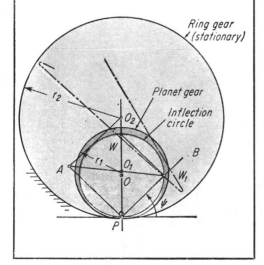

Ring gear (stationary)
Planet gear
Inflection circle

To find the inflection circle for a gear rolling inside a gear:
1. Draw arbitrary line PB from the contact point P.
2. Draw its parallel O_2A, and its perpendicular, PA. Locate A.
3. Draw line AO_1 through the center of the rolling gear. Locate W_1.
4. Draw a perpendicular through W_1. Obtain W. Line WP is the diameter of the inflection circle. Point W_1, which is an arbitrary point on the circle, will trace a curve of repeated almost-straight lines, as shown.

(continued next page)

6. Center of curvature—gear rolling on gear

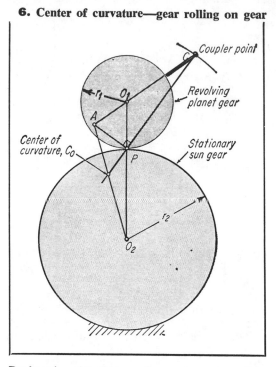

7. Center of curvature—gear rolling on a rack

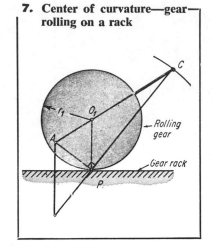

Construction is similar to that of the previous case.

1. Draw an extension of line *CP*.

2. Draw a perpendicular at *P* to locate *A*.

3. Draw a perpendicular from *A* to the straight suface to locate C_o.

By locating the centers of curvature at various points, one can then determine the proper length of the rocking or reciprocating arm to provide long dwells.

1. Draw a line through points *C* and *P*.

2. Draw a line through points *C* and O_1.

3. Draw a perpendicular to *CP* at *P*. This locates point *A*.

4. Draw line AO_2, to locate C_o, the center of curvature.

8. Center of curvature—gear rolling inside a gear

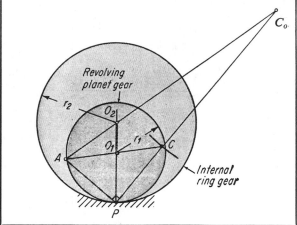

1. Draw extensions of *CP* and CO_1.

2. Draw a perpendicular of *PC* at *P* to locate *A*.

3. Draw AO_2 to locate C_o.

9. Analytical solutions

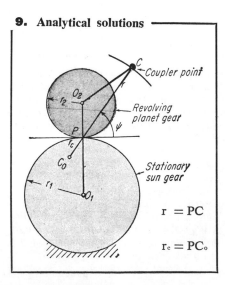

r = PC

r_c = PC$_o$

The centure of curvature of a gear rolling on a external gear can be computed directly from the Euler-Savary equation:

$$\left(\frac{1}{r} - \frac{1}{r_c}\right) \sin \psi = \text{constant} \quad (7)$$

where angle ψ and *r* locate the position of *C*.

By applying this equation twice, specifically to point O_1 and O_2 which have their own centers of rotation, the following equation is obtained:

$$\left(\frac{1}{r_2} + \frac{1}{r_1}\right) \sin 90° =$$

$$\left(\frac{1}{r} + \frac{1}{r_c}\right) \sin \psi$$

or

$$\frac{1}{r_2} + \frac{1}{r_1} = \left(\frac{1}{r} + \frac{1}{r_c}\right) \sin \psi$$

This is the final design equation. All factors except r_c are known; hence solving for r_c leads to the location of C_o.

For a gear rolling inside an internal gear, the Euler-Savary equation is

$$\left(\frac{1}{r} + \frac{1}{r_c}\right) \sin \psi = \text{constant}$$

which leads to

$$\frac{1}{r_2} - \frac{1}{r_1} = \left(\frac{1}{r} - \frac{1}{r_c}\right) \sin \psi$$

10. Hypocycloid substitute

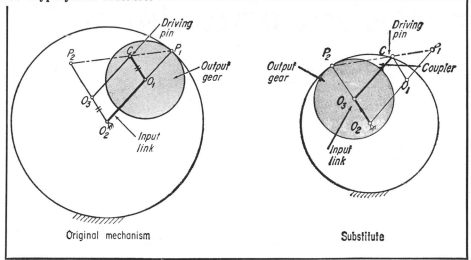

Original mechanism

Substitute

It is not always realized that cycloid mechanisms can frequently be replaced by other cycloids that produce the same motion and yet are more compact.

The mechanism (left) is a typical hypocycloid. Gear *1* rolls inside gear *2* while point *C* describes a hypocycloid curve. To find the substitute mechanism, draw parallels O_3O_2 and O_3C to locate point P_2. Then select O_2P_2 as the new radius of the large (internal) gear. Line P_2O_3 becomes the radius of the small gear. Point *C* has the same relative position and can be obtained by completing the triangles. The new mechanism is about two-thirds the size of the original.

11. Epicycloid substitute

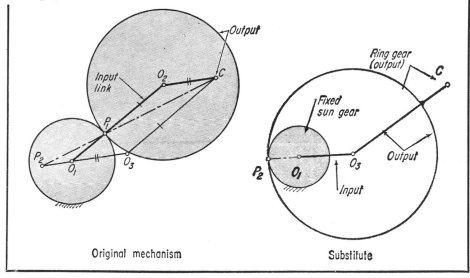

Original mechanism

Substitute

The equivalent mechanisms of epicycloids are pericycloids in which the planetary gear is stationary and the output is taken from the ring gear. Such arrangements usually lead to a more-compact design.

In the above mechanism, point *C* traces an epicycloidal curve. Draw the proper parallels to find P_2, then use P_2O_3 to construct the compact substitute mechanism shown at right of original.

12. Multigear substitute

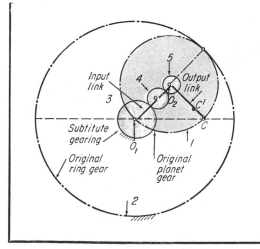

This is another way of producing a compact substitute for a hypocycloid mechanism. The original mechanism is shown in dashed lines—gear *1* rolls inside gear *2* and point *C* describes the curve. The three external gears (gears *3, 4,* and *5*) replace gears *1* and *2* with a remarkable savings in space. The only criterion is that gear *5* must be one-half the size of gear *3*; gear *4* is only an idler. The new mechanism thus has been reduced to approximately one-half that of the original in size.

Slider-crank mechanism

MERL D. CREECH, Professor, Department of Mechanical Engineering,

New Mexico State University

THE slider crank—an efficient mechanism for changing reciprocating motion to rotary—is widely used in engines, pumps, automatic machinery, and machine tools.

The equations developed here for finding such factors are in a more streamlined form than is generally available.

SYMBOLS

L = length of connecting rod

R = crank length; radius of crank circle

x = distance from center of crankshaft, A, to wrist pin, C

x' = slider velocity (linear velocity of point C)

x'' = slider acceleration

θ = crank angle measured from dead center (when slider is fully extended)

ϕ = angular position of connecting rod; $\phi = 0$ when $\theta = 0$

ϕ' = connecting-rod angular velocity = $d\phi/dt$

ϕ'' = connecting-rod angular acceleration = $d^2\phi/dt^2$

ω = constant crank angle velocity

$$\cos \phi = \left[1 - \left(\frac{R}{L} \right)^2 \sin^2 \theta \right]^{1/2}$$

Angular velocity of the connecting rod

$$\phi' = \omega \left[\frac{(R/L) \cos \theta}{[1 - (R/L)^2 \sin^2 \theta]^{1/2}} \right]$$

Linear velocity of the piston

$$\frac{x'}{L} = -\omega \left[1 + \frac{\phi'}{\omega} \right] \left(\frac{R}{L} \right) \sin \theta$$

Angular acceleration of the connecting rod

$$\phi'' = \frac{\omega^2 (R/L) \sin \theta [(R/L)^2 - 1]}{[1 - (R/L)^2 \sin^2 \theta]^{3/2}}$$

Slider acceleration

$$\frac{x''}{L} = -\omega^2 \left(\frac{R}{L} \right) \left[\cos \theta + \frac{\phi''}{\omega^2} \sin \theta + \frac{\phi'}{\omega} \cos \theta \right]$$

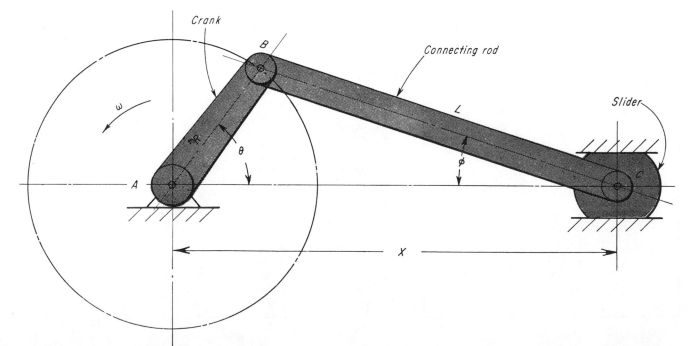

Linkage Design Techniques

*Comparison of 4 methods
—two approximate
and two exact—
for construction and design
of four bar linkages that
generate a path passing
through given points.*

J. C. WOLFORD AND J. C. NICKLAS

FOUR-BAR LINKAGE DESIGN may require that a point on the coupler link pass through a given series of positions. These positions may be on some specified curve, for instance, they may all be on a straight line, or they may have no particular relation to one another except for the sequence in which the coupler point passes through them. However, the path of the coupler point—hence the design of the linkage—must approximate the specified curve.

Four techniques—to fulfill this type of requirement—are generally considered for designing a linkage:

1. Coupler-curve method. This is an approximate method which involves the comparison of a constructed curve to the corresponding curves of known linkages such as might be found in a catalog or atlas of curves.

2. b-curve method. Similar to the coupler-curve method except a plot of the linkage angles must be made. As yet, there is no catalog of b-curves similar to those for coupler-curves. However a series is easy to construct.

3. Center-point curve method. This is a theoretically exact technique and involves a certain amount of construction. It is not as easily extended to a large number of given point positions as the first two methods, but it does not require that a catalog of curves be available.

4. Point-position reduction method. Also a theoretically exact technique involving construction. Technique permits a wider latitude as to the number of given points than the center-point curve method.

1. LINKAGE DESIGN BY COUPLER-CURVE METHOD

This method is often known as indirect synthesis since it is an approximate technique using a curve catalog. (Ref. 1) In the example used to compare all the techniques—a four-bar linkage having a coupler point path that passes through the points E_1, E_2, E_3, E_4 and E_5 of Fig. 1, must be determined. A convenient approach is to plot these five positions on tracing paper and to compare the curve through the points with curves from a catalog.

Several satisfactory fits may be found. The mechanism, Fig. 1, was selected from a curve catalog for the given conditions. The five specified coupler point positions do not all lie exactly on the coupler curve, but the error is slight. In any application, there would usually be some tolerance and a perfect fit would not be required.

(continued next page)

Poles and Pole Triangles (4)

Poles and pole triangles are used in the construction of the centerpoint curve. Here are some relationships involving poles.

A plane can be carried from one position to any other position by rotating it about a point called a pole. In Fig. A, two positions of a plane are defined by the lines A_1B_1 and A_2B_2. The Pole P_{12} is located at the intersection of the perpendicular bisectors of lines A_1A_2 and B_1B_2. Line A_1B_1 can then be moved to position A_2B_2 by rotating it about pole P_{12}. The angle of rotation is designated $2\phi_{12}$.

If three positions of a plane are given there would be three different poles. P_{12}, P_{13} and P_{23}. The poles P_{13} and P_{23} could be found in the same manner that pole P_{12} was found. These poles describe a pole triangle, Fig. B. The vertex angles are $\frac{1}{2}$ of the corresponding angles of rotation from one position to another. These angles are indicated in the figure.

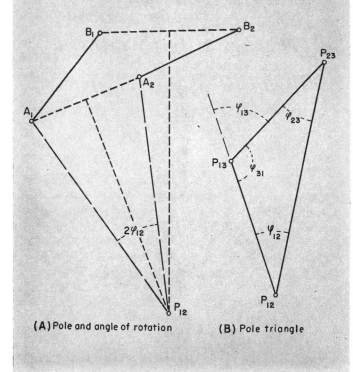

(A) Pole and angle of rotation   **(B)** Pole triangle

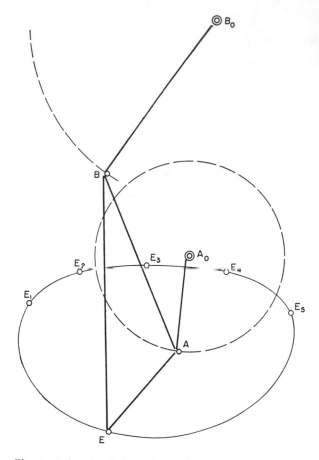

Fig. 1—A four-bar linkage designed by matching the given coupler point position, E_1 through E_5, with a coupler curve from a catalog. Coupler-curve method does not generally allow an exact matching of the given and desired curve.

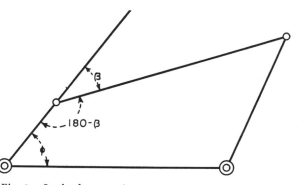

Fig. 2.—In the b-curve, the angle β of a linkage is plotted against the angle ϕ. In some instances, a plot of $180 - \beta$ vs ϕ is referred to as the b-curve. Method requires a catalog of curves for comparison.

2. b-CURVE METHOD FOR LINKAGE DESIGN

As mentioned, the term b-curve refers to a plot of the angle β of a four-bar linkage vs the angle ϕ (Ref. 2). See Fig. 2 for definitions of symbols. This technique is also classified as indirect synthesis since it is approximate and a collection of curves of known linkages must be used.

The coupler point is to pass through the five given point positions, E_1 through E_5, of Fig. 3. The location of crank pivot A_0 is chosen arbitrarily and the crank circle K_a is drawn with the assumed radius A_0A. This radius must be sufficiently large so that a line AE, the length of which is assumed, can have its one end E, on each of the five given points and its other end A, on the crank circle. Thus, using each of the five positions of E as a center and the assumed length AE as a radius, arcs can be drawn cutting the crank circuit at A_1, A_2, A_3, A_4, and A_5. These are the positions of the end of the crank A_0A cor-

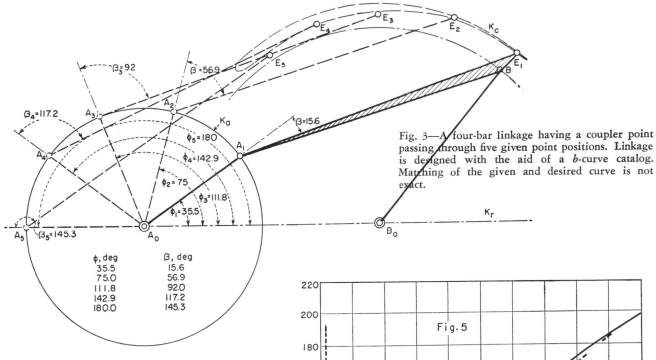

Fig. 3—A four-bar linkage having a coupler point passing through five given point positions. Linkage is designed with the aid of a b-curve catalog. Matching of the given and desired curve is not exact.

φ, deg	β, deg
35.5	15.6
75.0	56.9
111.8	92.0
142.9	117.2
180.0	145.3

Fig. 4—Plot of angle β vs angle φ. Values are taken from mechanism shown in Fig. 3. This is the b-curve of the desired four-bar linkage. Rotation of φ is measured from the line K_r. β is the angle between the crank arm and the coupler arm. This curve is shown dotted in Fig. 5. As noted the match is not perfect making the method only approximate.

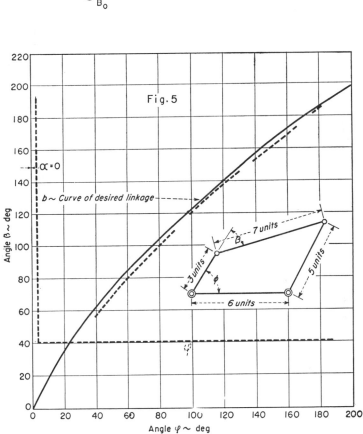

Fig. 5—Curve of four-bar linkage, shown by sketch, **to which** desired linkage most closely matches. Angle α locates the **arbitrarily** chosen reference line K_r. Final linkage is designed **proportional** to the sketched linkage values.

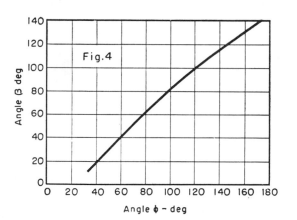

responding to the five coupler positions and $A_1 E_1$, $A_2 E_2$, etc. represents one side of coupler triangle in its five positions.

Crank angle φ is measured from some reference line K_r, drawn through A_0, in an arbitrary direction. Angle β is measured from the side of the coupler triangle AE to the crank A_0A extended. Angle measurements are made for each of the five positions and β vs φ plotted as the b-curve of the desired linkage, as shown in Fig. 4. The plotted b-curve is now compared with known b-curves until an approximate fit is found. The curve of the known

linkage to which the desired b-curve can be approximately fitted is shown in Fig. 5.

In obtaining a fit, the β and φ axes of the desired curve must be kept parallel to the axes of the known linkage curve. The two curves are made to fit exactly at the point corresponding to the design position. For this axample, the No. 1 position is the selected design point.

In general, when a fit is found, the β axis of the desired b-curve will be either to the right or left of the β axis of the known linkage curve. If it falls to the right or positive side, the angle φ of the linkage being designed must

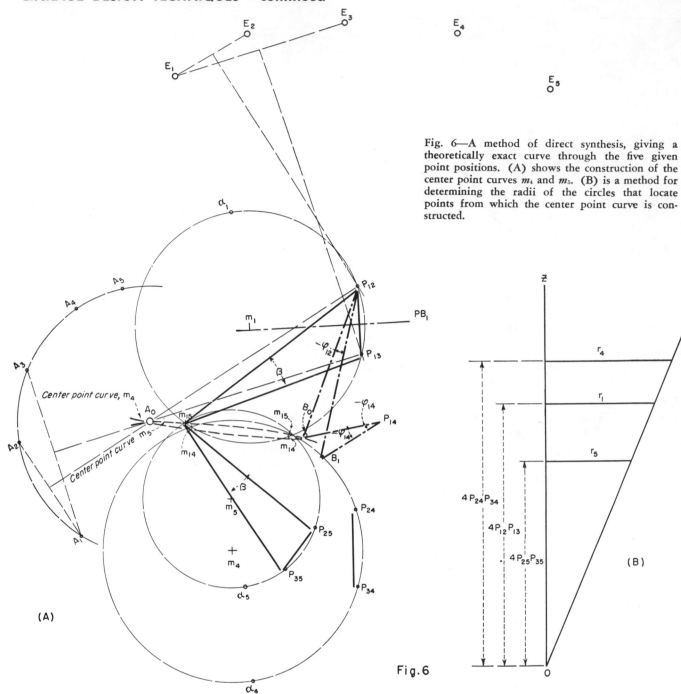

Fig. 6—A method of direct synthesis, giving a theoretically exact curve through the five given point positions. (A) shows the construction of the center point curves m_4 and m_5. (B) is a method for determining the radii of the circles that locate points from which the center point curve is constructed.

Fig.6

(A)

(B)

be increased by the corresponding number of degrees between the β axes. In Fig. 5, this is designated as α. If the curve falls to the left or negative side, the angle φ is reduced by a corresponding amount. The change is accomplished by rotating the reference line K_r (clockwise for positive valves; counterclockwise for negative valves) about A_0 through the angle α. For this example, α is zero, so the reference line remains in the assumed position.

The fixed link lies along the corrected reference line, K_r. The proportions of the link lengths which generated the known b-curve are known. The crank length and the length and direction of the side AE of the coupler triangle for the linkage being designed are known. Hence, the complete four-bar linkage with coupler triangle, ABE, can be drawn.

If a perfect fit of the b-curve is obtained, the point E will pass through the five given positions. If the curves do not match exactly at some points, there will be a corresponding lack of coincidence between the given and coupler points. In this example, a perfect fit was not found in the time allotted to the problem; hence, there is a minor variation between the given points and the final curve.

A catalog or atlas of b-curves, such as is used for the coupler curves, is not known to be available. However, a mechanism has been designed and built at Purdue University that will mechanically draw b-curves of different four-bar linkages and is used to find a curve fit with the desired motion. Some of the curves drawn by this device were used in finding the fit for the example used in this section.

3. CENTER-POINT CURVE METHOD

This is a method of direct mechanism synthesis involving the use of the center-point curve (Ref. 2). This curve is defined as the geometric locus of the centers of circles that can be drawn through four point positions of a plane when the four positions of the plane are given. If five positions of the plane are given, two center-point curves can be drawn. For instance, one would correspond to positions 1, 2, 3 and 4, and the other curve to positions 1, 2, 3 and 5. The intersections of these curves would locate the centers of circles that could be drawn through the five point positions of the given plane.

If the given plane is the coupler plane of a four-bar linkage, two of the intersections could be used as the fixed pivots. The radii of the circles passing through the five point positions would then be the lengths of the corresponding cranks. In this manner, it is possible to design a four-bar linkage having a coupler point passing through five given positions.

Assume that the five positions of a point on the coupler are E_1, E_2, E_3, E_4 and E_5, Fig. 6(A). Since these five points do not define the five positions of the coupler plane, it is necessary to assume a crank length, A_0A, and fixed pivot, A_0. Thus, link AE of arbitrary length can be used to determine the five points A_1, A_2, A_3, A_4 and A_5 on the crank arm arc, and the five positions of the coupler plane $A_1 E_1$ through $A_5 E_5$.

The center point curve for position, 1, 2, 3 and 5 can be determined by drawing perpendicular bisectors from lines $A_1 A_2$, $A_1 A_3$, $A_2 A_5$, $A_3 A_5$, and from $E_1 E_2$, $E_1 E_3$, $E_2 E_5$ and $E_3 E_5$. The intersection of $A_1 A_2$ with $E_1 E_2$, locates pole P_{12} (see pole and pole triangle explanation). Poles P_{13}, P_{25} and P_{35} are similarly located. The pole polygon $P_{12} P_{13} P_{35} P_{25}$ can be drawn. The polygon is constructed so that no number appears more than once in the subscripts of the opposite poles. Hence, opposite poles, for this example, are $P_{12} P_{35}$ and $P_{13} P_{25}$.

The point m_{15} is constructed, as shown in Fig. 6(B). A line is drawn to a base line at any agle. From point O, the chord length $P_{12} P_{13}$ and $P_{25} P_{35}$ are laid off an equal number of times so that the distance Or_1 is proportional to $P_{12} P_{13}$ and Or_5 is proportional to $P_{25} P_{35}$. r_1 and r_5 are the radii of circles m_1 and m_5 whose center is on the perpendicular bisector of $P_{12} P_{13}$ and $P_{25} P_{35}$. The intersection of the circles is point m_{15}. If lines are drawn from the opposite sides $P_{12} P_{13}$ and $P_{25} P_{35}$ of the pole polygon, to point m_{15} and if the included angle β between lines m_{15} P_{12} and m_{15} P_{13} and m_{15} P_{25} and m_{15} P_{35} are the same or supplementary, the point m_{15} lies on the center-point curve m_5 for positions 1, 2, 3 and 5. Additional points for this curve can be determined by varying the angle of the line OX in Fig. 6(B), with the base line OZ.

In a similar manner, the center-point curve m_4 can be plotted for positions 1, 2, 3 and 4. The intersections of the curves m_4 and m_5 are then points at which the center of a circle through five point positions lies. Since A_0 is the center of a circle drawn through five point positions, A_1, A_2, A_3, A_4 and A_5, it must necessarily lie at the intersection of m_4 and m_5. The other point at which m_4 and m_5 intersect can be used as the fixed pivot for the second crank, B_0 of a four-bar linkage.

The length of crank $B_0 B$ is determined by constructing lines $B_0 P_{12}$ and $B_0 P_{14}$. Lines are drawn from P_{12} and P_{14} at angles from $B_0 P_{12}$ and $B_0 P_{14}$ equal to $\frac{1}{2}$ the angle of rotation from $A_1 P_{12} A_2$ and $A_1 P_{14} A_4$ respectively. These are angle φ_{12} and φ_{14}. φ_{12} is also equal to angle $P_{24} P_{12} P_{14}$ and φ_{14} is equal to the supplementary angle of $P_{12} P_{14} P_{24}$

CONSTRUCTION TO FIND THE CENTER POINT CURVES FOR A FOUR-BAR LINKAGE (See Fig. 6)

ASSUME:

1. E_1 through E_5 are the five positions of a point on the coupler.
2. Crank length $A_0 A$ and fixed pivot A_0

CONSTRUCT:

1. Positions A_1 through A_5 on crank arm arc using arbitrary length AE.
2. Perpendicular bisectors from $A_1 A_2$, $A_1 A_3$, $A_2 A_5$, $A_3 A_5$ and $E_1 E_2$, $E_1 E_3$, $E_2 E_5$, $E_3 E_5$ to find poles P_{12} P_{13}, P_{35}, P_{25}. (For simplicity poles P_{12} and P_{13} only are constructed)
3. Lines between $P_{12} P_{13}$ and $P_{25} P_{35}$.
4. Line OX to any base line OZ at any angle (Fig. 6(B).
5. Lay off lengths equal to $P_{12} P_{13}$ and $P_{25} P_{35}$ along OZ any number of times.
6. r_1 and r_5 are radii of circles a_1 and a_5 whose centers are on the perpendicular bisectors of the chords, PB_1.
7. Intersection of circles is point m_{15}.
8. Repeat above to find center point curve m_{14}. Intersection of a_5 and a_4 is point B_0.
9. Lines $B_0 P_{12}$ and $B_0 P_{15}$.
10. Angles from above equal to $\frac{1}{2}$ angle of rotation $A_1 P_{12} A_2$ and $A_1 P_{14} A_4$.
11. Intersection of these lines locates point B_1.

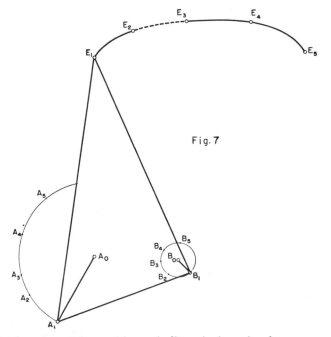

Fig. 7

Fig. 7—Final linkage designed by the center-point curve method for the five given point positions. A discontinuity exists between points E_2 and E_3. For mechanism to work a new fixed pivot point B_0 would have to be found. Center point curves usually permit a choice as to the B_0 position.

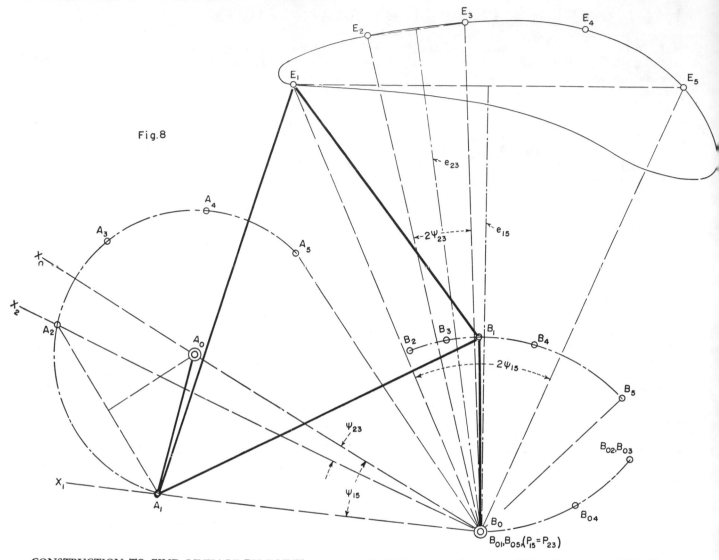

Fig. 8

Fig. 8—Construction of a four-bar linkage, by direct synthesis, that permits a theoretically exact curve through the five given point positions. Method will allow the design of a four-bar linkage with a coupler point passing as many as eight given points. With a greater number of links, more positions can be satisfied. Note that problem is reduced to three points.

CONSTRUCTION TO FIND LINKAGE BY POINT REDUCTION METHOD

ASSUME:

1. E_1 through E_5 are the five positions of a point on the coupler.

CONSTRUCT:

1. Perpendicular bisector from $E_1 E_5$ and $E_2 E_3$. Intersection gives B_0.

2. Radial lines from B_0 so that $X_1 B_0 X_0 = \phi_{15}$ and $X_2 B_0 X_0 = \phi_{23}$.

3. Arbitrary length line $E_1 A_1 = E_2 A_2$ and draw circle arcs from E_1, E_2. These intersect $B_0 X_1$ and $B_0 X_2$ locating A_1 and A_2.

4. Perpendicular bisector of $A_1 A_2$ which cuts $B_0 X_0$ locates A_0.

5. Circle arc with A_0 as center and radius $A_0 A$. Use AE as radius about points E_3, E_4, E_5 to locate A_3, A_4, A_5.

of the pole triangle. The intersection of these lines locates point B_1.

For the final linkage shown in Fig. 7, there is a discontinuity between points E_1 and E_2 on the coupler curve. This is because $A_1 B_1 + B_1 B_0 < A_1 A_0 + A_0 B_0$ which means that the linkages would have to be taken apart and reassembled to move from position 2 to position 3. Such interference cannot be determined until the final dimensions of the linkages have been determined. Point B_0 would have to be placed at another intersection of the center-point curve, or one or more of the arbitrary assumptions changed and the problem reworked.

In this example, the center-point curves, m_4 and m_5 were determined to such an extent that only two intersections were found. Actually, the center point curves may be such that more intersections can be obtained, and the additional intersections would allow a choice as to the B_0 location.

The center-point curve method is the only method that permits more than one solution without repeating the entire construction. Several locations of B_0 are possible when curves m_4 and m_5 are completely defined. Any discontinuity of the coupler point path allows that B_0 location to be ignored and another selected.

4. POINT POSITION REDUCTION METHOD

Point position reduction is a method of direct synthesis which consists of selecting certain important points of the given motion (which in general would all be separate points) such that two or more of these points fall together in a single point (Ref. 3). The end purpose is to arrive at the location of 3 or 4 points through which a circle can be drawn; these points actually corresponding to a somewhat greater number of system positions. It is possible under certain assumptions to design a four-bar linkage with a coupler point passing through eight given positions. Theoretically, the largest number of positions which can be fulfilled with a four-bar linkage is nine. For a mechanism with a greater number of links, a larger number of points can be satisfied.

Assume that a four-bar linkage is to be designed so that a coupler point passes through the five given positions, E_1 through E_5, of Fig. 8. The fixed pivot, B_0, of crank B_0B, is taken at the intersection of the perpendicular bisectors of lines $E_1 E_5$ and $E_2 E_3$. A family of radial lines, $B_0 X_0$, $B_0 X_1$, $B_0 X_2$, is drawn in an arbitrary direction from B_0, with angle $X_1 B_0 X_0 = \varphi_{15}$ and angle $X_2 B_0 X_0 = \varphi_{23}$. These angles are defined as $\frac{1}{2}$ the angle $E_1 B_0 E_5$ and $E_2 B_0 E_3$, respectively. Then with radius $E_1 A_1 = E_2 A_2$ of arbitrary length, circle arcs are drawn about E_1 and E_2 as centers, making intersections A_1 and A_2 with lines $B_0 X_1$ and $B_0 X_2$. The perpendicular bisector of $A_1 A_2$ cuts $B_0 X_0$ at A_0. $A_0 A_1 = A_0 A_2$ is the crank length A_0A. Points A_3, A_4 and A_5 are determined by getting the intersections of the crank circle with arcs drawn about points E_3, E_4 and

E_5 as center points and with $E_1 A_1$ as the radius.

All links have now been determined except the location of the coupler and of the second crank in the design position, point B_1. This can be found by considering the mechanism to be inverted with the coupler fixed in position 1 and plotting the five positions of B_0. This is done by taking $E_2 B_0$ as a radius and E_1 as the center, and $A_2 B_0$ as a radius with A_1 as the center. The intersection of the arcs is position B_{02}. Similarly, taking $E_3 B_0$ as a radius and E_1 as the center, and $A_3 B_0$ as a radius with A_1 as the center and swinging arcs, position B_{03} is located. Positions B_{04} and B_{05} are found in a similar way.

Because of the choice of B_0 as poles P_{15} and P_{23}, the points B_{01} and B_{05} will coincide, as well as points B_{02} and B_{03}. The center of a circle through the three distinct points—the intersection of the perpendicular bisectors of $B_{01} B_{04}$ and $B_{04} B_{02}$—will be B_1. The problem, originally one dealing with five points, is reduced to three points.

The procedure for locating the positions of B_0 can be expressed in another way by making triangle $E_1 A_1 B_{05} \sim$ triangle $E_5 A_5 B_{01}$; triangle $E_1 A_1 B_{02} \sim$ triangle $E_2 A_2 B_{01}$; triangle $E_1 A_1 B_{03} \sim$ triangle $E_3 A_3 B_{01}$; and triangle $E_1 A_1 B_{04} \sim$ triangle $E_4 A_4 B_{01}$.

Also, it should be noted that the family of radial lines, $B_0 X_0$, $B_0 X_1$ and $B_0 X_2$, are arbitrary as well as the length AE. These are, therefore, an infinite number of four-bar linkages having a coupler point passing through the given points. Several systems can be determined and the one most favorable in all respects can be used.

COMPARISON OF METHODS

It is difficult to say if any one method is better than another since each method has certain advantages and disadvantages. However, the techniques can be evaluated on the basis of: (1) reliability; (2) ease of application; and (3) selectivity.

The point position reduction method and the center-point curve method are probably the most reliable. The other two methods rely strongly on the availability of a good collection of coupler or b-curves as provided by a curve catalog. Also, the point position reduction method and the center-point method are more direct; however, the other two give more control of the complete path of the coupler point. One requirement of a linkage might be that the driving crank be capable of complete revolution. There is no assurance that the linkage determined by the first attempt with the two direct synthesis methods will be capable of this. For example, the linkage resulting from the first attempt by the center-point curve method was incapable of going from position 2 to 3. Furthermore, even if this had not occurred, the driving crank A_0A could not make a complete revolution. For any given problem several attempts might be necessary to get a satisfactory linkage. By the indirect synthesis methods, if small errors in the coupler paths are not objectionable, a single check of the curves is sufficient.

The method most easily applied is the one involving the use of a catalog of coupler curves. The most difficult method to apply is probably the center-point curve; one reason being the difficulty in obtaining the accuracy needed to get a solution that will check.

Selectivity can be defined as the number of solutions that are available and their accuracy at the five given points. Obviously, the coupler-curve and b-curve will not give exact solutions unless the curves fit exactly at the specified points. The point reduction method and the center-point curve method of an actual solution, however, will depend upon the accuracy of construction. The only method that might make more than one solution available without repeating the entire construction or curve fitting is the center-point curve method. The center-point curve might intersect at more than two points and give some choice of location of the second fixed pivot.

REFERENCES
1. Hrones, John A., and Nelson, George L., *Analysis of the Four-Bar Linkage*, New York: The Technology Press of M.I.T. and John Wiley and Sons, Inc., 1951.
2. Hain, Kurt, *Angewandte Getriebelehre*, Hanover, Germany: Hermann Schroedel Verlag K. G., 1952.
3. Hain, Kurt, *Angewandte Getriebelehre*, Hanover, Germany: Hermann Schroedel Verlag K. G., 1952, pp. 326-329.
4. Rosenauer, N. and Willis, A. H., *Kinematics of Mechanisms*, Sydney, Australia: Associated General Publications Pty. Ltd., 1953, pp. 360-367.

ROBERTS' LAW HELPS YOU FIND...

alternate four-bar linkages

For every linkage there are two substitutes that will produce the same desired motion—so says a little-known law that can be applied graphically to give quick results. Author furnishes three examples, including his own method of applying the law.

R T HINKLE, Professor of Mechanical Engineering
Michigan State University

Quite often, when a four-bar linkage has been designed or selected from a catalog to produce a desired coupler curve, it is found that one of the pivot points is inconveniently located or that the transmission angles are not suitable. (A coupler curve is produced by a point on the connecting rod joining the two cranks of the four-bar linkage). According to Roberts' Law there are at least two other four-bar linkages that will generate the same coupler curve. One of these linkages may be more suitable for the application.

Roberts' Law is not widely known and does not seem to be mentioned in any English-language textbook. The law states that the two alternate linkages are related to the first by a series of similar triangles. This leads to graphical solutions of which three examples are shown below—the first involving similar triangles, the second being a more convenient method developed by the author, and the third illustrating solution of a special case where the coupler point lies along the connecting rod.

Method of Similar Triangles

Four-bar linkage ABCD in Fig. 1 uses point P, which is actually an extension of the connecting rod BC, to produce desired curve. Point E is found by constructing EP parallel to AB, and EA parallel to PB. Then triangle EFP is constructed similar to triangle BPC. This involves laying out angle α and β.

Point H is found similarly and point G is located by drawing GH parallel to FP and GF parallel to HP.

The two alternate linkages to ABCD are GFEA and GHID. All use point P, to produce the desired curve; and given any one of the three, the other two can be determined.

The Author's Method

With the similar-triangle method described above, slight errors in constructing the proper angles lead to large errors in link dimensions. The construction of angles can be avoided by laying off the link lengths along a straight line.

Thus, linkage ABCD in Fig. 2 is laid off as a straight line from A to D in Fig. 3. Included in the transfer is point P. Points EFGHI are quickly found by either ex-

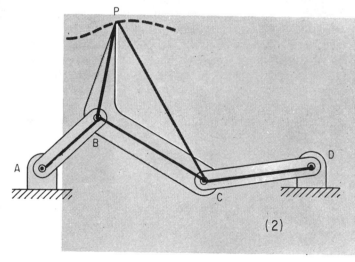

(2)

tending the original lines or constructing parallel lines. Fig. 3, which now has all the correct dimensions of all the links, is placed under a sheet of tracing paper and, with the aid of a compass, links AB and CD are rotated (see Fig. 4) so that linkage ABCD is identical with that in Fig. 2. Links PEF and PHI are rotated parallel to AB and CD, respectively. Completion of the parallelogram gives the two alternate linkages AEFG and GHID.

Special Case

It is not uncommon for the coupler point P to lie on a line through BC, Fig. 5. Links EA, EP and ID are quickly found by constructing the appropriate parallel lines. Point G is located by using the proportion: CB:BP = DA:AG. Points H and F are then located by drawing lines parallel to AB and CD.

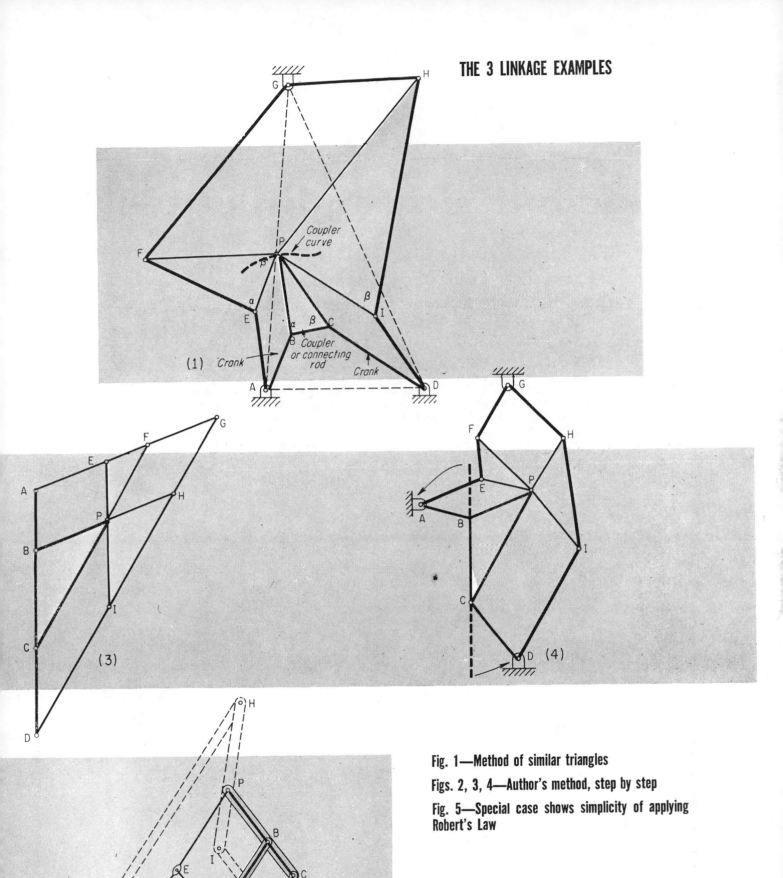

THE 3 LINKAGE EXAMPLES

Fig. 1—Method of similar triangles

Figs. 2, 3, 4—Author's method, step by step

Fig. 5—Special case shows simplicity of applying Robert's Law

Charts give best dimensions for
Four-bar power linkages

With large forces or high speeds, the transmission angle becomes highly important. These new German charts simplify design.

J. VOLMER, *Director, Institute for Mechanism Research, Chemnitz (now Karl-Marx-Stadt), East Germany*
PREBEN W. JENSEN, *Assistant Professor, University of Bridgeport, Bridgeport, Conn*

THE most common function of a four-bar linkage is transforming rotary motion into oscillating motion. Frequently, in such applications, a large force must be transmitted, or force must be converted at high speed. It is then that a factor called the *force-transmission angle* becomes of paramount importance.

The force-transmission angle, angle μ in Fig 1, is comparable to the pressure angle in cams. For best results, μ should be as close to 90 deg as possible during the entire rotation of the crank. This will reduce bending in the linkages and will produce the most favorable force-transmission conditions. (When μ becomes small, a large force is required to drive the rocker arm, and the force fluctuations increase.)

The charts presented here make it easier to find the best force-transmission linkage in a wide range of possible selections. Four examples show how to apply the charts.

continued, next page

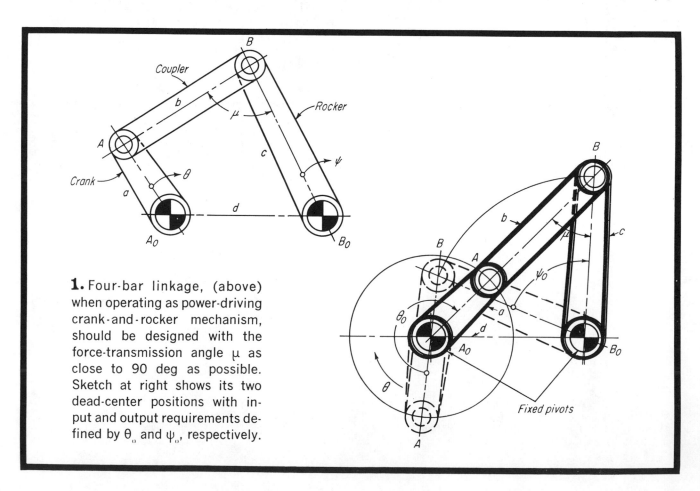

1. Four-bar linkage, (above) when operating as power-driving crank-and-rocker mechanism, should be designed with the force-transmission angle μ as close to 90 deg as possible. Sketch at right shows its two dead-center positions with input and output requirements defined by θ_o and ψ_o, respectively.

Layout techniques

For finding family of linkages which meet θ_o and ψ_o requirements. Pin B of the linkages will lie somewhere along arc LE — but only one linkage of each family will have optimum transmission angle.

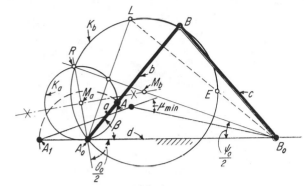

2. Where θ_o is less than 180 deg.

3. Where θ_o is greater than 180 deg.

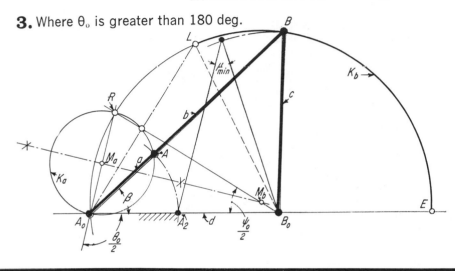

The linkage family

When a four-bar power linkage is designed to operate, for example, as a quick-return mechanism, angular displacement of the output link (the rocker) is usually prescribed in relationship to that of the input link (the crank). These angles are measured from the dead-center positions of the rocker (where the rocker reverses its direction of rotation). Thus, in Fig 1, ψ_0 is the angle between the two dead-center positions of the rocker, and θ_0 is the corresponding angle of the crank. Both angles are measured clockwise from the *inside* dead-center position, where crank and coupler are superimposed, to the outside dead-center position.

When values are given for ψ_0 and θ_0, and for the distance between centers, A_0B_0, a family of linkages that meets these conditions can be evolved by a graphical method developed

some years ago by H. Alt. His method, illustrated in Fig 2, is the first phase of the design procedure:

1) Lay out the line of centers, A_0B_0.

2) Construct angles $\theta_0/2$ with center at A_0 and $\psi_0/2$ with center at B_0. Both angles are measured in the same direction. This locates point R.

3) Draw M_aM_b, the perpendicular bisector of A_0R. Locate point M_b.

4) Draw circles K_a and K_b through point R with M_a and M_b as centers, respectively.

5) On circle K_b make $RL = A_0R$ and connect point L with B_0 to locate point E on circle K_b.

6) Choose any point on the circular arc LE as point B, which is the center of the moving joint. This will be one of a family of linkages.

7) Construct line A_0B to intersect circle K_a. This locates crank pivot point A, thus defining all dimensions of the required four-bar linkage.

This method, however, stops short of determining which of all possible mechanisms obtained from the construction is the best power linkage.

Transmission angles

The question is, which linkage, from the above family, has μ_{min} closest to 90 deg. Since angle μ can be either smaller or larger than 90 deg, it is useful to define it as the angle between AB and BB_0—or between the extension of line AB and BB_0. Thus μ is always taken as $\mu \leq 90$ deg. For example, if $\mu = 120$ deg, it is taken as $\mu = 60$ deg; a linkage in which μ varies from 75 deg to 120 deg ($\mu_{min} = 60$ deg) is more desirable than a linkage where μ varies from 45 deg to 90 deg ($\mu_{min} = 45$ deg).

The design charts

Previous investigations carried out by the first-mentioned author, J. Vol-

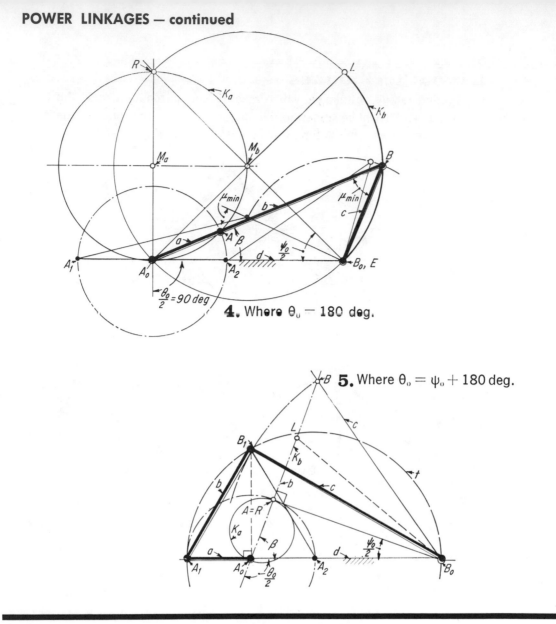

4. Where $\theta_0 - 180$ deg.

5. Where $\theta_0 = \psi_0 + 180$ deg.

mer, have shown how to find the crank positions where μ is minimum. For $\theta_0 < 180$ deg, μ_{min} occurs when crank pin A is at A_1 (see Fig 2); for $\theta_0 > 180$ deg when A is at A_2, see Fig 3; when $\theta_0 = 180$ deg the minima of μ at A_1 and A_2 are equal (see Fig 4). The linkage with $\theta_0 = 180$ deg is called a centric crank-and-rocker mechanism.

Recently the second author, Preben W. Jensen, showed that among the family of linkages with given angles θ_0 and ψ_0, the optimum linkage can be determined with the aid of a chart originally published by H. Alt in *Verein Deutscher Ingenieure*, Vol 85 (1941) p 69. Alt's chart, however, was not very exact. It has now been corrected and also completed for the whole range of angles θ_0 and ψ_0. The chart is shown in Fig 7.

Here is how to use the chart to find the linkage with the largest μ_{min} value

from the linkage family in Fig 2:

For the given values of θ_0 and ψ_0, find the value for angle β from the chart (dashed lines). Angle $\beta =$ angle AA_0B_0. This locates point B and thus defines the mechanism. Read also the value for max μ_{min} (solid lines). No better minimum transmission angle can be obtained for the given conditions—every other linkage for the same dead-center angles possess a lower value of μ_{min}.

Interpolation can be employed between the curves for β and μ_{min}. However, when more accurate values for β are needed, use the equations (by assuming values for β and d):

$$\frac{a}{d} = -\frac{\sin\frac{\psi_0}{2}\cos\left(\frac{\theta_0}{2}+\beta\right)}{\sin\left(\frac{\theta_0}{2}-\frac{\psi_0}{2}\right)}$$

$$\frac{b}{d} = \frac{\sin\frac{\psi_0}{2}\sin\left(\frac{\theta_0}{2}+\beta\right)}{\cos\left(\frac{\theta_0}{2}-\frac{\psi_0}{2}\right)}$$

$$c^2 = (a+b)^2+d^2-2(a+b)d\cos\beta$$

where $a = AA_0$, $b = AB$, $c = BB_0$, and $d = A_0B_0$.

The design chart in Fig 6 is for the special case where $\theta_0 = 180$ deg, and the chart in Fig 9 for the design of a slider crank mechanism. The following examples illustrate use of the three charts.

Example I—Typical design

The dead-center position construction for $\theta_0 = 160$ deg and $\psi_0 = 40$ deg is shown in Fig 2. From the chart in Fig 7 find $\beta = 50.5$ deg and max $\mu_{min} = 32$ deg. Although there is no linkage with more favorable force transmission characteristics, a linkage with such a low minimum value of transmission angle is not capable of running at high speeds or transmitting great forces.

Example II—When $\theta_0 = \psi_0 + 180$ deg

When θ_0 and ψ_0 are chosen so that $\theta_0 = \psi_0 +180$ deg at the dead-center position construction, then angle A_0RB_0 becomes a right angle, and circle K_b degenerates into the line A_0R. Fig 5 shows the construction for $\theta_0 = 220$ deg and $\psi_0 = 40$ deg. For all linkages within this family, the crank-pin center A coincides with point R, and line A_0R extended beyond point L is the locus of point B, where $A_0R = RL$. Therefore, angle β is useless for finding the optimum linkage.

To obtain this linkage, locate A, ($A_1 A_0 = A_0A$). Draw circle t, with A_1B_0 as the diameter, to intersect with a line from A_0 perpendicular to A_0B_0. This locates point B_1. The required optimum linkage is $A_0A_1B_1B_0$. Angle $A_2B_1B_0 = $ max μ_{min}. All mechanisms of this family lie on the diagonal dashed line in the chart, Fig 7. For this example, the chart shows that max $\mu_{min} = 30$ deg, and that $\beta = 70$ deg.

Example III—Centric linkage design

The centric four-bar linkage where the crank angle rotates 180 deg between the two dead center positions ($\theta_0 = 180$ deg) provides the greatest

amplitudes ψ_0 of the rocker with most favorable transmission angle. However, Fig 7 is not applicable for this case because it indicates that $\beta = 0$ deg for any desired rocker angle ψ_0. This means that the length of crank and rocker must be zero—a solution without practical significance. Thus, a second chart, Fig 6, is used. For example, if a total rocker displacement of $\psi_0 = 90$ deg is required, a mechanism with $\mu_{min} = 40$ deg will be constructed with angle of $\beta = 23$ deg, and a mechanism with $\mu_{min} = 30$ deg with an angle of $\beta = 35$ deg. The dead-center position construction for this mechanism is shown in Fig 4. Here, other conditions can also be prescribed, for instance, a desired length of crank, rocker, or coupler.

Example IV—Slider-crank mechanism

For $\psi_0 = 0$ deg, the four-bar linkage degenerates into the slider-crank mechanism. Instead of the rocker angle ψ_0 the stroke, s, of the slider is used. The construction is as follows (see Fig 8):

1) Draw line A_0B_0 perpendicular to the direction of stroke.

2) Construct angle $\theta_0/2$ and a line parallel to A_0B_0 with distance $s/2$ as shown. This locates point R.

3) Draw M_aM_b, the perpendicular bisector of A_0R.

4) Draw, through R, circle K_a and

K_b about M_a and M_b as centers.

5) The line parallel to A_0B_0 at distance s intersects circle K_b at points L and E. Arc LE on circle K_b is the locus of point B. Point A is on circle K_a in line with A_0B.

For example, suppose a ratio of 4:5 of the crank angles is required for a quick-return mechanism. This ratio provides a dead-center angle of $\theta_0 = 160$ deg and $\theta'_0 = 200$ deg (160:200 = 4:5). As in the case of the crank-and-rocker mechanism, there is a whole family of slider-crank mechanisms fulfilling this condition. Here, the optimum mechanism will be the one whose transmission angle is closest to 90 deg when the crank is perpendicular to the direction of stroke. To find this optimum linkage use the $\psi_0 = 0$ deg ordinate in the chart of Fig 7. Thus, for $\theta_0 = 160$ deg, the chart gives $\beta \approx 76$ deg, which permits completion of the construction in Fig 8 (angle β locates point B on arc LE). The chart also gives max $\mu_{min} = 43$ deg. If the supplementary angle, $\theta'_0 = 200$ deg, is used the construction provides the same linkage because the chart shows $\beta' = 104$ deg, which is the supplement of angle β. (The $c = b$ line in Fig 6 gives points for a linkage with equal coupler and rocker links).

Because an exact value for angle β cannot be found at the ordinate of the chart, a third chart, Fig 9, has

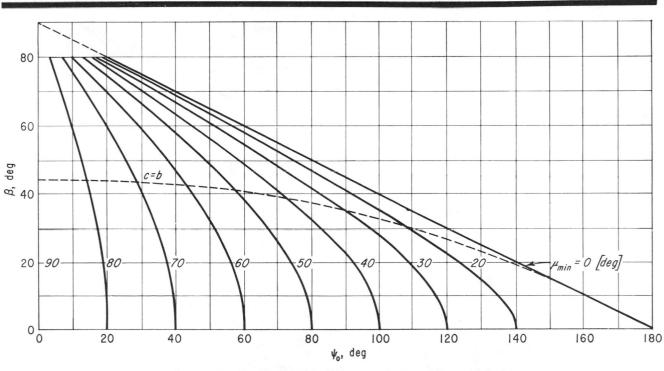

6. Optimum transmission angle — where $\theta_0 = 180$ deg.

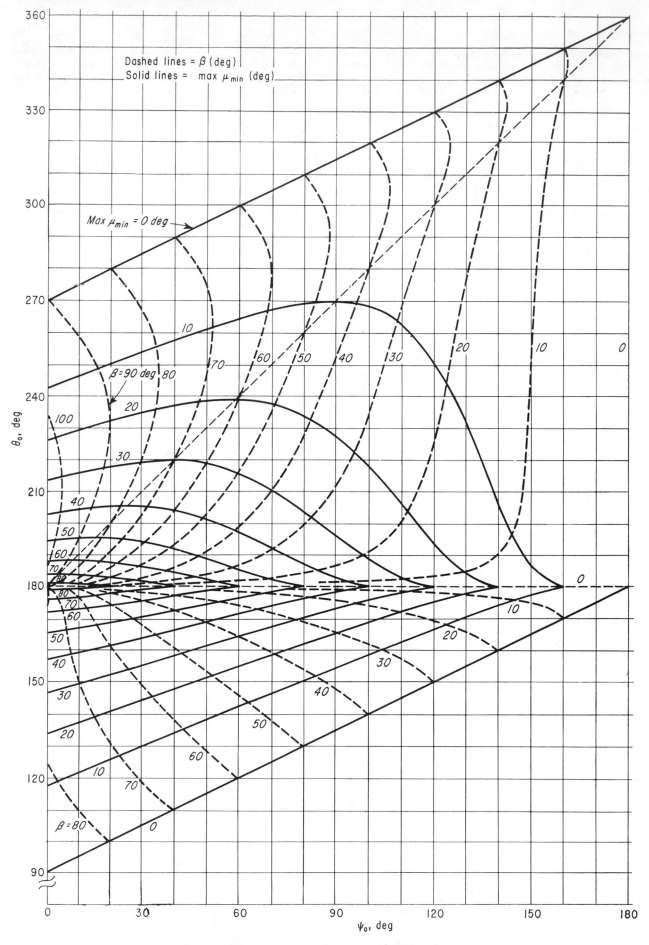

7. Optimum transmission angles — general case.

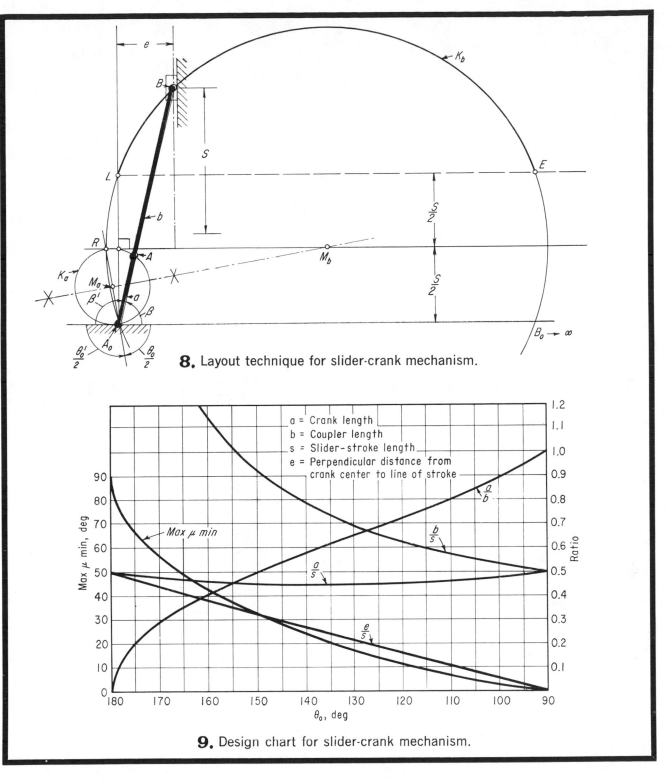

8. Layout technique for slider-crank mechanism.

9. Design chart for slider-crank mechanism.

been developed to provide greater accuracy. Here max $\mu_{\min}$ is plotted as a function of θ_0, along with ratios a/s, b/s, e/s, and a/b. For the desired angle of $\theta_0 = 160$ deg, max $\mu_{\min} = 43$ deg, $a/s = 0.465$, $b/s = 1.150$, $a/b = 0.406$, and $e/s = 0.378$. Instead of using angle β in Fig 8, draw a line from point A_0 perpendicular to A_0B_0 at a distance e—obtained from the ratio e/s—to locate point B on circle K_b. The line connecting A_0 and B intersects circle K_a at crank pin center, A, and the optimum slider-crank mechanism for the prescribed ratio of 4:5 is completely defined.

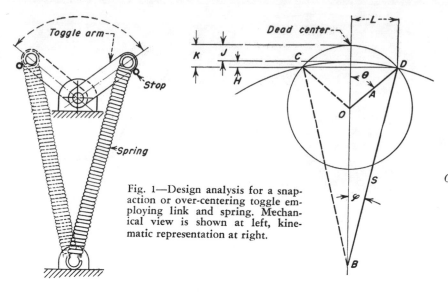

Fig. 1—Design analysis for a snap-action or over-centering toggle employing link and spring. Mechanical view is shown at left, kinematic representation at right.

Designing Snap-Action

ERWIN F. C. SCHULZE

Remington Rand, Division of Sperry Rand Corp.,
South Norwalk, Conn.

OVER-CENTERING TOGGLE MECHANISMS, Fig. 1, are widely used in mechanical and electrical switches, latch mechanisms and mechanical overload controls. Such toggles also serve as: (1) detent (holds other parts in selected position); (2) overload device in a mechanical linkage (shifts to opposite position when sufficiently loaded); and (3) energy storage device.

Two applications shown in Fig. 2 illustrate the "snap-action" of a toggle. As the toggle passes dead center it is snapped ahead of the actuating force by the toggle spring. In most applications it is desirable to obtain maximum snap action.

Snap-action is a function of the elongation per length of the toggle spring as it moves over dead center. Elongation at dead center is equal to:

$$J = K - H \qquad (1)$$

The elongation e in per cent of length is equal to:

$$e = (100)J/S \qquad (2)$$

Since the resisting force of the spring increases with elongation but decreases with an increase in length, the ratio J/S should be as large as possible within the capacity of the spring for best snap-action performance.

The ratio J/S as a function of angle θ can be derived as follows:

$$H = S - S \cos \varphi \qquad (3)$$

and

$$K = A - A \cos \theta \qquad (4)$$

Substituting Eqs (3) and (4) into Eq (1),

$$J = A(1 - \cos \theta) - S(1 - \cos \varphi) \qquad (5)$$

or

$$J/S = (A/S)(1 - \cos \theta) - (1 - \cos \varphi) \qquad (6)$$

The relationship between θ and ϕ is:

$$L = A \sin \theta = S \sin \varphi$$

or

$$\sin \varphi = (A/S)(\sin \theta) \qquad (7)$$

By trigonometric identity,

$$\sin \theta = (1 - \cos^2 \theta)^{1/2} \qquad (8)$$

Substituting Eq (8) into Eq (7) and squaring both sides,

$$\sin \varphi^2 = (A/S)^2(1 - \cos^2 \theta) \qquad (9)$$

By trigonometric identity,

$$\cos \varphi = (1 - \sin^2 \varphi)^{1/2} \qquad (10)$$

Substituting Eq (9) into Eq (10),

$$\cos \varphi = [1 - (A/S)^2 + (A/S)^2 \cos^2 \theta]^{1/2} \qquad (11)$$

and Eq (11) into Eq (6),

$$J/S = (A/S)(1 - \cos \theta) - 1 + [1 - (A/S)^2 - (A/S)^2 \cos^2 \theta]^{1/2} \qquad (12)$$

Eq (12 can be considered as having only three variables: (1) the spring elongation ratio J/S; (2) the toggle arm to spring length ratio, A/S; and (3) the toggle arm angle θ.

A series of curves are plotted from Eq (12) showing the relationship between J/S and A/S for various angles of θ. The curves are illustrated in Fig. 3; for greater accuracy each chart uses a different vertical scale.

Maximum Snap-Action

Maximum snap-action for a particular angle occurs when J/S is a maximum. This can be determined by setting the first derivative of Eq (12) equal to zero and solving for A/S.

Differentiating Eq (12),

$$\frac{d(J/S)}{d(A/S)} = 1 - \cos \theta + \frac{[-2(A/S) + 2(A/S)(\cos^2 \theta)]}{2[1 - (A/S)^2 + (A/S)^2 \cos^2 \theta]^{1/2}} \qquad (13)$$

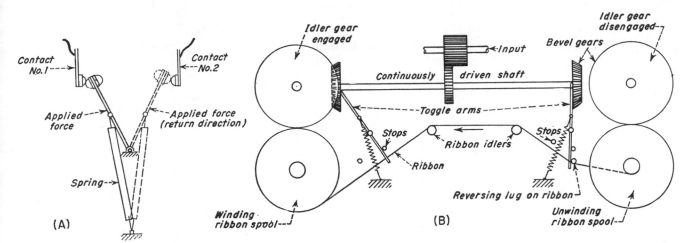

Fig. 2—Typical applications of toggles: (A) snap-action switches; (B) ribbon reversing mechanism for typewriters and calculators. The toggle in (B) is activated by a lug on the ribbon. As it passes dead center it is snapped ahead of the lug by the toggle spring, thus shifting the shaft and reversing the direction of the ribbon before next key is struck.

Toggles

Theory, formulas and design charts for quickly determining toggle dimensions to obtain maximum snap- action.

Setting Eq (13) equal to zero and re-arranging terms,

$$\frac{\cos\theta - 1}{\cos^2\theta - 1} =$$

$$\frac{A/S}{(A/S)[(S/A)^2 - 1 + \cos^2\theta]^{1/2}} \quad (14)$$

Cross-multiplying, squaring and simplifying,

$$(S/A)^2 - 1 + \cos^2\theta = \cos^2\theta + 2\cos\theta + 1$$

Reducing,

$$(S/A)^2 = 2\cos\theta + 2$$

and finally simplifying to the following equation of A/S when J/S is a maximum:

$$A/S = [2(\cos\theta + 1)]^{-1/2} \quad (15)$$

The maximum value of J/S can be determined by substituting Eq (15) into Eq (12):

$$J/S_{\text{max}} = \frac{1 - \cos\theta}{[2(\cos\theta + 1)]^{1/2}} - 1 +$$

$$\left[1 - \frac{1}{2(\cos\theta + 1)} + \frac{\cos^2\theta}{2(\cos\theta + 1)}\right]^{1/2} \quad (16)$$

which is simplified into the following expression:

$$J/S_{\text{max}} = \frac{2 - [2(\cos\theta + 1)]^{1/2}}{[2(\cos\theta + 1)]^{1/2}} \quad (17)$$

The locus of points of J/S_{max} is a straight line function as shown in Fig.

3. It can be seen from Eq (15) that the value of A/S at J/S_{max} varies from 0.500 when $\theta = 0$ to 0.707 when $\theta = 90$ deg. This relatively small range gives a quick rule-of-thumb to check if a mechanism has been designed close to the maximum snap-action point.

Elongation of the spring, Eq (2) is based on the assumption that the spring is installed in its free length S with no initial elongation. For a spring with a free length E smaller than S, the total elongation in per cent when extended to the dead center position is:

$$e = 100[(S/E)(1 + J/S) - 1] \quad (18)$$

Relationship between ϕ and θ at the point of maximum snap-action for any value of θ is:

$$\theta = 2\varphi \quad (19)$$

This can be proved by substituting Eqs (9) and (11) into the trigonometric identy:

$$\cos 2\varphi = \cos^2\varphi - \sin^2\varphi \quad (20)$$

and comparing the resulting equation with one obtained by solving for cos θ in Eq (15). This relationship between the angles is another means of quickly evaluating a toggle mechanism.

Design Procedure

A toggle is usually designed to operate within certain space limitations. When the dimensions X and W as shown in Fig. 4 are known, the angle θ resulting in maximum snap-action can be determined as follows:

$$A\sin\theta = S\sin\varphi = W/2 \quad (21)$$

Substituting Eq (19) into Eq (21),

$$A\sin\theta = S\sin(\theta/2) = W/2 \quad (22)$$

From Fig. 4:

$$X = S\cos(\theta/2) + A - A\cos\theta \quad (23)$$

Substituting Eq (22) into Eq (23),

$$X = \frac{W\cos(\theta/2)}{2\sin(\theta/2)}$$

$$+ \frac{W}{2\sin\theta} - \frac{W\cos\theta}{2\sin\theta} \quad (24)$$

Converting to half-angle functions and simplifying,

$$X = W/[2\sin(\theta/2)\cos(\theta/2)] \quad (25)$$

Using the trigonometric identity,

$$\sin\theta = 2\sin(\theta/2)\cos(\theta/2) \quad (26)$$

Eq (25) becomes:

$$X = W/\sin\theta$$

or

$$\sin\theta = W/X \quad (27)$$

Solving for θ permits determination

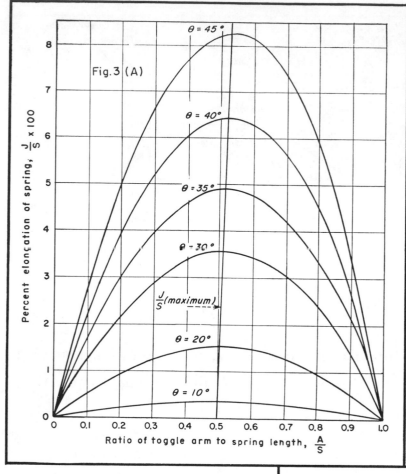

Fig. 3 (A)

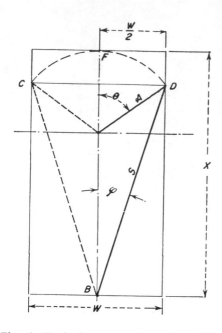

Fig. 4—Designing a toggle to lie within space boundaries W and X. It can be shown that for maximum snap-action, sin $\Theta = X/W$.

Fig. 3—Design charts for evaluating toggle arm and spring length for maximum spring elongation. Chart (B) is an extension of chart (A).

of ratios A/S and J/S from the charts in Fig. 3 when using the J/S(max) line. The values of S and A can then be obtained from Eq (22).

It can be seen from Fig. 3 that $\theta = 90$ deg results in maximum snap-action. Substitution of the sin of 90 deg in Eq (27) results in $W = X$; in other words, the most efficient space configuration for a toggle is a square.

EDITOR'S NOTE—In addition to the type discussed here, the term "toggle" is applied to a mechanism containing two links which line up in a straight line at one point of their motion giving a high mechanical advantage. A two-page mechanism spread, "Toggle Linkage Applications in Different Mechanisms" Thomas P. Goodman, appeared in the November 1949 issue of *Product Engineering*, p. 172, describing applications of this type to obtain: (1) high mechanical advantage, (2) high velocity ratio (3) variable mechanical advantage.

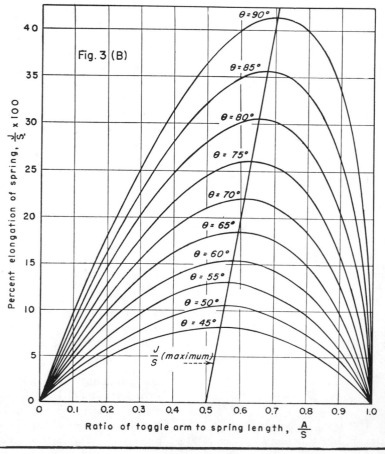

Fig. 3 (B)

Friction Wheel Drives Designed for Maximum Torque

Analysis of forces present in a friction wheel drive. Development of a design for drives that can be utilized to protect machines from excessive load torques.

RUDOLF KROENER

DURING THE POST WAR YEARS, as a consequence of the general scarcity of leather, rubber, and metals, in Germany efforts were made to replace belt drives and gear drives with friction wheel drives. The satisfactory results obtained are ascribed to:

1. Ability to manufacture a facing material having a high coefficient of friction. Cellulose type of materials have been developed possessing coefficients of friction ranging up to 0.5. When compared with materials having friction coefficients ranging from 0.15 to 0.2, the new materials offer an opportunity to reduce bearing pressures 60 to 70 percent.

2. Development of designs in which the contact or normal force between the friction wheels is varied automatically with changes in load torque of the driven machine. These designs make it possible to apply friction wheel drives to serve as disconnect clutches for limiting the transmission of torque before it becomes excessive.

When the faces of two friction wheels are pressed together, and where

μ = coefficient of friction of the materials in contact
P = radial force pressing the wheels together, lb
T = force transmitted tangentially to the wheels at their point of contact without slip, lb
r = radius of driving wheel, in.
n = speed of driving wheel, rpm
H = horsepower transmitted by the friction wheel drive

$$T = \mu P \qquad (1)$$

$$H = \frac{r\,n\,T}{63,025} \qquad (2)$$

Since the radial force P is equal and opposite to the force exerted by the wheels on their supporting bearings, it is evident that for constant values of T the bearing pressures increase as the coefficient of friction decreases. Low coefficients of friction, therefore, are conducive to resultant power loss and bearing wear.

In a friction wheel drive where the wheel centers are adjusted and fixed to obtain a radial force sufficient to transmit a desired torque, the bearing pressure remains at a constant value regardless of variations in the transmitted torque. When the load torque varies to a large extent, such an arrangement compares unfavorably with gear drives and belt drives, since in such drives the bearing pressures vary with the torque transmitted.

This disadvantage is overcome in types of friction drives in which the driving wheel is mounted on a swinging center.

The swing drive shown in Fig. 1 is designed to change the radial pressure P simultaneously and automatically with variations in load torque. In this arrangement the motor is fastened to a sub-base. The sub-base is free to swing on an axle at the right side. The opposite side of the base is supported by a spring. The driving friction wheel is pushed upward by the spring to maintain contact with the driven wheel. The driven wheel is mounted on a non-adjustable center.

When the torque load on the driven

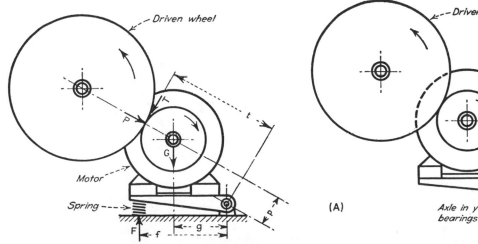

Fig. 1—Friction drive in which swing base is supported by a spring and axle.

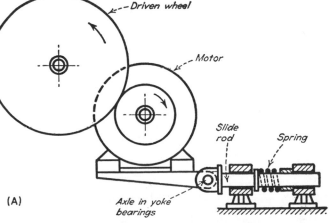

Fig. 2—(A) General arrangement of a maximum torque friction wheel drive with horizon-

wheel changes for any reason, the state of equilibrium is disturbed. The effect of an increase in torque load, until slipping occurs, is to cause the driving wheel to roll back or down on the driven wheel thus further compressing the spring. The spring force is thus increased, which results in an increased radial force P and an increase in the transmitted torque. Where

F = spring force, lb
f = horizontal distance from center of axle to line of spring force, in.
p = perpendicular distance from line of wheel centers to center of axle, in.
G = resultant of motor weight, driving wheel weight, and subbase weight, referred to axis of the motor, lb
g = horizontal distance from center of axle to vertical line passing through axis of motor, in.
t = perpendicular distance from tangent through point of contact of wheel faces to center of axle, in.

then to satisfy conditions of equilibrium

$$Gg - Ff - Pp + Tt = 0 \qquad (3)$$

and the spring force F is found by substituting in Eq (3) the value of P as given by Eq (1), or

$$F = \frac{Gg + T[t - (p/\mu)]}{f} \qquad (4)$$

In the design shown in Fig. 1, the extent to which the radial pressure P may build up, until slipping occurs, in response to increasing load torque is not limited. Excessive load torques may damage the friction facings, the driven machine, or the motor.

Any of many safety devices such as slip clutches, shear pins or keys, and breaking bolts, of course, can be used to protect the driven machine from excessive overloads. Fuses; overload relays, and thermal cut out devices can also be installed to protect the motor. Such protective devices

are not necessary, however, when the friction wheel drive is designed to perform as a maximum torque clutch in which contact at the wheel faces ceases when a predetermined value of load torque is exceeded.

In the friction wheel drive shown in Fig. 2 (A), the drive motor M is fastened to a swing plate, one side of which is supported on an axle. This axle is free to turn in yoke bearings on the ends of rods that are free to slide in fixed bearings. The spring F is compressed between a shoulder and a spacer on each slide rod.

In this arrangement, an increase in load torque on the driven wheel causes the tangential force T to increase, which in turn causes the driving wheel to ride at a lower position on the face of the driven wheel.

As the driving wheel drops to a lower position, the cosine of the angle included between the line of centers of the axle and motor and the horizontal centerline of the slide rods increases, thus compressing the spring F and increasing the contact force P. With an increasing load torque, the driving wheel will finally fall away from the driven wheel.

At the instant of last contact of the two wheels, the spring has its maximum compression. The maximum torque that the arrangement shown in Fig. 2 (A) can transmit, therefore, depends upon the spring rate of the spring.

The geometrical relations present in the drive shown in Fig. 2 (A) when operating under a normal load and under maximum load are shown in Figs. 2 (B) and (C), respectively. For normal load conditions, the notations for dimensions and angles carry the subscript 1; for maximum load conditions they carry the subscript 2.

The geometrical relations existing are.

AT A NORMAL LOAD,

$a_1 = (R + r) \cos \beta_1$
$h_1 = g - (R + r) \sin \beta_1$
$b_1 = \sqrt{s^2 - h_1^2}$
$p_1 = s \sin (\alpha_1 - \beta_1)$
$t_1 = r + s \cos (\alpha_1 - \beta_1)$
$c_1 = a_1 + b_1$

$$\sin \alpha_1 = \frac{h_1}{s} = \frac{g - (R + r) \sin \beta_1}{s}$$

AT MAXIMUM LOAD,

$\alpha_2 = \beta_2$
$a_2 = (R + r) \cos \beta_2$
$h_2 = g - (R + r) \sin \beta_2$
$b_2 = \sqrt{s^2 - h_2^2} = h_2 / \tan \beta_2$
$p_2 = s \sin (\alpha_2 - \beta_2) = 0$
$t_2 = r + s \cos (\alpha_2 - \beta_2) = r + s$
$c_2 = a_2 + b_2$
$\sin \alpha_2 = \sin \beta_2 = g/(R + r + s)$

Where

F = spring force or horizontal component of the reaction load exerted by the axle, lb
N = vertical component of the reaction load exerted by the axle, lb

the relations that satisfy conditions of equilibrium are

$$Gb + Tt - Pp = 0 \qquad (5)$$
$$P \cos \beta - T \sin \beta = F \qquad (6)$$
$$P \sin \beta + G + T \cos \beta = N \qquad (7)$$
$$\sqrt{N^2 + F^2} = S \qquad (8)$$
$$T = \mu P \qquad (9)$$

Substituting Eq (9) in Eq (6)

$$T_2 \left(\frac{\cos \beta_2}{\mu} - \sin \beta_2 \right) = F_2 \qquad (10)$$

The spring force F_2 required to maintain sufficient radial pressure P_2 to transmit a maximum horsepower H_2 from Eqs (2) and (10) is then

$$F_2 = \frac{63,025 \, H_2}{r n} \left(\frac{\cos \beta_2}{\mu} - \sin \beta_2 \right) \qquad (11)$$

by similar analysis

$$F_1 = \frac{63,025 \, H_1}{r n} \left(\frac{\cos \beta_1}{\mu} - \sin \beta_1 \right) \qquad (11A)$$

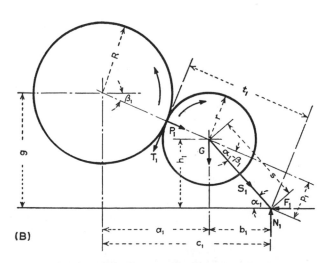

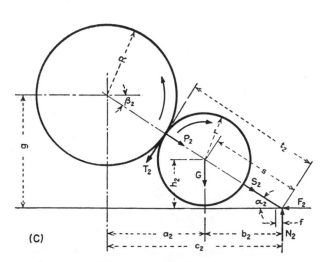

(B) **tal slide rods and compression springs. (B) Geometrical relation of parts under normal driving conditions. (C) Geometrical relation of parts under maximum torque driving conditions.**

The angle β_2 that gives the minimum value of F_2 for a given driving wheel diameter and speed at a given horsepower is found by differentiating Eq (11), setting the derivative equal to zero and solving for β_2, which results in the relation

$$\beta_2 = \sin^{-1}\left(\mu/\sqrt{1+\mu^2}\right) \quad (12)$$

Substituting the following values of μ in Eq (12) gives

For $\mu = 0.3$, $\beta_2 = 16$ deg 42 min
For $\mu = 0.4$, $\beta_2 = 21$ deg 48 min
For $\mu = 0.45$, $\beta_2 = 24$ deg 14 min

Employing an angle β_2 as determined by Eq (12) will assure full utilization of the coefficient of friction of the material up to the limit where sliding may occur, while simultaneously maintaining minimum radial pressure and bearing loads.

Where

= compression of the spring from spring load F_1 to spring load F_2 in.
$f = c_1 - c_2 = a_1 + b_1 - a_2 - b_2$

the spring rate k is

$$k = (F_2 - F_1)/f \quad (13)$$

The foregoing analysis of the drive shown in Fig. 2 (A) can be criticized on the basis that the design is expensive and that the vertical component N of the axle bearing reaction may introduce a frictional force that cannot be neglected. Furthermore, the analysis assumes that all the forces considered lie in the same vertical plane. Strictly speaking, the weights of motor, driving wheel, and swing base do not lie in the vertical planes that include radial pressure, tangential force, and spring force.

When the bearing rods are supported horizontally, however, these errors in assumption do not affect the spring calculatons to a large extent when the friction wheel lies in a vertical plane that is central between the two bearing rods. These errors do, however, affect the magnitude of the vertical component N, which acts on the two bearing rods.

The friction wheel drive shown in Fig. 3 is supported by two bearing rods separated by the distance d. The axial thrusts on these rods are counter-balanced by the reaction of compression springs. Each spring, its adjusting nut, and its rod thrust plate are contained within a sleeve. When the motor and swing plate have fallen through, the sleeve can be removed by lifting it from its enclosure. By lifting the motor, the sleeve can be replaced in its enclosure without changing the spring setting.

By resolving all the forces present into their components acting parallel to the plane passing through the centerlines of the bearing rods and writing equations of equilibrium, the following relations are obtained:

$G \sin \alpha_2 + T_1 \sin (\alpha_2 - \beta_1) +$
$P_1 \cos (\alpha_2 - \beta_1) - F_{A1} - F_{B1} = 0$ (14)
taking moments about B
$(d/2) G \sin \alpha_2 - d F_{A1} - e [T_1 \sin$
$(\alpha_2 - \beta_1) + P_1 \cos (\alpha_2 - \beta_1)] = 0$ (15)
taking moments about A
$(d/2) G \sin \alpha_2 + (d + e) [T_1 \sin (\alpha_2 - \beta_1) +$
$P_1 \cos (\alpha_2 - \beta_1)] - d F_{B1} = 0$ (16)

dividing Eq (15) through by d and solving for F_{A1}

$$F_{A1} = \frac{G \sin \alpha_2}{2} - \frac{e}{d} \times$$
$$[T_1 \sin (\alpha_2 - \beta_1) + P_1 \cos (\alpha_2 - \beta_1)] \quad (15A)$$

dividing Eq (16) through by d and solving for F_{B1}

$$F_{B1} = \frac{G \sin \alpha_2}{2} + \left(\frac{d + e}{d}\right) \times$$
$$[T_1 \sin (\alpha_2 - \beta_1) + P_1 \cos (\alpha_2 - \beta_1)] \quad (16A)$$

For the condition at the instant of maximum torque when the swing falls through

$$\alpha_2 = \beta_1 = \beta_2$$

therefore Eq (15A) becomes

$$F_{A2} = \frac{G \sin \alpha_2}{2} - \frac{e P_2}{d} \quad (15B)$$

and Eq (16A) becomes

$$F_{B2} = \frac{G \sin \alpha_2}{2} + \frac{(d + e) P_2}{d} \quad (16B)$$

The stroke or deflection Δl of the spring between the initial load and the maximum load is

$$\Delta l = R + r + s - [(R + r) \times$$
$$\cos (\beta_2 - \beta_1) + s \cos (\alpha_1 - \alpha_2)] \quad (17)$$

The spring constant for spring A is

$$k_A = (F_{A2} - F_{A1})/\Delta l \quad (18)$$

The spring constant for spring B is

$$k_B = (F_{B2} - F_{B1})/\Delta l \quad (19)$$

In similar manner, by resolving the forces into their components acting normal to the plane passing through the centerlines of the bearing rods and writing equations of equilibrium, the bending and twisting loads acting on the eyes of the bearing rods can be determined.

The maximum torque friction wheel drive is suitable and advantageous in applications where it is desirable to limit the magnitude of torque that can be delivered to a machine. This drive protects the machine from excessive steady loads and shock loads.

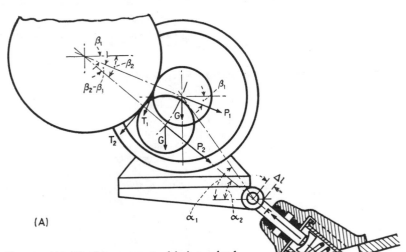

(A)

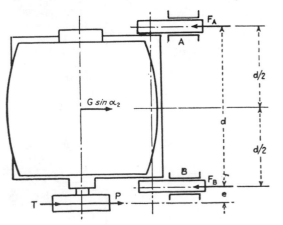

(B)

Fig. 3—(A) Maximum torque friction wheel drive with slide rods mounted at an angle to the base. (B) Forces acting in a plane passing through the centerlines of the slide rods.

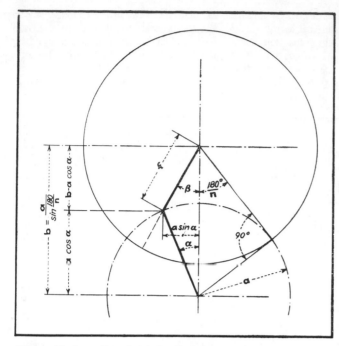

Fig. 1—Basic outline sketch for the external Geneva wheel. The symbols are identified for application in the basic equations.

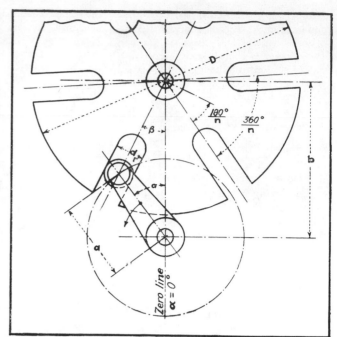

Fig. 2—Schematic sketch of a six slot Geneva wheel. Roller diameter, d_r, must be considered when determining D.

Kinematics of Intermittent Mechanisms
I—The External Geneva Wheel

Table I—Notation and Formulas for the External Geneva Wheel

Assumed or given: a, n, d and p

a = crank radius of driving member

n = number of slots

d_r = roller diameter

p = constant velocity of driving crank in rpm

$$m = \frac{1}{\sin \frac{180}{n}}$$

b = center distance = am

D = diameter of driven member = $2\sqrt{\dfrac{d^2_r}{4} + a^2 \cot^2 \dfrac{180}{n}}$

ω = constant angular velocity of driving crank = $\dfrac{p\pi}{30}$ radians per sec

α = angular position of driving crank at any time

β = angular displacement of driven member corresponding to crank angle α

$$\cos\beta = \frac{m - \cos\alpha}{\sqrt{1 + m^2 - 2m\cos\alpha}}$$

Angular Velocity of driven member = $\dfrac{d\beta}{dt}$ = $\omega\left(\dfrac{m\cos\alpha - 1}{1 + m^2 - 2m\cos\alpha}\right)$

Angular Acceleration of driven member = $\dfrac{d^2\beta}{dt^2}$ = $\omega^2\left(\dfrac{m\sin\alpha\,(1 - m^2)}{(1 + m^2 - 2m\cos\alpha)^2}\right)$

Maximum Angular Acceleration occurs when $\cos\alpha =$

$$\sqrt{\left(\frac{1 + m^2}{4\,m}\right)^2 + 2} - \left(\frac{1 + m^2}{4\,m}\right)$$

Maximum Angular Velocity occurs at $\alpha = 0$ deg, and equals

$\dfrac{\omega}{m - 1}$ radians per sec

ONE OF THE MOST commonly used mechanisms for producing intermittent rotary motion from a uniform input speed is the external Geneva wheel.

The driven member, or star wheel, contains a number of slots into which the roller of the driving crank fits. The number of slots determines the ratio between dwell and motion period of the driven shaft. Lowest possible number of slots is three, while the highest number is theoretically unlimited. In practice the 3 slot Geneva is seldom used because of the extremely high acceleration values encountered. Genevas with more than 18 slots also are infrequently used, since they necessitate wheels of comparatively large diameters.

In external Genevas of any number of slots, the dwell period always exceeds the motion period. The opposite is true of the internal Geneva, while for the spherical Geneva both dwell and motion periods are 180 degrees.

For proper operation of the external Geneva, the roller must enter the slot tangentially. In other words, the centerline of the slot and the line connecting roller center and crank rotation center must compose a right angle when the roller enters or leaves the slot.

Calculations that follow below are

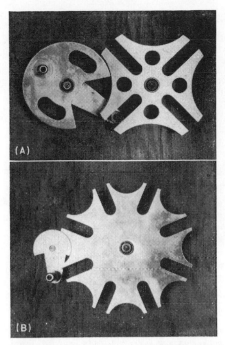

Fig. 3—Four slot Geneva (A) and eight slot (B). Both have locking devices.

S. RAPPAPORT

based upon these conditions stated.

Consider an external Geneva wheel, shown in Fig. 1, in which

n = number of slots
a = crank radius

From Fig 1, b = center distance = $\dfrac{a}{\sin \dfrac{180}{n}}$

Let $\dfrac{1}{\sin \dfrac{180}{n}} = m$

then $b = a m$

It will simplify the development of the equations of motion to designate the connecting line of wheel and crank centers as the zero line. This is contrary to the practice of assigning the zero value of α, representing the angular position of the driving crank, to that position of the crank where the roller enters the slot.

Thus, from Fig. 1, the driven crank radius f at any angle is

$$f = \sqrt{(am - a \cos \alpha)^2 + a^2 \sin^2 \alpha} = a\sqrt{1 + m^2 - 2m \cos \alpha} \qquad (1)$$

and the angular displacement β can be found from

$$\cos \beta = \frac{m - \cos \alpha}{\sqrt{1 + m^2 - 2m \cos \alpha}} \qquad (2)$$

A six slot Geneva is shown schematically in Fig. 2. The outside diameter

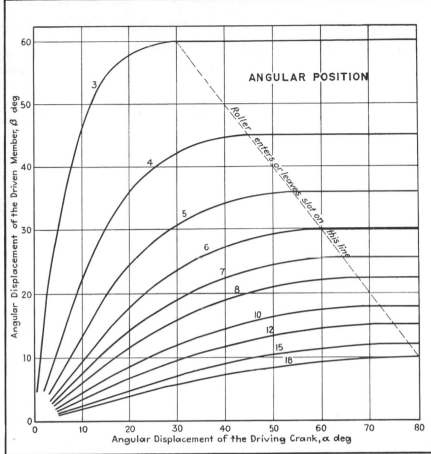

Fig. 4—Chart for determining the angular displacement of the driven member.

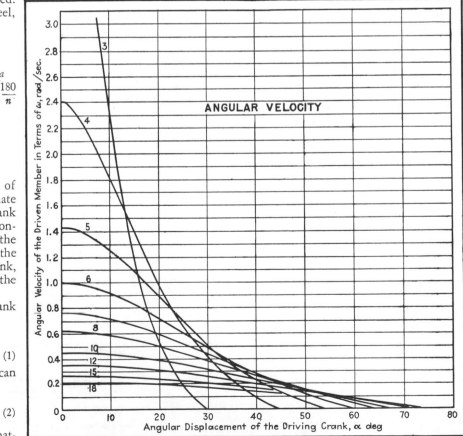

Fig. 5—Chart for determining the angular velocity of the driven member.

Table II—Principal Kinematic Data for External Geneva Wheel

No. of Slots	$\dfrac{360°}{n}$	Dwell period	Motion period	m and center-distance for $\alpha = 1$	Maximum angular velocity of driven member, radians per sec. equals ω multiplied by values tabulated. Crank at 0° position	Angular acceleration of driven member when roller enters slot, radians² per sec², equals ω^2 multiplied by values tabulated.			Maximum angular Acceleration of driven member, radians² per sec², equals ω^2 multiplied by values tabulated		
						α	β	Multiplier	α	β	Multiplier
3	120°	300°	60°	1.155	6.458	30°	60°	1.729	4°	27° 58'	29.10
4	90°	270°	90°	1.414	2.407	45°	45°	1.000	11° 28'	25° 11'	5.314
5	72°	252°	108°	1.701	1.425	54°	36°	0.727	17° 31'	21° 53'	2.310
6	60°	240°	120°	2.000	1.000	60°	30°	0.577	22° 55'	19° 51'	1.349
7	51° 25' 43"	231° 30'	128° 30'	2.305	0.766	64° 17' 8"	25° 42' 52"	0.481	27° 41'	18° 11'	0.928
8	45°	225°	135°	2.613	0.620	67° 30'	22° 30'	0.414	31° 38'	16° 32'	0.700
9	40°	220°	140°	2.924	0.520	70°	20°	0.364	35° 16'	15° 15'	0.559
10	36°	216°	144°	3.236	0.447	72°	18°	0.325	38° 30'	14° 16'	0.465
11	32° 43' 38"	212° 45'	147° 15'	3.549	0.392	73° 38' 11"	16° 21' 49"	0.294	41° 22'	13° 16'	0.398
12	30°	210°	150°	3.864	0.349	75°	15°	0.268	44°	12° 26'	0.348
13	27° 41' 32"	207° 45'	152° 15'	4.179	0.315	76° 9' 14"	13° 50' 46"	0.246	46° 23'	11° 44'	0.309
14	25° 42' 52"	205° 45'	154° 15'	4.494	0.286	77° 8' 34"	21° 51' 26"	0.228	48° 32'	11° 3'	0.278
15	24°	204°	156°	4.810	0.263	78°	12°	0.213	50° 30'	10° 27'	0.253
16	22° 30'	202° 30'	157° 30'	5.126	0.242	78° 45'	11° 15'	0.199	52° 24'	9° 57'	0.232
17	21° 10' 35"	201°	159°	5.442	0.225	79° 24' 43"	10° 35' 17"	0.187	53° 58'	9° 26'	0.215
18	20°	200°	160°	5.759	0.210	80°	10°	0.176	55° 30'	8° 59'	0.200

D of the wheel (when taking the effect of the roller diameter d_r into account) is found to be

$$D = 2\sqrt{\frac{d_r^2}{4} + a^2 \cot^2 \frac{180}{n}} \qquad (3)$$

Differentiating Eq (2) and dividing by the differential of time, dt, the angular velocity of the driven member is

$$\frac{d\beta}{dt} = \omega\left(\frac{m \cos\alpha - 1}{1 + m^2 - 2m\cos\alpha}\right) \qquad (4)$$

where ω represents the constant angular velocity of the crank.

By differentiation of Eq (4) the acceleration of the driven member is found to be

$$\frac{d^2\beta}{dt^2} = \omega^2\left(\frac{m \sin\alpha (1 - m^2)}{(1 + m^2 - 2m\cos\alpha)^2}\right) \qquad (5)$$

All notations and principal formulas are given in Table I for easy reference. Table II contains all the data of principal interest for external Geneva wheels having from 3 to 18 slots. All other data can be read from the charts: Fig. 4 for angular position, Fig. 5 for angular velocity, and Fig. 6 for angular acceleration.

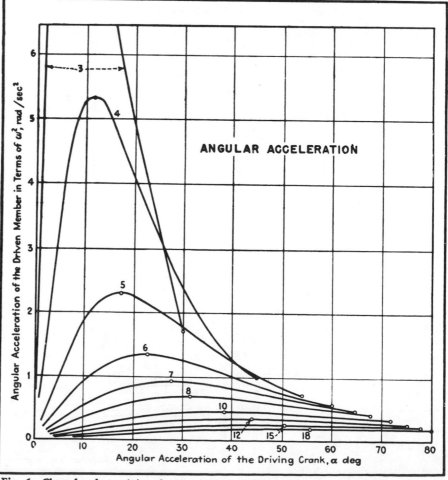

Fig. 6—Chart for determining the angular acceleration of the driven member.

Fig. 1—A four slot internal Geneva wheel incorporating a locking mechanism. The basic sketch is shown in Fig. 3.

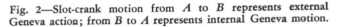

Fig. 2—Slot-crank motion from *A* to *B* represents external Geneva action; from *B* to *A* represents internal Geneva motion.

Kinematics of Intermittent Mechanisms
II—The Internal Geneva Wheel

S. RAPPAPORT

WHERE INTERMITTENT DRIVES must provide dwell periods of more than 180 deg, the external Geneva wheel design is quite satisfactory and is almost the standard device employed. But where the dwell period has to be less than 180 deg, other intermittent drive mechanisms must be used. The internal Geneva wheel is one way of obtaining this type of motion.

Dwell period of all internal Genevas is always smaller than 180 deg. Thus more time is left for the star to achieve maximum velocity, and acceleration is lower. The highest value of the angular acceleration occurs when the roller enters or leaves the slot. However, the acceleration curve does not reach a peak within the range of motion of the driven wheel. The geometrical maximum would occur in the continuation of the curve, but this continuation has no significance, since the driven member will have entered the dwell phase associated with the high angular displacement of the driving member.

The geometrical maximum lies in the continuation of the curve, falling into the region representing the mo-

Table I—Notation and Formulas for the Internal Geneva Wheel

Assumed or given: a, n, d and p

a = crank radius of driving member
n = number of slots
d = roller diameter
p = constant velocity of driving crank in rpm

$$m = \frac{1}{\sin \dfrac{180°}{n}}$$

b = center distance = $a\,m$

$$D = \text{inside diameter of driven member} = 2\sqrt{\frac{d^2}{4} + a^2 \cot^2 \frac{180°}{n}}$$

ω = constant angular velocity of driving crank in radians per sec = $\dfrac{p\pi}{30}$ radians per sec

α = angular position of driving crank at any time
β = angular displacement of driven member corresponding to crank angle α

$$\cos\beta = \frac{m + \cos\alpha}{\sqrt{1 + m^2 + 2m\cos\alpha}}$$

Angular velocity of driven member = $\dfrac{d\beta}{dt} = \omega\left(\dfrac{1 + m\cos\alpha}{1 + m^2 + 2m\cos\alpha}\right)$

Angular acceleration of driven member = $\dfrac{d^2\beta}{dt^2} = \omega^2\left[\dfrac{m\sin\alpha\,(1 - m^2)}{(1 + m^2 + 2m\cos\alpha)^2}\right]$

Maximum angular velocity occurs at $\alpha = 0°$ and equals = $\dfrac{\omega}{1 + m}$ radians per sec

Maximum angular acceleration occurs when roller enters slot and equals = $\dfrac{\omega^2}{\sqrt{m^2 - 1}}$ radians² per sec²

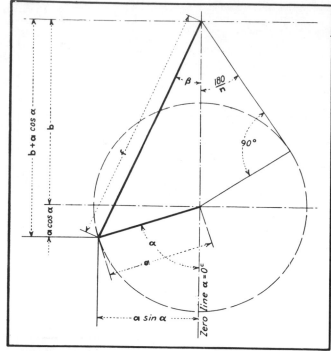

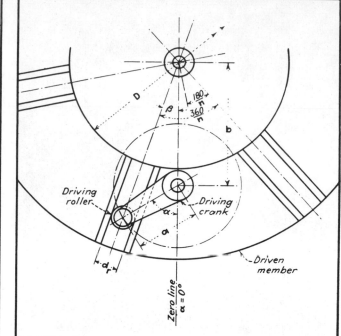

Fig. 3—Basic outline sketch for developing the equations of the internal Geneva wheel, using the notations as shown.

Fig. 4—Schematic sketch of a six slot internal Geneva wheel. Symbols are identified and motion equations given in Table I.

tion of the external Geneva wheel. This can be seen by the following considerations of a crank and slot drive, sketched in Fig. 2.

When the roller crank R rotates, slot link S will perform an oscillating movement, for which the displacement, angular velocity and acceleration can be given in continuous curves.

When the crank R rotates from A to B, then the slot link S will move from C to D, exactly reproducing all moving conditions of an external Geneva of equal slot angle. When crank R continues its movement from B back to A, then the slot link S will move from D back to C, this time reproducing exactly (though in a mirror picture with the direction of motion being reversed) the moving conditions of an internal Geneva.

Therefore, the characteristic curves of this motion contain both the external and internal Geneva wheel conditions; the region of the external Geneva lying between A and B, the region of the internal Geneva lying between B and A.

The geometrical maxima of the acceleration curves lie only in the region between A and B, representing that portion of the curves which belongs to the external Geneva.

Principal advantage of the internal Geneva, other than its smooth operation, is the sharply defined dwell period. A disadvantage is the relatively large size of the driven member, which increases the force resisting acceleration. Another feature, which is

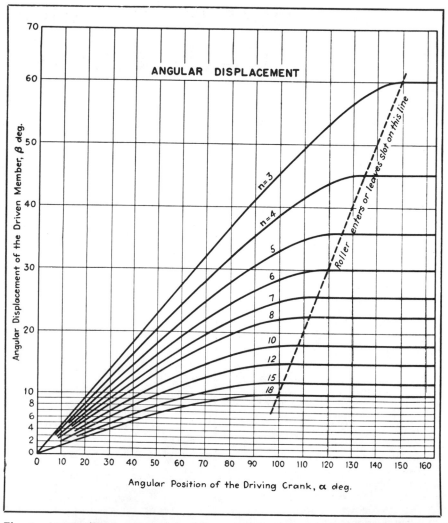

Fig. 5—Angular displacement of the driven member can be determined from this chart.

118

sometimes a disadvantage, is the cantilever arrangement of the roller crank shaft. This shaft cannot be a through shaft because the crank has to be fastened to the overhanging end of the input shaft.

To simplify the equations, the connecting line of wheel and crank centers is taken as the zero line. The angular position of the driving crank, α, is zero when on this line. Then the following relations are developed, based on Fig. 3:

n = number of slots
a = crank radius

b = center distance = $\dfrac{a}{\sin \dfrac{180°}{n}}$

Let

$$\dfrac{1}{\sin \dfrac{180°}{n}} = m,$$

then

$$b = am$$

To find the angular displacement, β, of the driven member, the driven crank radius, f, is first calculated from

$$f = \sqrt{a^2 \sin^2 \alpha + (am + a \cos \alpha)^2} = a\sqrt{1 + m^2 + 2m \cos \alpha} \qquad (1)$$

and since

$$\cos \beta = \dfrac{m + \cos \alpha}{f}$$

it follows:

$$\cos \beta = \dfrac{m + \cos \alpha}{\sqrt{1 + m^2 + 2m \cos \alpha}} \qquad (2)$$

From this formula, β, the angular displacement, can be calculated for any angle α, the angle of the driving member.

The first derivative of Eq (2) gives the angular velocity as

$$\dfrac{d\beta}{dt} = \omega \left(\dfrac{1 + m \cos \alpha}{1 + m^2 + 2m \cos \alpha} \right) \qquad (3)$$

where ω designates the uniform speed of the driving crank shaft, namely

$$\omega = \dfrac{p\pi}{30}$$

if p equals its number of revolutions per minute.

Differentiating Eq (3) once more develops the equation for the angular acceleration:

$$\dfrac{d^2\beta}{dt^2} = \omega^2 \left[\dfrac{m \sin \alpha (1 - m^2)}{(1 + m^2 + 2m \cos \alpha)^2} \right] \qquad (4)$$

The maximum angular velocity occurs, obviously, at $\alpha = 0$ deg. Its value is found by substituting 0 deg for α in Eq (3). It is

$$\dfrac{d\beta}{dt}_{max} = \dfrac{\omega}{1 + m} \qquad (5)$$

The highest value of the accelera-

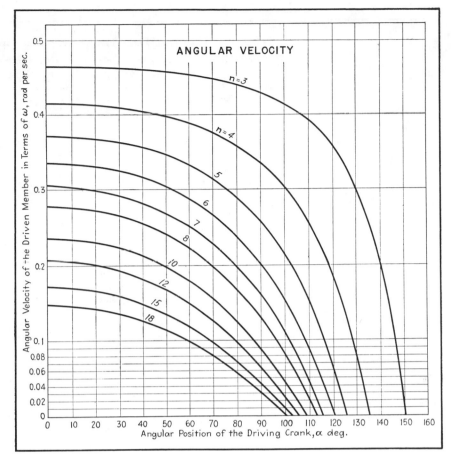

Fig. 6—Angular velocity of the driven member can be determined from this chart.

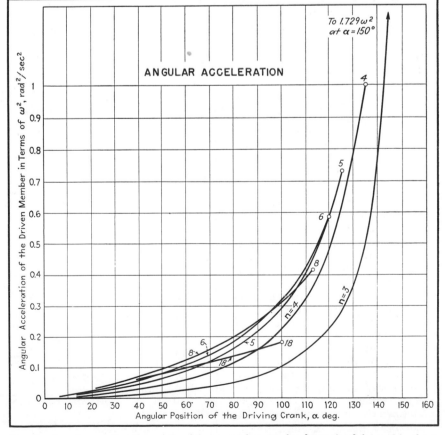

Fig. 7—Angular acceleration of the driven member can be determined from this chart.

Table II—Kinematic Data For the Internal Geneva Wheel

Number of slots, n	$\dfrac{360°}{n}$	Dwell period	Motion period	m and center-distance for $a=1$	Maximum angular velocity of driven member equals ω radians per sec. multiplied by values tabulated. Both α and β in 0° position	Angular acceleration of driven member when roller enters slot equals ω^2 radians² per sec² multiplied by values tabulated		
						α	β	Multiplier
3	120°	60°	300°	1.155	0.464	150°	60°	1.729
4	90°	90°	270°	1.414	0.414	135°	45°	1.000
5	72°	108°	252°	1.701	0.370	126°	36°	0.727
6	60°	120°	240°	2.000	0.333	120°	30°	0.577
7	51° 25′ 43″	128° 30′	231° 30′	2.305	0.303	115° 42′ 52″	25° 42′ 52″	0.481
8	45°	135°	225°	2.613	0.277	112° 30′	22° 30′	0.414
9	40°	140°	220°	2.924	0.255	110°	20°	0.364
10	36°	144°	216°	3.236	0.236	108°	18°	0.325
11	32° 43′ 38″	147° 15′	212° 45′	3.549	0.220	106° 21′ 49″	16° 21′ 49″	0.294
12	30°	150°	210°	3.864	0.206	105°	15°	0.268

tion is found by substituting $180/n + 90$ for α in Eq (4):

$$\frac{d^2\beta}{dt^2}_{max} = \frac{\omega^2}{\sqrt{m^2-1}} \qquad (6)$$

A schematic sketch for a six slot internal Geneva wheel is shown in Fig. 4. All the symbols used in this sketch, and throughout the text, are compiled in Table I for easy reference.

Table II contains all the data of principal interest on the performance of internal Geneva wheels having from 3 to 18 slots. Other data can be read from the charts: Fig. 5 for angular position, Fig. 6 for angular velocity and Fig. 7 for angular acceleration.

THE CARDIOID DRIVE

Short dwell periods, with correspondingly low accelerations, make possible higher speed operation with this intermittent motion drive.

S. RAPPAPORT

INTERMITTENT ROTARY MECHANISMS with extremely short dwell periods have the inherent advantage of smooth operation because of the comparatively low acceleration forces involved. As a corollary benefit, this feature enables the mechanism to operate at high speeds. Obviously, a short dwell leaves more time for the mechanism to attain its maximum velocity, thus lowering the necessary acceleration. If the designer must incorporate an intermittent mechanism in his machine, he should choose the one that has the shortest dwell compatible with the given operating conditions.

An example, concerning a machine of European design for making cigarette tubes, illustrates this. A metal

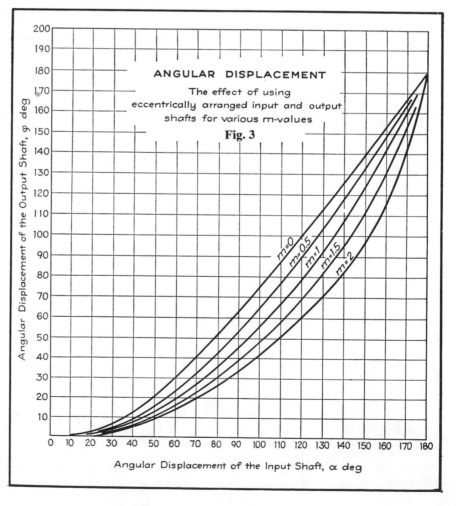

ANGULAR DISPLACEMENT

The effect of using eccentrically arranged input and output shafts for various m-values

Fig. 3

Angular Displacement of the Output Shaft, g deg

Angular Displacement of the Input Shaft, α deg

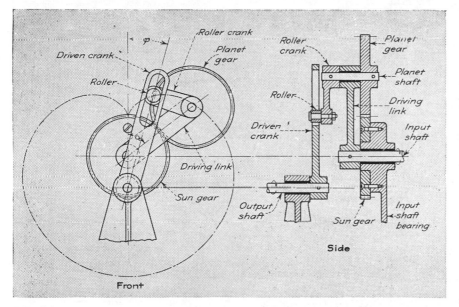

Fig. 1—Schematic arrangement of the Cardioid drive. Note that the front and side views illustrate the mechanism in two different positions of angular displacement.

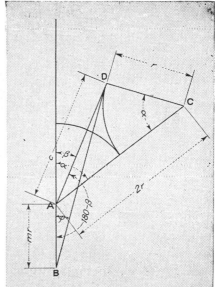

Fig. 2—Construction for calculating the displacement curve of the output shaft.

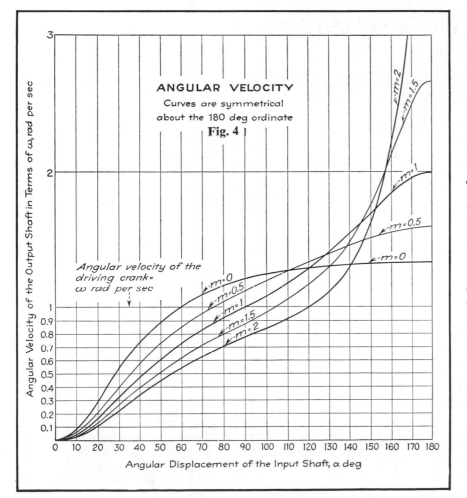

ANGULAR VELOCITY

Curves are symmetrical about the 180 deg ordinate

Fig. 4

Angular Velocity of the Output Shaft in Terms of ω, rad per sec

Angular velocity of the driving crank = ω rad per sec

Angular Displacement of the Input Shaft, α deg

tube of small diameter and having a longitudinal slot, received into this slot the heavy paper for the mouthpiece. The tube then rotated and the precut paper was wrapped around it.

Since the metal tube had to be motionless while the paper was fed into the slot, an intermittent drive was employed for the tube. This was first done with a mechanism of an unnecessarily long dwell period, 180 deg, which limited the speed of the machine to 240 rpm. Investigation showed that a dwell of only a few degrees would allow sufficient time to feed the paper through the short distance into the slot of the metal tube. The choice for such a suitable mechanism lay between the Three-Gear drive, PRODUCT ENGINEERING, Jan 1950, p 120, and the Cardioid drive, both having similar characteristics. Constructive and space considerations, however, favored the Cardioid drive, In Fig. 1 a sketch is shown to aid in understanding the construction.

Use of the Cardioid drive made it possible to raise the speed of the machine from 240 to 650 rpm, without developing excessive forces or rough action.

The working principle of a Cardioid drive is shown schematically in Fig. 1. The name comes from the shape of the path traced by the roller in the driven crank slot. The sun gear is fastened rigidly to the input shaft bearing, while the input shaft carries the driving link. Other end of the driving link carries a bearing for the planet shaft. On one end of the planet shaft the planet gear is fastened, and on the other end is the roller crank. The sun gear and the planet gear are of the same pitch diameter, $2r$, and the length of roller crank equal r. As shown, the roller fits into the slot of the driven crank, which in turn is fastened to the output shaft.

When the input shaft rotates, the roller follows the path of a cardioid, sliding up and down the slot of the driven crank and imparting to it, and thus to the output shaft, an intermittent motion.

Input and output shaft may or may not be located eccentrically to each other. Their center distance, mr, where m is the factor by which r is multiplied to equal the center distance, influences the characteristic curves. Usually m equals 1 produces satisfactory results by providing an apparent dwell of sufficient length for practical purposes and giving good acceleration characteristics.

Geometrical conditions from which the displacement curve can be calculated are shown in Fig. 2, using following notations:

Point A is the center of rotation of the input shaft.
Point B is the center of rotation of the output shaft.

r = pitch radius of both sun and planet gears.
α = angular position of driving crank at any time.
ϕ = angular position of driven crank corresponding to α
Point C is the center of the plant gear at the position α
Point D is the center of the roller at the position α

From the triangle ACD is found

$$c = \sqrt{r^2 + 4r^2 - 4r^2 \cos \alpha} = r \sqrt{5 - 4 \cos \alpha} \quad (1)$$

$$\tan(\alpha - \beta) = \frac{r \sin \alpha}{2r - r \cos \alpha} = \frac{\sin \alpha}{2 - \cos \alpha} \quad (2)$$

or

$$\frac{\tan \alpha - \tan \beta}{1 + \tan \alpha \tan \beta} = \frac{\sin \alpha}{2 - \cos \alpha} \quad (3)$$

solving for $\tan \beta$:

$$\tan \beta = \frac{2 \sin \alpha - \sin 2\alpha}{2 \cos \alpha - \cos 2\alpha} \quad (4)$$

From the triangle ABD is found

$$\tan \phi = \frac{c \sin(180 - \beta)}{mr - c \cos(180 - \beta)} \quad (5)$$

$$\tan \phi = \frac{r \sqrt{5 - 4 \cos \alpha} \quad \sin \beta}{mr + r \sqrt{5 - 4 \cos \alpha} \quad \cos \beta} = \frac{\sin \beta \sqrt{5 - 4 \cos \alpha}}{m + \cos \beta \sqrt{5 - 4 \cos \alpha}} \quad (6)$$

Substituting for

$$\cos \beta = \frac{1}{\sqrt{1 + \tan^2 \beta}} \Big]$$

$$\tan \phi = \frac{\tan \beta \sqrt{5 - 4 \cos \alpha}}{m \sqrt{1 + \tan^2 \beta} + \sqrt{5 - 4 \cos \alpha}} \quad (7)$$

From Eq (4) and (7) is finally found the curve of angular displacement, Fig. 3, from:

$$\tan \phi = \frac{2 \sin \alpha - \sin 2\alpha}{m + 2 \cos \alpha - \cos 2\alpha} \quad (8)$$

By differentiation of Eq (8) is found the curve of angular velocity, which Fig. 4 represents:

$$\frac{d\phi}{dt} = 2\omega \left[\frac{3 + (m-3)\cos \alpha -}{5 + m^2 + 4(m-1)\cos \alpha -} \right. \left. \frac{m \cos 2\alpha}{2 m \cos 2\alpha} \right] \quad (9)$$

where ω = uniform angular velocity of the driver in radians per seconds.

It is somewhat tedious to develop the second derivative in general terms of m, to find the acceleration curves of Fig. 5. However, the calculations are appreciably simplified, if the actual values of m are substituted. So, for instance, for $m = 1$, the acceleration is

$$\frac{d^2\phi}{dt^2} = 2\omega^2 \left[\frac{3 \sin \alpha - \sin \alpha \cos 2\alpha +}{9 - 6 \cos 2\alpha +} \right. \left. \frac{2 \sin 2\alpha \cos \alpha}{\cos^2 2\alpha} \right] \quad (10)$$

in radians per second per second.

As can be seen from the displacement curves, an increase of m increases also the apparent dwell—for the price of an increased acceleration. The acceleration curves have generally two maxima which are equal only when m equals 1. For most applications, m should be chosen between 0.8 and 1.5. As mentioned before, m equals 1 gives satisfactory results for average conditions.

Wherever practicable, the mechanism should be enclosed in an oil bath. Then good lubrication and protection from dirt are assured for the roller-crank slot contact.

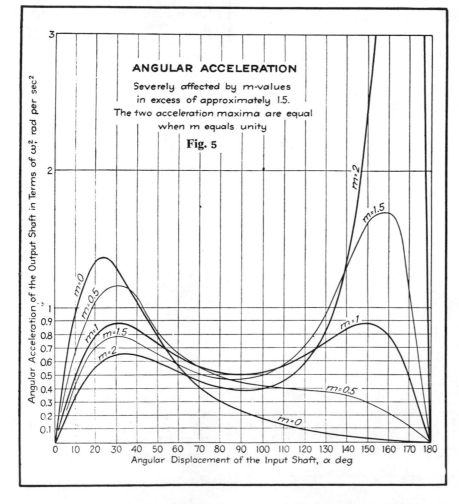

ANGULAR ACCELERATION
Severely affected by m-values in excess of approximately 1.5. The two acceleration maxima are equal when m equals unity

Fig. 5

Angular Acceleration of the Output Shaft in Terms of ω^2, rad per sec^2

Angular Displacement of the Input Shaft, α deg

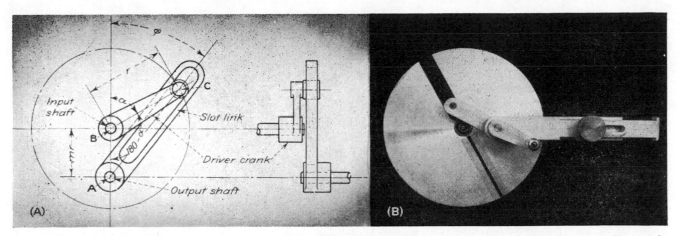

Fig. 1—(A) Schematic sketch of the crank and slot drive. By changing distance *mr*, the non-uniform rotary motion can be varied. The driven member will perform a complete revolution as long as *mr* is kept smaller than *r*. (B) Model of the crank and slot drive having an adjustable center distance. Slot link is replaced by a slot carrying disk for balancing purposes.

Kinematics of the Crank And Slot Drive

A low-cost substitute for elliptical gearing

S. RAPPAPORT

APPLICATION OF NON-UNIFORM RO-TATION is sometimes unavoidable —. and even to be desired. One frequent application is on rotary cross-cutting knives for continuously moving paper or foil webs.

Here, a fixed length of the web passes beneath the knife during one cycle of the machine, while the knife performs one rotation per cycle. The knife's peripheral speed, while cutting, should approximately equal the web speed, which in turn determines the cut length. Obviously, these conditions can be fulfilled for one particular cut length only if the knife diameter is kept constant. If the paper feed is set for a larger cut length, the web speed increases and the peripheral speed of the knife is relatively too slow.

To overcome this difficulty, elliptic gears are sometimes employed to drive the knife shaft. They cause the knife to accelerate in its cutting position to the approximate web speed and slow

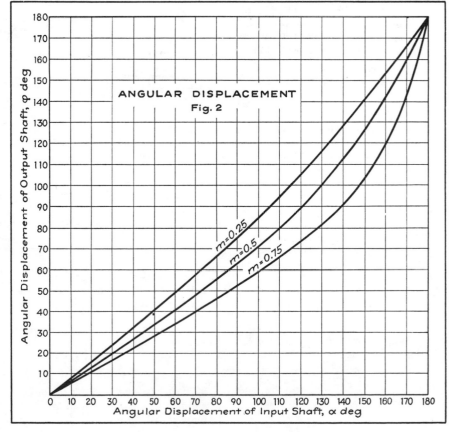

ANGULAR DISPLACEMENT
Fig. 2

Angular Displacement of Output Shaft, φ deg

Angular Displacement of Input Shaft, α deg

m=0.25
m=0.5
m=0.75

down in the remainder of its cycle.

There are other machines for which non-uniform output speed is desired, but elliptic gears are difficult to make and accordingly are expensive. There is, however, another solution for this kind of drive—the crank and slot drive.

It is a comparatively simple mechanism giving similar results. Fig 1(A) shows a schematic sketch.

It is obvious that the driven member, the slot link, will perform a complete revolution for each turn of the driving crank as long as their center distance is smaller than r, the crank length, or $m < 1$; (where m equals a constant by which r is multiplied to equal the distance between input and output shaft centers). For $m > 1$, the slot link will perform oscillations.

The equations of motion then will equal those of the Internal Geneva, where the direction of rotation is that of the driving crank. The equations will be those of the External Geneva, when the slot link is on its backstroke, rotating in an opposite direction to the driving crank.

An advantage of this drive over the elliptic gear drive is the possibility of making the center distance adjustable. Thus it is possible to change the degree of circular irregularity to meet the particular requirement. Fig. 1(B) shows a photograph of a model with adjustable center distance.

For the development of the equations of motion refer to Fig. 1(A). The displacement of the output shaft, ϕ, is found from triangle ABC, where α is the driving crank displacement:

$$\tan \phi = \frac{r \sin (180 - \alpha)}{mr - r \cos (180 - \alpha)} = \frac{\sin \alpha}{m + \cos \alpha} \qquad (1)$$

Curves, Fig. 2, represent this equation for different values of m.

By differentiating Eq (1) the angular velocity of the driven shaft is found:

$$\frac{d\phi}{dt} = \omega \left(\frac{1 + m \cos \alpha}{1 + m^2 + 2m \cos \alpha} \right) \qquad (2)$$

where ω is the uniform angular velocity of the driving crank in radians per second. This is plotted in Fig. 3. The minimum velocity occurs at $\alpha = 0$ deg and equals

$$\omega \left(\frac{1}{1 + m} \right)$$

The maximum velocity occurs at $\alpha = 180$ deg and equals

$$\omega \left(\frac{1}{1 - m} \right)$$

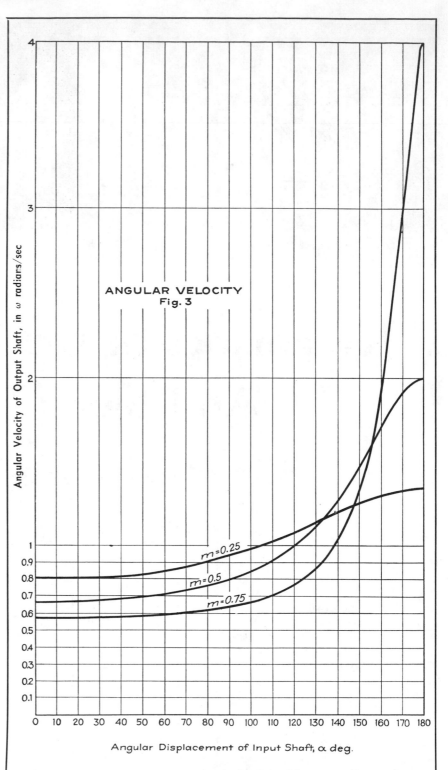

ANGULAR VELOCITY
Fig. 3

Angular Velocity of Output Shaft, in ω radians/sec

Angular Displacement of Input Shaft, α deg.

These relations can also be clearly seen from Fig. 1(A) taking the ratios between driving crank radius and the limits of the driven slot radius.

The degree of circular irregularity follows as

$$\frac{1 + m}{1 - m} \qquad (3)$$

It is significant that Eq (2) closely resembles the velocity equation of elliptic gears which is

$$\frac{d\phi}{dt} = \omega \left(\frac{1 - e^2}{1 + e^2 + 2e \cos \alpha} \right) \qquad (4)$$

Where $\quad e = \frac{1}{a} \sqrt{a^2 - b^2}$

Here $2a$ is the large axis, and $2b$ the small axis of the pitch ellipse.

The difference between the velocity outputs of elliptic gears and the crank and slot drive lies in the fact that the elliptic gear drive produces a lower velocity minimum than the crank and slot drive if the velocity maximum is kept alike in both drives. Accordingly, the degree of circular irregularity is larger for elliptic gears; namely:

$$\left(\frac{1+e}{1-e}\right)^2$$

as compared to Eq (3).

The acceleration curves, Fig. 4, are obtained by differentiation of Eq (2):

$$\frac{d^2\phi}{dt^2} = \omega^2\left[\frac{m\,(1-m^2)\sin\alpha}{(1+m^2+2m\cos\alpha)^2}\right] \quad (5)$$

The designer is interested mainly in the maximum acceleration, chiefly to calculate the highest force encountered.

To find at what position, a, of the driver the maximum acceleration of the slot link occurs, let

$$\frac{d^3\phi}{dt^3} = 0$$

or:

$$(1+m^2+2m\cos\alpha)^2\,m(1-m^2)\cos\alpha + 4m^2(1-m^2)\sin^2\alpha\,(1+m^2+2m\cos\alpha) = 0 \quad (6)$$

from which follows:

$$\cos\alpha = \frac{1+m^2 - \sqrt{(1+m^2)^2 + 32m^2}}{4m} \quad (7)$$

Substituting the value of a thus found into Eq (5) gives the maximum acceleration for the specified dimensions and input speed.

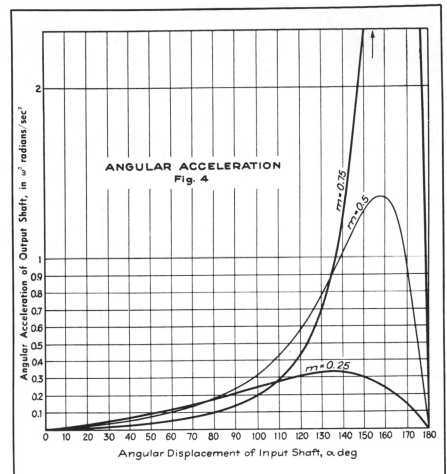

ANGULAR ACCELERATION
Fig. 4

Angular Acceleration of Output Shaft, in ω^2 radians/sec^2

Angular Displacement of Input Shaft, α deg

$m=0.75$

$m=0.5$

$m=0.25$

Constant Torque Power Cams

- *Procedure for*

  designing power cams—as distinguished from time-displacement cams.

- *Numerical examples*

  are included, and the analysis is extended to include friction.

CARL THUMIM
Lawson Machinery Corporation

CAMS ARE COMMONLY USED for obtaining desired motions, for timing, and for getting mechanical advantage. In most of these applications, the cam curve is determined either by the velocity or by the desired acceleration characteristics. Another application, equally useful but not so well known, is that of obtaining variable output forces while the input torque remains essentially constant. A system like this is useful in isolating the effects of fluctuating or cyclic loadings from the driving motor and gear boxes. Thus, obvious advantages are its smaller power unit, smaller transmission parts—such as gears—smaller overall size, and therefore, lower total cost.

There are several possible methods for designing such a mechanism. The underlying principles are the same in all cases, but the details differ with various types of desired output characteristics. The basic steps are as follows:

1. Starting with the force-displacement curve of the required output, determine the total area under the curve. This equals the work to be done.

2. Divide this area and the total angular travel of the cam into the same number of equal parts, thus defining the equal increments of work to be done for each corresponding increment of cam rotation.

3. On the curve, find the coordinates that form the boundaries of the equal areas in terms of rise of the cam follower and the load.

4. From the total work, calculate the uniform input torque required.

5. From the torque and load, obtain the approximate moment arm of the load force at each increment of cam rotation.

6. Plot the shape of the cam, using the rise of the cam follower (Step 3) and the corresponding cam position as coordinates, taking into account the point of tangency obtained by plotting the line of action of the load normal to the moment arm that has been calculated in the previous step.

In the three examples that follow, the cam follower is a roller rising along a path intersecting the center of the cam radially. These were chosen to illustrate basic problems that frequently arise. The solutions all follow the procedure just outlined; only the details of analyzing the various curves differ. A final section shows how friction effects can be included.

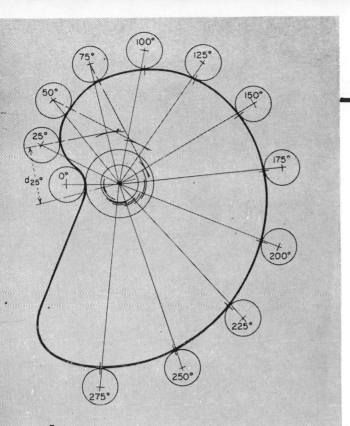

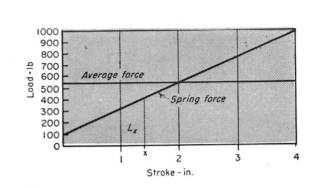

Fig. 1—Plot of spring load vs stroke is typical example of an output curve following Hooke's Law.

Fig. 2—Constant torque cam for cocking spring with load-displacement relationship shown in Fig. 1.

Table I—Design Data from Curve in Fig. 1, f$=$0

Cam Rotation Degrees	25	50	75	100	125	150	175	200	225	250	275
Area, In.-lb	200	400	600	800	1,000	1,200	1,400	1,600	1,800	2,000	2,200
$4ac$ (−)	576	1,152	1,728	2,304	2,880	3,456	4,032	4,608	5,184	5,760	6,336
$b^2 - 4ac$	640	1,216	1,792	2,368	2,944	3,520	4,096	4,672	5,248	5,824	6,400
$x = \dfrac{-b + \sqrt{b^2 - 4ac}}{2a}$	0.96	1.49	1.90	2.25	2.56	2.85	3.11	3.35	3.58	3.79	4.00
L_x	316	436	528	607	676	741	800	853	906	951	1,000
d	1.45	1.25	0.87	0.76	0.68	0.62	0.57	0.54	0.51	0.48	0.46

1. Output Curve Following Hooke's Law

A typical problem is one requiring the stressing of a spring by means of an electric motor. The usual solution is to use a screw for which the mechanical advantage does not change, and the input torque rises at a constant rate that is determined by the spring gradient.

The spring to be stressed is shown in Fig. 1, the load rises from 100 lb to 1,000 lb, in a 4 in. stroke. If a frictionless screw is used, the maximum torque can be expressed by 1,000K where K is a constant. But if a constant torque device is used, the torque has a uniform value of 550K. Obviously, all forces and powers in the latter case are only 55 percent of those in the former, with resultant savings. Applying the general method above, the solution follows:

STEP 1. From the area under the curve, the total work is

$$4\left(\frac{100 + 1,000}{2}\right) = 2,200 \text{ in.-lb}$$

STEP 2. Assuming the cam is to rotate 275 deg while doing the work, both work and angular motion can be divided into 11 equal parts, with 200 in.-lb of work to be done every 25 degrees.

STEP 3. At any point of the stroke. x, the value of the spring force is:

$$L_x = 100 + \left(\frac{1,000 - 100}{4}\right)x = 100 + 225x$$

The value of x for the first increment of area is expressed by:

$$x\left(\frac{100 + (100 + 225x)}{2}\right) = 200$$

or

$$9x^2 + 8x - 16 = 0, \text{ and}$$

$$x = \left(\frac{-8 \pm \sqrt{64 + 576}}{18}\right) = 0.96$$

Thus, the spring force is:

$$L_x = 100 + (225)(0.96) = 316$$

Similarly, the sum of the first and second areas is:

$$x\left(\frac{100 + (100 + 225x)}{2}\right) = 400$$

Reduced to lowest terms,

$$9x^2 + 8x - 32 = 0$$

This indicates that the binomial coefficients a and b remain the same and that c changes by multiples of 16. The other values can be found in Table I.

STEP 4. The constant torque input, T, required to move the cam is balanced by a torque output consisting of the load, L_x, at any given point, x, multiplied by its arm, d. The constant torque can be evaluated as follows:

$$T \times 2\pi \times \text{cam deg}/360 = \text{work}$$

For the sample problem,

$$T = \frac{2,200 \times 360}{2\pi \times 275} = 459.5 \text{ lb-in.}$$

STEP 5. Since T is also the output torque at every point, an approximate

value of the moment arm at every incremental area can be found from $d = T/L_x$. Values of d at 25 deg intervals are tabulated in Table I.

STEP 6. The shape of the cam shown in Fig. 2 is obtained by first laying in the rise, x, and then drawing a line from the center of the roller tangent to an arc of radius, d, whose center is the axis of the cam. The intersection of this line with the roller circumference gives the approximate point of tangency.

2. Output Following Curve of Known Equation

When the equation of the output curve is known, or when it can be found, the area of the curve can be obtained by integration. For the type of curve shown in Fig. 3, where y increases as x increases, the equation can be found by solving for the coefficients of

$$y = a + bx + cx^2 + dx^3 \ldots$$

Coordinates taken from the curve are:

$$x = 0 \quad 0.9 \quad 1.2 \quad 1.6 \quad 2.1$$
$$y = 2 \quad 7 \quad 8 \quad 9 \quad 10$$

Substituting some of these values of x and y in the general equation,

the following simultaneous equations ensue:

$$x = 0, \quad y = 2; \quad a = 2$$
$$x = 1.2, \quad y = 8; \quad a + 1.2b + 1.44c = 8$$
$$x = 2.1, \quad y = 10; \quad a + 2.1b + 4.41c = 10$$

Solving simultaneously,

$$a = 2$$
$$b = 6.59$$
$$c = -1.33$$

The equation of the curve then becomes

$$y = 2 + 6.59x - 1.33x^2$$

Using the general method, the design now proceeds as follows:

STEP 1. Integrating the equation to obtain the area under the curve,

$$\int_0^{2.1} \frac{d(y)}{dx} = 2x + \frac{6.59x^2}{2} - \frac{1.33x^3}{3}$$

Evaluating this integral for the given limits, the area equals 14.6 in.-lb of work.

STEP 2. Divide this area into 10 equal parts of 1.46 in.-lb and the cam travel of 300 deg into 10 corresponding arcs of 30 degrees.

STEP 3. The value of x bounding each incremental area can be found algebraically by equating the cubic

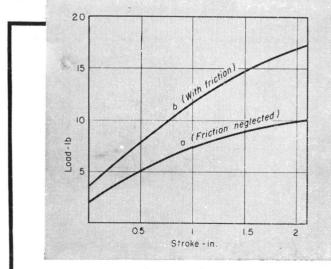

Fig. 3—Curve (a) is typical of Example 2, friction being neglected. To include friction, new curve (b) is calculated, and design continued as for zero friction.

Fig. 4—Plot of area for curves (a) and (b) of Fig. 3.

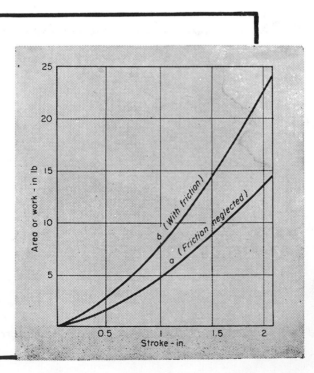

Table II—Data for Fig. 3, f=0

Increment	1	2	3	4	5	6	7	8	9	10
Cam Travel, Deg.	30	60	90	120	150	180	210	240	270	300
Area, In.-lb	1.46	2.92	4.38	5.84	7.30	8.76	10.2	11.7	13.1	14.6
x	0.39	0.69	0.93	1.14	1.33	1.49	1.66	1.80	1.96	2.1
$6.59x$	2.57	4.55	6.12	7.50	8.75	9.80	11.0	11.8	12.9	13.9
$1.33x^2$	0.20	0.62	1.15	1.73	2.36	2.95	3.68	4.32	5.13	5.87
y	4.37	5.93	6.97	7.77	8.39	8.85	9.28	9.53	9.77	10.0
d	0.62	0.47	0.40	0.36	0.33	0.32	0.30	0.29	0.28	0.28

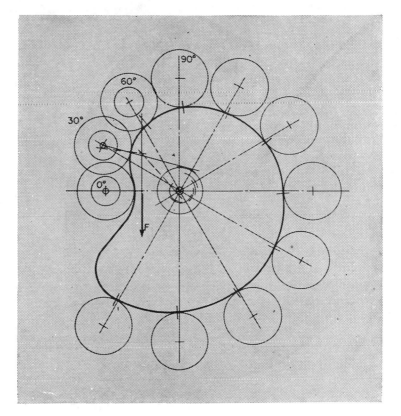

Fig. 5—Constant torque cam for curve of Fig. 3. At the 30 deg position of the follower, construction is modified to show how friction can be included. See Table IV.

equation to values of areas that vary by equal increments, or by plotting assumed values of x as shown in curve a of Fig. 4 and reading the coordinates which are shown in Table II.

STEP 4. The constant torque is

$$T = \frac{14.6 \times 360}{2\pi \times 300} = 2.775 \text{ lb-in.}$$

STEP 5. To find y at each incremental area, the corresponding value of x is inserted into the equation of the curve and tabulated. The value of the arm d is then obtained by dividing T by y.

STEP 6. The cam, Fig. 5, is then laid out by plotting the rise x at each increment of motion, and by determining the point of tangency as before.

3. Output Curves of Irregular Shape

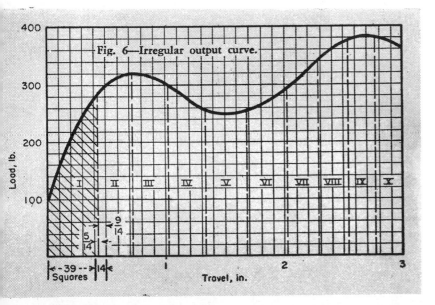

Fig. 6—Irregular output curve.

Although the shape of the force-travel curve can often be expressed as an equation, there are occasions, as shown in Fig. 6, where this is practically impossible. Here, the curve cannot be approximated satisfactorily with a usable equation. The solution can be obtained by counting the squares under the curve and then dividing the area into equal increments as before.

STEP 1. In the curve shown, the number of squares is found to be 438.

STEP 2. If the cam is to act in 300 degrees, both area and travel can be

129

Fig. 7—Constant torque cam for the irregular curve shown in Fig. 6. Details of constructing cone shape are identical to those of the two previous examples, with friction neglected.

divided into ten equal parts corresponding to 43.8 squares and 30 degrees.

STEP 3. The area boundaries can usually be determined graphically with sufficient accuracy for practical use. However, care should be taken to prevent an accumulation of error. For example, in Area I of Fig. 6, the area under the curve after 0.4 in. of travel is equal to 39 squares. The next 0.1 in. of travel must then be divided to obtain the equivalent of 5 squares to get a total for Area I of 44 squares. Since this column of travel is equal to 14 squares, it is split vertically in the ratio of 5 to 9, the former being assigned to Area I and the latter to Area II. The same procedure is followed for each remaining increments.

STEPS 4-6. Essentially unchanged.

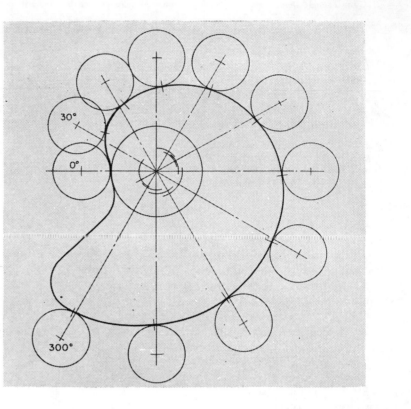

4
MECHANICAL COMPONENTS FOR AUTOMATIC CONTROL

MECHANICAL COMPONENTS FOR AUTOMATIC CONTROL

Gearing for Closed Loop Systems

Automatic Control Clutches

Mechanical Apparatus for Servo Construction

Gearing for Closed Loop Systems

SIDNEY A. DAVIS

AUTOMATIC CONTROL SYSTEM applications require high quality gears to satisfactorily perform the various functions listed in Table I. To achieve these functions the following factors are important in the selection and specification of control system gearing:

1. Gear ratio — for optimum matching of motor and load.

2. Gear materials — chosen not only for adequate life under a specific duty cycle, but also for minimum incremental system inertia. This latter factor is closely related to the closed loop stability (freedom from hunting) of high performance systems. Environmental conditions that can induce corrosion and accelerate wear are also important material selection factors.

3. Precision — related directly to the accuracy of the gear drive computer components. Gear accuracy is often the limiting factor in the accuracy of a control function.

4. Backlash—resulting from the imperfect location of centers, tooth wear and inaccurate gear contours — can be the source of closed loop instability.

5. Power handling ability and the rigidity of the tooth and shaft under

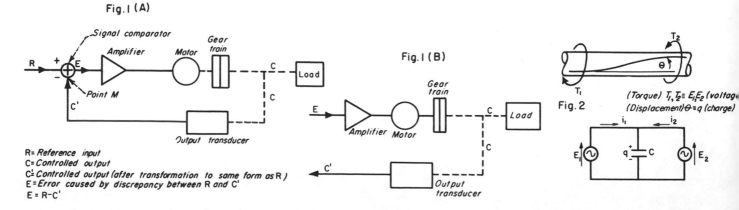

Fig. 1 — Characteristic schematic of closed loop system, (A). The arrangement obtained by opening the loop at point *M*, as shown in (B) is useful in establishing stability criteria.

Fig. 2 — Equivalent circuit of a shaft under torsion showing analogous quantities.

R= Reference input
C= Controlled output
C'= Controlled output (after transformation to same form as R)
E= Error caused by discrepancy between R and C'
E = R−C'

rapid reversal and impact — influence life and stability.

6. Special features—such as the use of a slip clutch to avoid peak loads, the use of a spring-loaded anti-backlash gear, the choice of enclosure and bearing seals to minimize the possibility of foreign particles becoming lodged in the tight meshes, the choice of lubricant and the type of shaft bearing — are additional design factors.

Effect of Gearing on System Performance

A system of ideal gearing would give the designer a transforming device that uniformly converts between torque and speed with no residual irregularities to disturb the analysis. Actually all gearing contributes certain irregularities that must be considered when designing a system.

The effect of these residual irregularities can be seen from an examination of the basic cause of instability in closed loop systems. Fig. 1 (A) shows the characteristic schematic for closed loop systems. The condition for instability can be established by opening the loop at point M and comparing the signal C' at M with the error signal E. Assuming that E oscillates sinusoidally, then the response will also oscillate sinusoidally. The relative response amplitude and phase shift of C' with respect to E will be a function of frequency. If the response-to-error ratio, C'/E, is one or greater at a frequency that will give a 180 deg phase shift, then there is sufficient response energy to cause oscillation or instability when the loop is closed. The phase shift of 180 deg means that the correction or response C' adds to the error rather than subtracting from it. Thus, if the amplification around the loop is sufficiently high, and the phase shift gives

effective positive feedback, oscillation will occur.

The important factor is the phase shift that results from either the residual or inherent inertial and spring properties of the members. These can be taken as respectively analogous to the inductive and capacitive elements of an electrical circuit. Because of their capacity to delay the flow of energy by momentarily absorbing it, they prevent the immediate application of the correction and thereby cause phase shifts. Components of this nature are known as energy storage elements and the number and capacity of these elements should be minimized to achieve system stability.

The stability characteristics of a set of gears in a feedback system can be directly measured by the residual energy storage elements that the gears add to the system. These can take the form of inertias, dead space and resilience.

In Fig. 2 is shown the electrical analog of a shaft having a certain amount of resilience. In effect the resilience is similar to shunt (stray) capacitance in electrical systems. For a perfectly rigid shaft θ equals 0. Strain beyond the elastic limit, such as can occur under shock loads, tends to reduce stiffness and introduces nonlinearity. The electrical equivalent would be a hypothetical nonlinear dielectric condenser. In systems having high inertias and insufficiently rigid shafting, severe oscillation can be induced by this energy storage.

An elementary system consisting of two coupled rigid members having dead space (backlash) in the coupling is shown in Fig. 3. It is assumed that the input shaft is oscillating sinusoidally. Since backlash is a type of nonlinear compliance, the electrical equiva-

lent can again be represented by a shunt capacitor. In establishing system stability, it is necessary to consider the above resilient shaft, or the coupling with backlash, as cascaded elements in the loop contributing phase shift and therefore instability. Since nonlinearity is involved, the stability criteria must be made more general.

Applying a sinusoidal torque (or voltage) to the coupling, the output torque (or voltage) will take the distorted form shown in Fig. 3 (C). A good approximation of the transfer characteristic of the coupling can be obtained by using only the fundamental Fourier component of the output, neglecting the harmonics. The relative phase shift and attenuation of the fundamental output with respect to the input or complex gain are also illustrated. In this specific example, the value of this complex gain is independent of frequency, so that the coupling can be directly introduced into the servo loop as a complex quantity. However, the complex gain is a function of error amplitude with maximum nonlinearity introduced at small input amplitudes, since backlash is constant and does not vary with error. Thus the system must be checked for stability for all possible values of complex gain. Oscillation at any realizable value of this gain means instability. This broader stability criterion emphasizes the increased difficulty in stabilizing systems in the presence of nonlinearity.

The above examples show that the nonlinearities that are present in mechanical elements contribute to the difficulty of securing satisfactory control system performance. Fig. 4 extends this method of analysis to a complete gear train, demonstrating the numerous energy storage elements that are encountered. Additional components of

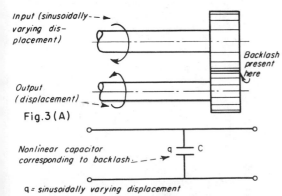

Fig. 3(A) — Gear coupled shafts in the presence of backlash with equivalent electrical circuit. The input shaft is subjected to a sinusoidally varying displacement.

Fig. 3 (B)

(B) — Plot of the reciprocal capacitance versus charge for a nonlinear capacitor with the charge varying sinusoidally. In a gear system with backlash this diagram represents a plot of displacement versus force transmitted by the teeth.

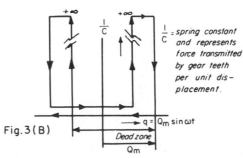

(C) — Displacement or charge as a function of time for a sinusoidal input. The phase shift, ψ, and distorted output wave form (represented by the shaded portion of curve) are caused by the dead space or backlash.

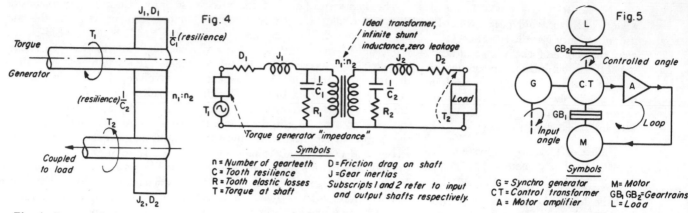

Fig. 4 — Exact equivalent circuit for a gear train. The numerous energy storage elements can contribute to the tendency toward oscillation.

Fig. 5 — The effect of gearing GB1 is to include additional storage elements within the closed loop. By substituting the equivalent circuit of Fig. 4 for GB1, the loop stability can be determined. GB2, which is outside the loop, does not contribute to instability, although backlash here can result in inaccurate positioning of the load.

lower order importance can complicate the picture further where high quality performance specifications require a more detailed study. An example of this is the effect of end play and side play in the bearing mounts of the gearing or motor. In high performance systems these factors can force the use of preloaded bearings even though the harmful effects of increased friction and reduced accuracy are introduced.

In Fig. 5 is shown a schematic of a complete servomechanism which indicates the nature of the instability caused by residual mechanical energy storage elements. In well designed systems, the resiliences can be kept small, minimizing undesired resonances. This is particularly important in systems where a wide servo band width is required since even slight resilience can cause trouble. The principal difficulties encountered in wide band systems result from unexpected resonances occurring at some frequency within the desired band width. This is analagous to the deleterious effects of stray capacitance in wide-band amplifiers.

Choosing the Motor-Load Gear Ratio

For a given control system there is an optimum gear ratio that will minimize errors. The exact determination of this optimum for the general case is a complex task and requires a statistical knowledge of the nature of the input. In addition, a clear mathematical statement of what constitutes minimum error is required. System nonlinearities, such as may be introduced by a fan load (where power increases as the cube of the speed) or by the curved speed-torque characteristic of a real two-phase servo motor, add complications. Where maximum overall precision is required, as in problems of fire control requiring maximum hit density, the object of system optimization is to control the statistical error for probable target paths so as to achieve the maximum number of target hits. It is usually a difficult problem to reduce a set of physical conditions to a satisfactory statistical statement of what constitutes optimization.

For most control problems, simplified criteria can be set up to facilitate an approximation of the optimum gear ratio. The gear ratio figure can be refined through a series of successive approximations, including more detail in the final stages of calculation. In practice an accuracy within plus or minus 20 percent is usually satisfactory. Table II lists some of the frequently encountered selection situations.

The equivalent circuit method of gear train analysis can be used to determine the optimum gear ratio for specified conditions. Fig. 6 (A), (B), and (C) show three simplified circuits, that can be used for this purpose. In these circuits the tooth resilience (including backlash) and the tooth elastic losses are considered to be negligible.

Fig. 6 (A) involves finding the gear ratio for the maximum dissipative (friction) load velocity under steady state conditions.

Since equivalent circuit calculations are made using electrical quantities,

Table II—Common Situations in Gear Ratio Selection

1. When the reference signal varies at a relatively constant speed, the gear ratio should permit following at this speed.

2. When the reference signal experiences sudden increments (high acceleration) the gear ratio should be selected to achieve maximum torque to inertia ratio at the output.

3. Where static accuracy or slow smooth following is a principal consideration, the gear ratio should amplify motor torque so that the output torque is capable of maintaining the error within allowable limits. This gear ratio is usually inefficient in terms of power transfer to the load.

4. When there are special requirements such as the ability to simultaneously maintain a specified velocity and acceleration, or the need for rapid reversal, or the requirement of minimum time to come up to speed or a maximum allowable braking time.

5. When a specified friction load is to be carried at a given speed. (Either a constant friction or a linear speed-varying drag).

electrical symbols have been substituted for the mechanical symbols shown in Fig. 4. These symbols correspond as follows

$$E \equiv T = \text{torque at shaft}$$
$$L \equiv J = \text{gear inertia}$$
$$R \equiv D = \text{friction drag on shaft}$$
$$I \equiv \text{load velocity}$$
$$a \equiv n_1/n_2 = \text{reciprocal gear ratio (less than one)}$$
$$Z = \text{electrical impedance of } L \text{ and } R \text{ in in series.}$$

From the circuit configuration comes

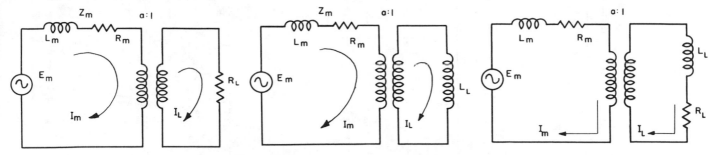

Fig. 6 (A)　　　　　　　　　　Fig. 6 (B)　　　　　　　　　　Fig. 6 (C)

Fig. 6 — Simplified equivalent circuits used to solve three practical problems in the selection of proper gear ratio. (A) is for condition of maximum dissipative load velocity under steady conditions, (B) is for condition of maximum inertial load acceleration, and (C) is for a condition of minimum required motor torque to attain a specified load velocity and load acceleration.

the following relationships:

$$I_m = \frac{E_m}{Z_m + a^2 R_L} \quad (1)$$

and

$$I_L = \frac{a E_m}{Z_m + a^2 R_L} \quad (2)$$

Under steady state conditions the drop across the inductance L_m is zero (or input gear inertia does not affect system performance under a condition of constant angular velocity). Thus the load velocity can be expressed by

$$I_L = \frac{a E_m}{R_m + a^2 R_L} \quad (3)$$

To determine optimum parameters for a given condition let the change in I_L with respect to a be zero.

$$\frac{dI_L}{da} = \frac{E_m (R_m + a^2 R_L) - 2a^2 E_m R_L}{(R_m + a^2 R_L)^2} = 0 \quad (4)$$

and $R_m + a^2 R_L - 2a^2 R_L = 0$

$$R_m = a^2 R_L \quad (5)$$

$$a = \sqrt{\frac{R_m}{R_L}} \quad (6)$$

This means that the optimum gear ratio for this condition is equal to the square root of the ratio of motor frictional drag to load frictional drag. This is analogous to the condition of matching electrical impedances.

Fig. 6 (B) shows the gear ratio for maximum load acceleration for an inertia load. Assume that the velocity is initially zero (I_m equals 0) and that a torque E_m is suddenly applied.

Under this condition the motor torque can be expressed approximately by the following equation

$$E_m \cong (I_m + a^2 L_L) \frac{dI_m}{dt} \quad (7)$$

and load acceleration, A_L, is:

$$A_L = \frac{I_L}{dt} = a \frac{I_m}{dt} \quad (8)$$

Combining Eq(7) and Eq(8), the load acceleration is equal to

$$A_L = \frac{a E_m}{L_m + a^2 L_L} \quad (9)$$

which is similar in form to Eq (3) of the previous problem. To determine the system parameters for the condition of maximum inertial load acceleration, derive the expression for the change in A_L with respect to a and equate to zero.

$$\frac{dA_L}{da} = \frac{E_m (L_m + a^2 L_L) - 2a^2 E_m L_L}{(L_m + a^2 L_L)^2} = 0 \quad (10)$$

and $L_m + a^2 L_L - 2a^2 L_L = 0$

$$a = \sqrt{\frac{L_m}{L_L}} \quad (11)$$

Thus the optimum gear ratio for this condition is equal to the square root of the ratio of motor inertia to load inertia.

Fig. 6 (C) gives the gear ratio that will require minimum motor torque to achieve a specified maximum load velocity and maximum load acceleration with the load having both friction and inertia. The given quantities are the motor and load frictional drag, R_m and R_L, the motor and load inertia, L_m and L_L, and the specified load velocity, I_L, and specified load acceleration, dI_L/dt. To find the optimum gear ratio express the motor torque, E_m, as a function of the circuit constants.

$$E_m = R_m I_m + L_m \frac{dI_m}{dt} + a R_L I_L + a L_L \frac{dI_L}{dt} \quad (12)$$

substitute $I_m = \frac{1}{a} I_L$ and $\frac{dI_m}{dt} = \frac{1}{a} \frac{dI_L}{dt}$

and differentiate Eq(12) with respect to a

$$\frac{dE_m}{da} = -\frac{R_m I_L}{a^2} - \frac{L_m}{a^2} \frac{dI_L}{dt} + R_L I_L + I_L \frac{dI_L}{dt}$$

Equating this to zero and solving for the gear ratio gives

$$a = \sqrt{\frac{R_m I_L + L_m \frac{dI_L}{dt}}{R_L I_L + L_L \frac{dI_L}{dt}}} \quad (13)$$

This is the optimum gear ratio for the given conditions of load.

Once the correct overall gear ratio has been selected, such design factors as the number of stages, stage ratios and manufacturing tolerances must be considered.

Gear Design Factors

Low gear inertia is a principal design factor, and together with backlash constitute 95 percent of the problems encountered in the design of gearing for control system applications. The important points that affect gear train inertia are:

Choice of materials — Gear materials should have minimum density consistent with the requirements of satisfactory durability under specified duty cycles. Aluminum gears are being widely used in instrument servos.

Width of face — This depends on the required load torques and the strength of the gear material. The minimum width in low power instrument servos is established by the need for rigidity rather than the load demands.

Gear blank design — A minimum of material should be used with the unstressed sections designed out.

Number of stages and choice of stage ratios — The effective system inertia for a given overall gear ratio between the driving element and the load can be minimized by the proper choice of ratio per stage of gearing. (Overall

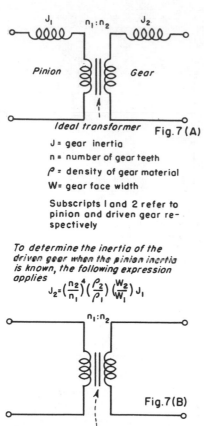

Fig. 7 (A)

J = gear inertia

n = number of gear teeth

ρ = density of gear material

W = gear face width

Subscripts 1 and 2 refer to pinion and driven gear respectively

To determine the inertia of the driven gear when the pinion inertia is known, the following expression applies

$$J_2 = \left(\frac{n_2}{n_1}\right)^4 \left(\frac{\rho_2}{\rho_1}\right)\left(\frac{W_2}{W_1}\right) J_1$$

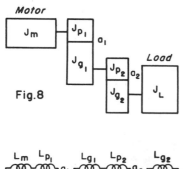

Fig. 7(B)

Ideal transformer.

Fig. 7 — Approximate equivalent circuits for simplified gear train analysis. Circuit in (A) assumes an ideal gear train but includes effects of gear inertia. In actual applications the pinion diameter is kept to a practical minimum. (B) neglects gear inertia and is useful in well-designed systems where the inertia of the motor and load predominate.

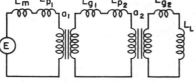

Fig. 8

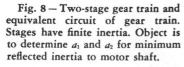

Fig. 8 — Two-stage gear train and equivalent circuit of gear train. Stages have finite inertia. Object is to determine a_1 and a_2 for minimum reflected inertia to motor shaft.

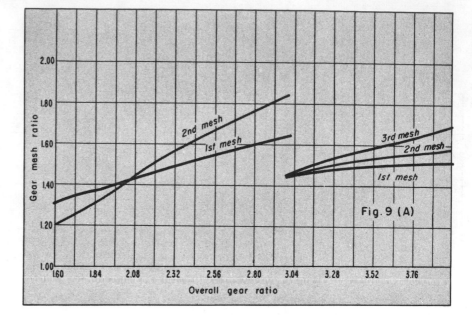

Fig. 9 (A)

gear ratio is determined as discussed above.) Usually where a high speed motor drives a low speed load, the first stage or two have relatively low ratios in a good design. The gears beyond the second stage contribute little to the overall inertia reflected to the motor shaft.

Within the limits of mechanical gear design, the equivalent circuit is useful in minimizing gear inertia by indicating the optimum stage ratios. As a necessary prerequisite to obtaining suitable closed loop stability margin, the resiliences, backlash, mechanical strength and nonlinear friction characteristics are made negligible by proper gear design. Thus in most practical problems the equivalent circuit can be simplified in comparison with the exact version. Fig. 7 (A) shows an approximate equivalent circuit that is suitable for the dynamic analysis of most closed loop systems. Where gear inertias are also negligible, the equivalent circuit further reduces to the form shown in Fig. 7 (B).

A two-stage gear train with finite inertia in the separate stages and the equivalent circuit of this gear train are illustrated in Fig. 8. The problem is to select the stage gear ratios a_1 and a_2 so that minimum inertia is reflected back to the motor shaft. In this example the overall ratio of load speed to motor speed, a, is specified at some value less than one and

$$a = a_1 a_2 \qquad (14)$$

To simplify the approach it is assumed that the same gear materials, and face widths are used throughout, and that the shafts, clamps and other required hardware contribute negligible inertia. None of these assumptions is essential and they are only made to facilitate the solution of the problem. The equivalent circuit approach is suitable for any general situation.

Using the equation shown in Fig. 7 (A), for a condition of equal face widths and similar materials, the ratio of gear to pinion inertia in the two stages can be represented by

$$\frac{J_{g1}}{J_{p1}} = \frac{1}{a_1^4} \qquad (15)$$

and

$$\frac{J_{g2}}{J_{p2}} = \frac{1}{a_2^4} \qquad (16)$$

Assume for convenience that the inertia of the two pinions is equal so that

$$J_{p1} = J_{p2} = J_p$$

Therefore,

$$J_{g1} = \frac{1}{a_1^4} J_p \qquad (17)$$

and

$$J_{g2} = \frac{1}{a_2^4} J_p \qquad (18)$$

To determine the reflected inertia as seen at the motor shaft, add up the inertia of each element taking into account the relative speed (gear ratio) relative to motor shaft speed. Electrical symbols from the equivalent circuit are used.

$$L_T = L_m + L_p + (L_{g1} + L_p)a_1^2 + (L_{g2} + L_L)a^2 \qquad (19)$$

where L_T = total inertia reflected to motor shaft.

Substituting Eqs (15) and (16) in Eq (19)

$$L_T = L_m + L_p + \left(\frac{L_p}{a_1^4} + L_p\right)a_1^2 + \left(\frac{L_p}{a_2^4} + L_L\right)a^2 \qquad (20)$$

Substituting Eq (14), the above

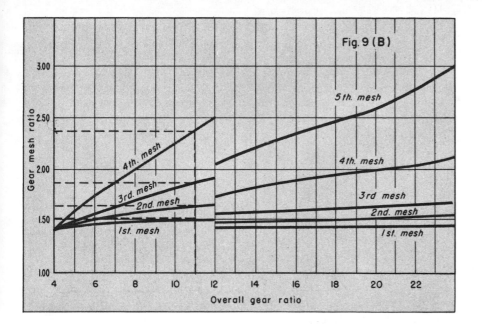

Fig. 9 (B)

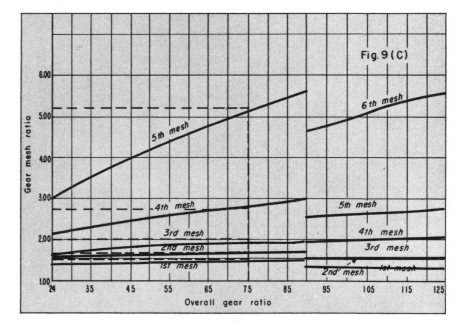

Fig. 9 — Optimum number of gear stages and the individual mesh ratios for minimum reflected moment of inertia.

Fig. 9 (C)

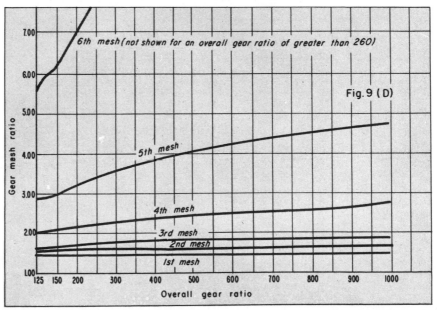

Fig. 9 (D)

equation can be simplified

$$L_T = L_m + L_p + L_p \left(\frac{1}{a_1^4} + 1\right) a_1^2 + \left(\frac{L_p}{a^4} a_1^4 + L_L\right) a^2$$

(21)

To determine the first stage ratio, a_1, in terms of the overall gear ratio, a, differentiate the left hand term with respect to a and equate the result to zero:

$$\frac{dL_T}{da_1} = -\frac{2L_p}{a_1^3} + 2a_1 L_p + 4\frac{L_p}{a^2} a_1^3$$

(22)

Equating to zero and solving for a_1

$$2 = 2a_1^4 + \frac{4}{a^2} a_1^6$$

(23)

The first term is numerically negligible in most systems and therefore a_1 becomes approximately

$$a_1 = \sqrt[6]{\frac{a^2}{2}}$$

(24)

This means that for minimum reflected inertia in a two-stage gear train, the first stage ratio should bear this relation to the overall gear ratio.

Using the first stage gear ratio calculate the ratio of gear train inertia to motor pinion inertia.

$$L_T' = L_p + L_p a_1^2 \left(\frac{1}{a_1^4} + 1\right) + \frac{L_p a_1^4}{a^2}$$

(25)

where L_T' = gear train inertia as seen from motor shaft.

$$\frac{L_T'}{L_p} = 1 + \frac{1}{a^2} (\frac{1}{2})^{2/3} a^{4/3} + (\frac{1}{2})^{1/3} a^{1/3} + (\frac{1}{2})^{-1/3} a^{-2/3}$$

(26)

Simplify this expression to

$$\frac{L_T'}{L_p} = 1 + \frac{3}{(2a)^{2/3}} + \sqrt[3]{\frac{a^2}{2}}$$

(27)

This represents the inertia for a two-stage gear train. For comparison with a single-stage gear train having the same overall ratio, a, the ratio of total inertia

137

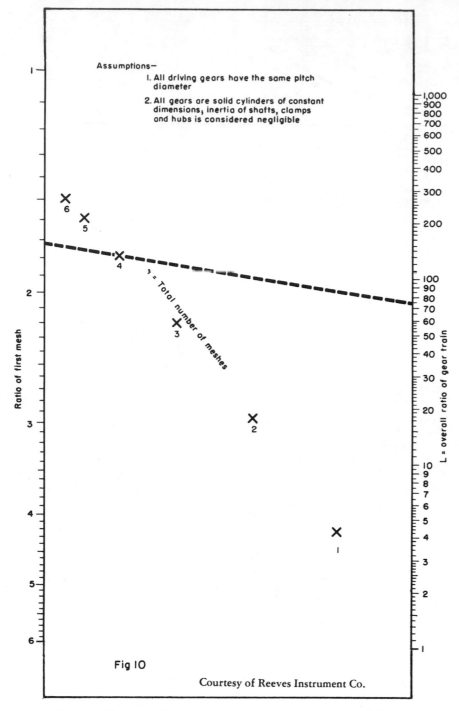

Fig 10

Courtesy of Reeves Instrument Co.

Fig. 10 — Nomogram for approximating the optimum ratio for each gear mesh when the number of gear stages and overall gear ratio are specified.

to motor pinion inertia for a single stage can be expressed by

$$\frac{L_T'}{L_p} = \frac{1}{a^2} + 1 \qquad (28)$$

Substitute a known total ratio, say a equals $1/27$, in Eqs (28) and (27). For a single-stage train

$$\frac{L_T'}{L_p} = 27^2 + 1 \cong 27^2 \qquad (29)$$

and for an ideally scaled two-stage train

$$\frac{L_T'}{L_p} \quad \frac{27}{2^{2/3}} + \frac{1}{2^{1/3}}\left(\frac{1}{9}\right) + 1 \qquad (30)$$

The second and third terms of Eq (30) are negligible in a first approximation so that for this particular overall ratio the ratio of total gearing inertia with one stage to total inertia with two stages is

$$27(2)^{2/3}$$

Thus the use of multiple staged gearing results in a lower gearing inertia. However, there are other factors to be considered such as required manufacturing tolerances, space limitations and cost.

In Figs. 9 (A) to (D) are shown four sets of curves that can be used to determine the number of gear meshes and the ratios of the individual meshes for minimum total reflected gear train inertia to the driving shaft. These curves can be used for overall gear ratios ranging from 1.60 to 1,000. For example, if the overall gear ratio is 11, refer to Fig. 9(B). The optimum number of gear stages is four and the approximate mesh ratios for minimum inertia are:

> 1st mesh — 1.51
> 2nd mesh — 1.63
> 3rd mesh — 1.86
> 4th mesh — 2.36

or if the overall ratio is 75, Fig. 9 (C), then five stages will give the minimum reflected inertia and the approximate

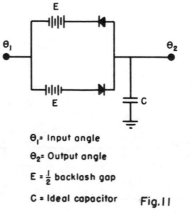

θ_I = Input angle
θ_2 = Output angle
$E = \frac{1}{2}$ backlash gap
C = Ideal capacitor

Fig. 11 — (right) Circuit used for the simulation of gear backlash in analog computers.

Fig. 12 (far right) — Backlash effects in a simple second order servo. (A) shows the servo block diagram including a gear reduction stage with an overall ratio of $\bar{\theta_c}/\bar{\theta_m}$. The hysteresis loop of (B) shows the input-output angular relations of the gear train including the effects of total backlash 2δ. (C) shows a plot of the ratio of motor oscillation amplitude to backlash as a function of the system gain and motor time constant.

Fig. 11

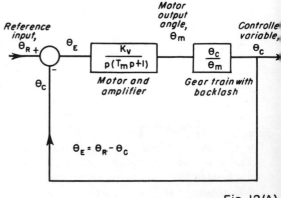

Fig. 12(A)

mesh ratios are:

    1st mesh — 1.55
    2nd mesh — 1.65
    3rd mesh — 2.00
    4th mesh — 2.77
    5th mesh — 5.20

These values can be rounded out to give feasible gear ratios and to obtain the exact overall ratio.

While the curves shown in Fig. 9 are useful if the optimum number of stages are used for a required overall gear ratio, there can be a condition where for simplicity one or two fewer gear stages are specified for the same overall ratio. If this is done, the nomogram shown in Fig. 10 is useful as an auxiliary tool to determine the individual stage ratios that will give minimum reflected inertia for any given overall ratio and any given number of stages. Thus this nomogram can be used for the optimum number of stages or fewer than the optimum number of stages.

For example, as indicated above, the optimum number of stages for an overall gear ratio of 75 is five. However, if simplicity of the mechanical set up and conservation of space are important factors in design a four mesh system can be used with only a small increase in reflected inertia. Assume this is the desired condition.

Referring to the nomogram, place a straight edge through the point representing the total number of stages (4), and the overall gear ratio on the right hand scale (75:1). From the left hand scale it can be seen that the gear ratio of the first stage is 1.72 (compared to 1.55 as obtained above for five stages). Round this off to 1.75 and determine the remaining gear ratio, 75/1.75 equals about 43. Repeat this process using 43 as the overall ratio and 3 as the number of stages to determine the second stage ratio. The other stage ratios are found in a similar manner.

The convenience criterion for the use of Figs. 9 and 10 is as follows: if the optimum number of stages is used, determine the total number of stages and the individual stage ratios from Fig. 9; if any other than the optimum number of stages is used determine the individual stage ratios from Fig. 10.

Extended Use of Equivalent Circuits

The exact and approximate equivalent circuits that are given in Figs. (4) and (6) are useful where it is desired to set up an analogous electrical equivalent of a servo loop. The effects on stability, a study of stress under rapid reversal, or the impact of an inertia load against a limit stop can be evaluated. Fig. 11 shows a second circuit for the simulation of backlash in analog computer stability studies. This analogy is quite distinct from the equivalent circuits shown previously, since analog computers operate directly by integrations and differentiations performed on the dynamic equations and do not depend on a one-to-one correspondence between electrical and mechanical elements.

Gear Backlash

Backlash is the most difficult of the residual effects to control and consequently merits special atention. As a theoretical problem, backlash can be represented by a nonlinear capacitor as shown in the equivalent circuit of Fig. 3. Backlash introduces a phase shift in a servo loop that is independent of frequency but varies with amplitude. This phase shift reaches a maximum at a relatively small signal amplitude and any tendency to oscillate because of

backlash will manifest itself as a small amplitude oscillation.

Coulomb friction has been found satisfactory as a damping medium for oscillations derived from backlash. This is because the fixed coulomb drag contributes a high damping coefficient when velocity and amplitude are small. However, coulomb friction cannot be applied indiscriminately because of its deleterious effect on static accuracy.

In sluggish systems having one major time constant that is effective in the frequency band width, or in systems where the normal mode of operation is steady tracking, backlash requirements can be somewhat relaxed.

In Fig. 12 (A) is shown a simple second order servo with backlash in the motor output gear train, while Fig. 12 (B) shows the hysteresis loop relating gear train angular input and output where δ is $\frac{1}{2}$ of the total backlash. The curve of Fig. 12 (C) is a plot of the ratio of motor oscillation amplitude versus the product of system gain and motor time constant. This plot shows that if the product $K_v T_m$ is greater than 3.046, oscillation will occur. Conversely, if the system gain is low enough or the motor time constant is so small that $K_v T_m$ is less than the critical value, there will be no oscillation. Thus, whether oscillation will occur or not is a function of the system constants and not of the magnitude of the backlash. The curve shows that a reduction in backlash, δ, will cause a corresponding reduction in oscillation amplitude, $\bar{\theta}_m$ since the ratio of $\bar{\theta}_m/\delta$ is fixed depending on the value of the product $K_v T_m$.

The presence of coulomb friction limits the usefulness of a curve such as this. Regardless of the critical value at which oscillation theoretically starts,

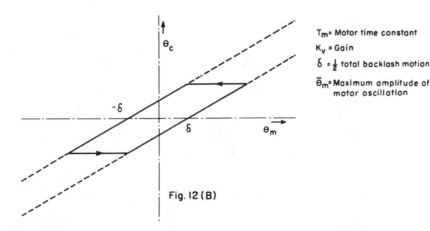

T_m = Motor time constant

K_v = Gain

$\delta = \frac{1}{2}$ total backlash motion

$\bar{\theta}_m$ = Maximum amplitude of motor oscillation

Fig. 12 (B)

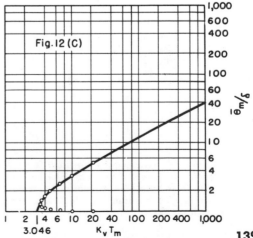

Fig. 12 (C)

when the amplitude of the backlash oscillation falls below a certain limit (depending on the amount of friction) the oscillation will cease.

Backlash is especially severe in high-gain wide-band servo systems, where the sensitivity is sufficient to detect the slightest irregularities in the transmission characteristics of the gears. Backlash chatter and noise generated by high frequency tooth irregularities cause jerky and uneven following by the output member. For optimum performance, many common groupings of components are manufactured as basic sub-assemblies, with direct shaft coupling in lieu of gearing wherever possible. For example, an induction motor generator that is used as a combined damping and drive element in instrument servo-mechanisms. Even a minute dead space between a motor and its tachometer damping element effectively

disconnects the damping temporarily, causing instability.

Where required speed ratios or mechanical considerations make direct coupling impossible, spring-loaded gears can be used to prevent backlash, Fig. 13. These are used in precise coupling applications; however, they are expensive and contribute excessive friction and wear. Tests on spring-loaded instrument gears indicate that the wear can be many times greater than might be expected from direct consideration of the effective load, including the additional spring force. This is caused by bounce under transient conditions that results in repeated impact of the spring-constrained inertial masses.

The springs used in anti-backlash gearing must be of a high uniform quality if constant specified tooth loading is to be maintained in mass produc-

tion. Gears are available with either tension or compression springs, both types being equally satisfactory. Some designs totally enclose the springs to avoid the possibility of a spring being disconnected from its mounting and interfering with the gear meshes. Fig. 14 shows assemblies of precision gearing in a complex control device. Two split spring-loaded gears are used.

Anti-backlash gearing cannot be considered a totally satisfactory solution to the precision gear problem. Although the backlash can be held at zero, tooth wear will destroy the exact contour producing irregularity at tooth frequency and the erosion of material will cause the zero setting to shift in accurately aligned computer equipment.

In high powered equipment where it may be impossible to maintain exact gear center distances and where wear may be excessive, spring-loaded gears

Fig. 13 — Spring-loaded instrument gears manufactured by Servomechanisms, Inc. This type is used in applications where backlash cannot be permitted.

Fig. 14 — Precision gearing used in computing device manufactured by the Arma Corp. Shows use of both conventional and spring-loaded gears.

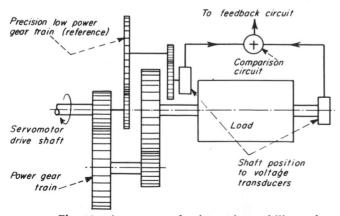

Fig. 15 — Arrangement for improving stability and accuracy of power gear train. The high precision reference gear train permits continuous monitoring of the error in load position. The feedback voltage compensates for backlash.

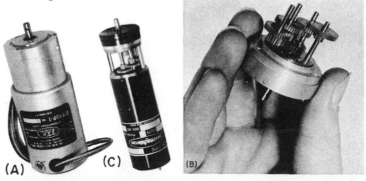

Fig. 16 — Servo motors with integral gear heads. (A) Servo motor manufactured by Eastern Air Devices, Inc. with gear head by Bowmar Instrument Corp. This gear head is shown in (B). Unit has ratio of 314:1. A universal design combination gear head and motor by Servomechanisms, Inc. is shown in (C). First stage pinion is machined directly on motor output shaft.

cannot be used because of their low power efficiency. For these applications a variety of backlash compensation techniques have been developed of which the arrangement shown in Fig. 15 is typical.

This system includes an auxiliary precision gear train that has the same overall gear ratio as the power gear train. The output angular position of this reference gear train is compared with the output angular position of the power gear train or load and the error is introduced into the main feedback loop. This corrects for the inaccuracies in the power gear train and improves system stability.

While this compensating technique is straight-forward and widely applied, it is only useful in large systems where the cost of the additional low power reference equipment is small compared to total system cost.

Practical Factors in Gearing

The factors in selecting gearing for feedback control systems are little different than in the usual high quality gear application. The major differences are in the close tolerances, the minimization of wear to maintain low backlash, the need for frame rigidity to maintain perfect center distances and the transient nature of the tooth loading, where rapid reversal and shock are common. The low static friction requirement often dictates the use of high precision anti-friction bearings and spring loading of the bearings may be necessary to prevent end play.

In many installations, the wide range of environmental conditions may require the use of special lubricants and corrosion resistant finishes. Anodized aluminum gears are frequently used in airborne instrument servos, where the light weight and low inertia features make aluminum superior to the usually preferred brasses and bronzes. A common lightweight combination consists of stainless steel pinions and aluminum mating gears.

Among the most useful of the specialized gear applications are the packaged gear trains built integrally with servo motors, Fig. 16. Because of the compactness of the design and the close control of packaging, these units are economical and accurate. Design simplification and a reduction in system assembly costs can also be achieved by the use of these combination units.

These small instrument servo gear trains are available permanently lubricated, totally enclosed and designed to meet the load and environmental requirements of an application. For minimum inertia and in the interests of economy it has become standard prac-

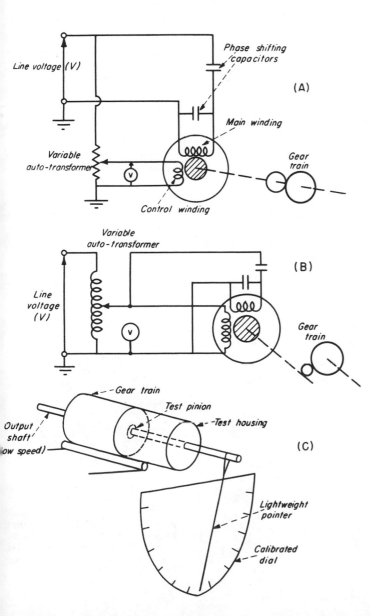

Fig. 17 — Methods of checking gear quality — Servo motor starting voltage is a measure of the sensitivity of the motor — gear train combination to small input signals, and is also a rough measure of gear quality. Since the stall torque developed by a two-phase servo motor varies as the product of the voltages on the two fields, the voltage required to just produce starting is a measure of the friction in the gear train.

In the method shown in (A), full main field voltage is applied to the motor, and torque is proportional to the control field voltage. This arrangement has the disadvantage that it is impossible to separate motor cogging and friction torques from the resistance of the gear train. If the motor rotor is eccentric or if side motion of the rotor is permitted, the rotor will be pulled to one side by the strong main field. This side thrust varies as the square of the main field voltage. This condition will tend to produce high friction points in the gearing and realistically represents the actual situation.

The circuit of (B) is more useful in directly examining the gear friction. Since main field voltage is not at its full value, side thrust is reduced to a negligible amount. This technique gives a relatively true measure of gear friction.

In a good servo motor, v is about 1/20 to 1/50 of rated control field voltage for the first method. In the second method, v varies from 1/5 to 1/10 of rated line voltage.

To use either of these methods, v is slowly increased until the motor just starts. This process is repeated several times and the maximum is the final test figure. By measuring v at different points, any tendency of the gears to bind will be discovered. A convenient way to determine the worst point in a gear train is to slowly reduce motor voltage from a running condition until the motor just stops. The stopping point will generally be a high friction spot. In small servo motors, gear friction as measured at the motor shaft should be about 0.001 to 0.002 oz-in.

A method of measuring gear friction to evaluate a gear trains suitability for assembly with a servo motor is shown in (C). A dummy pinion is made to mesh with the unloaded gear train. The test housing rotates on rollers. In the absence of gear friction, gravity will cause the pointer to remain vertical. Any irregularities in the gearing will cause pointer motion. The pointer can be designed to require a torque of 0.005 oz-in. to deflect it to a horizontal position. Before performing this test the gears should be run in to wear down the high spots and to distribute the lubricant.

tice to cut a pinion directly on the motor shaft. This also permits a maximum gear reduction in the first stage. Gear trains are usually designed to limit the additional system inertia to a fraction of the inertia of the servo motor.

Since the use of integral gear head servo motors is relatively new, little standardization exists and delivery time is often several months. In addition, the cost of the gear head is usually several times motor cost. To improve this situation, some manufacturers are standardizing on gear heads and offering certain discrete ratios as stock items. One manufacturer has designed a gear head having universal jig-bored centers. By using various combinations of 25 stock gears almost any ratio between 4 and 3,000 can be obtained.

For satisfactory performance, the gears must contribute negligible irregularity and starting friction and must not add sufficient coulomb friction to introduce static eror. Also the torque efficiency should be high; a good gear train stage will transmit more than 95 percent of its input torque. Where many gear train stages are cascaded, this loss of torque can present a serious problem.

Rough spots in the gearing and eccentricity resulting in localized loading and high friction will reveal themselves after a 24 hr run-in period, and in critical applications such a run-in is advisable. Local instabilities are characteristic of such gear trains once the high spots have been worn down. A good method of checking gear train quality in a servo is to determine the starting voltage of the servo motor (the minimum signal to which it will respond). Fig. 17 shows two methods of checking servo motor starting voltage, and one method of measuring gear friction.

The gear train precision must be maintained over the entire temperature range of the motor, including its own temperature rise and during transient heating and cooling cycles.

Commercially available motor gear trains have backlash tolerances of $1/4$ to $1/2$ deg. Closer tolerances become very costly.

Often system loop gain rather than torque determines the choice of gear ratio. This is common in instrument servos where a motor is required to drive a stack of potentiometers or resolvers at low speed. In this application, total friction may be of the order of two ounce-inches and gear ratios in the thousands are used.

Where loads have appreciable inertia, it is important that provision be made to limit transient torques on the output shaft and final gear stages. Sometimes a servo design will specify a maximum motor torque on sudden reversal. More often a spring loaded slip clutch will be put on the output shaft as a torque limiting device.

The most precise gear trains are required in the scaling or coupling of computer components. When accuracies of 0.1 percent or better are required in a system, angular inaccuracies of the critical gears must be limited to less than 1 min. In the new computer components having diameters of 1 in. or less, the gear tolerances must be held within 0.0003 in. For example, in multi-speed synchro systems driving computer components, the ultimate accuracy limits are imposed by gearing errors. Fortunately the most precise gearing is required where the speeds are low.

Where magnetic steels such as 416 stainless are used in gears or bearings they can accidentally become magnetized resulting in increasing friction. Simple demagnetization is the solution. However, in sensitive situations this factor and the effects of stray magnetic fields must be considered.

Differential Gearing

In closed loop control systems differentials are used for mechanical comparison or error measurement. They are also used as basic computing elements for the addition or subtraction of two shaft motions, Fig. 18. The selection of a mechanical differential as opposed to an electrical comparison device is a function of design, convenience and price.

A typical computing differential is shown in Fig. 19. This type of unit is designed for highest accuracy of tooth form and minimum friction and backlash. Note that the end gears are customer selected to facilitate application in a specific control system. For maximum economy, some manufacturers classify their differentials according to mesh accuracy. Fig. 20 shows a differential with a hollow output shaft. This feature permits convenient axial positioning.

The accuracy of high quality differentials (about 5 min) is inadequate for the most exacting applications unless the differential is operated at a relatively high speed through precision spur gears. The accuracy of the spur gears and the upper speed limit of the differential represent factors in limiting maximum overall accuracy.

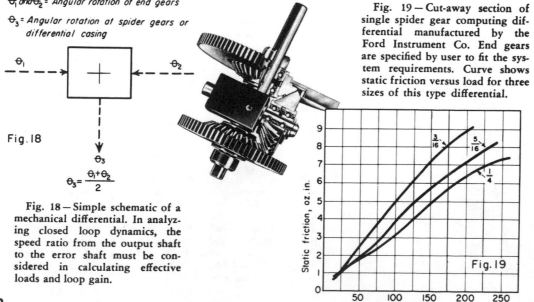

θ_1 and θ_2 = Angular rotation of end gears

θ_3 = Angular rotation at spider gears or differential casing

Fig. 18

$$\theta_3 = \frac{\theta_1 + \theta_2}{2}$$

Fig. 18 — Simple schematic of a mechanical differential. In analyzing closed loop dynamics, the speed ratio from the output shaft to the error shaft must be considered in calculating effective loads and loop gain.

Fig. 19 — Cut-away section of single spider gear computing differential manufactured by the Ford Instrument Co. End gears are specified by user to fit the system requirements. Curve shows static friction versus load for three sizes of this type differential.

Static friction, oz. in.

Load on each gear, oz. in.

Fig. 20 — Librascope hollow shaft differential including shaft clamp. Unit weighs 1.25 oz with an inertia of 0.0745 oz-in.² Total backlash is less than 10.0 min. Recommended maximum shaft speed is 800 rpm under a maximum load of 6 oz-in.

Automatic Control Clutches

Emphasizing fractional and low integral horsepower applications, which account for a large majority of control applications, the basic requirements for a clutch operating in a closed loop system are defined. As a guide to selection, the characteristics of the specific types that can satisfy these requirements are then presented.

CLUTCHES AND BRAKES are used to control the coupling between two shafts by means of relatively low power signals. In control system applications this coupling can either be of the continuous proportional type where the degree of coupling varies with the magnitude of the control signal, or it can be of the on-off variety where the coupling is either zero or maximum.

The principal types of clutches that are of interest to control system designers are electrically operated friction disk, hysteresis, eddy current, magnetic fluid, magnetic powder, crystal, and "loudspeaker" clutches. While the specific features of each clutch will be covered in detail in a later section, all of these types of clutches or brakes must have the following characteristics to perform satisfactorily in closed loop applications:

a. Smooth coupling throughout the specified speed range and ease of control by electrical signals.

b. Rapid response to prevent time delays that can cause instability.

c. Low control power required for actuation.

d. Minimum stickiness or hysteresis in the response of the output to a control signal.

e. Minimum zero signal clutch torque, since residual torque can cause system errors and heating.

f. Sensitivity to small error signals.

g. Linearity of output response to control signal is often desirable but usually not absolutely necessary.

Clutches are not widely used in the small instrument servos where the controlled power is under 10 or 20 watts since the additional hardware represented by the clutch increases the packaging problem and the cost. Exceptions are made in certain specialized applications where high response speed is required.

Where the power level exceeds this low figure, clutches are widely used in control systems that range in size up to thousands of horsepower. The clutches and applications presented here emphasize the low integral and fractional horsepower ranges. These cover the majority of the clutch application problems.

Some typical control applications of clutches (or brakes — essentially similar to clutches in design and appearance except that output shaft is held stationary) are precise rapid positioning, synchronizing of shafts, speed control, rapid cycling, and rapid starting and stopping. The technical advantages that make clutch control suitable for these types of applications are:

a. High intermittent torques can be obtained.

b. Reduced control power requirements mean that excitation can be supplied by a low power amplifying device.

c. High accelerations of several hundred thousand radians per sec² can be obtained by abruptly coupling a high inertia rotating flywheel to a load. This exceeds the accelerating ability of electric motors and is comparable to the performance of high quality hydraulic drive units.

d. Suitable clutches can reduce shock loading such as can occur during synchronizing of a control system.

e. A single drive motor can be used to drive several loads in turn through a suitable clutching arrangement.

f. Clutch application flexibility permits a large variety of special purpose circuits to be constructed.

g. All of the listed types of clutches can be controlled remotely.

Since a clutch is not a source of torque, but rather a transmitter of torque, it controls speed by reducing the input speed from a prime mover to the desired level. The method by which this is accomplished necessitates the absorption of energy by the clutch. Thus a clutch, when slipping, generates a large quantity of heat. This often means that elaborate cooling methods must be used, and a part of any clutch selection problem involving speed control is a consideration of the heating effect. This must include an examination of the duty cycle and the inertial and/or dissipative characteristics of the load. Heat dissipation is of maximum concern in clutches that require the slipping of coupled friction disks,

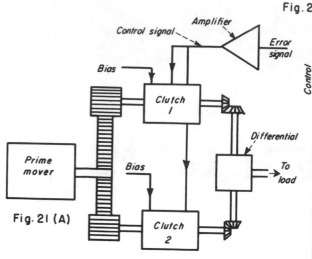

Fig. 22 (A)

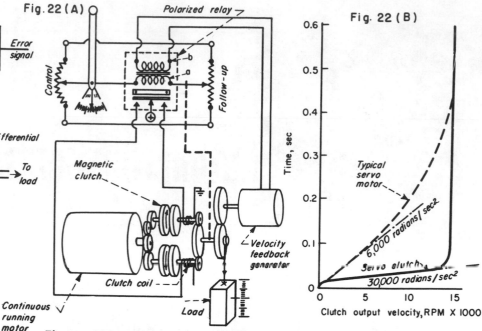

Fig. 22 (B)

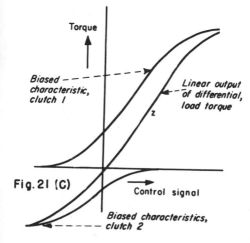

Fig. 21 (A) — Schematic of a clutch type bi-directional actuator for use in control systems. Linear performance is obtained by biasing both clutch control coils and using a push-pull amplifier. (B) — Typical non-linear clutch characteristic, X, and same characteristic after the application of a bias signal to the control coil, Y. (C) — Two biased clutches combined as shown in (A) give a resultant output curve, Z, that is linear over a specified range.

Fig. 22 (A) — Follower servomechanism driven by a relay operated clutch system. The use of velocity feedback results in a continuous high frequency chatter around the closed loop that effectively averages out the nonlinearity of the clutch. (B) — Comparison of system response using a servo clutch and a typical servo motor. The clutch drive unit is capable of five times the acceleration of the servo motor.

where heat is localized and wear is high.

In analyzing the torque and dissipation requirements of a system, each mode of the cycle must be considered and the results determined by the application of conventional dynamics. Most manufacturers provide curves relating steady torque and dissipation to slip.

Linearity Characteristics of Clutches

In continuous closed loop operation is is usually desirable to achieve effectively linear performance with a clutch. If a clutch is inherently linear (in other words, if the amount of coupling varies directly with the magnitude of the control signal), it can be combined in a servo system in much the same manner as the other servo components. If a clutch is nonlinear, the techniques that are used to obtain essentially linear response are varied and depend on the specific nature of the clutch. However, there are two basic approaches to this problem.

The first approach includes those clutches that can reasonably be considered approximately linear. With these clutches a further improvement towards linearity is obtained by using special devices such as push-pull operation or biasing. A typical circuit using this mode of linearization is shown in Fig. 21 (A). The bi-directional assembly is driven by a push-pull amplifier (which can also supply the clutch bias as quiescent plate current) and gives highly linear performance in a servomechanism.

The principle of operation of this circuit is shown by the curves of Figs. 21 (B) and (C). The basic operating mode of the clutch is represented by the nonlinear curve, X, of Fig. 21 (B). The application of a bias signal to the clutch control coil shifts this basic curve to the left, curve Y, so that with no control signal the clutch will deliver a torque represented by point a. Fig. 21 (C) shows the result of combining two clutches, each biased an equal amount. The no-signal torques of the two clutches cancel one another and the application of a control signal will cause a linear response of torque as shown by curve Z. Clutch operation is designed to be sensitive to control signal polarity.

Where a clutch behaves essentially in an on-off manner (for example, the usual frictional surface type), there is another general method for achieving linear performance. This method requires the introduction of a system oscillation of high frequency compared with the natural frequency of the system and is similar to the methods used for linearizing relay or on-off type amplifiers. The oscillation can be intro-

Table I—Clutch Types and Characteristics[1]

Type	Power Rating	Time Delay[2] Milliseconds	Nature of Control	Power Gain[3]	Durability
Friction disk	250 watts	5	On-off	200	Fair
Hysteresis	Low hp	3	No slip, continuous control	5-20	Excellent
Eddy-current	Up to thousands of hp	10	Slips several per cent continuous control	50-200	Excellent
Magnetic fluid	250 watts	3	Continuous control, nonlinear torque curve	200	Good
Magnetic powder	250 watts	3	Continuous control, nonlinear torque curve	200	Good
Crystal	25 watts	0.2	On-off, poor ratio of idling to rated torque	Many thousand	Fair
Loudspeaker	25 watts	0.5	On-off	——	Excellent

Notes: 1. Because of diverse nature of possible applications, characteristics are given for typical rather than extreme applications.
2. Time delay figures apply when clutch is operated from a high impedance excitation source.
3. Power gain is for closed loop control applications.

duced from an external source or can be generated internally by suitable feedback circuits.

When a control signal is superimposed on this high frequency oscillation, either the positive or negative half cycle of the oscillation is accentuated, depending on the polarity of the signal. This results in a net average value of direct control and the average control force is approximately proportional to the control signal over a useful range, even though the clutch itself is inherently highly nonlinear.

In Fig. 22 (A) is shown a typical follower servomechanism operating in this mode. The control signal input to this system is through a bridge network consisting of a variable control potentiometer and a variable follow-up potentiometer. Any unbalance in the bridge will cause a current of the proper polarity to flow in relay actuating coil a, energizing the proper clutch coil to rebalance the bridge. Thus load position is determined by control potentiometer position, and load position is mechanically fed back to the follow-up potentiometer to balance the circuit.

To introduce the high frequency oscillation necessary to linearize clutch operation, a velocity feedback generator is geared to the output shaft of the double clutch unit. The output of the generator feeds an auxiliary coil, b, on

the polarized relay so that the direction of relay actuation bucks the direction of load movement. In the presence of a small error signal on relay coil, a, a high frequency system oscillation is set up that alternately energizes one clutch and then the other to maintain the correct average load position. The proper clutch is energized a greater portion of the time depending on signal polarity. If the control signal is large enough, only one clutch will be energized and the load will be slewed at maximum rate to the null position. Fig. 22 (B) shows the improvement in response time that is possible with a clutch servomechanism compared to the response of a typical servo motor.

Since this latter mode of operation can be used with sturdy, inexpensive and fast-acting friction disk clutches that are capable of handling large forces in small sizes, it has found applications where compactness and cost are important. The accuracy of this arrangement is comparable to that obtained from high performance linear systems. However, the rapid oscillation characteristic of this mode of operation means increased wear, relatively short life, and reduced net amplification as compared with the nonoscillating direct-acting system.

To show the variety of uses for clutching devices (including brakes)

in closed loop systems, Fig. 23 covers four typical schematic application diagrams. The choice of the type of clutch to be used in one of these applications depends on the specific load and duty requirements.

Types of Clutches

Magnetically operated friction disk clutches are general purpose components and constitute the large majority of clutches that are presently being used in automatic control systems. While wear at the friction surfaces can cause failure by the destruction of the clutch faces or by excessive gap increase, satisfactory life for many applications is obtained through the suitable choice of friction materials.

Good wear properties have been achieved by using combinations of steel against steel. Case hardening and chrome plating will increase the life. Also, stainless steel has been satisfactorily used with case hardened steels.

This type of clutch is compact; operating characteristics can be predicted in the design stage; and it can be designed into integral assemblies with servo actuators and other devices. Units are available for control system applications with response times of 5 milliseconds and better. Power amplifications of several thousand can be obtained with carefully designed magnetic circuits

Fig. 23—Clutch Application Diagrams

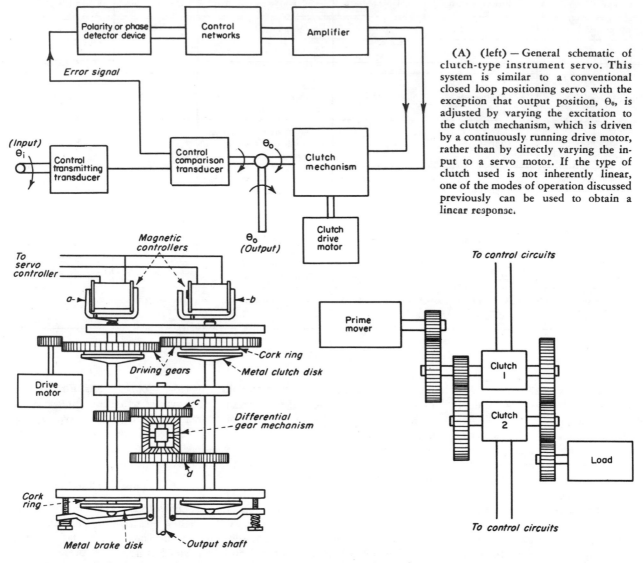

(A) (left) — General schematic of clutch-type instrument servo. This system is similar to a conventional closed loop positioning servo with the exception that output position, θ_0, is adjusted by varying the excitation to the clutch mechanism, which is driven by a continuously running drive motor, rather than by directly varying the input to a servo motor. If the type of clutch used is not inherently linear, one of the modes of operation discussed previously can be used to obtain a linear response.

(B) — Detailed schematic of a clutch type instrument servo manufactured by Norden. This system incorporates simultaneous clutching and braking. In the diagram, magnetic controller *a* is energized. This engages the clutch from the driving motor and disengages the brake for the left hand shaft, by axially shifting the shaft. Thus the output shaft is being driven by the left hand shaft through differential gear *c*. Since only one controller can be energized at a time, the right hand shaft is held stationary by its brake. This means that gear *d* is locked so that the differential can be driven through gear *c*. This arrangement permits rapid starting and stopping.

(C) — This diagram shows two clutches used to obtain two-speed operation. This is a simple on-off arrangement that is useful in multiple-mode servo systems.

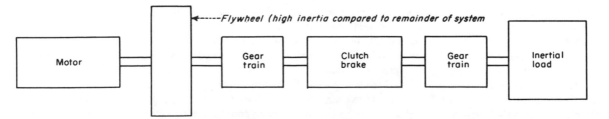

(D) — Schematic of system that is useful for rapid starting and stopping. When the clutch is energized, the load is coupled to the high inertia flywheel and motor. This results in high load accelerations. When the clutch is de-energized, the load is disconnected from the flywheel and motor and is coupled to the brake. This brings it to a rapid stop. The flywheel supplies pick-up energy during acceleration.

This high gain permits the control of integral horsepower loads from conventional small receiving tubes.

The operation of this clutch is decidedly nonlinear, since it is essentially an on-off device. For use in proportional systems, the high frequency linearizing technique described above can be applied.

In Fig. 24 (A) is shown a typical high power capacity friction disk clutch and brake combination. In this unit both the brake and clutch are magnetically actuated, with the clutch actuating coil being through slip rings from the brushes. The speed-torque curves and speed-power dissipation curves for various sizes of this unit are plotted in Figs. 24 (B) and (C). These curves are necessary for predicting system performance and for sizing the clutch to meet specific duty cycle conditions.

Another type of brake-clutch combination is shown in Fig. 25. In these devices the clutching function is obtained by the use of a conventional magnetic actuating coil, while the braking function is spring-actuated and operates whenever the clutch coil is de-energized. This unit is useful for rapid start-and-stop operation shown in Fig. 23 (D) and is especially useful in servos where the motor rotor constitutes the bulk of the system inertia.

One manufacturer produces a flexible brake-clutch combination that uses various arrangements of crown tooth coupling and/or friction plate coupling in the standard housing shown in Fig. 26 (A). The types of drive and brake arrangements that are available are

Fig. 24 (A) (left) — Friction type magnetically actuated brake and clutch combination manufactured by the Warner Electric Brake and Clutch Co. (B) (below) — Torque-speed curves for various sizes of clutch shown in (A). These curves are important in establishing clutch rating and in predicting the dynamics of a clutch actuated system.

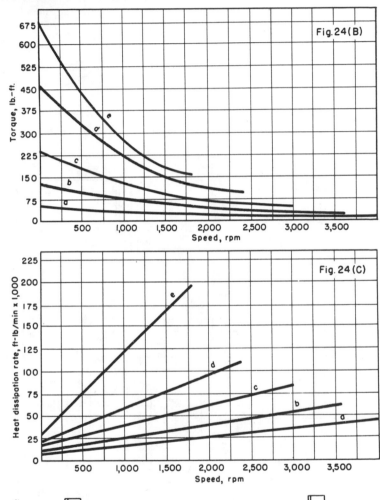

Fig. 24 (B)

Fig. 24 (C)

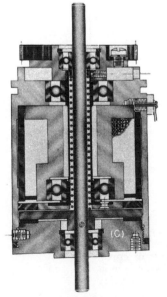

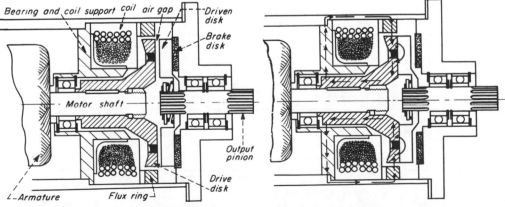

Fig. 25 — Fastop clutch-brake unit for servo use by Lear, Inc. In (A) (center) the clutch is de-energized and the load is coupled to the brake. The motor is disconnected and coasts to a halt at will. (B) (right) shows the clutch energized so that the motor drives the load. (C) is a similar type of clutch-brake combination manufactured by the Belock Instrument Co. Unit is designed for use as a separate element in a control circuit.

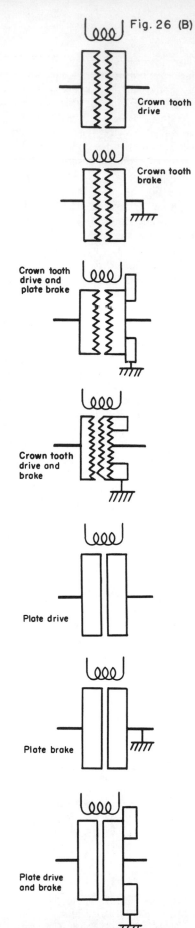

Fig. 26 (B)

Crown tooth drive

Crown tooth brake

Crown tooth drive and plate brake

Crown tooth drive and brake

Plate drive

Plate brake

Plate drive and brake

shown in Fig. 26 (B). The crown tooth coupling is used where a high torque must be transmitted with no slip, while plate (friction disk) coupling is used where the clutch or brake must engage in any contact position without angular shaft displacement. This latter arrangement also has the torque limiting feature in that the clutch or brake will slip if a certain peak torque is exceeded. Fig. 26 (C) shows the relation between static torque and control voltage for the crown tooth type of coupling.

Hysteresis Clutches

In the hysteresis clutch, d-c control excitation generates a steady field in the clutch, Fig. 27. The flux passes through and magnetizes the permanent magnet ring. Because of hysteresis, the resultant flux poles generated by the ring lead the axis of d-c excitation by some angle. This angle depends on the control excitation and on the choice of permanent magnet material. The attraction between the induced poles of the

Fig. 26 (A)

Fig. 26 (C)

Rated torque 80 oz.-in.

Minimum static torque, oz.-in.

Percent of rated voltage

Fig. 26 — (A) (left, above) Reeves Instrument Corp. standard magnetic clutch and brake housing for control and instrumentation applications. Crown tooth type will transmit 80 oz-in., while plate type will transmit 16 oz-in. (B) (right) shows various arrangements of crown tooth coupling and plate coupling that can be obtained in housing shown in (A). Curve in (C) (above) is plot of static torque against rated voltage for crown tooth coupling. Rated value is shown to be 80 oz-in.

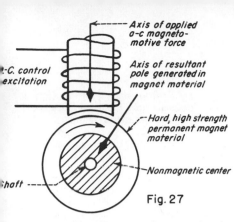

Fig. 27 — Schematic diagram showing operating principle of hysteresis clutch. Torque is developed as a result of the angle of lag between the pole generated in the ring and the axis of the applied d-c excitation.

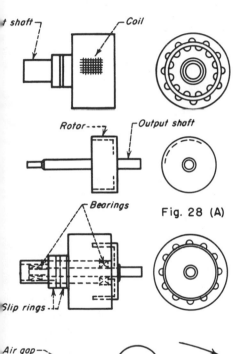

Fig. 28 (A)

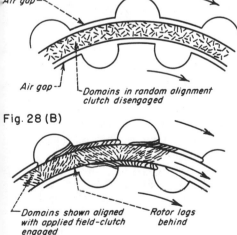

Fig. 28 (B)

Fig. 28 (A) — Component parts of a typical hysteresis clutch manufactured by Magtrol, Inc. (B) shows clutch performance for the disengaged and engaged conditions. When control excitation is applied, the magnetic fields between the input and output members will resist relative motion of the members. This produces an output torque.

ring and the control magnetomotive force results in a torque opposing rotation. Quantitatively, the torque can be deduced from the fact that the work done in turning the rotor must equal the hysteresis loss in the rotor iron.

A hysteresis clutch has the following characteristics:

1. Power gain is low; usually ranges from about 5 to 20.

2. Hysteresis torque is independent of speed. (In an actual unit, induction torques may also be developed because of rotational eddy current losses in the permanent magnet ring. These torques can be of the order of 3 to 10 percent of total torque per 1,000 rpm).

3. Operation is smooth because of the perfect symmetry of the rotor design.

4. Residual drag at zero excitation is low.

This type of clutch permits close control and can carry full load with no slip and consequently no heat generation. When slipping under overloads, heat is generated proportional to slip. The power dissipated is equal to the product of torque and slip speed. Dissipation limits the upper operating speed of the hysteresis clutch.

The unit is reliable and stable, maintaining its initial performance indefinitely. It can be used as a torque-limiting cushion against shock loads, and the uniform torque characteristics have resulted in its application in tension control devices. Because of its flat characteristic, the hysteresis clutch cannot

be used in speed control applications unless the load has a sharply rising speed-torque curve.

In special designs the hysteresis clutch can be built with torque to inertia ratios of 50,000 rad/sec² or higher, with time constants of the order of a few milliseconds.

Although a hysteresis clutch is capable of developing speed independent torques, it cannot be used where a duty cycle includes small rapid reversals, for example, in damping backlash oscillations. During reversal a dead zone is encountered before the opposing torque builds up.

In Fig. 28 (A) is shown the component parts that form a typical hysteresis clutch. The output or rotor assembly is driven by the input assembly through air gaps by an applied magnetic field. The output rotor is constructed from a permanent magnet material. The input assembly consists of two multi-polar members arranged so that all poles of each are of similar polarity. The permanent magnet rotor is assembled into the circular opening between these members and is itself polarized by the applied field that is driven through the air gaps and the permanent magnet rotor when excitation is applied to the coil through the slip rings.

Clutch operation is shown in Fig. 28 (B) for the energized and de-energized conditions. The magnetic domains within the rotor ring are caused to align with the controllable flux path

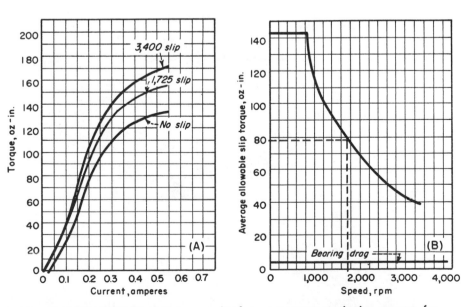

Fig. 29 — (A) (left) Maximum transmitted torque versus excitation current for hysteresis clutch manufactured by Duncan and Bayley. Three conditions of slip are shown. In (B) (right) is shown average allowable slip torque as a function of slip speed. Dotted lines indicate that for difference in speed between input and output of 1,725 rpm, the continuous torque must not exceed 80 oz-in.

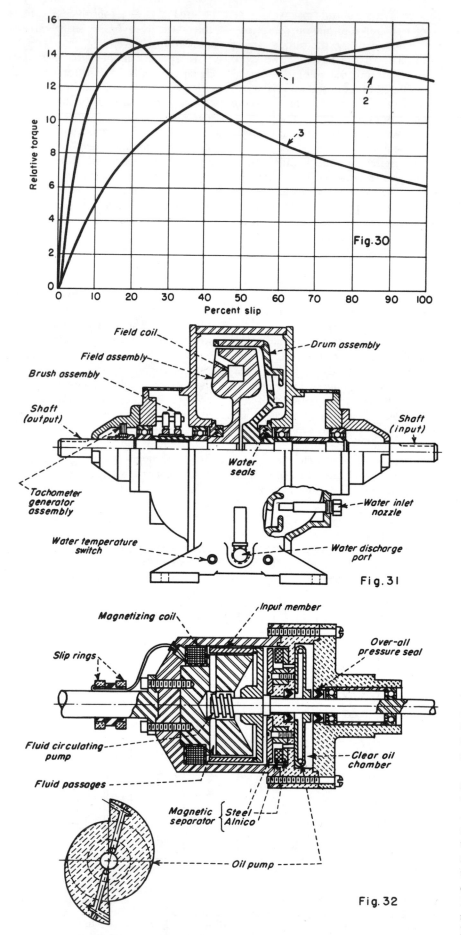

Fig. 30

Fig. 31

Fig. 32

Fig. 30 — Typical shapes of slip-torque characteristics for three types of eddy-current clutches manufactured by Dynamatic. Various characteristics are obtained by modifying the pole design of the d-c field.

Fig. 31 — Cross-section of Dynamatic water-cooled eddy-current clutch. The unit incorporates a tachometer generator for use as the feedback element in a closed loop velocity control system. Speed can be controlled to 0.1 percent over speed ranges exceeding 5 to 1.

Fig. 32 — Hermetic seal for magnetic fluid clutch developed by the National Bureau of Standards. Clear oil from a reservoir is continuously pumped into the interior of the clutch. The clear oil is then returned to the reservoir through a magnetic separator that prevents passage of the iron powder.

across the air gaps. Unless overloaded, the input and output units will rotate in synchronism.

Performance curves for a typical hysteresis clutch are shown in Figs. 29 (A) and (B). The curves in (A) show the torque that can be transmitted as a function of clutch excitation current for a condition of no slip and for two different slip speeds. (B) indicates the average allowable slip torque as a function of slip speed. Note the relative insensitivity to speed and the high degree of linearity for excitation currents below saturating values.

Eddy-Current Clutches

Eddy-current braking and clutching units are available in sizes up to thousands of horsepower. Since there are no contact surfaces required for torque transmission, these devices are reliable and have infinite life characteristics.

The basic operating principles are somewhat analogous to those of a conventional induction motor. A d-c field rotates relative to a conducting material, inducing eddy currents in this material and generating a drag torque. In an eddy-current clutch, torque is a function of slip and unlike the hysteresis clutch, torque cannot be developed unless there is a difference in speed between the input and output members. It can be shown from induction motor theory that the relation between the in-

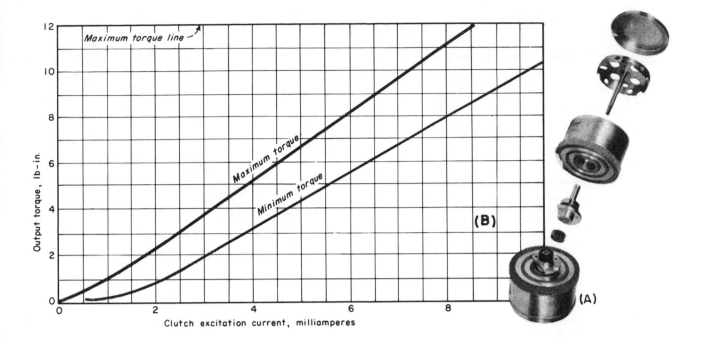

Fig. 33 (A) — Exploded and assembled views of Lear magnetic powder clutch for servo applications. Torque is transmitted between pinion on inner shaft and gear machined on casing. (B) shows the torque versus excitation current characteristics for this unit. Except at low signal levels, clutch performance is extremely linear.

herent eddy-current losses generated in the conducting material and the developed shaft power can be expressed as follows:

$$\frac{P_{EC}}{P} = \frac{\text{slip}}{\text{speed}} \qquad (31)$$

where

P_{EC} = eddy-current loss
P = shaft power to load
Slip = speed difference between input and load
Speed = load speed

For maximum clutch efficiency, the slip must be small. For a given output torque, slip is determined by the slip-torque characteristics of the clutch. The shape of the characteristic curve is dependent on machine design parameters. As with conventional induction machines, both low slip units and high slip units are available. While the latter type is low in running efficiency it is capable of developing high starting torque. Fig. 30 shows performance curves for three types of clutches. Note that the high slip clutch, 1, develops a much high starting torque (100 percent slip) than the low slip clutch, 3.

The control power required for eddy-current clutches varies from several percent of the output power in the small sizes to a fraction of a percent in large units. Since both the d-c flux and the induced eddy currents increase with control current (neglecting saturation), the drag in eddy current clutches varies as the square of the control current.

While this feature is somewhat undesirable in feedback control systems, it does not prevent the use of these clutches in this type of system.

The efficiency of this type clutch compares favorably with that of Ward-Leonard drives and other speed control systems, particularly at low slips. The efficiency of an air-cooled clutch is approximately equal to that of a wound rotor induction motor of equal rating. Typical units, Fig. 31, slip between 1.5 and 5 percent at rated loads.

In large systems, a wide range of speed control can be obtained by using feedback control of the d-c field. In the very large sizes, water cooling is used. One manufacturer circulates water between the rotating members so that in addition to cooling directly at the heat source, extra drag is obtained because the water is subjected to shear. Efficiencies as high as 96 percent can be obtained in this manner.

Magnetic Fluid and Magnetic Powder Clutches

These clutch types consist basically of a pair of plates separated by a powder or powder-oil combination of finely divided magnetic particles. The application of a magnetic field causes the powder to form a rigid mass capable of transmitting torque and oriented along the lines of flux. While the fluid

type operates more smoothly, maintains more uniform distribution of the iron particles and has superior cooling characteristics, leakage caused by inadequate sealing techniques has in many instances forced the use of the dry powder.

The slipping action that occurs under load, while it generates the usual heat inherent in slip clutches, does not cause excessive wear since the sliding iron particles and all interior surfaces of the clutch are lubricated. Lubricants based on talc or molybdenum have been used successfully in dry powder units.

Labyrinth seals have been employed in magnetic clutches, with varying degrees of success. If the speed of the clutch is always high, the labyrinth can be made effective by utilizing the centrifugal forces on the powder. Where the speeds are variable and the positions of the clutch are undetermined, as in some military airborne applications, the use of labyrinths has not proved satisfactory. Labyrinths, moreover, do not prevent breathing. Thus, as the clutch warms up, air is driven out, and as the clutch cools, cold air enters again, carrying with it fresh oxygen and moisture, which corrode the internal parts of the mechanism and the iron powder.

For these reasons, hermetic sealing is often used. One type of hermetic seal, Fig. 32, consists of a reservoir of

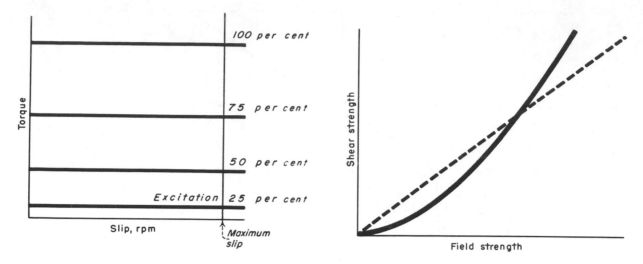

Fig. 34 — (A) (left) Slip-torque characteristics of Clark Dynamatic magnetic powder clutch. Family of excitation curves are flat out to maximum allowable slip. (B) indicates the field-shear variation of same unit. Dotted line represents desired linear performance, while solid line represents actual clutch performance.

Fig. 35 — Magnetic fluid clutch servo drive unit developed by the National Bureau of Standards. These units use the hermetic seal shown in Fig. 32.

clear oil, mounted adjacent to the clutch proper, so designed that the clear oil is continuously pumped along the shaft into the interior of the clutch. The clear oil is then returned to the reservoir through a magnetic separator which prevents iron particles from flowing with the oil. The magnetic separator consists of a ring magnet of Alnico having a short air gap. The iron powder does not pass the air gap, while the oil does so freely. An impeller-type pump then recirculates the oil back through the shaft seal. The whole system is provided with a second seal which operates entirely in clear oil. Such seals are commercially available.

When thick grease lubricants are used in magnetic fluid clutches, the sealing problem is somewhat simpler since the iron-grease mixture tends to stay in the working gap. Air intake, however, causes trouble, and hermetic seals are still required to make the clutch independent of ambient conditions. This is also true of clutches employing dry lubricants.

In Fig. 33 is shown an exploded and an assembled view of a typical magnetic powder clutch for servo applications, and the torque-excitation current characteristic for this clutch. This unit transmits a normal torque of 0.8 lb-in. with a maximum rating of 12 lb. in. at a maximum recommended speed of 1,500 rpm. With a 100 percent slip, the maximum continuous frictional power dissipation is 15 watts. With zero ex-

Fig. 36—Experimental crystal clutch designed by National Bureau of Standards. The three crystal elements bend when a d-c voltage is applied. This bending pinches the output disk between the rotating mounting plate and the rotating crystal pressure plate.

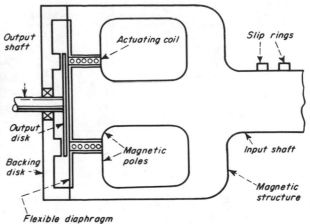

Fig. 37 — (right) Schematic diagram of National Bureau of Standards loudspeaker clutch. When current is applied to the actuating coil, which is located in a magnetic field, the coil moves forward and presses a flexible diaphragm against a disk attached to the output shaft.

citation the drag torque is 0.2 lb-in. maximum. By using forced air cooling, increased energy dissipation ratings can be obtained.

The perfomance characteristics of Fig. 33 (B) show the ordinary production variations. The slight nonlinearity at low signals can be overcome by biasing. This bias can be obtained from the quiescent plate current of the driving amplifier tube.

The torque-slip characteristics of another commercially available magnetic powder clutch are shown in Fig. 34 (A). The uniform flat characteristic is similar to the characteristic obtained with a hysteresis clutch. However, the power amplification of the magnetic powder clutch is inherently higher.

The flatness of the curves indicates that no velocity lag will be introduced in a simple servomechanism during tracking. This is in contrast to the lag that is inherent in the speed-torque curves of a conventional two-phase servo motor. Fig. 34 (B) shows a plot of shear strength versus field strength for this same unit. The dotted line in this curve represents the desired linear performance. The solid line is actual clutch performance. While the nonlinearity is objectional, where necessary, push-pull circuits can be used to minimize this effect.

In Fig. 35 is shown a servomechanism power unit using two magnetic fluid clutches driven by a constant speed motor.

Crystal Clutches

The crystal clutch is actuated by a direct current applied to a piezo-electric crystal. This causes a change in the dimensions of the crystal, pressing the clutch output disk against the input disk. The unit is noted for its high speed of response and negligible current drain. Although not widely used as yet, these features make the crystal clutch valuable in a few specialized closed loop control applications.

Since the only excitation current that is required is the insulation leakage current necessary to charge the crystal capacitors, current drain is negligible. There is no magnetic field generated. One model that has been constructed, Fig. 36, delivers useful torque about 0.2 milliseconds after the application of the exciting voltage. An output torque of 21 oz-in. was obtained with 500 v excitation. However, the zero excitation drag was about 7.5 oz-in., an appreciable fraction of the engaged torque.

If resistance is present in the excitation circuit, the crystal voltage rises exponentially while the crystal is charged (crystal capacity is about 0.0065 mfd). Speed of response is related to this voltage rise. Because of nonlinearity in the crystal, there is an optimum value of series resistance that will give a firm response.

In the first clutch models, Rochelle salt crystals were used. However, this material is easily fractured, melts at 55

C and will absorb water unless protected from humidity. Barium titanate crystals are stronger mechanically and are usable at temperatures up to 100 C, although they have a lower sensitivity and a higher electrical capacity.

Loudspeaker Clutches

Another experimental development in the field of high speed servo clutches is the loudspeaker type clutch. This unit operates on the same principle as the electrodynamic loudspeaker of an ordinary radio receiver and is actuated by applying d-c to a coil located in a constant magnetic field, Fig. 37. The force resulting from the interaction of the coil current and the magnetic field moves the coil and causes the clutch output disk to be pressed against the rotating input members. In one model, full output-shaft torque of 10 oz-in. was attained in less than a third of a millisecond after the application of the actuating voltage. Possible applications include rapid starting and stopping of magnetic wire or tape recording media in high speed electronic computers and high speed switching in telephone dial systems.

The loudspeaker clutch is inherently capable of faster response than conventional electrical or magnetic friction clutches. In a conventional clutch, time as well as energy is required to build up a field after the actuating voltage is applied, while in the loudspeaker clutch, the necessary magnetic field is

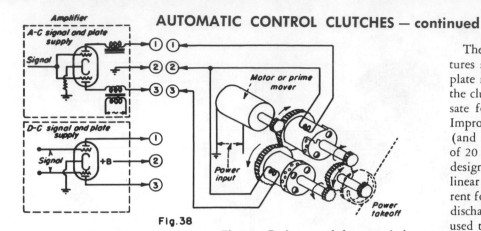

Fig. 38

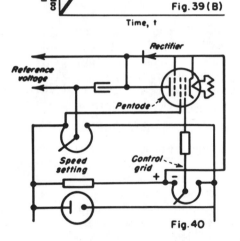

Fig. 39 (A)

Fig. 39 (B)

Fig. 40

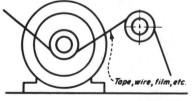

Fig. 41

Fig. 38—Basic a-c and d-c control circuitry for servo actuator incorporating two magnetic power clutches. These systems are available from Lear, Inc. Sensing circuits can be used to activate either of the two clutch circuits.

Fig. 39—(left) (A) One circuit used by Dynamatic obtaining exponential control of acceleration in clutch speed control systems. Load velocity will vary with time in the same manner as capacity voltage varies with time, (B), after a sudden change in speed setting.

Fig. 40 — Clutch control circuit used by Dynamatic to obtain linear control of acceleration. By using the pentode, a constant capacitor charging rate and consequently a linear acceleration can be achieved. Acceleration is adjusted by setting the control grid potential.

Fig. 41 — Typical brake tensioning setup as recommended by Magtrol. If instead of using this method, the unwinding reel is attached directly to the brake, the changing diameter of the roll is compensated for by having a follower roll actuate a variable resistor whose change of resistance with motion matches the slope of the torque — current curve of the brake.

already in existence before the clutch is actuated. The inductance of the moving coil is normally small and can be made negligible by means of compensating coils. Thus the time required for the coil current to build up to press the clutching surfaces together is equally negligible.

Clutch Applications and Control Circuits

The clutch excitation signal must be d-c to achieve high forces at a high efficiency. In ordinary single-ended control circuits, a full-wave rectifier bridge can be used to supply direct current. A capacitance-resistance filter is normally required for smoothing the clutch chatter caused by the a-c excitation current component. Where excitation is derived from a polarity sensitive a-c error detector, a combination of a phase sensitive detector and a d-c amplifier must be used.

The schematic of Fig. 38 shows two basic vacuum tube circuits for controlling the clutch excitation coils of an actuator using magnetic powder clutches. The addition of feedback, stabilizing means and a preamplifier enables the resulting control system to control a variety of functions.

The amplifier can incorporate features such as current feedback or high plate resistance pentodes that can force the clutch control current and compensate for the inherent coil time delay. Improvements in the time constant (and closed loop stability) by factors of 20 to 100 can be obtained by careful design. Where intermittent instead of linear clutch torques are developed, current forcing methods based on capacitor discharge through a thyratron can be used to increase the speed of response.

When high inertia loads must be accelerated or when processing equipment requires a smooth increase of driving torque, acceleration control can be used. Systems incorporating clutch control can be used in many of these applications including the manufacture of wire, paper, linoleum, plastics, rubber and other materials. Since acceleration rates can be closely matched, two or more drives can be started simultaneously.

When clutches are used for speed control by bucking a reference voltage against the output voltage of a load-coupled tachometer, controlled acceleration can be obtained by using the circuit shown in Fig. 39 (A). If there is a sudden change in the speed setting from zero, then the voltage across the capacitor can be expressed as

$$e = e_m (1 - \epsilon^{-t/RC})$$

where e = instantaneous voltage across capacitor
e_m = voltage corresponding to new speed setting
t = time
R = resistance
C = capacitance

If the servo loop can respond rapidly enough to accelerate as desired, the curve indicating the variation of velocity with time will follow the exponential relation representing the variation of capacitor voltage, e, with time, Fig. 39 (B). This exponential type of acceleration control, gives high accelerations for starting, with a logarithmic decrease in acceleration as the unit approaches the preset speed.

When logarithmic acceleration is desired and a longer time base is required than is possible with the circuit shown in Fig. 39 (A), a triode tube can be substituted for the resistor. By controlling the grid of the tube, the charging rate of the capacitor can be adjusted. Thus the circuit can be set for any desirable time base within practical limits.

A circuit that can be used to obtain linear acceleration is shown in Fig. 40.

With this arrangement a pentode tube is substituted for the fixed resistor. In addition to the basic tube elements of the cathode, plate and grid, a pentode contains a suppressor grid and screen grid. By keeping the screen grid at a constant positive voltage with respect to the cathode, the plate current is reduced to the function of control-grid voltage only, supplying a constant charging rate in spite of the leveling off of the plate-to-cathode voltage. Since the capacitor charging rate is constant, the voltage across it must increase linearly with time. The control grid voltage is adjustable so that the capacitor charging rate or load acceleration can be set as required. When the control is reset for a lower speed, the rectifier serves as a discharge path for the capacitor.

Another function of clutch systems is to protect against overload by limiting the transmitted torque. This function is required where heavy intermittent overloads occur during starting or operation. For example, processing equipment is subjected to occasional overloads because of the nonuniformity of feeding mechanisms, or because foreign objects are mixed in with the material being processed. Specific applications are conveyor drives, pulverizing mill drives and various machine tool drives.

One torque-limiting system uses main drive-motor current as an indication of transmitted torque, since this current is closely related to motor torque. A d-c voltage proportional to current regulates the grid of a tube. The tube plate current is supplied to a potentiometer. The setting of this potentiometer determines the speed control reference voltage. Heavy currents in the motor windings subject the control grid to a large negative bias, limiting the reference voltage and eventually forcing this voltage to assume a value of zero.

This reduces load coupling by reducing clutch excitation. As load speed is reduced, an equilibrium of limited torque is reached. Increased flexibility can be obtained by using potentiometers and resistor switching.

When used with a synchronous motor drive, torque limiting prevents the loss of synchronism because of transient overloads.

In typical designs, brakes and clutches are identical with the exception that simpler mechanical design is in-

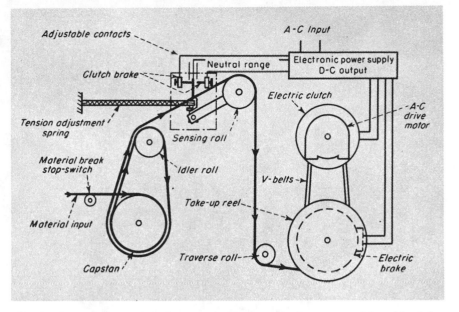

Fig. 42 – Intermittent power pulse control of brake – clutch system used for maintaining constant tension. System was designed by Warner Electric Brake and Clutch Co. The system continually hunts to maintain the proper tension.

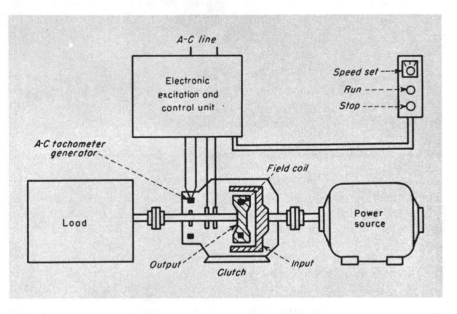

Fig. 43 – Dynamatic eddy-current clutch with feedback tachometer on the output shaft. Load speed can be adjusted by varying the speed-set device.

herently possible in the brake and that slip rings are usually omitted. Fig. 41 shows a hysteresis brake used to maintain the desired value of tension in an unwinding reel.

A combination braking-clutching system for controlling tension is shown in Fig. 42. Power is applied in intermittent pulses as the sensing roll in the material take-off moves a switch arm to energize clutch or brake, depending on the tension requirements. When the motor starts, the clutch drives the reel until the tension is sufficient to break the clutch contact on the sensing arm.

This interruption relieves the tension, restores clutch control and repeats the cycle, causing a perpetually hunting control, pulsating at a frequency above resonance.

In Fig. 43 is shown a clutch control system for controlling load speed. This system uses a water-cooled eddy current such as the one that is illustrated in Fig. 31. The eddy current clutch incorporates an a-c tachometer on the output shaft for feedback purposes. Fractional percent precision over a speed range of several hundred is feasible with this arrangement.

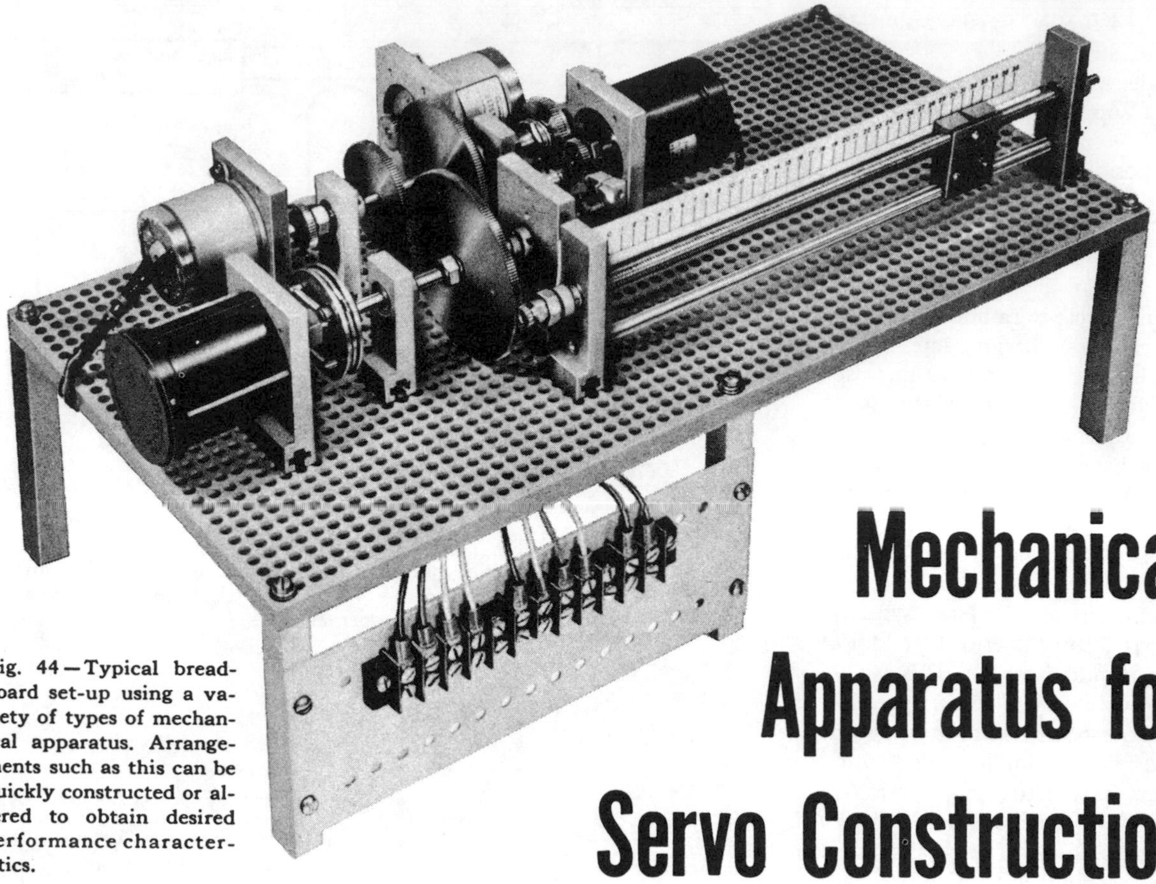

Fig. 44 — Typical bread-board set-up using a variety of types of mechanical apparatus. Arrangements such as this can be quickly constructed or altered to obtain desired performance characteristics.

Mechanical Apparatus for Servo Construction

To PERMIT THE RAPID ASSEMBLY of mechanical breadboards, or permanent or semi-permanent servo systems, an assortment of standardized precision-built components is available. All of these components are stock items with various manufacturers and include not only the usual servo hardware such as gear trains and differentials, but in addition a variety of general purpose adapters aimed at achieving maximum flexibility.

In Fig. 44 is shown a typical bread-board set-up incorporating many of these devices. The development of this line of components was made possible largely because various government agencies standardized on specific outlines and performance features for synchros, motors, tachometers and other rotating components common in automatic control systems. Of particular importance was the establishment of standard frames, mounting methods and shaft diameters.

While this mechanical hardware is still relatively expensive, it has been adopted by many organizations doing development work in control systems. Where educational institutions require flexibility and functional variety at minimum cost this equipment has found use. Although breadboards of these standard parts do not give the finished compact appearance of a specialized design, they have found application in finished equipment of such a specialized nature that final production-line designs are uneconomical.

By using breadboard arrangements, designs can be tested in mock-up form prior to the packaging of a final system. An engineer may save development time by working on a breadboard, adjusting parameters to achieve performance requirements and in some instances omitting altogether the paper design stage. By experimental manipulation, tolerances can be varied and producibility evaluated. The effects of nonlinearities such as backlash and resiliences in shafts, and the nature of transient shock loads and amplifier saturation can be observed beforehand and tolerances that are appropriate for production can be established.

Manufacturers of this apparatus are adding components (such as servo dampers and magnetic clutches) to their standard line with the view toward increasing versatility. To simplify stocking needs and to reduce the variety of devices that are of a different size or shape but perform the same function, various items have been standardized by the different manufacturers. These items include gear materials (which are usually limited to stainless steel and aluminum), shaft diameters (although adapters are available), height of component centerlines above baseboard, gear pitch and face widths. However, most manufacturers are willing to supply special purpose parts to order.

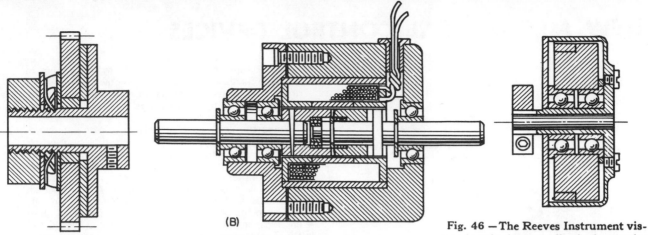

Fig. 45 — Slip and regulating clutches. The Reeves Instrument adjustable slip clutch, (A) (left), is used for limiting peak mechanical loads. Within limited ranges it can be adjusted by varying the spring tension. The magnetic clutch shown in (B) (right), is similar to those discussed in the section on clutches. It can be used in small clutch type control systems or for the remote coupling of elements in a complex mechanical assembly. The unit is of the crown-tooth type.

Fig. 46 — The Reeves Instrument viscous inertia damper effectively couples a flywheel to a servo shaft through the medium of a viscous silicone fluid. This technique gives satisfactory damping with extremely high velocity constants. Units such as this are available as independent elements to be coupled into a servo system.

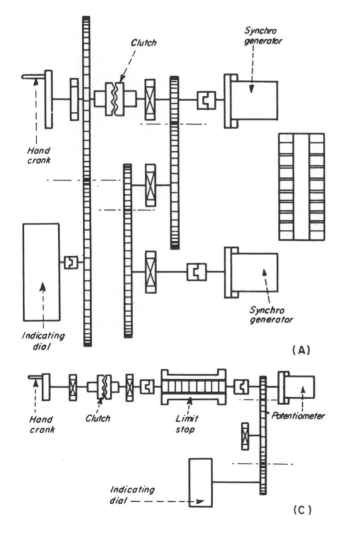

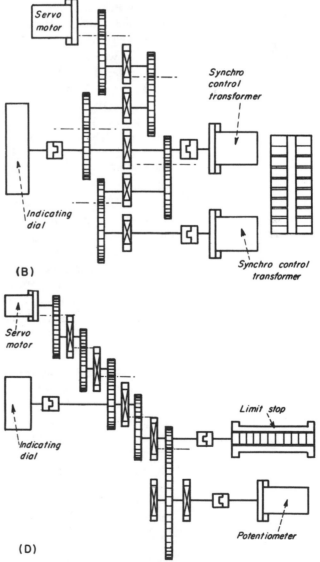

Fig. 47 — These schematic diagrams represent typical assemblies that can be constructed using Belock standard mechanical parts. A variety of arrangements is possible with a minimum number of different components. (A) (above, left), represents a multi-speed synchro transmitter, (B) (above, right), a multi-speed synchro receiver.

(C) (above), a potentiometer transmitter and (D) (right), a potentiometer receiver.

NEW MECHANICAL CONTROL DEVICES

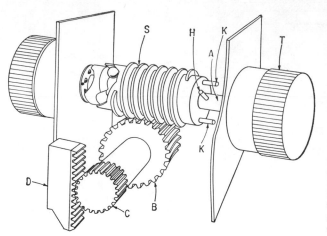

One-knob control—New and controversial in microscopy is this single knob control for coarse and fine adjustment, available in three series of Leitz microscopes, particularly those for classroom and student

use, or for rapid observations. It is most suitable in high magnifications, less so for low-power work where a greater range of fine adjustment is necessary. The mechanism runs in ball bearings, totally enclosed so lubrication is unnecessary.

Turning the knob continuously in one direction provides the coarse adjustment. When direction is reversed, the fine adjustment is automatically engaged for about 1/3 turn of the knob. Turning beyond this amount at either end shifts back to coarse adjustment.

Worm **S** is loosely mounted on shaft **A**, along which it can move a short distance. Drive knob **T** is rigidly attached to the shaft. As soon as drive pin **H** on shaft **A** engages one of the stop pins **K** on the worm, the latter is rotated directly. It in turn rotates worm wheel **B** and pinion **C**, which in turn drives rack **D** on the table lift. This is the coarse adjustment. But a reversal of the knob disengages the coarse feed and moves the worm gear **(S)** along the shaft a very short distance through a mechanism consisting of an inclined plane and ball. This causes very slight rotation of the worm wheel **(B)** and pinion **(C)**, so movement of rack **D** is correspondingly limited. This fine feed can be continued, or reversed, within the limits of stops **(K)**.

A new British design for lead screws and bolt and stud attachments is aimed at improved thrust distribution and more uniform wear.

The design, developed and patented by Vickers-Armstrong, uses a screw of constant effective diameter with a convex-profile thread (elliptical, involute, or semicircular). The nut thread is concave and the nut itself tapered internally toward the center plane so that the depth of its thread is reduced toward the outside (see diagram). Thus, when assembled, contact between the nut threads and the screw thread also diminishes progressively, and the mean flank angle (α, β, γ) varies progressively. In this way, the thrust distribution can be controlled and spread among the nut threads instead of being

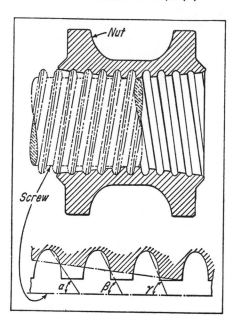

concentrated in one or two. It also permits progressive transition from static to dynamic conditions and allows for more effective lubrication.

A variable-throw cam designed by Atomic Energy Commission engineers is among the new devices being released for royalty-free licensing and use.

The cam consists of two eccentric sleeves, one inside the other (see diagram), adjustably locked together. The throw of the cam at any setting is equal to twice the distance between driveshaft and inner sleeve axes, and this can be varied by loosening the collar, rotating the outer sleeve relative to the inner, and then locking them together again. The inventors, E. C. Godsil and E. Y. Robinson, believe the device should be useful in ram-and-die presses, cyclic fatigue testers, and similar devices. They point out that the design has a special advantage: Once the collar has been tightened,

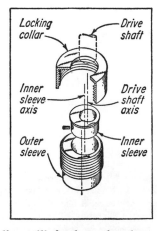

any subsequent relative rotation tends to tighten the collar still further, thereby preserving the original cam setting.

5

CHUCKING, CLAMPING, AND SPECIAL-FASTENING DEVICES

6 SPRING-LOADED CHUCKS (and) HOLDING FIXTURES

Spring-loaded fixtures for work-holding are sometimes preferable to other types. Their advantages are: Shorter setup time and quick workpiece change. And work distortion is much reduced because spring force can be easily and accurately adjusted.

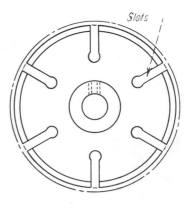

Spring-loaded Nest . . .

has radial slots extending into face. These ensure even grip on work, which is pushed over rim. Slight lead on rim makes work-mounting easier. Chief use of this fixture is for ball-bearing race grinding where only light cutting forces are necessary.

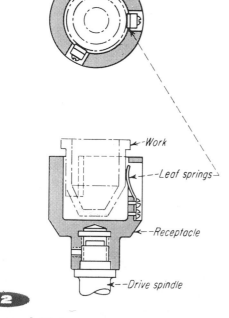

Cupped Fixture . . .

has three leaf-springs equally spaced in wall. Work, usually to be lacquered, is inserted into cup during rotation. Because work is placed in fixture by hand, spindle is usually friction driven for safety.

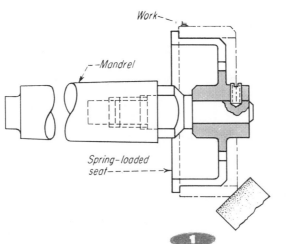

Lathe Center . . .

is spring loaded and holds work by spring pressure alone. Eight sharp-edged notches on the conical surface of driving center bite into the work and drive it. Spring tension is adjustable.

SIGMUND RAPPAPORT

Project Supervisor, Ford Instrument Co.,
Adjunct Professor of Kinematics
Polytechnic Institute of Brooklyn

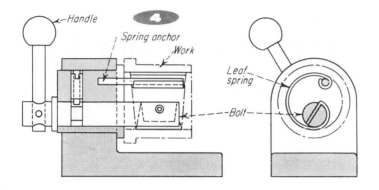

Leaf-spring Gripper . . .

is used mainly to hold work during assembly. One end of flat coil-spring is anchored in housing; other end is held in bolt. When bolt is turned, spring is tightened and its OD decreased. After work is slid over spring, bolt handle is released. Spring then presses against work, holding it tight.

Spring Clamp . . .

has cam and tension spring to apply clamping force. Tension spring activates cam through steel band. When handle is released, cam clamps work against V-bar. Two stop-pins limit travel when there is no work in the fixture.

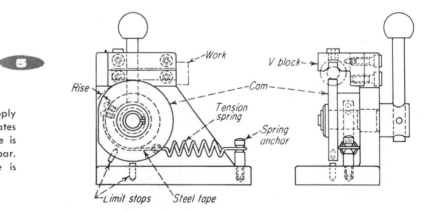

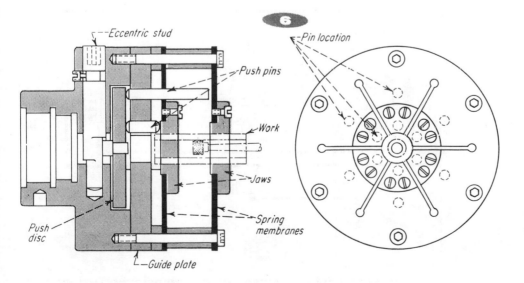

Slotted Membranes . . .

have holding jaws attached. ID of holding jaws hold work. When eccentric stud is turned it forces two sets of push-pins against the spring-membrane. This action deflects membrane, opening jaws for receiving or releasing work. Turning the eccentric stud back relieves the push-pins, allowing spring to snap back and grip work.

Hydraulic Chucking Devices

INTERNAL HYDRAULIC CHUCKING

Hydraulic fluid enters rotating cylinder when directional hydraulic control valve is shifted. Rotating cylinder piston then pushes on bell crank of chuck through drawrod. False jaws operated by bell crank then grip work. To release grip, drawrod is pulled back when control valve lever is reversed.

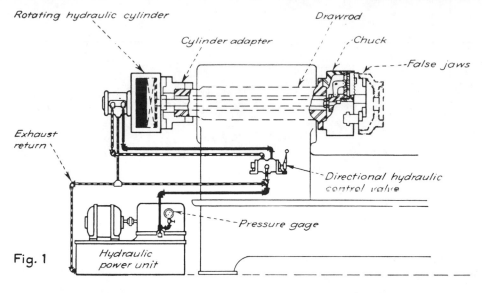

Fig. 1

EXTERNAL HYDRAULIC CHUCKING

After operation of directional hydraulic control valve, pull on bell crank through drawrod closes false jaws on work. Upon reversal of control valve, jaws are opened and work is released. Hydraulic accumulator in power unit maintains pressure for relatively long periods of chuck operation.

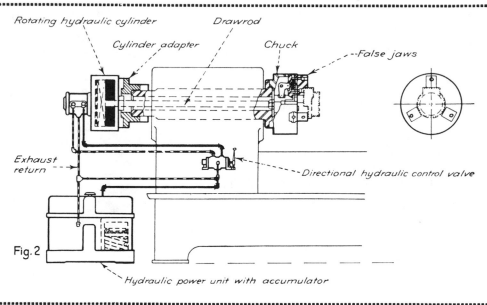

Fig. 2

HYDRAULIC CHUCK AND TAILSTOCK

After operation of directional hydraulic control valve, fluid enters non-rotating cylinder, and tailstock moves into position, and sequence valve A opens. Hydraulic fluid then admitted to rotating cylinder causes mandrel to grip work. When machine operation is completed, control valve is reversed. Tailstock retracts and sequence valve B opens, causing mandrel to release work.

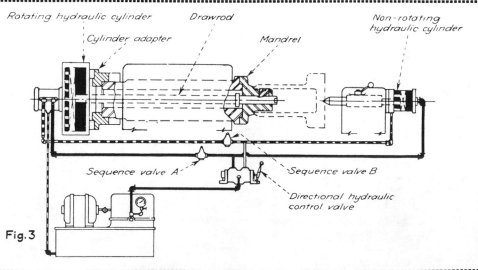

Fig. 3

for Lathe Applications

HARRY L. STEWART
Logansport Machine Company, Inc.

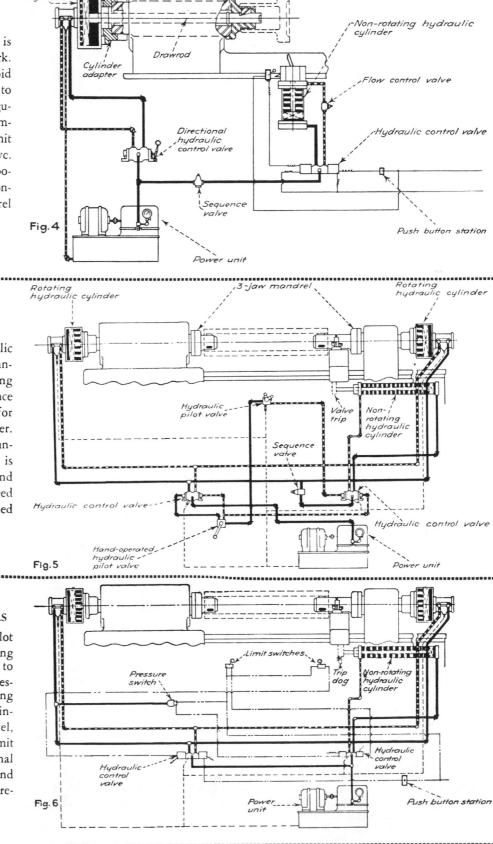

HYDRAULIC CHUCK AND FEED

After directional control valve is shifted, mandrel grips work. Push button operated solenoid valve admits hydraulic fluid to tool feed cylinder at a rate regulated by flow control valve. Completion of tool travel trips limit switch reversing solenoid valve. Tool then returns to original position. Reversing directional control valve then causes mandrel to release work.

Fig. 4

HYDRAULIC CHUCK AND AUTOMATIC FEED

Shifting hand operated hydraulic pilot valve causes push type mandrels to grip work. Gripping work automatically trips sequence valve, opening control valve for non-rotating hydraulic cylinder. Tool is then fed hydraulically until hydraulic pilot valve is tripped. This reverses righthand control valve to return tool feed cylinder. Shifting hand operated pilot valve releases work.

Fig. 5

HYDRAULIC CHUCK WITH ELECTRIC CONTROLS

Electric controls replace the pilot valves shown in Fig. 5. Pressing push button causes mandrels to grip work. This trips the pressure switch causing non-rotating hydraulic cylinder to feed cylinder. At the end of the tool travel, tripping the left hand limit switch returns tool to original position. This trips righthand limit switch, which initiates release of work.

Fig. 6

163

NEW CHUCKING AND HOLDING DEVICES

Hydrostatic chucking devices . . .

. . . with interesting features are appearing on both sides of the Iron Curtain.

One, from Britain, is a self-contained diaphragm-type that operates by internal hydrostatic pressure. As the assembly diagram (left, below) indicates, the chuck has two diaphragms, one of which carries the chucking ring and jaw pads, so that when the diaphragm is pressed outward, the jaws are opened. An axial piston A compresses the hydrostatic mass in chamber B, bulging an inner diaphragm C which, in turn, is pressed against a second diaphragm D attached to the split chucking ring E. As the diaphragm is pressed outwards, the ring opens, and the grip on workpiece F is loosened. Advantage,

the designer says, is that a high clamping load can be applied with a system actuated by a very small stroke. Integral Ltd., Wolverhampton, makes it.

The other new chuck diagrammed below, designed in Hungary, also uses a hydrostatic material, but the prime actuator is centrifugal force. As the chuck turns, the weights A are flung outwards, turning the double-armed levers B which push the radial pistons C inwards. This compresses the hydrostatic material D, moving the axial pistons E and actuating the axial sleeve F. This, in turn, pushes the conical clamping sleeve G backwards, gripping the workpiece. Springs return the flyweights to their original position when the machine stops.

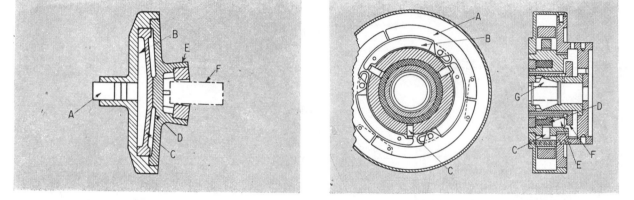

British chuck (above) features two diaphragms, operates simply by compressing the piston. Other is the **Hungarian chuck**. It uses both hydrostatic pressure and centrifugal force, but is so designed that flyweights will re-set themselves.

Simple Mandrel Expands Like a Collet

INGENIOUS MANDREL simplifies the holding of work pieces during machining operations. Made in one piece, it is slotted to form three cantilever sections that deflect to positively engage the work piece. Each mandrel has one, two or three gripping diameters and is made in the standard C-5 collet sizes; diameters range from 7/32 to 1½ in. in 1/32-in. steps. These mandrels are manufactured by E. Westberg Co., 800 Beley Ave., East Syracuse, N. Y.

As the tapered part of the mandrel is tightened in the machine, the spiral segment is forced to deflect outward. In this manner, the gripping portion engages the inside diameter of the work. With a 10 deg taper, the total radial force exerted by each of the three gripping shoulders is about equal to the axial force on the mandrel. Three equally-spaced segments insure concentricity.

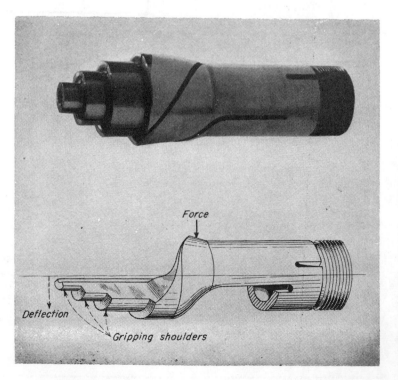

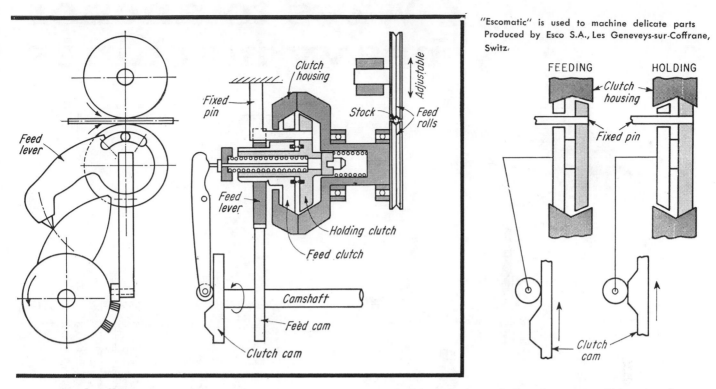

"Escomatic" is used to machine delicate parts
Produced by Esco S.A., Les Geneveys-sur-Coffrane,
Switz.

Feed rolls . . .

have dual function: moving stock, and holding it during machining. Cam-operated clutches control all feed-roll movement. Clutch cam, on same shaft as feed cam, positions clutches for the operation selected. Feed cam rotates feed rolls through a clutch and lever. After this clutch is engaged, feed lever is cammed through an arc sufficient to advance required length of stock. At end of this stroke the holding clutch is engaged to hold the stock for machining; the feed clutch is released. When released, feed lever and clutch return to starting position for next stroke. Fixed pin prevents rotation of holding clutch and feed rolls during machining.

Denison Multi-press.

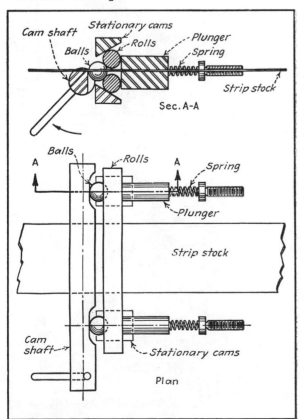

HOLDING MECHANISM allows material to be fed in one direction only. In each cycle, the spring pushes the plunger and forces the rolls against the stationary cams. These in turn force the rolls against the strip stock, gripping it firmly. The stock is released as the rotating cam shaft pushes balls against rolls away from the stationary cams, allowing them to spread.

12 Ways to anchor heavy machines

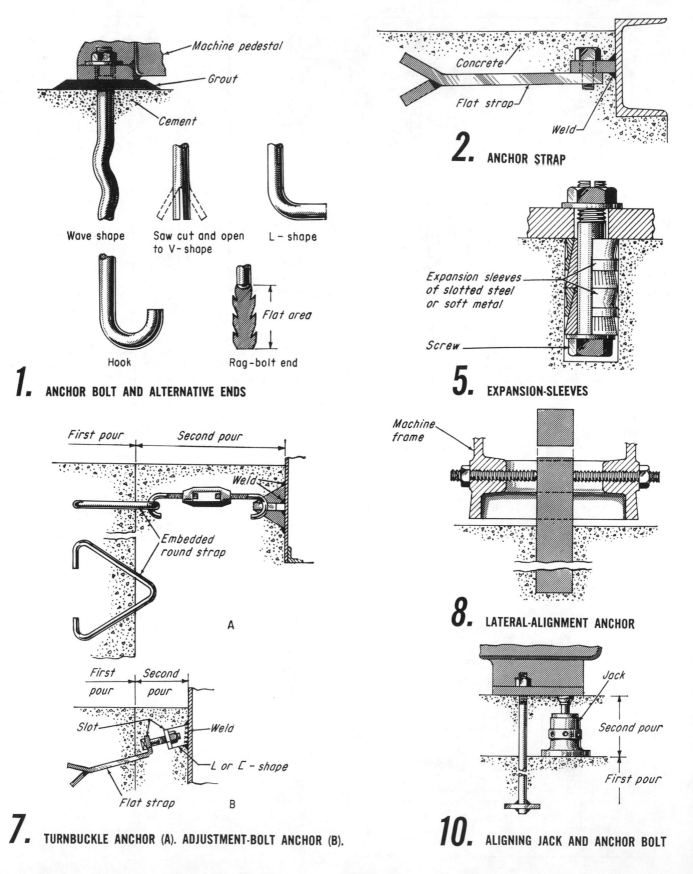

Machine pedestal
Grout
Cement

Wave shape

Saw cut and open to V-shape

L-shape

Hook

Flat area

Rag-bolt end

1. ANCHOR BOLT AND ALTERNATIVE ENDS

Concrete
Flat strap
Weld

2. ANCHOR STRAP

Expansion sleeves of slotted steel or soft metal
Screw

5. EXPANSION-SLEEVES

First pour
Second pour
Weld
Embedded round strap

A

First pour
Second pour
Slot
Weld
L or C - shape
Flat strap

B

7. TURNBUCKLE ANCHOR (A). ADJUSTMENT-BOLT ANCHOR (B).

Machine frame

8. LATERAL-ALIGNMENT ANCHOR

Jack
Second pour
First pour

10. ALIGNING JACK AND ANCHOR BOLT

Machine design is not really finished until anchoring and levelling methods have been decided. Here's a selection from which to choose.

LOUIS DODGE, Consulting Engineer, New Richmond, Ohio

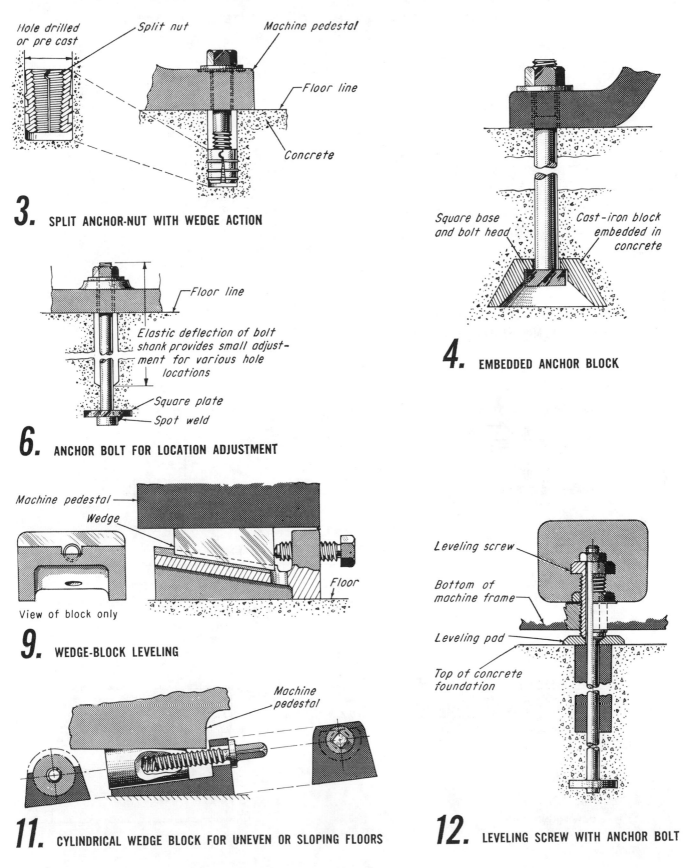

Hole drilled or pre cast — Split nut — Machine pedestal — Floor line — Concrete

3. SPLIT ANCHOR-NUT WITH WEDGE ACTION

Floor line / Elastic deflection of bolt shank provides small adjustment for various hole locations / Square plate / Spot weld

6. ANCHOR BOLT FOR LOCATION ADJUSTMENT

Square base and bolt head — Cast-iron block embedded in concrete

4. EMBEDDED ANCHOR BLOCK

Machine pedestal — Wedge — Floor — View of block only

9. WEDGE-BLOCK LEVELING

Machine pedestal

11. CYLINDRICAL WEDGE BLOCK FOR UNEVEN OR SLOPING FLOORS

Leveling screw — Bottom of machine frame — Leveling pad — Top of concrete foundation

12. LEVELING SCREW WITH ANCHOR BOLT

Isolating machines

Here is a selection of resilient pads, spring and rubber mounts, as they are commonly arranged to absorb vibrations

LOUIS DODGE, Consulting Engineer, Richmond, Ohio

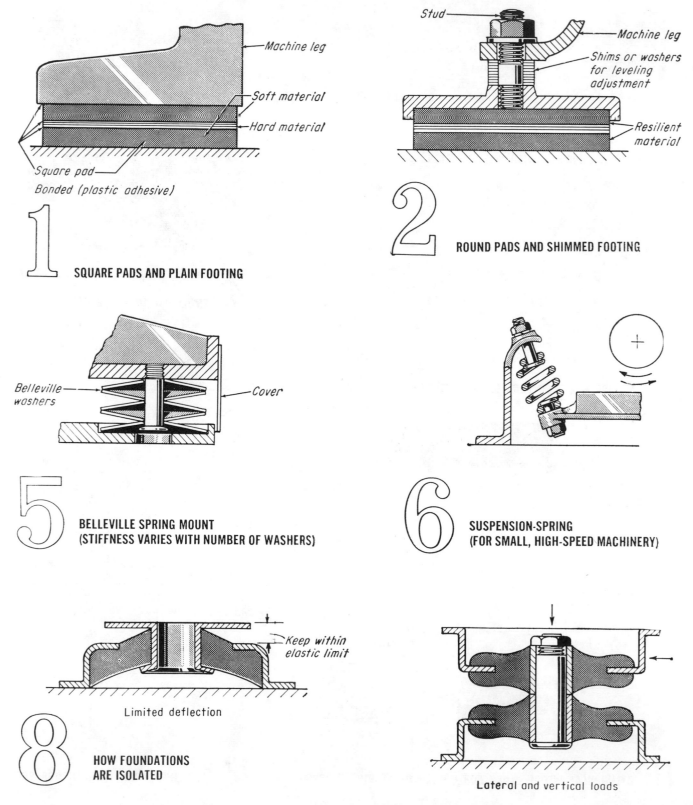

1 SQUARE PADS AND PLAIN FOOTING

2 ROUND PADS AND SHIMMED FOOTING

5 BELLEVILLE SPRING MOUNT
(STIFFNESS VARIES WITH NUMBER OF WASHERS)

6 SUSPENSION-SPRING
(FOR SMALL, HIGH-SPEED MACHINERY)

8 HOW FOUNDATIONS ARE ISOLATED

Limited deflection

Lateral and vertical loads

from vibration

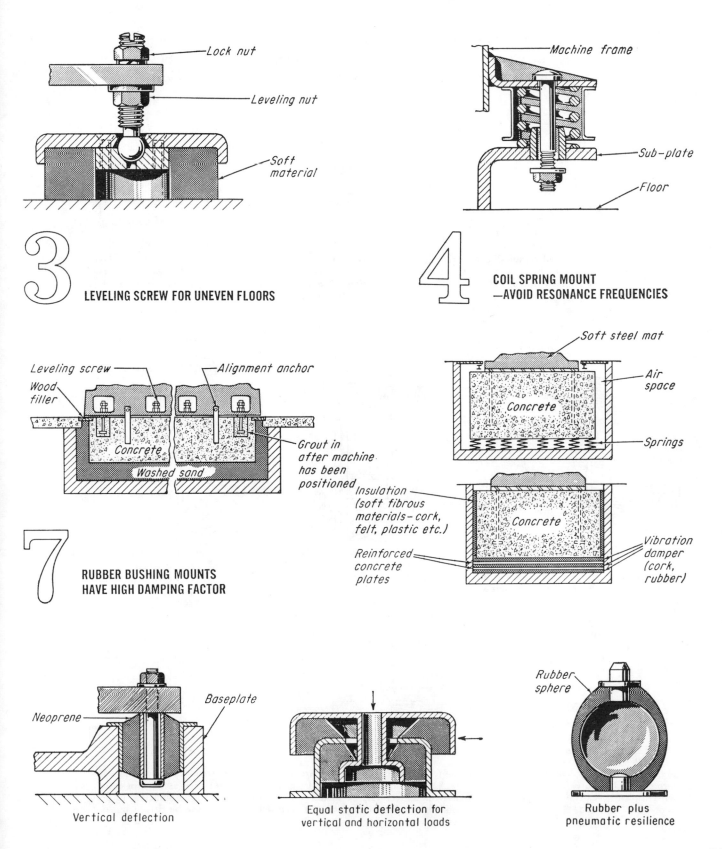

3 LEVELING SCREW FOR UNEVEN FLOORS

Lock nut

Leveling nut

Soft material

4 COIL SPRING MOUNT —AVOID RESONANCE FREQUENCIES

Machine frame

Sub-plate

Floor

Leveling screw

Wood filler

Alignment anchor

Concrete

Washed sand

Grout in after machine has been positioned

7 RUBBER BUSHING MOUNTS HAVE HIGH DAMPING FACTOR

Soft steel mat

Air space

Concrete

Springs

Insulation (soft fibrous materials—cork, felt, plastic etc.)

Reinforced concrete plates

Concrete

Vibration damper (cork, rubber)

Neoprene

Baseplate

Vertical deflection

Equal static deflection for vertical and horizontal loads

Rubber sphere

Rubber plus pneumatic resilience

20 Tamper-proof

Ways to prevent or indicate unauthorized removal of fasteners in vending machines, instruments, radios, TV sets and other units. Included are positively retained fasteners to prevent loss where retrieval would be difficult.

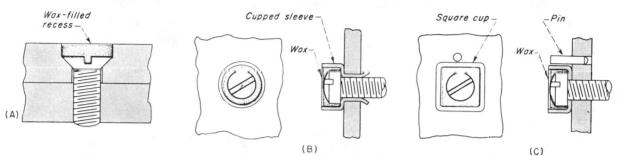

Fig. 1—(A) Wax or other suitable material fills recess above screw. Wax flush with plate hides screw position if surface is painted. (B) Cupped sleeve riveted in screw hole provides cavity for wax when plate is too thin for recessing. (C) Pin prevents rotation of square cup which would allow screw to be removed without disturbing wax.

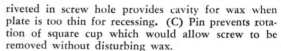

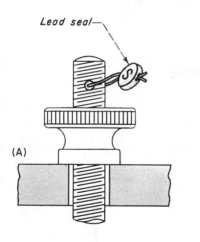

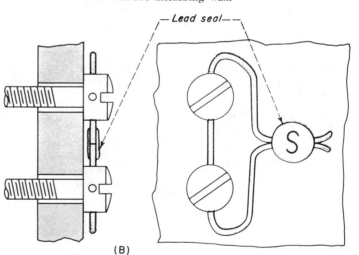

Fig. 2—(A) Lead seal crimped over twisted ends of wire passing through screw allows only limited slackening of nut. (B) Two or more screws strung through heads with wire are protected against unauthorized removal by only one seal. Code or other signet can be embossed on seals during crimping.

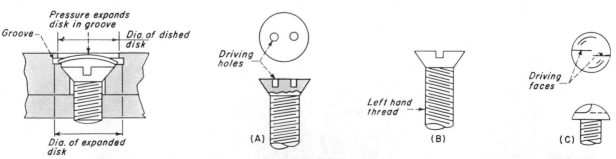

Fig. 3—Sheet-metal disk pressed into groove can only be removed with difficulty and discourages tampering.

Fig. 4—(A) Spanner-head screws are available in all standard heads and sizes from U.S. manufacturers. Special driver is required for each screw size except ¼-in. dia and above. (B) Left-hand screw thread is sometimes sufficient to prevent unauthorized loosening, or (C) special head lets screw be driven but not unscrewed.

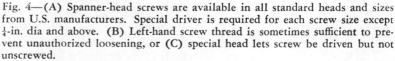

Fasteners

POSITIVELY RETAINED FASTENERS

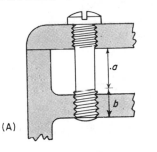

(A)

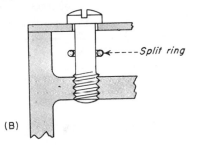

Split ring

(B)

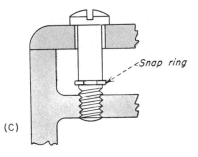

Snap ring

(C)

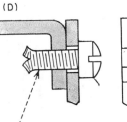

Pin

(D)

Fig. 5—(A) Tapped cover and casing allows screw (a > b) with reduced shank diameter to be completely unscrewed from casing yet retained positively in cover. For thin sheet-metal covers, split ring on reduced shank (B) is preferable. Snap ring in groove (C) or transverse pin (D) are effective on unreduced shank. Simple and cheap method (E) is fiber washer pushed over thread.

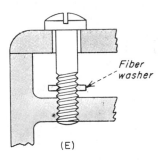

Fiber washer

(E)

Staked screw

Slot in sliding cover

Fig. 6—Open-ended slot in sliding cover allows screw end to be staked or burred so screw cannot be removed, once assembled.

Staked end

(A)

Binding-head screw

(B)

Tangential pin

(C)

Riveted but free to move

(D)

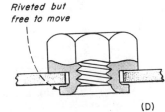

Fig. 7—(A) Nut is retained on screw by staking or similar method but, if removal of nut is occasionally necessary, coaxial binding-head screw (B) can be used. Where screw end must be flush with nut, pin through nut tangential to undercut screw (C) limits nut movement. Rotatable nut (D) or screw (E) should have sufficient lateral freedom to accommodate slight differences in location when two or more screws are used.

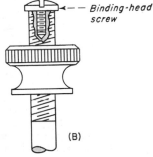

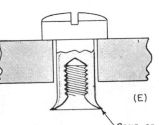

(E)

Spun or riveted over

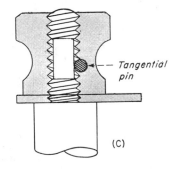

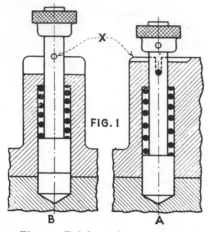

FIG. 1

Fig. 1—Driving plunger, shown in engagement at *A* is pulled out, and given a 90-deg. turn, pin *X* slipping into the shallow groove as shown at *B*, thus disengaging both members.

Many forms of detents are used for positioning gears, levers, belts, covers and similar parts. Most of these embody some form of spring in varying degrees of tension, the working end of the detent being hardened to prevent wear

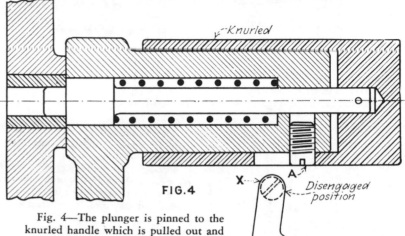

FIG. 4

Fig. 4—The plunger is pinned to the knurled handle which is pulled out and twisted, the screw *A* dropping into the locked position at *X* in the bayonet slot.

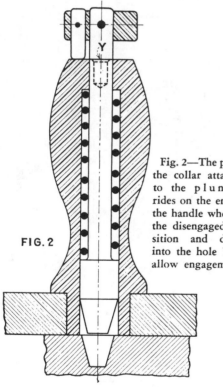

FIG. 2

Fig. 2—The pin in the collar attached to the plunger rides on the end of the handle when in the disengaged position and drops into the hole *Y* to allow engagement.

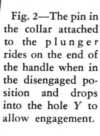

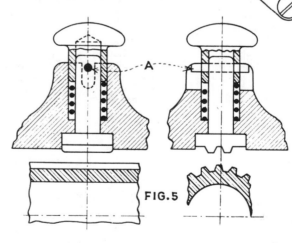

FIG. 5

Fig. 5—In this design, the pin *A* engaging in the slot prevents the plunger from turning. This detent is used as a temporary gear lock which is engaged for loosening a drawback rod through the gear.

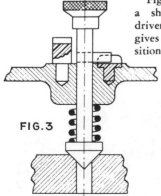

FIG. 3

Fig. 3—A long and a short slotted pin driven into the casting gives two plunger positions.

Fig. 6—An adjustable gear case cover lock. Pushing the door shut, it is automatically latched, while pulling out the knurled knob *A* disengages the latch.

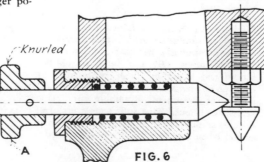

FIG. 6

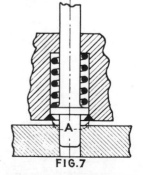

FIG. 7

Fig. 7—In this design the plunger is retained by staking or spinning over the hole at *A*.

Locking Detents

ADAM FREDERICKS

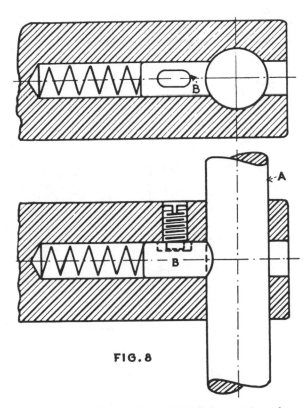

FIG. 8

Fig. 8—End of the plunger *B* bearing against the hand lever *A* is concaved and prevented from turning by the dog point setscrew engaging the splined slot. Friction is the only thing that holds the adjustable hand lever *A* in position.

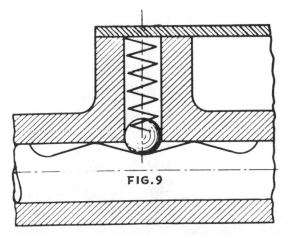

FIG. 9

Fig. 9—A spring-backed steel ball makes a cheap but efficient detent, the grooves in the rod having a long, easy riding angle. For economy, rejected or undersized balls can be purchased from manufacturers.

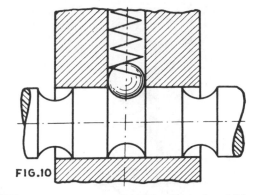

FIG. 10

Fig. 10—Another form in which the grooves are cut all around the rod, which is then free to turn to any position.

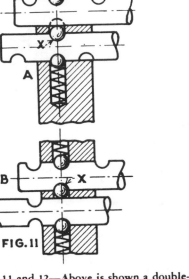

FIG. 11

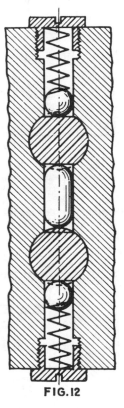

FIG. 12

Figs. 11 and 12—Above is shown a double-locking device for gear shift yoke rods. At *A* the neutral position is shown with ball *X* free in the hole. At *B* the lower rod is shifted, forcing ball *X* upwards, retaining the upper rod in a neutral position. The lower rod must also be in neutral position before the upper rod can be moved. To the right is shown a similar design wherein a rod with hemispherical ends is used in place of ball *X*.

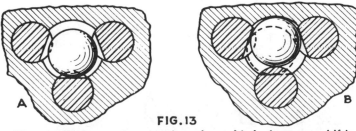

FIG. 13

Fig. 13—Without using a spring of any kind, three gear-shifting rods are locked by a large steel ball. At *A*, the neutral position is shown. At *B*, the lower rod has been shifted, forcing the ball upwards, thereby locking the other two rods. The dashed circle shows the position of the ball when the right-hand rod has been shifted.

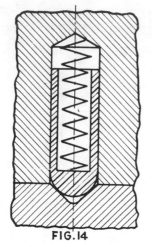

FIG. 14

Fig. 14—Instead of a ball, a hollow plunger is used which accommodates the spring. The end is hemispherical.

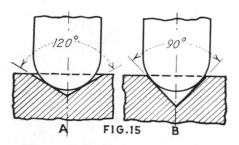

120°   90°

A   **FIG.15**   B

Fig. 15—At *A* is shown the usual 120 deg. conical spot made with a drill. At *B* is shown a 90-deg. spot which gives a more positive seat, one which will not permit the plunger to disengage as readily and which is preferable when considerable vibration is encountered.

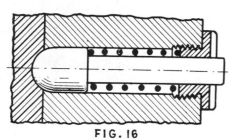

FIG. 16

Fig. 16—The plunger is turned down slightly smaller than the inside diameter of the spring which gets its other bearing against the threaded plug, the hole in the plug guiding the stem of the plunger.

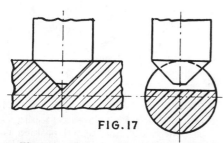

FIG. 17

Fig. 17—Instead of a hole, a slot is milled across the rod. The plunger being conical, it is obvious that only line contact is obtained.

Retaining and

ADAM FREDERICKS

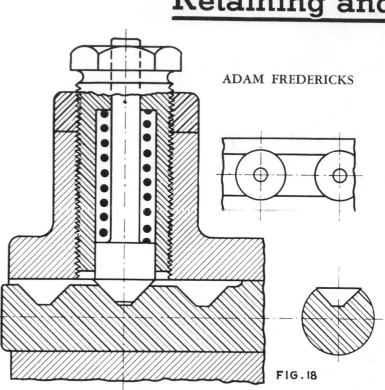

FIG. 18

Fig. 18—The spring tension may be increased or decreased as desired by the long hollow threaded plug, which is then locked in position by means of the check nut. In this design, the rod is flattened and the locating holes which are truncated cones in shape, are machined into the flat surface.

Fig. 19—Below to the left, the round plunger is flat milled to a 90-deg. included angle and prevented from turning by pin *A* engaging milled slots in the threaded plug. In the end view shown at *B* it can be seen that if the spring tension is to be adjusted, at least a half turn must be given in order that the flattened point will coincide with the slot in the rod.

Fig. 20 — When the plunger diameter and the wall thickness are sufficiently large, a keyway can be milled into the plunger for engaging a pin which prevents it from rotating.

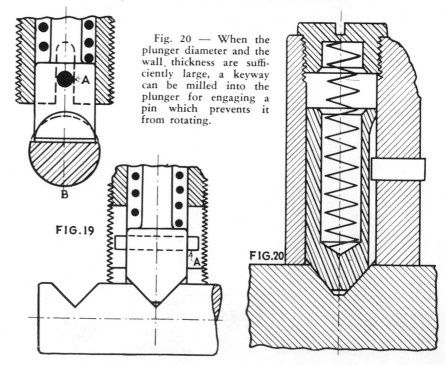

FIG.19

FIG.20

Locking Detents (continued)

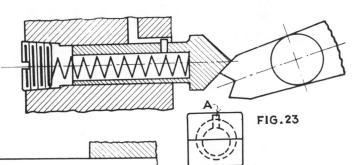

FIG. 23

Fig. 23 — Here is shown a square-headed plunger with its body turned round to accommodate the spring in an eccentric hole, thereby giving a support to the pin *A* which acts as a key.

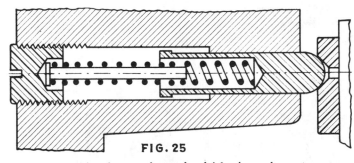

FIG. 24

Fig. 24—Probably one of the simplest yet **most highly efficient** forms of detent is merely a flat spring bent to a 90-deg. included angle and seating in Vees milled in the rod.

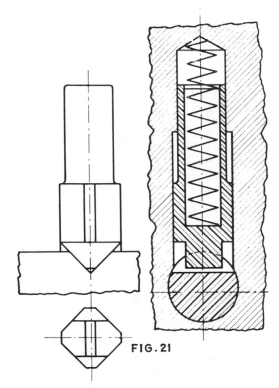

FIG. 21

Fig. 21—The plunger is milled square with round corners and the hole partially broached, doing away with the necessity of a key. The point is flat milled.

FIG. 25

Fig. 25—With a long spring and a fairly short plunger, a common flat-head wire nail can be used to support the spring against buckling. The spring also fits closely into the plunger hole to gain support and the plunger is flanged at its upper end to prevent its slipping through the hole.

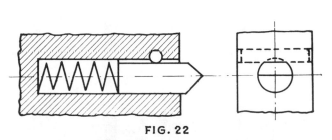

FIG. 22

Fig. 22—Sometimes the plunger can be milled with a flat which bears against a pin as shown in the end view to the right, thus preventing the plunger from turning in the hole, which design is particularly suitable for solid-type plungers.

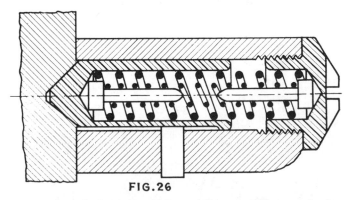

FIG. 26

Fig. 26—This design is similar to Fig. 20. When confined to a small diameter, a smaller spring is placed within the larger. Using a $\frac{9}{16}$ O.D. outer spring. 25 per cent spring tension can be gained by the addition of the inner spring. The larger one has a sliding fit in the plunger and screw plug holes. Two guide pins, the heads fittings closely into the larger spring, keep the inner spring central and free from buckling.

Flexure devices—for

Advantages: Often simpler, friction and wear are virtually nil, no lubrication.

Disadvantages: Limited movement, low force capacity.

JAMES F. MACHEN, Machen Products Company, Toledo

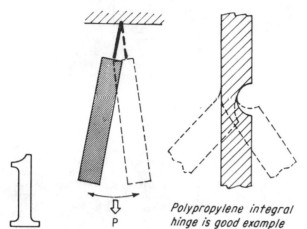

Polypropylene integral hinge is good example

1 BASIC FLEXURE connection (single-strip pivot) eliminates need for bearing in oscillatory linkages such as relay armatures

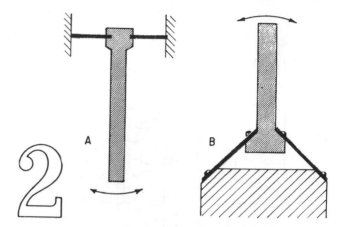

2 TWO EXAMPLES of two-strip pivots

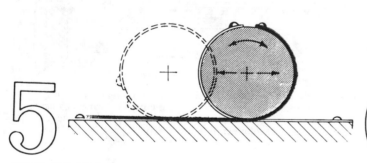

5 "RACK AND PINION" equivalent of rolling pivots

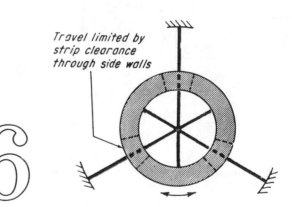

Travel limited by strip clearance through side walls

6 120° Y CROSS-STRIP pivot holds center location to provide frictionless bearing with angular spring rate

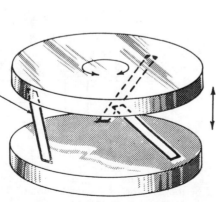

Three (or more) skewed strips spaced around circular disks at equal angles

9 SKEWED STRIP converts angular motion into linear motion or vice versa

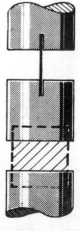

10 LIGHT-DUTY UNIVERSAL JOINT is ideal for many sealed instrument actions

economic action

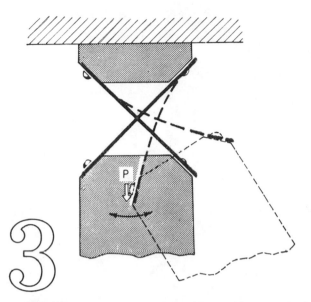

3 CROSS-STRIP PIVOT combines flexibility with some load-carrying capacity

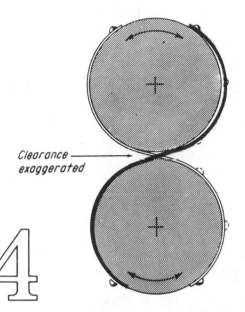

4 CROSS-STRIP ROLLING PIVOT maintains "geared" rolling contact between two cylinders — different diameters give "gear" ratio

Clearance exaggerated

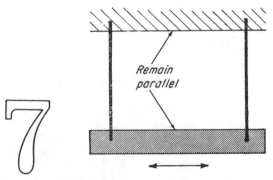

Remain parallel

7 PARALLEL-MOTION linkage has varying spacing

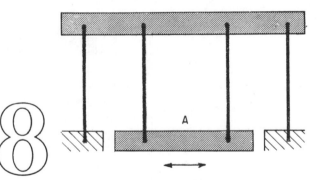

8 IN THIS PARALLEL-MOTION linkage, platform A remains level and its height does not change with sideways oscillation

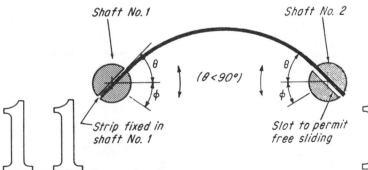

Shaft No.1   *Shaft No. 2*

$(\theta < 90°)$

Strip fixed in shaft No. 1   *Slot to permit free sliding*

11 FLEXURE TRANSMITS equal but opposite, low-torque, angular motion between parallel shafts

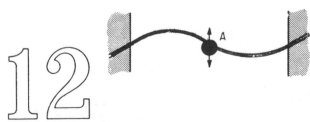

12 SINE SPRING, straight line mechanism lets point A move in approximately a straight line for short distances.

SELF-ADJUSTING WRENCH

A novel hand tool, a self-adjusting open-end wrench, is being made by HIPO-KG, Karolinenstrasse 3, Hamburg 6, West Germany. It looks like an ordinary wrench, except that its jaw is filled with spring steel leaves that will slide back into the body of the wrench under pressure. Thus, as the wrench is applied to the nut, the leaves give way to provide an opening exactly the size of the nut—and they hold the shape until released by the button at the base of the handle. HIPO says one wrench will handle nuts from about 0.04 to 0.80 in. dia (1 to 20 mm), and the leaves are only about 0.02 in. thick, so the fit is very close.

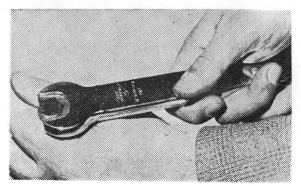

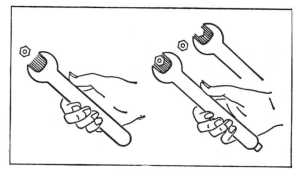

NEW ELECTRICAL CONNECTOR

Electrical connectors that attach without screws, nuts, or special tools and are "simple, reliable, robust, inexpensive, foolproof, noncorroding, and resistant to shock and vibration" are claimed by Kaye Tex Products Trust, Vaduz, Liechtenstein. All that's necessary, says Kaye Tex, is to insert the wire into the terminal. As the wire slides past the metal ball (see diagram) it is pressed against the conical sleeve and held as the ball rides forward on its spring. Any pull on the wire will jam the ball even more tightly into position. To remove the wire, just press down on the ball with a small pointed tool—a pin or toothpick will do the trick.

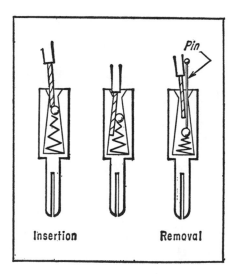

Insertion   Removal

6

ELECTRICAL COMPONENTS FOR AUTOMATIC CONTROL

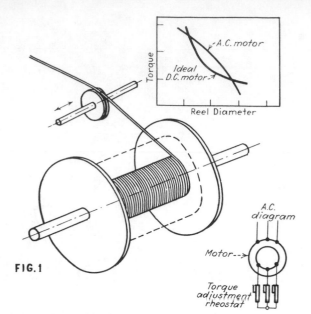

FIG.1

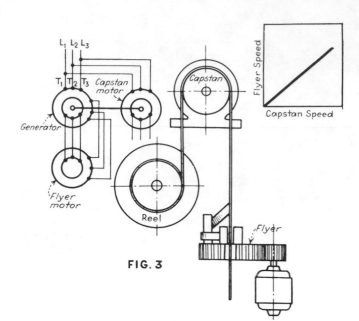

FIG. 3

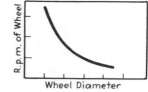

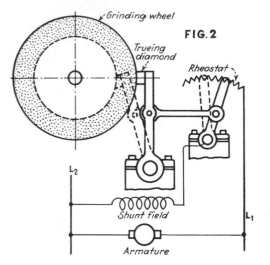

FIG.2

Methods of Electric Control—I

R. S. ELBERTY, JR.
Machinery Electrification Division
Westinghouse Electric & Manufacturing Company

How electrical controls can be applied to machinery for regulating peripheral speeds, rates of feed, controlling speed ratios, maintaining constant loads and for machine reversal

Fig. 1—Constant tension with constant peripheral speed is required in this wire reel application. The application can be used on wire drawing machines, insulating machines or any other reeling operation. As the reeling diameter increases, the reel speed decreases, and at the same time the reeling torque is increased. The required constant hp. characteristic is obtained accurately with a d.c. motor and regulator type of control on shunt field. An a.c. wound rotor motor with secondary resistance control approximates ideal conditions

Fig. 2—For automatically limiting the peripheral speed of a grinding wheel, the truing diamond is mechanically interlocked with the wheel motor field rheostat. The wheel r.p.m. is increased as the wheel diameter decreases.

Fig. 3—A wire insulating machine requires a constant speed ratio between capstan motor and flyer for starting and running. The capstan motor drives a frequency changer or transmitter electrically connected to the synchronous motor of the flyer. The speed ratio between flyer and capstan is constant at all times.

Fig. 4—For high-speed cutting on a metal planer, the tool enters the work at a slow speed to prevent tool breakage, cutting speed is then increased and near the end of the cut the cutting speed is reduced to prevent breaking out of edge of work. This speed control is accomplished by limit switches which put full field on the motor before the tool leaves work. After the return stroke de-

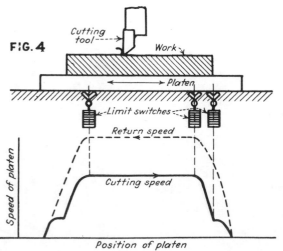

FIG. 4

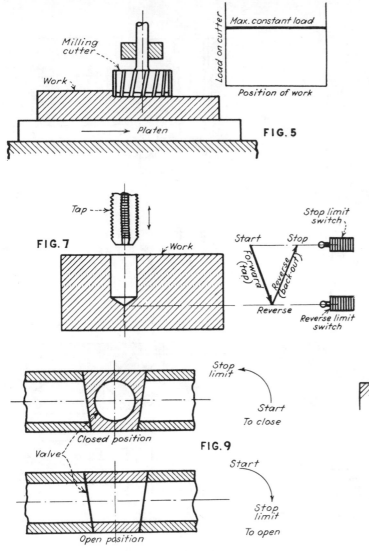

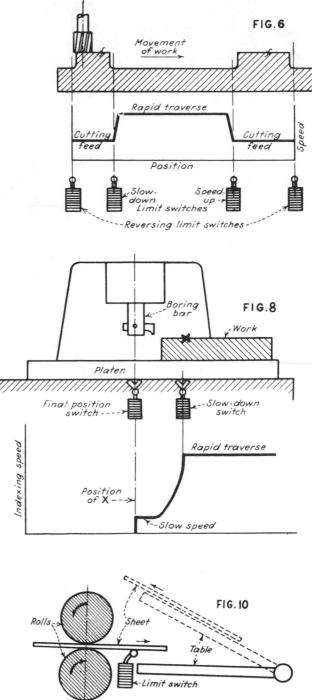

layed acceleration keeps full field on motor until tool enters work, upon which fast cutting speed is resumed.

Fig. 5—To keep load constant on the cutter and spindle of a milling machine for maximum production, a relay controlled by the armature circuit of the d.c. spindle motor regulates the field of d.c. feed motor. This automatically controls the feed within limits to maintain a maximum constant load on the spindle motor.

Fig. 6—When milling work having a gap between machined surfaces, production is increased by rapid traverse between machining positions. Jump feed control is accomplished by means of adjustable limit switches, multi-speed motors, and suitable magnetic controls.

Fig. 7—Accurate positioning of reversing and stop limits is necessary on tapping machines, especially when tapping blind holes. Special a.c. reversing motors for tapping service permit as many as 60 reversals per min. The use of two or four-speed motors reduces the number of gear changes required. Accurate limit switches, quick-acting contactors, and high torque motors are used. A plug stop is used for braking at the "out" position.

Fig. 8—Accurate location of boring tool for indexing requires extremely slow speed of work table to prevent over-travel when stop limit is reached. A d.c. motor

and control is used; heavy armature series resistance and armature parallel resistance provide for creep speeds for final positioning.

Fig. 9—For accurately stopping a slowly moving body, such as a rotary type valve, a geared switch is mounted on the motor, operating at motor speed. The motor can be stopped within one-fourth revolution and with a gear reduction of 100 to 1 between the motor and valve, the valve can be accurately located to within less than 1 degree.

Fig. 10—On a sheet catcher, the table must reverse and return the sheet as soon as it passes through the rolls. Since the length of the sheet varies, the sheet itself is used to operate the limit switch which reverses the table. This application requires specially designed motors and exceptional ruggedness in the control equipment.

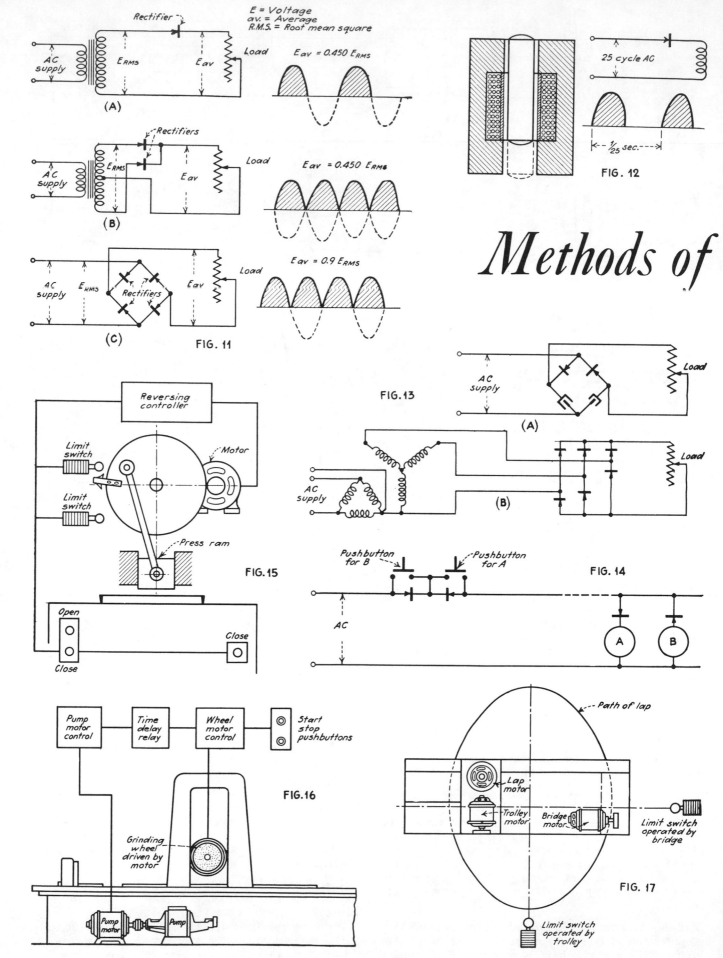

E = Voltage
av. = Average
R.M.S. = Root mean square

AC supply — Rectifier — E_{RMS} — E_{av} — Load

(A)

$E_{av} = 0.450\ E_{RMS}$

AC supply — Rectifiers — E_{RMS} — E_{av} — Load

(B)

$E_{av} = 0.450\ E_{RMS}$

AC supply — E_{RMS} — Rectifiers — E_{av} — Load

(C)

FIG. 11

$E_{av} = 0.9\ E_{RMS}$

25 cycle AC

$\frac{1}{25}$ sec.

FIG. 12

Methods of

FIG. 13

AC supply — Load

(A)

AC supply — Load

(B)

FIG. 14

Pushbutton for B   Pushbutton for A

AC

A   B

Reversing controller

Limit switch
Limit switch
Motor

Press ram

FIG. 15

Open
Close
Close
Close

Pump motor control — Time delay relay — Wheel motor control — Start stop pushbuttons

FIG. 16

Grinding wheel driven by motor

Pump motor   Pump

Path of lap

Lap motor
Trolley motor
Bridge motor

Limit switch operated by bridge

FIG. 17

Limit switch operated by trolley

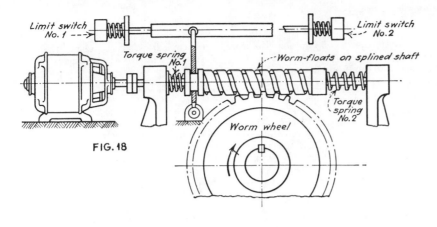

Limit switch No. 1 --

Limit switch No. 2

Torque spring No. 1

Worm-floats on splined shaft

Torque spring No. 2

Worm wheel

FIG. 18

Electric Control–II

R. S. ELBERTY, JR.
Machinery Electrification Division
Westinghouse Electric & Manufacturing Company

Fig. 11—Single-phase rectifier circuits generally used. (*A*) Half-wave rectifier circuit used in radio, also in industrial equipment such as vibrating machinery or electric razors, requiring reciprocating motion. (*B*) Full-wave rectifier circuit used in radio work and magnetic chucks. (*C*) Full-wave rectifier circuit used in industrial applications to obtain d.c. from a.c. source.

Fig. 12—Showing the use of a pulsating d.c. on a vibrating machine. In most instances, frequency of pulsations is important and on hammer shown, 25 cycle a.c. is used with a single-wave rectifier.

Fig. 13—Other rectifier circuits. (*A*) Single-phase voltage-doubler rectifier circuit used in radio work to obtain higher than line voltage without transformer. (*B*) A 3-phase, full-wave rectifier circuit, one type of rectifier used to obtain a large amount of d.c. power for power circuit.

Fig. 14—Illustrating the use of rectifiers in conjunction with magnetic control equipment on relays. Through the use of a rectifier in conjunction with d.c. relay, multiple control can be obtained over a single control circuit.

Fig. 15—Motor-operated press with safety control requiring operator to use both hands to start press. In starting, if either "close" button is released, the motor stops. To guard against blocking in one close button, the control is wired so that both close buttons must be fully released or press will not operate. Limit switches are used.

Fig. 16—Large grinders use pumps driven by separate motors. Pump motor need not be in operation when grinding wheel is not running but it is sometimes desirable to allow wheel motor to coast to rest before shutting down pump motor. This can be done electrically by means of time delay relay to permit pump motor to operate for predetermined time after wheel motor is shut down. For the starting sequence, an arrangement similar to that in Fig. 19 may be used.

Fig. 17—In a machine for polishing telescope mirrors, an elliptical motion of the polishing lap is sometimes required. Controls are arranged to reverse bridge motor at center of trolley motion; and to reverse trolley motor at center of bridge motion.

Fig. 18—Combination mechanical and electrical torque or load limiting device for control of motor-operated valves, chucks and clamps. When load becomes sufficiently high to stall wormwheel, the worm sliding on a splined shaft moves axially, similarly to a screw threading through a nut. This movement compresses a calibrated torque spring and opens a limit switch, thereby shutting off the motor.

Fig. 19—Electrical interlocking or sequencing of motors for large milling machine insures that coolant pump motor is running and pressure obtained before spindle motor starts, and that spindle motor is running before feed motor can be started. A master "stop" button dominates all controls.

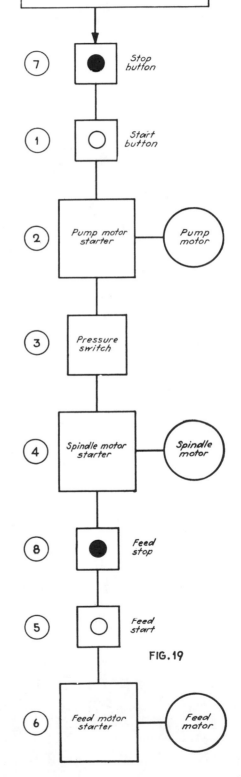

TABLE FOR SEQUENCE
OF OPERATIONS
1. Press start button
2. Pump motor starter closes
3. Pressure switch closes
4. Spindle motor starter closes
5. Press feed start button
6. Feed motor starter closes
7. Stop button stops all motors
8. Feed stop stops feed motor

7 — Stop button
1 — Start button
2 — Pump motor starter — Pump motor
3 — Pressure switch
4 — Spindle motor starter — Spindle motor
8 — Feed stop
5 — Feed start
6 — Feed motor starter — Feed motor

FIG. 19

POTENTIOMETER TYPES

POTENTIOMETERS are electromechanical devices that develop an electrical output signal proportional to the product of an electrical input signal and some function of shaft position.

Examples illustrated are typical of those used in machine tool application, test instrumentation, inspection devices and process control.

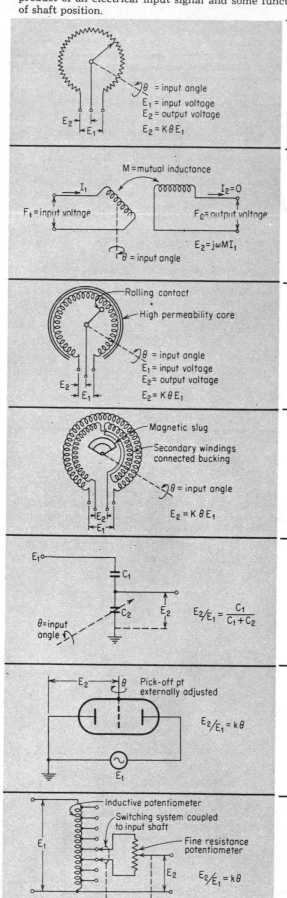

RESISTANCE POTENTIOMETERS — Resistance units use a sliding contact or wiper on a resistance element. It is a flexible component, ac or dc, operates to very high frequency ranges, introduces no distortion of the output signal, and can be manufactured to high accuracies at a relatively low cost. Its principal limitations are: limited life due to sliding contact, poor ratio of output to input impedance, and noise generation at the wiper.

INDUCTION POTENTIOMETERS — Operates by varying the mutual inductance between a primary coil and an output or secondary coil. The instrument is distinguished by exceptionally long life (hundreds of millions of cycles at speeds up to several thousand rpm). Resolution is infinite, and accuracies are comparable to resistance pots. It provides isolation between input and output. Its principal limitation is the expensive electronic auxiliary equipment required for phase correction and temperature and nonlinearity compensation. It has a low ratio of output to input impedance, and is not as load-sensitive as the resistance types.

INDUCTIVE POTENTIOMETERS—Essentially a variable auto-transformer, with a contact for varying the output tap point. Present units avoid a sliding action by using a rolling wiper. Life is somewhere between that of the resistance pot and the induction pot. The ratio of output impedance to input impedance is extremely low, high accuracies can be achieved even when heavily loaded. Properly designed units have practically infinite resolution, and thus are suitable for use in high-gain servo systems. Their principal limitation is their size, large in comparison with equally accurate resistance or induction pots.

RELUCTANCE POTENTIOMETERS—Mutual inductance of two coils is varied by moving a magnetic slug. The differential transformer, responding to linear-motion inputs, is a useful special variety of this unit. Since there is no contact with the rotor, the reluctance pot is simple, rugged, and long-lived. This, and the following types, are not as generally used as first three above.

CAPACITIVE POTENTIOMETERS — Capacitance is varied by an angular shaft motion. It is useful as a control element in high-frequency circuits. Used in computers for the generation of linear and nonlinear functions. Shielding is an important prerequisite to satisfactory operation.

DIELECTRIC POTENTIOMETERS—Operates by varying the position of a pickup point or tap in a current-carrying field. They are principally used on a-c because of ionization problems. The total resistance of a dielectric pot varies considerably with temperature. However, the accuracy of the tap voltage as a percentage of applied voltage can be held to very close tolerances. Infinite resolution and unlimited life are the two major features.

COMBINED TYPES—Many potentiometers are combinations of several types. A common form includes one potentiometer, suitably tapped, with a second, fine potentiometer interpolating between taps. Synchronized switching is required in this application. Accuracies of 0.003 per cent have been achieved this way.

POTENTIOMETER FUNCTIONS

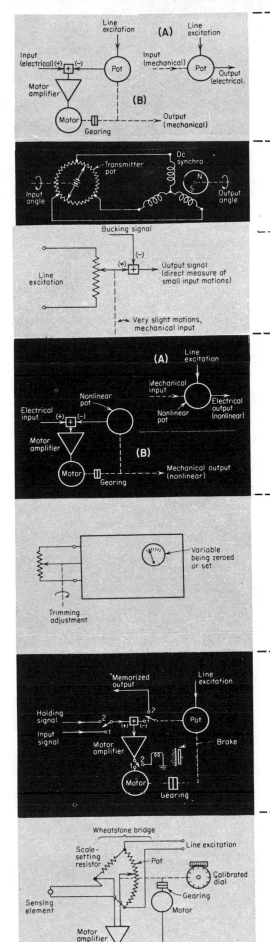

DATA CONVERSION — The electromechanical computer for analog computation and automatic control uses the potentiometer as a converter between shaft angle and electrical signal. (A) shows the mechanical to electrical conversion, and (B) the electrical to mechanical conversion. The accuracy must be sufficient to meet the requirements of the application, while resolution must be consistent with the stability requirements of the closed loop. Note also the possibility of multiplying or dividing with line excitation as one variable.

ANGLE TRANSMISSION — Since the potentiometer must do work in providing the energy for positioning the dc synchro, it must be capable of a large amount of heat dissipation. Inherently, open-loop systems of this type are not highly accurate. Frictional torque is apt to be appreciable since heavy contacts are required for current conduction. However, in the open-loop system, resolution is important only as it affects accuracy.

DETECTING SMALL MOTIONS — Potentiometers can be used to detect small motions in open- and closed-loop systems. Typical examples are pressure pick-ups, gyro pickups, accelerometers, and strain gages. Resolution and low noise level are principal factors, total resistance and accuracy less important.

FUNCTION GENERATION — A potentiometer can develop a nonlinear function of a mechanical or electrical input in addition to the normal straight-line characteristic. (A) and (B) show the mechanical-to-electrical and electrical-to-mechanical conversions, respectively. The requirements are similar to those for data conversion. Depending on the way the nonlinearity is developed, resolution may be a function of shaft position, in which case stability must be investigated under worst conditions. In (B), servomechanism stiffness can vary according to the potentiometer gradient. Adequate stiffness must be achieved under the sloppiest conditions, while at the same time stability must be maintained at the other high-gain extreme. Nonlinear servo techniques ease the design problem.

TRIMMING — Potentiometers can be used to make circuit adjustments where normal variations in the system cause shifts in calibration. Principal trimmer characteristics are precise maintenance of setting and adequate resolution to meet the finest adjustments required in an application. Where these units are used as variable resistance elements, rather than as straight voltage dividers, low-temperature coefficient and low contact resistance are necessary. Since trimmers are often used in electronic equipment, they are designed to operate at temperatures up to 350 F. Locking features are required to maintain the initial setting. Since accuracy is not a factor, they can be extremely small. Recent designs use metal films as the resistance element.

NULLING — In nulling circuits, a servomechanism positions a potentiometer so that it bucks out an input signal. Since precise nulling is important in a high-gain servo, resolution must be adequate if oscillation is to be avoided. The diagram shows a pot as a nulling device in a "memory" circuit. After the pot is positioned to balance the input signal, it may be locked in that position by a brake. Then the "memorized" output voltage may be switched to another circuit.

BALANCING — When used as a balancing device, potentiometer accuracy must be consistent with the requirements of the application. High resolution is also necessary because of the closed loop. Balancing-potentiometer shaft position is an indication of the quantity being measured.

POTENTIOMETER APPLICATIONS

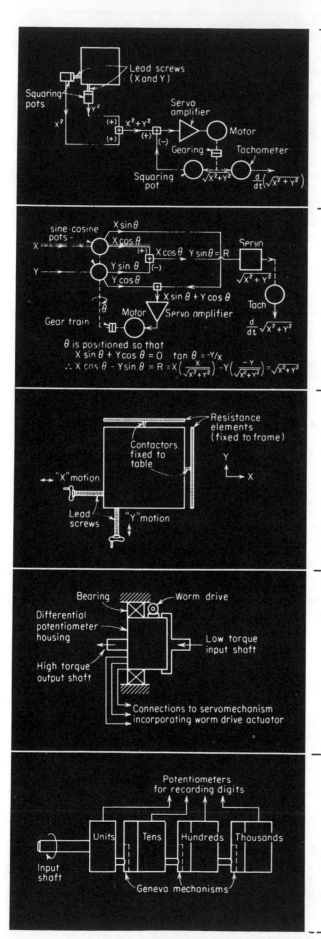

CIRCUIT FOR DETERMINING TANGENTIAL CUTTING SPEEDS—The table of a milling machine is oriented by the motion of X and Y leadscrews to permit cutting a contour, such as a plate cam. The assembly of components delivers an output voltage proportional to the tangential speed of the cam-cutting operation. The squaring potentiometer on the lead screws are function generators, with accuracy important but resolution not a problem. The potentiometer in the feedback loop is both a function generator and balancing device. Both high accuracy and high resolution are required. Servo has variable stiffness as noted in section on basic system functions.

ALTERNATE CIRCUIT FOR DETERMINING TANGENTIAL CUTTING SPEED —In this alternate computational method, two trigonometric function-generating potentiometers supply the nonlinear functions instead of the three squaring potentiometers in the previous diagram. Since they are both in the loop, resolution and accuracy are problems. Again, variable servo gain (depending on the magnitude of X and Y) is characteristic of this type system. An additional linear potentiometer is also required in the servo to convert the electrical signal, R, into a shaft rotation.

TABLE-POSITION INDICATION—Linear-motion potentiometers convert mechanical displacement to a proportional electrical signal. In this data-converting function, accuracy is the problem, not resolution.

TORQUE AMPLIFIER—Differential potentiometer used for torque amplification. Motion of low-torque input (wiper) shaft produces an output signal, which, amplified, actuates the worm drive and delivers a high torque output. Performs a nulling function; potentiometer accuracy and total resistance unimportant, resolution critical.

REVOLUTION COUNTER — Potentiometers for data conversion. The voltages from the four potentiometers indicate corresponding digits. In this application, the digital nature of the output minimizes potentiometer requirements in general.

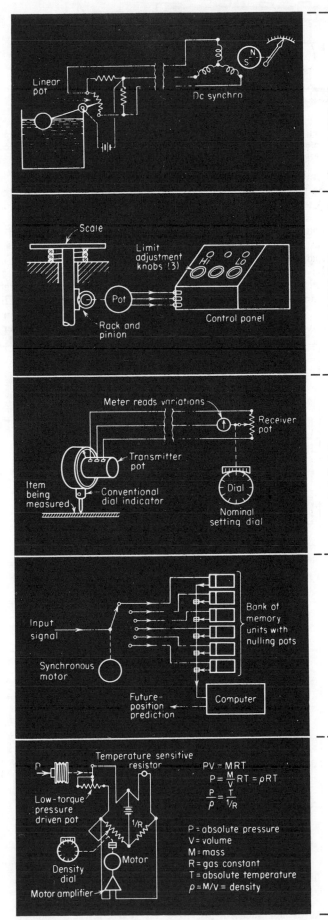

LIQUID-LEVEL INDICATION — Remote transmission of liquid level by means of potentiometer and dc synchro. The basic function is angle transmission. Resolution is unimportant, and accuracy better than a few tenths of a per cent is unnecessary due to friction and intrinsic system errors.

HI-LO WEIGHT INDICATOR — This arrangement is useful in repetitive industrial weighing operations. The potentiometers in the control panel, preset to required limits, buck the transmitting potentiometers coupled to the scale. Basic function is detecting small motions, so that the transmitting pot must have sufficient resolution to detect small variations from the present nominal weight. Total resistance and accuracy are less important.

THICKNESS GAGE — Potentiometer on conventional dial indicator simultaneously detects small motion variations, and remotely transmits them to an output meter. Transmitter pot must be of low-torque variety and have high accuracy. Accuracy of meter reading depends completely on accuracy of transmitting potentiometers. Receiving potentiometer is not critical.

MEMORY UNITS — Potentiometers, used here as memory units, serve as nulling devices. The input signal is switched in turn to the servo-actuated bucking potentiometers. These bucking potentiometers thus "remember" a uniformly spaced sequence of input signals, which, when applied to the computer, permit prediction of the input signal at some given future time. Accuracy and total resistance are unimportant, but resolution must be adequate to avoid servo instability.

AIR-DENSITY COMPUTER — Computer operates on the perfect gas law, uses two potentiometers as variable resistors. Bellows-driven potentiometer must be of low-torque variety and highly accurate. Balancing potentiometer coupled to the density dial must have good resolution to avoid closed-loop instability.

DIFFERENTIAL TRANSFORMERS

The differential transformer is used to measure small motions and has a linear variation of output with armature displacement. The power source is electrically isolated from the output circuit, with negligible phase shift throughout the operating range.

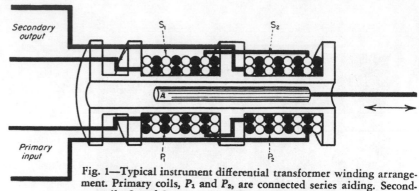

Fig. 1—Typical instrument differential transformer winding arrangement. Primary coils, P_1 and P_2, are connected series aiding. Secondary coils, S_1 and S_2, are connected series bucking.

A DIFFERENTIAL TRANSFORMER is a transducer that will generate an a-c signal directly proportional to the displacement of its armature from the electrical center of the transformer winding. It can be used where relatively small motions must be accurately measured, recorded, or controlled, and consists of two primary coils, two secondary coils, and an armature of magnetic material, Fig. 1. The primary coils are connected series aiding, and the secondary coils series bucking. The primary winding is energized from a suitable source of alternating current, and since the secondary coils are connected opposing their output voltages are 180 deg out of phase. The armature is located so that it can alter the relative flux distribution which exists between the primary windings and the two secondary coils.

Motion of the armature, A, toward secondary coil S_1 results in an increased output of one phase, and motion of A toward S_2 results in an increased output of the opposite phase. If S_1 and S_2 are identical coils and A is located so that each receives an equal amount of flux, the voltages induced in the secondary coils will be equal and out of phase and a theoretical output of zero will result. This condition denotes the null or balance point of the differential transformer.

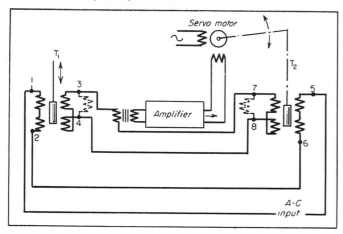

Fig. 2 (A)—Standard null type balancing circuit. At balance point outputs of T_1 and T_2 are equal and there is no input to amplifier. Displacing the armature of T_1 will cause a differential output which energizes the servo motor in the proper direction to rebalance system.

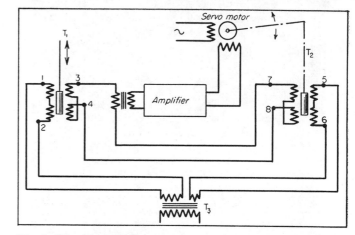

Fig 2 (B)—Two-winding supply transformer, T_3, changes range of transformers T_1 and T_2. Increased voltage input to T_1 and decreased input to T_2 cause servo motor to move further to balance movement of T_1 and thus increase sensitivity of system. Ratios of up to 40:1 are used.

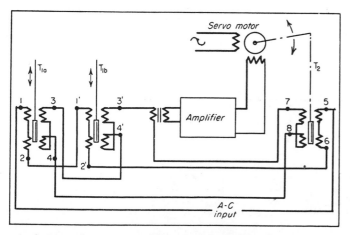

Fig 2 (C)—Algebraic summation circuit. When T_{1a} and T_{1b} are properly connected, the algebraic sum of their outputs is delivered to the input of balancing transformer T_2. The phase of this signal indicates the sign of the sum. The motion of armature T_2 is proportional to the sum.

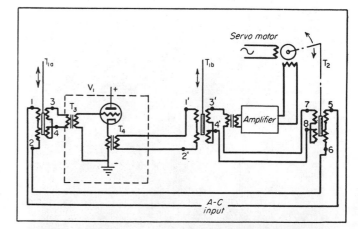

Fig. 2 (D)—Multiplication circuit in which outputs of transformers T_{1a} and T_{1b} are multiplied together to furnish input to balancing transformer, T_2. Since output of T_{1a} is not sufficient to drive T_{1b}, the electronic amplifier (dotted box) consisting of cathode follower must be used.

Differential Transformer Sensing Devices

W. D. MACGEORGE   Automatic Temperature Control Co.

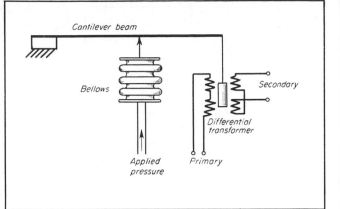

GAGE PRESSURE BELLOWS TRANSMITTER. Bellows is connected to cantilever beam with a needle bearing. Beam adopts a different position for every pressure; transformer output varies with beam position. Bellows are available for ranges from 0-10 in. to 0-200 in. of water for pressure indication or control.

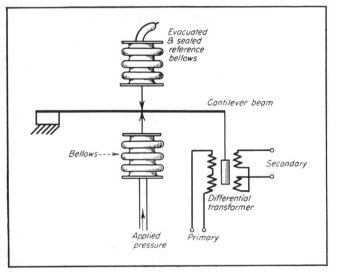

ABSOLUTE PRESSURE BELLOWS TRANSMITTER. Similar to above except for addition of reference bellows which is evacuated and sealed. Used for measuring negative gage pressures with ranges from 0-50 mm to 0-30 in. of mercury. Reference bellows compensates for variations in atmospheric pressure.

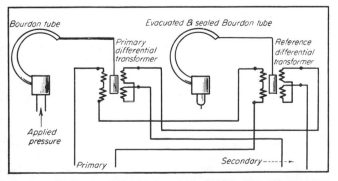

ABSOLUTE PRESSURE BOURDON TUBE TRANSMITTER. Device is used to indicate or control absolute pressures from 15 to 10,000 psi, depending on tube rating. Reference tube is evacuated and sealed, and compensates for variations in atmospheric pressure by changing output of reference differential transformer. Signal output consists of algebraic sum of outputs of primary and reference differential transformers.

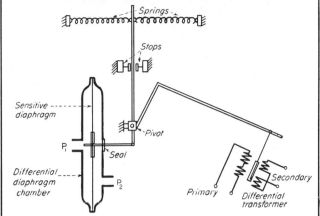

DIFFERENTIAL DIAPHRAGM PRESSURE TRANSMITTER. Differential pressures P_1 and P_2 act on opposite sides of sensitive diaphragm and move the diaphragm against the spring load. Diaphragm displacement, spring extension, and transformer core movement are proportional to difference in pressure. Device can be used to measure differentials as low as 0.005 in. of water. It can be used as the primary element in a differential pressure flow meter, or in a boiler windbox to furnace draft regulator.

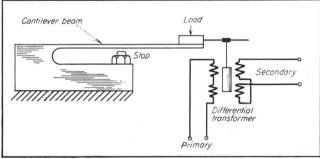

CANTILEVER LOAD CELL. Deflection of cantilever beam and displacement of differential transformer core are proportional to applied load. Stop prevents damage to beam in the event of overload. Beams are available for ranges from 0-5 to 0-500 pounds and can be used for the precise measurement of either tension or compression forces.

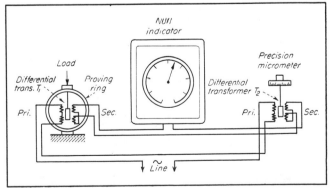

PROVING RING. The core of the transmitting transformer, T_1, is fastened to the top of the proving ring, while the windings are stationary. The proving ring and transformer core deflect in proportion to applied load. The signal output of the balancing transformer, T_2, opposes the output of T_1, so that at the balance point the null point indicator reads zero. The core of the balancing transformer is actuated by a calibrated micrometer screw which indicates the proving ring deflection when the differential transformer outputs are equal and balanced.

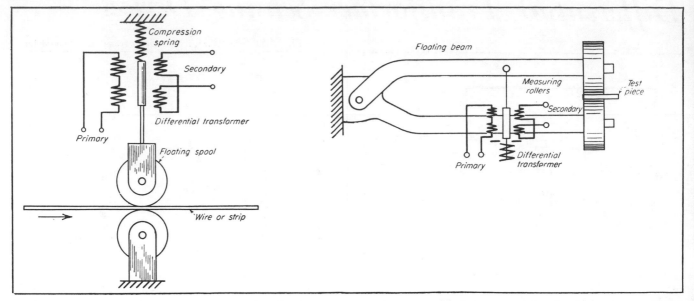

GAGING AND CALIPERING. Above, left, the thickness of a moving wire or strip is gaged by the position of the floating spool and transformer core. If the core is at the null point for proper material thickness, the transformer output phase and magnitude indicate whether the material is too thick or thin and the amount of the error. The signal may be amplified to operate a controller, recorder, or indicator. The device at the right can be used as a production caliper or as an accurate micrometer. If the transformer output is fed into a meter indicator with *go* and *no-go* bands, it is a convenient device for gaging items.

Typical Circuit Applications

PRESSURE COMPENSATED GAS FLOW METER (Right). Since all gases are compressible, a gas flow meter must either have a constant inlet pressure or else be compensated for variation in inlet pressure. This meter uses a circuit similar to the multiplication circuit, Fig. 3 (D), to compensate for variations in gas density caused by inlet pressure changes. The differential cell transmits a motion proportional to P_1 minus P_2 to the flow metering transformer. A signal is generated which is proportional to the square root of the flow and can be fed into a square root indicator. The input voltage to the flow metering transformer is controlled by the compensating transformer through the amplifier. The bellows pressure transmitter has a signal output proportional to inlet pressure, P_1, and consequently proportional to the density of the gas. Thus when properly calibrated, the meter will always indicate volume of gas flow at a specified reference pressure, regardless of inlet pressure.

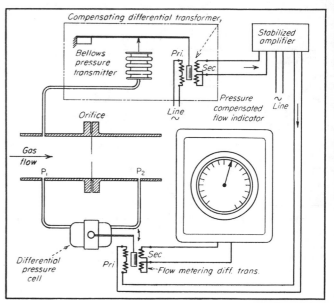

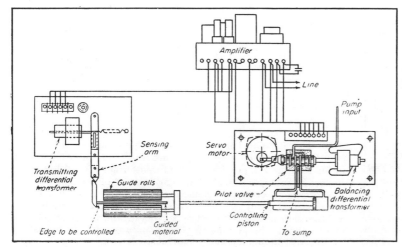

EDGE GUIDE CONTROL (Left). A null balance circuit, Fig. 3 (A), with a mechanical finger pickup and a servo controlled hydraulic system, positions guide rolls to keep processed material in register. Any motion of the sensing arm, which moves the core of the transmitting transformer, unbalances the circuit and causes the servo motor to move the pilot valve in the proper direction to bring the guided material back into register. The core of the balancing transformer moves with the pilot valve stem in a direction to rebalance the circuit so that the stem will only move a distance proportional to the amount the material is off register. Thus, the rate of correction will also vary with the amount of the error. With a 10:1 ratio on the sensing arm and a ¼ oz. force on the edge of the web, this system will position the material within 0.001 inch. The speed of an electrically transmitted signal is combined with the power of a hydraulic control system.

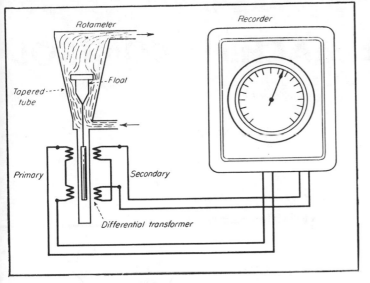

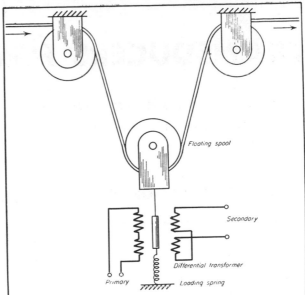

FLOW METER. The flow area varies as the float rises or falls in the tapered tube. High flows cause the float to rise, and low flows cause it to drop. The differential transformer core follows the float travel and generates an a-c signal which is fed into a square root recorder. A servo can be equipped with a square root cam to read on a linear chart. The transformer output can also be amplified and used to actuate a flow regulating valve so that the flow meter becomes the primary element in a flow controller. Normally meter has an accuracy of better than 2 percent, but the flow range is limited.

TENSION CONTROL. The loading spring is adjusted so that when the transformer core is at the null point, the proper tension is maintained in the wire. The amplified output of the transformer is transmitted to some type of tension controlling device which increases or reduces the tension in the wire depending on the phase and magnitude of the differential transformer signal.

AUTOMATIC TARE ADJUSTMENT WEIGHING SYSTEM. This scale uses a variation of the summation circuit, Fig. 3 (C), to automatically compensate for the tare weight of a container during a weighing operation. The secondary windings of the transmitting, weighing and tare-adjustment transformers are connected in series and feed into the amplifier. The amplifier output operates either the tare-adjustment or weighing servo through contacts RL2 and RL1 depending on whether relay RL is energized.

In the starting arrangement, the indicator arm contact is open since the scale indicator is at zero. The weigh push button also is open. Therefore, relay RL is deenergized and contact RL2 closed. When the empty container is placed on the scale, the transmitting transformer generates a signal proportional to the tare weight. The secondary winding circuit is unbalanced, and the tare-adjustment servo moves the core of its transformer an amount suf-

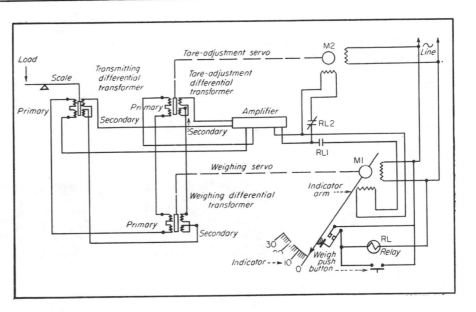

ficient to balance the output of the transmitting transformer. The weigh push button is then pressed, energizing RL which in turn opens RL2, closes RL1, and completes the circuit to the weighing servo. The tare-adjustment servo, being deenergized, remains in the tare position. When the material to be weighed is placed in the container on the scale, the secondary circuit is unbalanced again and must this time be rebalanced by the weighing transformer actuated by its servo. Since the zero adjustment of the system has been displaced by an amount equal to the signal output of the tare-adjustment transformer, the weight shown on the indicator is only that of the material and does not include the weight of the container. During the weighing operation the indicator arm contact closes as soon as the arm moves from zero and locks in RL so that it is not necessary to continue pressing the weigh button. At the completion of weighing, when the container and material are removed from the scale, the indicator arm drops to zero, the contact opens, and relay RL is deenergized. The circuit is completed through RL2 to the tare-adjustment servo and it runs to its zero position, placing the system in readiness for another weighing operation with all parts in their original position.

In order to maintain accuracy of weighing, the motion of the tare adjustment servo must be limited to a maximum of 10 percent of the full scale travel of the weighing servo. Thus the weight of the empty container must be no more than 10 percent of the maximum container weight.

EXTENSOMETER. Another interesting application of the differential transformer is its use as an indicating element in a creep measuring and recording system. In this case two transformers are attached to a test specimen, one on each side, in such a manner that the motion of the armatures is equal to the extension of the section under test. The output of the transformers are proportional to the strain on the opposite sides of the specimen. By combining the two signals in a variation of the summation type circuit, the average strain of the test section can be accurately obtained.

This type extensometer has the advantages that the strain can either be read from an indicating instrument, or the average output can be fed into a recording instrument and a continuous record of the test made available.

TRANSDUCERS FOR MACHINE CONTROL

Here are 40 ways to keep track of machine movement, or to establish position of an object.

FRANK YEAPLE, associate editor

ROTARY POSITION TRANSDUCERS

mechanical

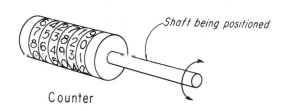

Counter

COUNTERS are the simplest digital visual-readout devices for shaft positioning. They are coupled or geared to the shaft and can have any desired resolution within the limits of the gearing. A counter has no error, but measuring systems using counters are usually limited to 0.0001 in. accuracy because of rack and gear tolerances.

variable induction

Rotary induction position transducers (and linear too) work on the same principle as transformers: Alternating current in one coil (the primary) induces alternating current in an adjacent coil (the secondary). In most position transducers the coils are mechanically separate—the induced secondary voltage vector varies with the physical position of the secondary winding rela-

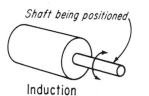

Induction

tive to the primary. This position can be deduced accurately with external electrical instruments. Examples of induction-type devices used as position transducers are: synchros, resolvers, induction potentiometers, differential transformers (here the coils are not separable), and the special linear transformers.

Either rotary or linear action is available in most types. For instance, a linear resolver is in effect a "stretched-out" rotary resolver. The accompanying brief discussion of individual types is based mostly on rotary transducers but also applies in general to linear.

variable resistance

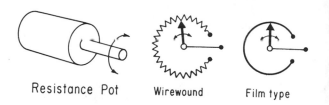

Resistance Pot   Wirewound   Film type

ROTARY POTENTIOMETERS, divide voltage in proportion to position of the sliding brush along the resistive element. (This also applies to linear pots, which are "stretched-out" versions of a rotary pot.) Pots are usually simple, will work on ac or dc, and are well understood. Costs range from a few dollars to several hundred—depending on design and accuracy. Accuracies can be in tenths of a percent of full travel. One problem with sliding-contact transducers of any type is wear—particularly if the slider hovers near a single point. For normal positioning applications, this is not a problem, because the device is not used constantly, and adjustments can be made to change the point of wear. Film-type pots are less sensitive to wear: the coatings are relatively thick; and damage at a single point will not open the circuit.

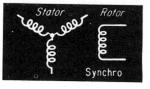

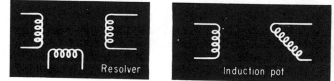

A SYNCHRO resembles a 3-phase motor, but its function is to produce an electrical output corresponding to the angular position of its shaft. This electrical output can be modified electrically and used as input to a servo element of any type, or can be fed to a second (repeater) synchro which moves its own shaft to correspond with the shaft position of the transmitting synchro.

RESOLVERS are similar to synchros — they "resolve" shaft angular position into electrical vectors. A resolver has two coils in the stator at right angles to one another; a synchro has three coils, 120° apart. They are functionally similar and the terms synchro and resolver are often used interchangeably. Typical cost is over $100, and electrical accuracy is in seconds of arc.

INDUCTION POTENTIOMETERS *(see PE—Aug. '54 p 130)* are single-phase resolvers with a voltage output that varies linearly with shaft position — at least for the 45° on either side of null.

SYNTHETIC TRANSMITTERS, called "digital transformer networks" often replace the rotating variety. Stepping relays (or the equivalent) select transformer taps, and the resulting voltage signal is identical (in phase and amplitude) to a hypothetical synchro or resolver output for a given shaft position. Such networks can be more accurate than the resolvers and synchros they replace.

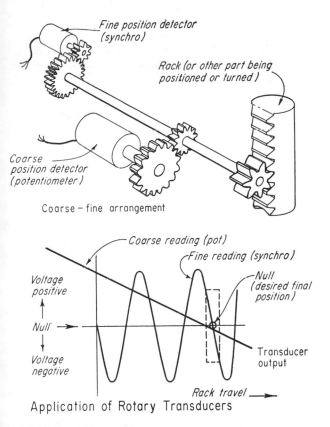

Fine position detector (synchro)

Rack (or other part being positioned or turned)

Coarse position detector (potentiometer)

Coarse – fine arrangement

Coarse reading (pot)

Fine reading (synchro)

Null (desired final position)

Voltage positive

Null

Voltage negative

Transducer output

Rack travel →

Application of Rotary Transducers

COARSE AND FINE ROTARY TRANSDUCERS are combined to increase range and improve accuracy of a positioning system. Synchro is the fine sensor and turns many revolutions for each pot revolution. Accompanying graph shows how voltage output of pot changes gradually while synchro passes through many complete voltage cycles. Pot output indicates rough position of rack but is not sensitive near null. An error-sensing control switches off the pot when the null is nearly reached, and the more sensitive synchro takes over for final positioning.

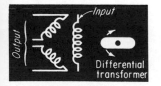

Output | Input

Differential transformer

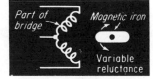

Part of bridge | Magnetic iron

Variable reluctance

DIFFERENTIAL TRANS-FORMERS are rotary or linear induction transducers that normally have a wound stator with three coils and a movable magnetic-iron core. In the rotary version, one stator coil (the primary) is energized with ac; there is inductive coupling with the two secondary stator windings via the iron rotor core, and output depends on rotor position. If the rotor is centered output is approximately zero. Output increases with the rotor movement—phase depending on direction. Typical cost for a rotary differential transformer is over $200 or $300.

VARIABLE - RELUCT-ANCE position transducers vary in output with rotor or plunger position because impedance of each coil leg is affected by the amount of magnetic iron in its ac field. They are not "induction" devices in the full sense, but they fit that category better than any other. Bridge circuits perform the readout. Costs are lower than for the differential type.

electrical digitizers and encoders ⎯⎯⎯

Digitizing means converting shaft rotation — an analog quantity—into distinct digital or pulse quantities. Encoders are digitizers whose outputs are in binary or decimal code. Digitizing is done with rotating disks that have discrete points built-in. These points can be holes, slots, gearteeth, magnetic spots, conductive areas, or any means of generating a pattern of pulses of light, electricity, or magnetism. Simplest example is the ordinary tap-switch: shaft rotation operates electrical contacts in sequence.

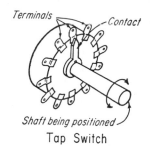

Terminals | Contact

Shaft being positioned

Tap Switch

Encoders

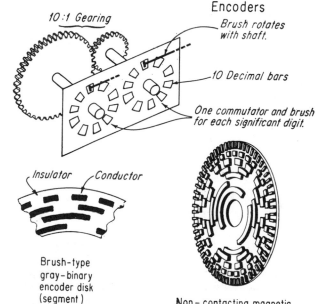

10:1 Gearing

Brush rotates with shaft.

10 Decimal bars

One commutator and brush for each significant digit.

Insulator | Conductor

Brush-type gray-binary encoder disk (segment)

Non–contacting magnetic encoder disk

BRUSH-TYPE ROTARY ENCODERS have electrically conductive and nonconductive areas arranged in a pattern on a disk. The pattern is in code (binary, decimal, binary-decimal, or gray scale). Although each type scale is important and different, most will resemble one of the sketches. The tracks (four are shown in the gray binary version) each have at least one brush, and the electrical circuit is completed through the brush when it contacts a conductive area. Either the brush or disk will rotate with shaft. Note that there is a different pattern at each angular position of the coded disk. With gearing and multiple disks, half a million discrete indications can be generated in a single revolution of the main shaft.

Brush wear is a problem, but most encoders are only operated part of the time. Typical life is 500 to 2000 hr at speeds of a few hundred rpm. Costs range from over $100 to about $3000, depending on the number of disks.

NON-CONTACTING-MAGNETIC ROTARY ENCODERS are similar to the brush-type in appearance and operation. However, instead of "brushes" the pickups are magnetic

continued next page

coils, and the disk is magnetic material etched or machined with coded pattern. The impedance of the sensing head changes when a machined-out portion of the scale is underneath. Costs are similar to those for brush-type encoders, but size is many times larger and the readout circuitry is not as simple. Life is longer—typical is 10,000 hr at 10,000 rpm—because there is no physical contact.

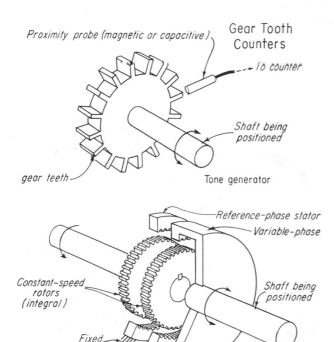

Gear Tooth Counters

Proximity probe (magnetic or capacitive)

To counter

Shaft being positioned

gear teeth

Tone generator

Reference-phase stator

Variable-phase

Constant-speed rotors (integral)

Shaft being positioned

Fixed

Phase-shift angle encoder

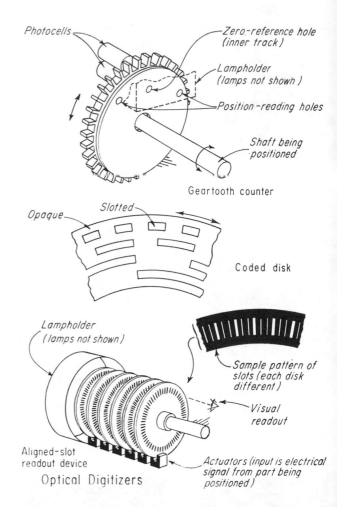

Photocells

Zero-reference hole (inner track)

Lampholder (lamps not shown)

Position-reading holes

Shaft being positioned

Geartooth counter

Opaque

Slotted

Coded disk

Lampholder (lamps not shown)

Sample pattern of slots (each disk different)

Visual readout

Aligned-slot readout device

Optical Digitizers

Actuators (input is electrical signal from part being positioned)

MAGNETIC-IMPEDANCE GEAR-TOOTH COUNTERS need no motion to detect presence or absence of a tooth. Magnetic heads sense impedance change when tooth is under head; external electronic counters keep track of teeth, number of revolutions, and direction of rotation. Number of teeth determines resolution—500 to 1000 teeth are typical. Speeds to 2400 rpm are not unusual.

CAPACITIVE GEAR-TOOTH COUNTER is an electrostatic tone generator that senses a change in capacitance as each tooth goes by. A thousand teeth are not unusual. The dual-gear (phase-shift) version works on the same principle. Theory is this: the two gears on the constant-speed shaft are integral, and each generates a constant-frequency signal in its associated stator. But the variable-phase stator is free to take any angular position relative to the reference stator, and the electrical phase of its signal will depend on this position. Phase difference between the variable and reference stators is a measure of angular displacement. One problem: there is a full 360-deg relative phase change each time the shaft angular displacement moves through one tooth pitch with no way to distinguish one cycle from the next. To allow measurements greater than one tooth pitch, one tooth is left out of each gear and ring—the "missing tooth" causes a discrete pip each revolution.

OPTICAL SHAFT DIGITIZERS are opaque disks with holes or slots to pass light. A small section on one face of the disk is illuminated, and photocells detect the presence (or absence) of a slot. The disks can be simple toothed gears, optical gratings (10,000 radial lines on a 10-in. disk), drilled plates, or printed patterns on optical-glass disks in a complicated array of decimal or binary-coded slots that give thousands of discrete indications (in code) per revolution.

Unusual **visual-readout** device is shown in the sketch: a sliver of light is transmitted through aligned slots (only one group can line up at a time) thus illuminating a dial face at the appropriate position with a pointer of light. Interesting fact is this: each disk has only two positions —de-energized, and about 1/3 deg (about 1/1000 rev) from the de-energized position. Electrical actuators (controlled by signal from a commutator on the remote shaft being positioned) select which disks will move, and 512 discrete dial indications are possible with only 9 disks.

special rotary devices

ELECTROSTATIC-COUPLING between the stationary driver disk and rotating coupler disk produces an electrical output that is a function of their relative angular displacement. Input voltage is applied to the conductive areas on the stationary disk (those areas above and below the sine waves); the resulting fields of potential are electrostatically coupled to the stationary output conductive rings via the conductive pattern on the rotating disk. The output is a voltage vector that always has the same amplitude but varies in phase with angular position of the rotating disk. (This is done with a 4-phase input whose effective amplitiude sum at the output is a constant.) Because phase is measured instead of voltage, voltage variations in the supply line will have negligible effect on accuracy. Final readout, with the help of external circuitry, can be in any desired form—analog or digital. Typical costs are over $15,000 but devices can be accurate to seconds of arc.

STRAIN-GAGE BRIDGE CIRCUIT on a torsion shaft indicates angular deflection as a strain reading. Angular deflections to 60° are possible (with torques less than 16 oz-in.) and typical terminal linearity is ±½%.

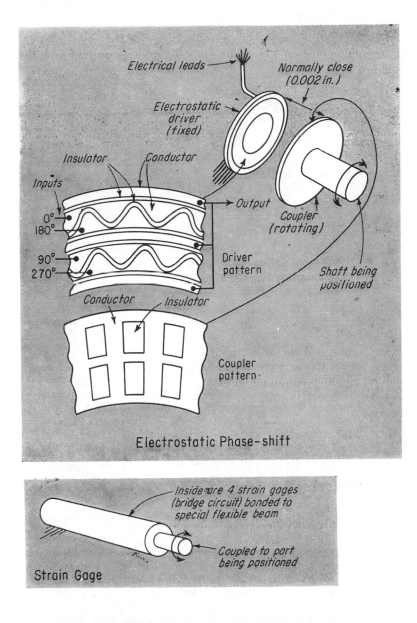

Electrostatic Phase-shift

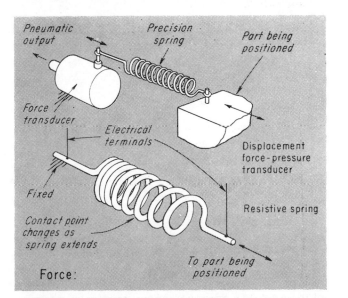

Strain Gage

special linear devices

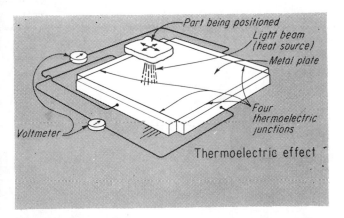

Thermoelectric effect

THERMOELECTRIC position sensor has four sensitive junctions capable of detecting the heat (from a beam of light) absorbed by a metal plate. Voltmeter signals depends on relative closeness of the heat spot to each edge

Force:

EXTENSION SPRING measures position indirectly when a force transducer senses spring tension or when the spring is electrically resistive and contact point changes with movement.

continued next page

mechanical_____

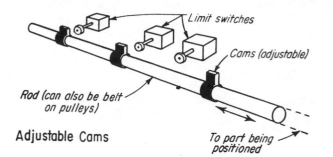

Adjustable Cams

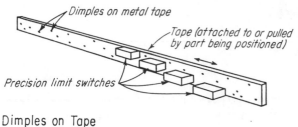

Dimples on Tape

ADJUSTABLE CAMS AND LIMIT SWITCHES signal the control when the desired linear position is reached. For most applications six positions are sufficient, and accuracy can be about 0.005 in.

DIMPLED METAL TAPE instead of adjustable cams operate precision limit switches to signal the control. Accuracy is good—about 0.001-in. repeatability is claimed possible (depends on switch accuracy).

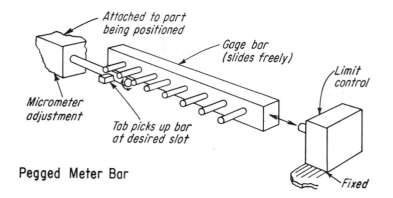

Pegged Meter Bar

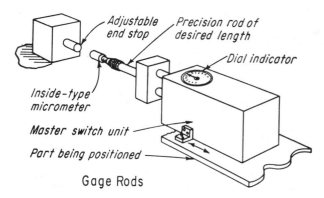

Gage Rods

SPACED PRECISION PINS in a meter bar insure accurate "coarse" positioning; an auxiliary device (it can be of any type) interpolates between the pins for "fine" positioning. For example, a star-wheel can move into mesh with any preselected pin, driving a rotary potentiometer or a linear resolver. Or a micrometer-adjusted tab (pictured) can pick up a pin on the meter bar at just the right point, carrying the bar along until it hits the limit switch.

MECHANICAL GAGING is one of the basic ways to measure or preset length or position. Accuracy is limited only by the gage blocks or rods. Some machines automatically place the gage blocks in position at a signal from the control—but it takes a lot of blocks. Others (sketch above) have a limited selection of manually inserted gage rods, with a special micrometer adjustment for in-between settings.

resistance _____

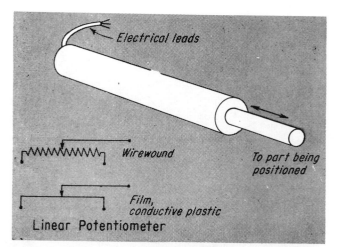

Linear Potentiometer

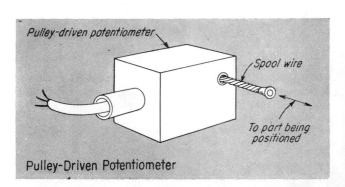

Pulley-Driven Potentiometer

LINEAR POTS are stretched-out versions of rotary pots —the sketches show how they are built. Some are 10 to 15 ft long. Typical positioning accuracy for precision types is in tenths of a percent full scale or better.

PULLEY-DRIVEN POT has a wire or cord wound on a constant-force spring-loaded pulley—similar to the return pulley on a typewriter. As the cord is extended it rotates the potentiometer shaft.

DIAL INDICATOR with a built-in pot (pot shaft carries the pointer) is another way to get linear measurements with a rotary device.

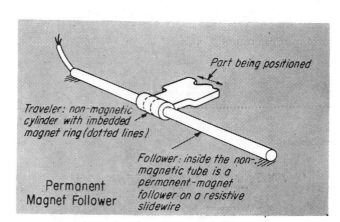

PERMANENT-MAGNET inside a non-magnetic tube slides along a resistance wire (part of an electrical bridge circuit) in response to movement of the external magnet-ring traveler. Position reading can be direct (voltage unbalance corresponds with traveler position) or nulled (servo-balanced bridge). Supply can be 115 v, 60 cycle ac. Transducers of this type can be submerged in water because the coupling is magnetic and the tube is hermetically sealed. One application is for measuring liquid level in tanks. Typical accuracy is about 0.25 in.

commutator ————————————

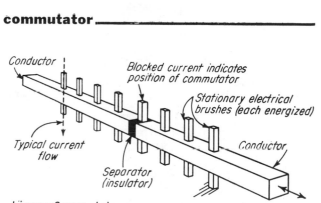

LINEAR COMMUTATOR depends on interruption of electrical current to indicate position—the insulating spacer does it. Or the spacer can be the conductor, the long bars the insulators; then current flow indicates position.

induction ————————————

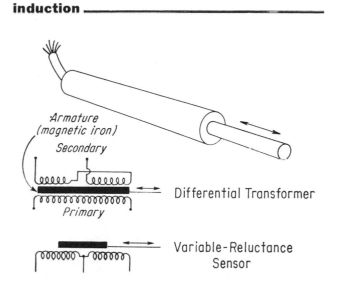

LINEAR INDUCTION TRANSDUCERS are analog devices; sensing depends on voltages and nulls. Discussion on rotary types applies to linear too.

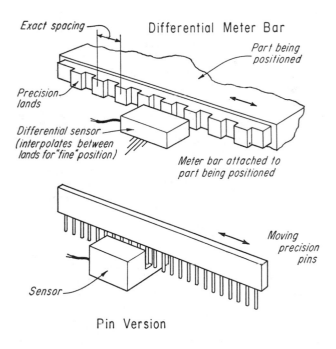

Pin Version

INDUCTION-SENSED METER BAR has precision lands (or pins) accurately spaced. A variable-reluctance sensor or some similar device nulls at dead-center on each land with accuracies of about 0.0001 in. For interpolation between lands the transformer position can be adjusted with a micrometer, an electrical null shifter or by any suitable precision control. Auxiliary coarse controls are needed to guide moving part to proper land.

continued next page

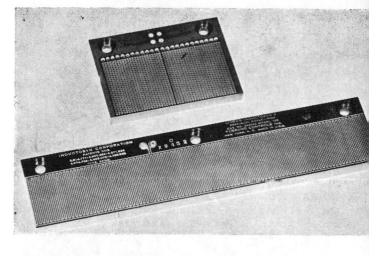

SYMMETRICAL LINEAR RESOLVER has flat slider and scale, with the coils printed on in the form of hairpins. (The principles are the same as those for ordinary wound induction coils). The slider-coil pattern matches the scale-coil pattern, and a full cycle of voltage occurs each time the relative position changes by one coil. Position to within about 0.0001 in. is determined by sensing electrical null, and null can be offset electrically to occur at any point between two coils (interpolation). Medium and rough positioning to locate a given coil and a given scale section can be accomplished in two ways: with a slidewire, potentiometer, or synchro coupled or geared to the part being positioned; or with special coarse scales on the linear transformer itself. The coarse scales have wider-spaced divisions—up to 400 in. apart if necessary.

VERNIER LINEAR RESOLVER is also a hairpin coil transducer and is similar to the symmetrical version except that the slider does not have exactly the same pattern as the scale it slides along. Although the slider hairpin coils are the same width as those on the scale, they are spaced 0.001 in. closer. This 0.001 in. accumulates so if there are 25 coils in the slider, the total difference is 0.025 in. compared with the length of 25 similar coils on the scale. By selecting particular slider coils, you can find nulls every 0.001 in. Interpolation between nulls gives resolution of about 0.0001 in., accuracies of about 0.0005 in., repeatability of about 0.0001 in. Coarse positioning elements such as rotary resolvers bring the part within less than 1/16 in. of final position before the final control takes over.

PERMANENT-MAGNET-POLE SCALE and inductive sensor detect position of a part by comparing phase angle of alternating current induced in pickup coil with an identical-frequency reference ac in the command control (not shown). Poles in scale magnetize this path: pole to screw land, through pickup coil, back to scale. A fluctuating field is needed to generate the current in pickup, so synchronous motor turns screw to cyclically vary the magnetic impedance (the screw action moves lands from one pole to next continuously). Pickup coil then generates ac. If sensing assembly is stationary, the

SYMMETRICAL LINEAR RESOLVER depends on transformer effect: plated hairpin "coils" on one scale are electrically energized with ac, and signal is induced in coils of opposing scale.

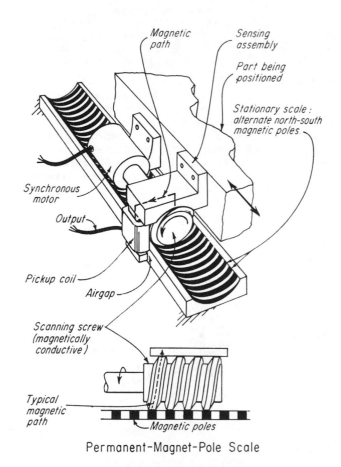

Permanent-Magnet-Pole Scale

ac will have a fixed phase relationship with the command reference signal (external). But if the sensor moves to a new position, the phase relationship will be different, and this difference indicates the position change. (It is position and not movement that does it.) Device can detect part movement of less than 0.000,15 in.

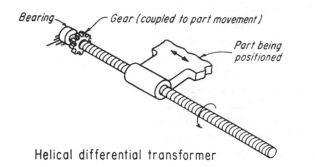

Bearing
Gear (coupled to part movement)
Part being positioned

Helical differential transformer

HELICAL DIFFERENTIAL TRANSFORMER has a cylindrical bar with a double thread cut into the surface for the primary winding (winding is bifilar with both terminals emerging via sliprings at one end of the rod). The secondary winding (in the sliding sleeve) is also bifilar and matches the primary. The part being positioned carries the sleeve, and also rotates the cylindrical bar (with gearing): One turn of the bar is equivalent to a slider movement of one coil, and serves as an interpolation between nulls. Resolvers or induction potentiometers coupled to the bar help measure angular rotation precisely and establish which turn of the long winding is under the sleeve (coarse setting). Final accuracy depends on coil spacing and ability of slider to detect the electrical "null" preset by the control (fine setting). Accuracy can be 0.0001 in., repeatability 0.000,05 in.

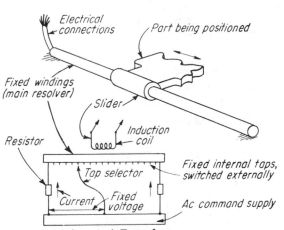

Electrical connections
Part being positioned
Fixed windings (main resolver)
Slider
Induction coil
Resistor
Tap selector
Current
Fixed voltage
Fixed internal taps, switched externally
Ac command supply

Tapped Differential Transformer

TAPPED DIFFERENTIAL TRANSFORMER primary is a continuous coil with precisely spaced internal taps connected to external switches which select the desired tap. If slider (the secondary) is not centered over a chosen tap, a voltage is induced in it proportional to the direction and amplitude of the displacement (position error). As the slider approaches the tap, voltage approaches zero. Points between taps are preset or located by biasing the null voltage with the control. Accuracy is about 0.001 in., repeatability about 0.0005 in.

optical

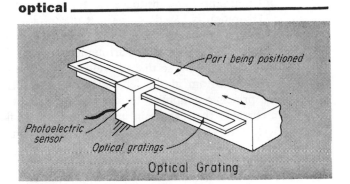

Part being positioned
Photoelectric sensor
Optical gratings
Optical Grating

LINEAR OPTICAL GRATINGS are fine rulings on a glass plate (up to 6350 lines per in. are available). Two such plates superimposed but slightly askew will show a fringe pattern of light when a lamp is held behind them. If one plate is moved along the other, the fringes move transversely with greatly magnified movement (each fringe moves completely past a given point with a plate forward movement of a single grating line). Photocells help count the fringes, and resolutions of 0.0001 in. are practical.

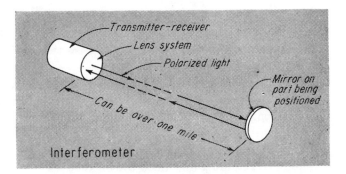

Transmitter-receiver
Lens system
Polarized light
Mirror on part being positioned
Can be over one mile
Interferometer

LIGHT-BEAM INTERFEROMETER aims a narrow beam of light at a mirror attached to the object whose distance is being measured. The reflected beam is compared with the outgoing beam by measuring phase shift of the modulated light waves. Phase shift is zero if the total distance is an integral number of wavelengths (plus a constant). For in-between distances, the instrument can interpolate between nulls with accuracies of a few centimeters at distances of hundreds of yards. Recent developments (*PE—July 3, '61, p 5*) of optical masers (microwave amplification by stimulated emission of radiation) have produced extremely precise light beams that are narrow and have a pure waveform—important in long-distance optical measurements.

NEW TRANSDUCER DEVICES

A low-cost transducer that uses closed-cell expanded rubber or foamed plastic as its operating mechanism has been designed at Scovill Mfg Co, Waterbury 20, Conn. Its first application: a pressure gage for automobile tires. Here, it offers the performance advantage of being independent of altitude and the sales advantage of being simple and inexpensive. It's cheap enough to be used as a promotion item.

Operation is based on the fact that a closed-cell expanded elastomer immersed in a fluid or gas will increase or decrease in volume in response to changes in the pressure of the medium surrounding it, and the response will be in accordance with Boyle's Law, so that the value of pressure times volume will be a constant.

The diagram at the left below, from a British patent to Scovill, shows how the principle is applied to a pressure-regulator valve. The unit consists simply of a chamber that can be inserted in the fluid flow line. The chamber is equipped with a valve and contains a block of the foamed material, held between pressure

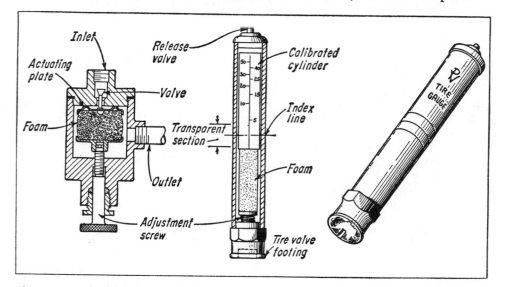

plates, one of which is attached to the inlet valve. As the pressure increases, the elastomer shrinks in all directions, pulling the valve down and automatically shutting off the flow. By adjusting chamber size and the size and characteristics of the foam, and making use of the adjusting screw, it is possible to set the unit for any desired outlet pressure.

The tire gage, which Scovill calls a PV gage, is sketched center and right. As the unit is fully enclosed, and connects only to the air in the tire itself, it will give a true reading regardless of outside pressure. This is why it is independent of altitude. Furthermore, it's small, light in weight, and poses no special sealing problems.

An optical transducer for pressure measurements that's said to achieve marked improvements in performance, reliability, and ruggedness has been designed by Northrop Corp's Ventura Div.

It's another light beam-and-photocell device (PE— Dec 7 '64, p 86) in which the light beam is directed at the photocells through a movable shutter (see diagram).

As outside pressures are sensed (by either a diaphragm or aneroid capsule), the shutter is deflected, thereby altering the light intensity falling on the photocells and, in turn, causing a change in resistance which is converted into electrical output.

One advantage of this "optical bridge" technique, Northrop says, is that the transfer of information between input and output is achieved without amplifiers or associated electronics. Fewer parts are needed

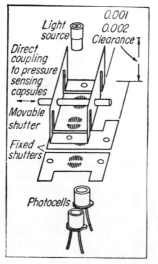

An electromechanical transducer for fluid pressure measurements that takes advantage of the fact that conventional rod-type resistance elements will vary in electrical resistance under an applied pressure has been designed and patented in England by Coutant Electronics Ltd, Richfield, Reading, Berkshire.

The transducer consists of a cylindrical body containing a grooved piston-like element carrying an O-ring seal. This divides the body into two chambers (see upper diagram), each containing a resistance element. The upper chamber is filled with fluid under pressure; the lower is at atmospheric pressure. (The dual-chamber system is not essential, but helps to minimize the effects on temperature variations; and the two chambers may both be under pressure if desired, one by a calibrated amount.)

Electrical connections from the resistance elements are brought out through the plug in the lower chamber and connected to a conventional bridge network (lower diagram). Then, changes in the resistance of the upper element resulting from changes in fluid pressure can be indicated on a calibrated instrument.

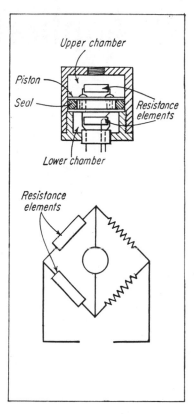

J. S. Dean of Sanderstead, the inventor, claims the advantage of the system is its wide working range as compared with diaphragm-type pressure sensors, and the fact that it is simple and economical to manufacture.

A magnetoelectric transducer that converts dc voltages or current input signals into high-frequency voltage is described in USSR Author's certificate 119,924. The inventors say it can accept either electrical or mechanical inputs, and may be applied as a zero indicator in automatic control systems or as a rotary transformer in computers.

It consists of two moving coils mounted on the same shaft. One is a galvanometer coil, with its loop located in the field of a permanent magnet. The second coil is located in a high-frequency field created by stationary coils which also operate as an inductance in the tank circuit of an hf oscillator.

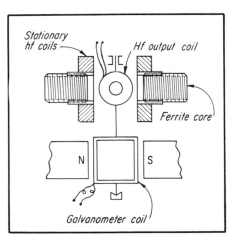

When an input signal is supplied to the device, the moving coils are angularly displaced and a high-frequency voltage is produced. Magnitude of this voltage is proportional to the angle of rotation.

The Soviets claim the device has an unusually high conversion factor (3.1 v/degree at 220 kc with 1200 turns on the hf output coil and an effective voltage of 10 v on the oscillator circuit); also that the circuit is unusually stable.

An article describing the device appeared in *Priborostroyeniye*; No 9, 1960; and a one-page abstract, in English, may be found in *Current Review of the Soviet Technical Press*, 21441-28, available from OTS, Dept of Commerce, Washington 25, DC.

6 Applications of Ultrasonic

They will:

- **clean**
- **drill**
- **solder**
- **weld**
- **test and measure**

Certain materials undergo a reversible change when subjected to magnetic or electric fields, and thus can serve as transducers for high-frequency vibrations. Cobalt and nickel are magnetostrictive (Jan. '57, p. 162); barium-titanate ceramic is electrostrictive (Sept. '55, p. 173).

Power is supplied to the transducer from an electronic

1 Ultrasonic cleaning . . . ▶

of objects immersed in a treatment vessel results from violent cavitation throughout the liquid. Frequency is about 30,000 cps for the type of equipment illustrated. Optimum relationship exists between surface tension, vapor pressure and temperature of the liquid. Water plus a mild detergent is often used, but other liquids such as cyclohexane or trichlor-ethylene with lower viscosity are sometimes more suitable, especially for greasy articles. The liquid is usually heated to about 120 to 140 F for more effective cleaning. Small units such as this require about 450-w input to the ultrasonic generator. Water and oil cooling prevent excessive heating of the transducer.

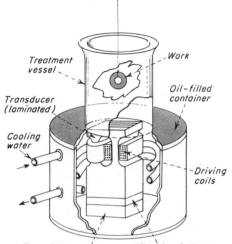

4 Ultrasonic welding . . .

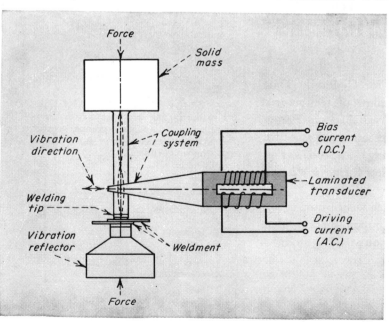

of similar or dissimilar metals gives metallurgical bond with low deformation, low clamping load, and no fusion. Pieces to be joined are clamped between two welding members. Vibratory energy briefly introduced produces a solid-state bond; the phenomenon occurs without high pressures or temperatures at the weld zone. Thicknesses can be 0.00015 to 0.040 in.

5 In thickness gage . . . ▶

transducer is applied to test piece and excited at varying frequencies, and an oscilloscope indicates amplitude of vibrations. Resonant frequency of test piece varies with thickness, and when the exciting frequency passes through resonance, the oscilloscope trace shows a peak which corresponds to a previously calibrated thickness. For curved test pieces such as pipe or bearing sleeves, curved crystals are used in searching unit. Accuracy of method is within 1%.

Transducers

oscillator, usually at frequencies from 20,000 to 60,000 cps for magnetostrictive transducers, and up to 500,000 cps for the electrostrictive type. The transducer is designed to be in resonance with the oscillator at such frequencies—which are in the ultrasonic range (above the frequencies of audible sound).

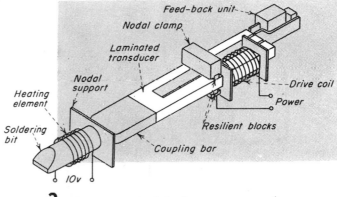

2 Vibrating tool . . .
can drill various materials

such as hardened steel and glass. Hole shape will be the same as tool section and end face, hence intricate holes or cavities can be sunk quickly. Velocity transformer and detachable toolholder are specially shaped to increase amplitude of transducer vibrations. Cutting tool vibrates at about 20,000 cps on the axis of cone. Abrasive fed between tool and work grinds corresponding outline of tool in work area at about 0.01-0.30 in. per min depending on particle size, material, tool area and pressure. Power for ultrasonic drills varies from 50 w for small units to 2 kw for larger machines.

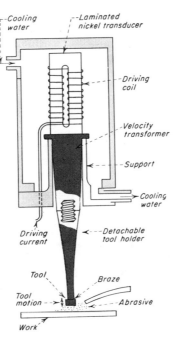

3 Aluminum soldering . . . ▲

with ultrasonic vibrator can be done without flux. Oxide scale is loosened by cavitation. Soldering bit may be heated directly, or heat may be supplied to work by a hot plate or other external source. Resonance can be maintained by capacitance feedback at end of transducer, but this method, although inexpensive, is not considered efficient by some authorities. The system oscillates at 20,000 to 60,000 cps with an input of 50 w or more depending on bit size. Bits are interchangeable.

6 Flaws detected . . ▶

by echo-sounding are mainly those in metals, but non-metallic materials can be inspected by same method. One vibrating crystal transmits the wave; the other converts the reflected vibrations into electric impulses. Good acoustic contact is essential between transducers and test-piece surface. Film of oil or glycerine between surfaces is simple method for providing good contact. Surface roughness should be less than 125 micro-inches. As only a small volume can be inspected at one time, examination tends to be lengthy for large billets or castings.

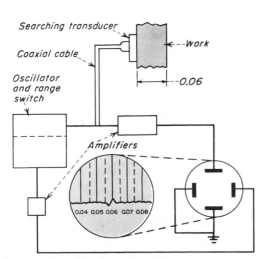

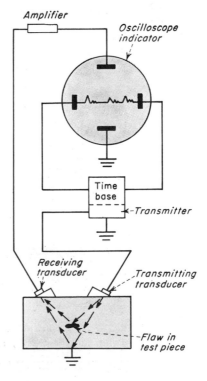

TYPES OF AUTOMATIC TIMERS

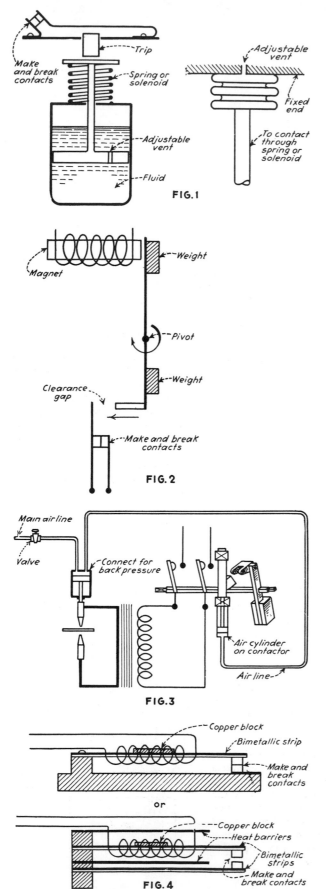

FIG. 1

FIG. 2

FIG. 3

FIG. 4

Thermal, Mechanical and Electronic Methods for Automatic Timing of Industrial Machinery, Welding Operations and Motor Control Devices

GILBERT SMILEY
Chief Engineer, General Control Co.

FIG. 1—Dashpot principle. Simplest form consists of a piston or plunger operating in oil, mercury, or air. Adjustable small orifices or bleeders provide time adjustment. A by-pass may be provided near the end of the piston travel for snap action closing of the contact. Widely used because of its simplicity and low cost. When air is used, changing clearances due to dust, gumming of lubricant, and leakage affect the timing. If oil is used, the temperature will change oil viscosity and affect the timing. Also subject to error because of clearance changes from wear.

FIG. 2—Inertia mechanism. Time-delay is by virtue of the inertia of two weights mounted on a pivoted arm, and the length of arc to be traversed before mechanical contact is made. Tilted by gravity, this device gives a relatively short interval and becomes clumsy for long time intervals.

FIG. 3—Contactor works on back pressure from the main cylinder on the welder, assuring pressure between the welding points before the welding contactor closes. When the back pressure has built up to a predetermined value, the plunger moves upward at a definite rate of speed and the hardened cam closes the main contacts. After a predetermined time, the cam moves by the roller that it engages and the main contacts open. One adjustment sets the back pressure at which the contactor plunger starts to move, and therefore determines the lag in applying the current after pressure has been applied. A second adjustment changes the needle valve opening to the contactor air cylinder and thus times the upstroke. This determines the welding time. A third adjustment varies the time of the down stroke and is of importance only when used with a repeater.

FIG. 4—Thermal relays. Inexpensive time-delay utilizing the effect of a heating coil around a bimetallic strip. Least accurate device. Has a slow make and break action. For longer time intervals, a copper block may be mounted to absorb some of the heat; the larger the block of copper the longer the time interval. Time intervals ranging from ½ sec. to 5-10 min. are possible with this device.

FIG. 5—Magnetic time-delay, used on direct current only. Relatively inexpensive, effects time-delays up to 10 sec. by means of residual magnetism. Magnet may be copper jacketed, or may have copper rings, or may have short-circuited turns around the magnet. Variation in the amount of copper, or in the resistance of short-circuited turns will affect the time-delay.

FIG. 6—Magnetic drag time-delay. A small electro-magnet is used, and the motion of the relay plunger is made to revolve a metal disk in the field of the magnet. The rotation of the disk is retarded by magnetic induction. Reliable device, trouble free, but relatively expensive.

FIG. 7—Vacuum tube. Condenser charged or discharged through a resistor closes a relay after definite time, using direct current. When switch is open, the condenser discharges slowly through shunt resistor. This lowers the negative potential on the grid, and at the critical value the plate current will rise enough to operate the relay. Full line voltage may be applied to the condenser to obtain longer time delay. See article beginning on page 132 of this number.

FIG. 8—In this circuit, operation is maintained for a pre-determined time after the starting impulse has stopped. When the button has been pressed, the filament gets current in series with relay winding No. 1, and the relay pulls up, locking in the circuit. The second contact charges the condenser negative, and no plate current flows. When button is released, the relay stays closed until condenser discharges. Then the plate current flows through the second relay winding in opposition to the first, releasing the armature. Applicable to direct current or rectified alternating current only.

FIG. 9—In the Westinghouse electronic relay there is no temperature error, reset is instantaneous, adjustment is easy and first cost is low. When the switch is closed, the tube passes current. As the current increases, the increasing IR drop from the potentiometer causes a charging current through condenser. The IR drop across the resistor due to this current applies the negative bias to the grid. Plate current cannot build up very rapidly, because the faster it increases the more negative the grid becomes. After a time period, adjustable through potentiometer, the plate current will operate relay. The time-delay is proportional to the product of resistance and capacitance. Long delays require large resistors, and short delays correspondingly small resistors. Maximum time-delay with this device is about 3 min. About 0.05 sec. is the minimum.

Various mechanical devices have been adapted to replace the dashpot: one uses an escapement pendulum similar to those for clocks. Time is varied by changing the length of the pendulum. Mechanical clocks may be used, driving a cam or traveller, or tilting a mercury switch, or any type of make and break mechanism.

Motor-driven timers are used where long time intervals are required and where starting is infrequent. Generally a small pilot motor drives a contact cylinder through reduction gearing. For motor-driven timing devices a synchronous motor is generally used, driving through gearing. These motors offer timing intervals from 1 sec. to infinity. A non-synchronous direct current shunt or an a.c. induction motor of the capacitor type may also be used to drive a timer, since these motors maintain approximately constant speed. However, the accuracy of this type of timing is variable.

Electronic time-delay devices for long time intervals are expensive. Circuits employing thermionic tubes will give a time-delay of more than 30 min. by the use of carbon resistors. Condensers and resistors vary with use, humidity and temperature, and adjustable resistors do not always hold their characteristics.

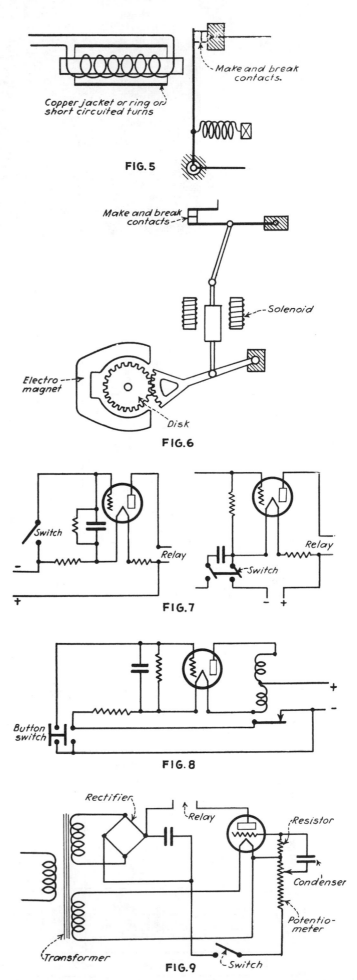

FIG. 5

FIG. 6

FIG. 7

FIG. 8

FIG. 9

TYPE		COMMON RANGES	MINIMUM ERROR	CONTROL MEANS	TIMING ADJUSTMENT	REMARKS	DIAGRAMS
FREQUENCY GENERATORS	GENERAL	Used as precision standard when intervals are short (1 sec to 1 micro sec). If time is broken into minute parts, as in duration of a cycle in 100KC signal, and frequency is constant, it is only necessary to count the cycles in an interval to measure its length.					
	QUARTZ CRYSTAL OSCILLATOR	10 micro sec to 1 sec	1-10 micro sec	Control tube fires to operate relay	Switches set predetermined cycle count in gated counter circuit	Electronic multiplying and dividing circuits are added to give higher and lower frequencies, and output can be amplified. Errors are as low as 1 part in 10^8 if stable electronic components are used and temperature, humidity, barometric pressure, voltage, and loading are closely controlled.	 CRYSTAL
	TUNING FORK OSCILLATOR	1 sec to 30 min	10 microsec			Fork is driven by one electromagnet. Output is delivered to other electromagnet, which is excited by vibrating tines. Frequency can be changed as in crystal oscillator, or by clamping fork at different points. Output frequency can be constant within 1 part in 10^5 if ambient conditions listed above are constant.	 TUNING FORK
SYNCHRONOUS MOTORS	GENERAL	Synchronous motors, because of their inherent timing accuracy, are generally used to drive timers of greater than 1 min range. Motors count cycles and are as accurate as frequency of power source (instantaneous error of 60 cps is about plus or minus 0.1 cps). Outputs are normally between 2 and 75 in.-oz at 1 rpm. Speed not affected by ordinary voltage fluctuations. Time to reach synchronous speed can cause 2 cps timing error. For this reason clutches may connect continuously running motor.					
	SHADED POLE	1 sec to 1 week	0.01 sec abs. 2 sec/day	Dogs, notches, or cams operate contacts or valves directly or through levers; feelers on tape operate contacts.	Motor circuit is interrupted for adjustable periods by any of numerous arrangements listed in next box below.	Squirrel-cage rotor. Copper shading coils produce supplementary flux, shifted in phase with main flux, to create starting torque. Nonreversible and can be stalled.	 ARMATURE FIELD SHADING COILS LINE
	PERMANENT MAGNET					Salient pole with permanent magnet field. More efficient and higher torque than shaded-pole. Permanent magnet reduce: coasting. Clutches, magnetic or dynamic braking, or large gear recutions are used with other motors to prevent coasting.	

TIME-DELAYING DEVICES

Device	Description	Adjustment	Output	Accuracy	Time range
INDUCTION MOTORS	Used when controlled frequency is unavailable or high starting torque is required. Speed varies with load. Capacitor-start, capacitor-run, and shaded-pole types are most often used.	Placing dogs, pins, keys on, or cutting notches in, dial or drum; adjustable cams, change gears, rotating arm or screw; variable radius pulleys or friction discs; punched, notched or embossed tape; interrupting circuit to electric motor for adjustable periods. Dc motors can be adjusted by varying series resistance either locally or remotely.	Dogs, notches, or cams operate contacts or valves directly or through levers; feelers on tape operate contacts.	3-10 per cent	1 min to 24 hrs
DC MOTORS	Used on dc power and where timing must be controlled remotely. Constant speed dictates shunt-wound, but permanent magnetic are smaller and cheaper. Speed varies with voltage, load, and temperature. Voltage ranges from 4.5 to 115 v.			5-10 per cent	1 sec to 4 hr.
REGULATED DC MOTORS	One type uses centrifugal governor. Line contacts are opened when motor overspeeds. Unit shown here uses balance wheel and escapement. Pulses of line voltage are applied at regular intervals. Maximum error at 1 rpm is ± 0.1 per cent despite voltage variations of ± 20 per cent and load variations of 0–30 in.-oz. Principal problems are contact wear or failure and radio interference.			0.1-1 per cent	1 min to 24 hr.
SPRING ACTUATED DEVICES	Intervals can vary from fractional set to a month or more. Diagram shows lever-type escapement. Accuracy depends on precision of manufacture, temperature compensation, and external load. Pendulum escapements are bulky and only good for stationary service. Spring movements are limited by low and irregular torque.			Escapement 0.2 sec/day to 5 sec/day — Escapement 0.5 sec/day	Lever 1 sec to 1 week — Pendulum 12 to 24 hrs.
AIR MOTOR	Used in hazardous conditions. High speed air turbine drives a gear train regulated by escapement. Accuracy depends on escapement. Typical characteristics: operating pressure 20-25 psig; air consumption 0.1 cfm; torque output 2-8 in.-oz at 1 rpm.			0.3-3 per cent	1 hr to 24 hr.
CAPACITOR CHARGE OR DISCHARGE	Uses time required for transient voltage and current changes in a resistance-capacity circuit. In circuit shown, capacitor discharge rate depends on RC product. After time RC, capacitor voltage drops to 37 per cent of initial value. V_R equals voltage across R. Timing is adjusted by varying resistance or changing capacity. Accuracy depends on constancy of charging voltage and component characteristics. If capacitor operates load directly, delay is limited due to required capacitor size. Using capacitor voltage to fire a gas tube overcomes this. Capacitor charging time can also be used.	Variable resistor local or remote; switching different resistance or capacitance into circuit.	Vacuum tube or Thyratron operates load directly or through relay; relay can also be operated directly through capacitor.	1-5 per cent	0.1 sec to 1 min

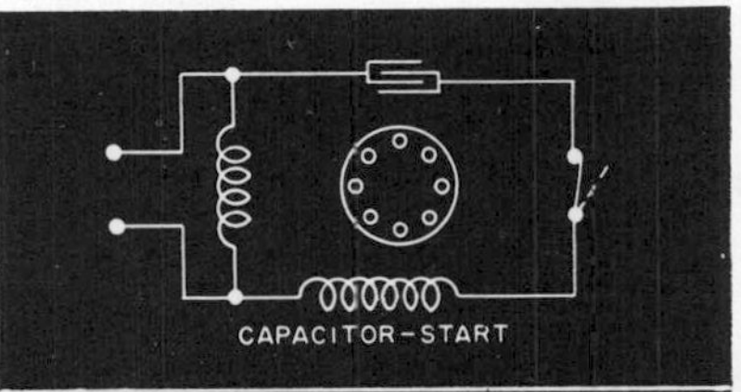

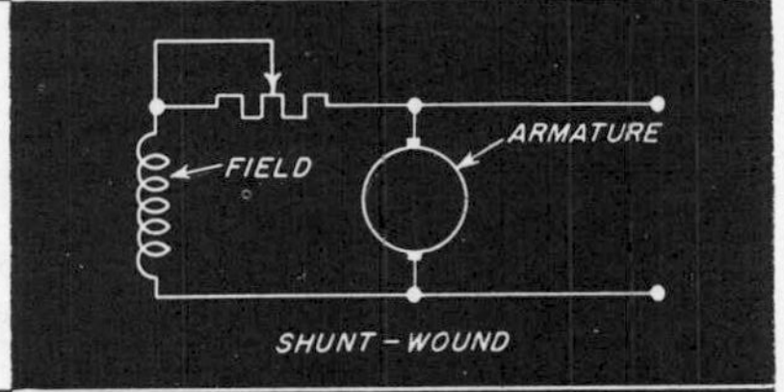

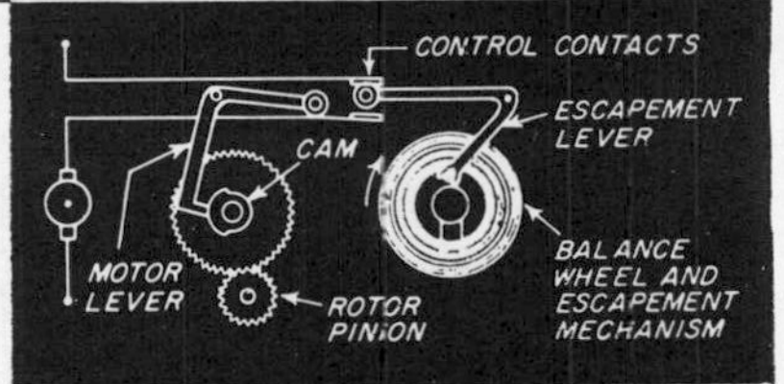

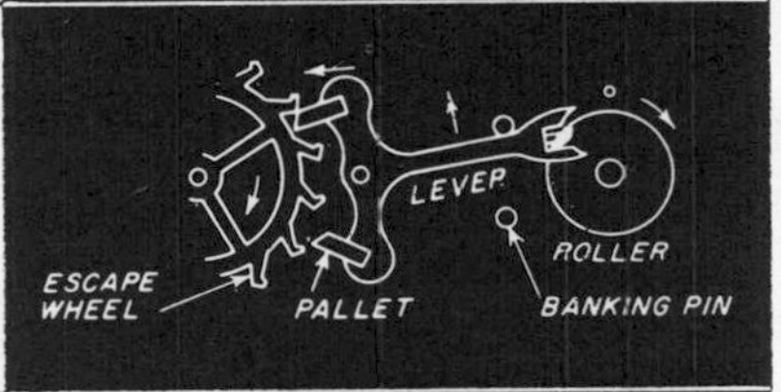

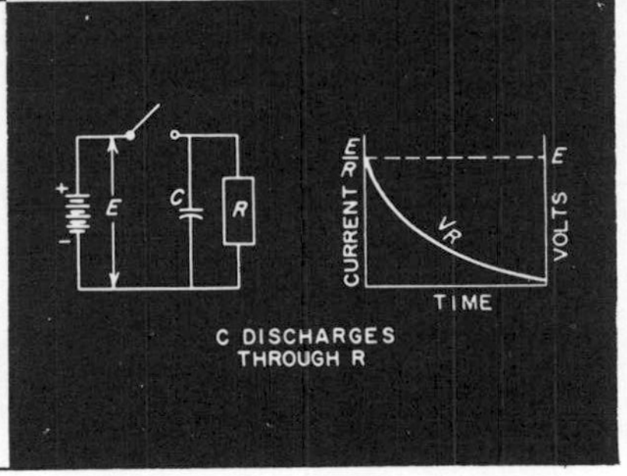

TYPE	DIAGRAMS	REMARKS	TIMING ADJUSTMENT	CONTROL MEANS	MINIMUM ERROR	COMMON RANGES
FLUX-DECAY RELAY		Dc electro magnet has heavy copper ring or highly inductive short-circuited coil around the core, inside the main coil. When circuit opens, magnet drop-out is retarded by current induced in copper slug. Time constant, L/R of slug, determines delay.	Local: movable copper sleeve; local or remote: rheostat in series with neutralizing coil.	Relay armature operates contacts.	5-10 per cent	0.1 sec to 4 sec
THERMAL DEVICES		Either ac or dc. Uses rate of expansion of metal or differential expansion of bimetal. Unit shown here uses bimetallic strip. If moving and fixed contacts are both mounted on bimetal strips, uni is temperature compensated. Heater is wrapped around moving bimetal. Another type (6-14 v range) has a wire attached to bent strip. Heat expands wire and contact on strip makes. Accuracy depends on ambient temperature voltage fluctuation and elapsed time between successive operations (for cooling). Units are cheap, silent, and not affected by positioner frequency.	Variable resistor in series with thermal element or adjustable contact; usually fixed.	Hot wire straightens bow, or heater bends bimetal to operate contacts.	5-10 per cent	1 sec to 8 min
DASH POT		Ac or dc solenoid armature motion is retarded by fluid passing plunger. Repeatability requires constant viscosity fluid; therefore is affected by temperature changes. Silicone oils help between minus 30 and plus 120 deg F. For rapid recycling, quick-return check valves are used.	Usually fixed washer opens or closes by-pass passages.	Solenoid armature operates contacts.	5-10 per cent	1 sec to 2 min
PNEUMATIC DEVICES		Uses time required for fixed volume of air to pass through a restriction. Armature of solenoid may be attached to a diaphragm. When solenoid is de-energized, spring-aided movement of diaphragm and armature is retarded by rate at which air flows through the restriction. Not affected by ambient temperature but air must be clean.	Adjustable needle valve.	Solenoid armature operates contacts.	5-10 per cent	0.1 sec to 5 min
INERTIA DEVICES		Weights added to armature of ac or dc relays increase inertia and cause time delay. Where shock, vibration, or change in position affect operation, the armature can be coupled to a flywheel. Flywheel rotates as armature moves and inertia effect can be varied by changing its travel.	Usually fixed; flywheel type may have adjustable stop pins.	Relay armature operates contacts.	5 per cent	0.08 sec to 2 sec

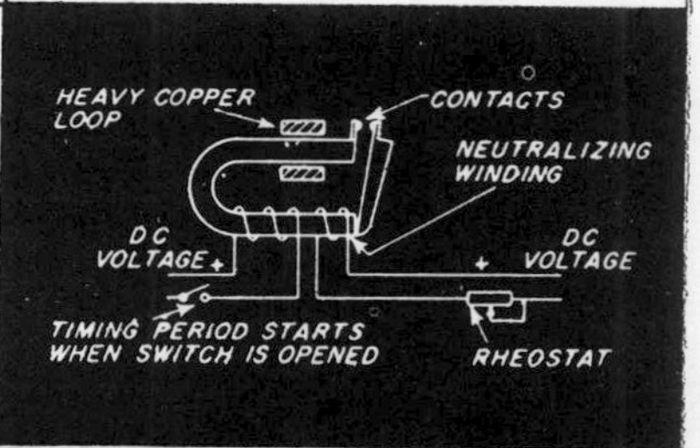

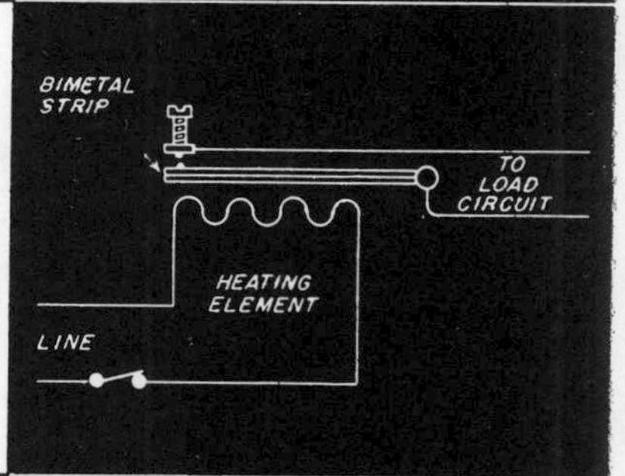

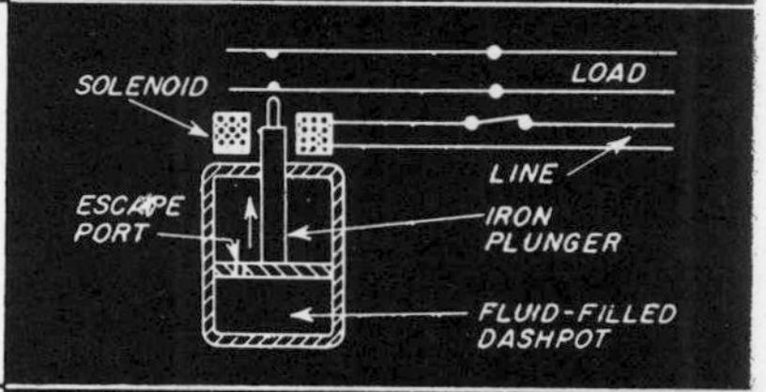

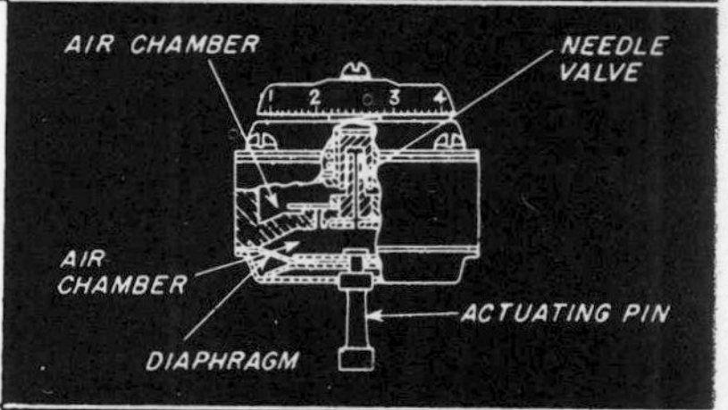

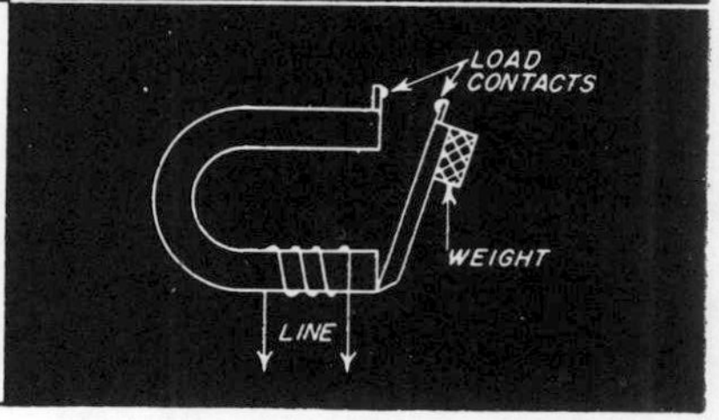

TIME INDICATING MEANS

TYPE	REMARKS	DIAGRAMS
DIAL	Dial can be fixed or movable. Some types have a pointer which is manually set at the desired time interval, plus a concentric pointer that rotates during timing to indicate remaining or elapsed time. Movable dials have functions other than mere indication. The time markings may be on a disc that carries trippers to operate contacts (see diagram), or on a knob that carries an arm to be actuated by the driving means at the end of a timed interval.	
RECORDER	Recorders plot a curve on a chart with time as one coordinate. Accuracy depends on uniformity of time graduations and constancy of chart speed. High-speed recorders, for very short intervals, use photographic film and a light source, or electro-sensitive paper and a stylus; others use pen and ink on round, strip, or drum charts.	
ILLUMINATED	High-speed short-interval units with crystal oscillators use illuminated read out. A series of lights indicates the time interval as a total number of cycles counted, as in a standard electronic counter. In the form of read-out indicated, a digit in each decade is illuminated to show the cycle count as it progresses. The right hand decade represents units, the next one tens, etc.	

MEANS OF INITIATING TIMING

	TYPE	SPECIFIC REMARKS	GENERAL REMARKS
MANUAL STARTING METHODS	MOMENTARY ELECTRIC CONTACT	Push-button start for electrically driven timers with electromagnetic or cam-operated lock-in devices. Used with timers that stop at the end of each cycle, but whose operation is repeated regularly (stop-cycle timers).	Starting means selection factors:
	MAINTAINED ELECTRIC CONTACT	Closing a switch energizes driving or controlling means. Used on continuously operating (repeat-cycle) timers; can also be used on stop-cycle types, but switch must be opened at completion of timing to reset for new cycle.	1. Duration of interval—short intervals require automatic starting, since time for manual operation of pilot contact is long relative to interval measured.
	SPRING WINDING	Some spring driven timers are started by turning a knob that winds the spring. Releasing the knob initiates timing. The same action, using a friction clutch and electric contacts, is used on simple electric-motor-driven models.	2. Accuracy—automatic starting used where accuracy greater than plus or minus 0.1 sec is required.
	LEVER RELEASE	Used in stop watches and other spring-operated timers where spring is separately wound.	3. Driving means—spring wound and simple electrical types are often started manually. Most electrical timers can be started manually or automatically. Air-motor units use quick opening valves.
AUTOMATIC STARTING	MOMENTARY ELECTRIC CONTACT	Used principally in single interval timing. An impulse from the event or process to be timed initiates timing.	
	MAINTAINED CONTACT	Used with continuously repeating timers. Contact is closed (or opened) by process or operation to be timed. In stop-cycle types, circuit must reopen before timer can repeat its cycle unless a suitable lockout is used.	

SETTING AND CONTROL MEANS

TYPE	REMARKS	DIAGRAMS
SPEED CHANGERS	GENERAL: How timers are adjusted for the desired time intervals (setting means) and how the load contacts are actuated at the proper time (control means) depend primarily on the driving means. (Common methods are itemized above under timing means (Measuring and Driving).	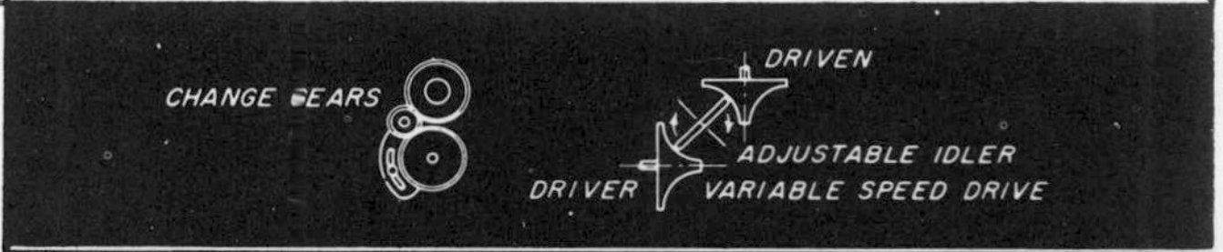 CHANGE GEARS — DRIVEN, DRIVER, ADJUSTABLE IDLER, VARIABLE SPEED DRIVE
CAMS		 LOAD SW., SPLIT CAM — LOAD CONTACTS, DIAL WITH STOP ARM, ARM ROTATED BY TIMER MOTOR, CAM WITH DETACHABLE SEGMENT, LOAD SW.
DISCS AND DRUMS		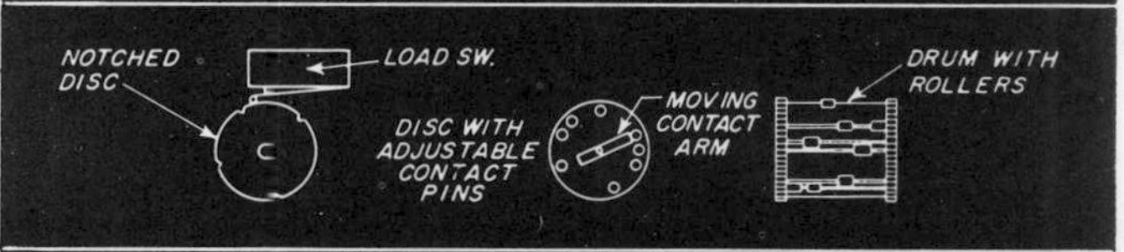 NOTCHED DISC, LOAD SW., DISC WITH ADJUSTABLE CONTACT PINS, MOVING CONTACT ARM, DRUM WITH ROLLERS
THREADED AXLE AND PINION	Control means for accurate dial-type motor-driven timer with fine adjustment. Pinion is positioned on threaded axle according to desired time setting. During timing, the driving means rotates pinion. At end of travel, the pinion actuates an arm to operate load contacts. Time interval can be set to 0.1 per cent.	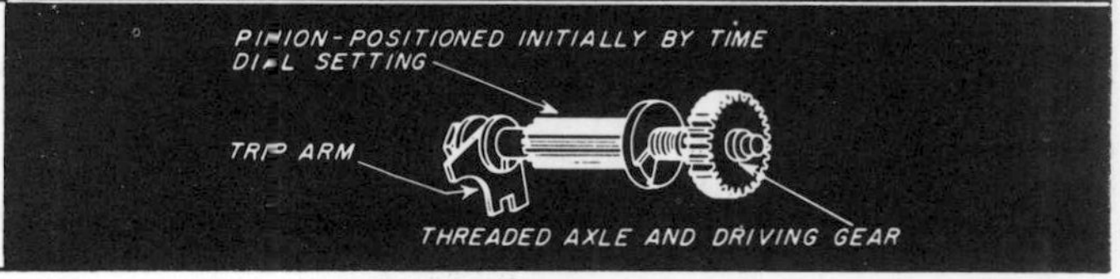 PINION-POSITIONED INITIALLY BY TIME DIAL SETTING, TRIP ARM, THREADED AXLE AND DRIVING GEAR

FOR MOTOR-DRIVEN TIMERS

	GENERAL REMARKS
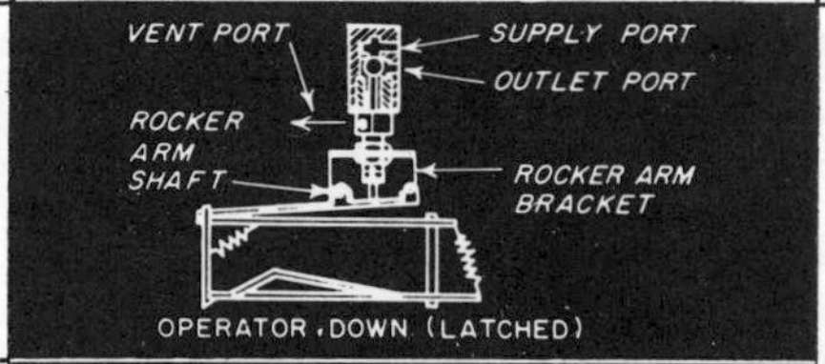	Usually consist of some form of electric or pneumatic switch arrangement. Some common configurations for motor-driven timers are shown to the left. Timers that are not motor driven usually depend on the armature of a relay or the plunger of a solenoid to operate the control contacts. Some electronic types develop enough current to operate a load connected in series with the plate circuit of a control tube. Also, some thermal types do not require auxiliary relays.

LOAD CONTACTS

TYPE	SPECIFIC REMARKS	DIAGRAMS
PNEUMATIC OPERATOR	Usually a small poppet valve. Diagram shows one operated by a latching mechanism. Trip pins, located at select spots on a motor-driven drum, alternately latch or release the hinged plates that move the valve plunger.	SUPPLY PORT, OUTLET PORT, ROCKER ARM BRACKET, VENT PORT, ROCKER ARM SHAFT, OPERATOR-DOWN (LATCHED)
ELECTRIC OPERATOR	Contacts can be closed, open, or mercury tube, and can be found in a variety of current ratings, number of poles, and operating sequences. The latching-type operator is shown with a SPDT snap-acting switch.	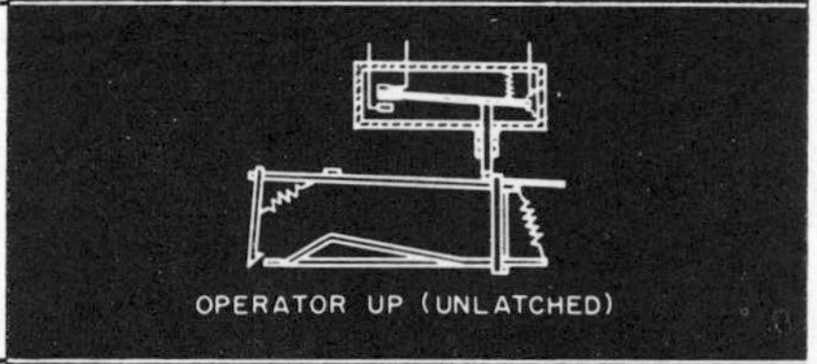 OPERATOR UP (UNLATCHED)
CAM OPERATED	Switch plungers or contact leaves ride directly on cams. Cams shown here are separately adjustable. On and off points and interval between operations can be adjusted.	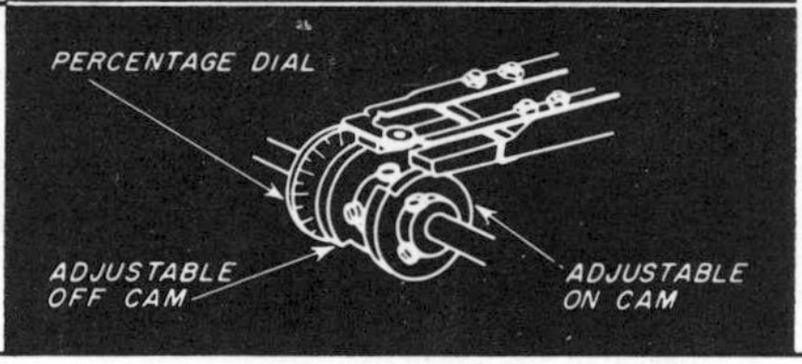 ADJUSTABLE ON CAM, PERCENTAGE DIAL, ADJUSTABLE OFF CAM

1. TIME SWITCHES

TYPE	DESCRIPTION	DIAGRAM	DESIGN DETAILS	APPLICATIONS
MOTOR DRIVEN	A 24 hr timing device generally used to open or close electrical circuits according to the time of day, on a continually repeating basis.		Motor driven; electric types often have spring reserves because of infrequent attention and importance of regular operation. Control means is usually a dial, graduated in two 12 hr sections, although some, called calendar dials, rotate once in 7 days. Calendar type is more flexible but size limitations prevent operations being as closely spaced as on 24 hr dial. Minimum spacing on 24 hr dial varies from 5 to 60 min and number allowable range from 6 to 288. Load contact operation can be either maintained or momentary. When controlling a large number of operations daily, time switch is called a program timer. Contacts may be momentary and a "duration" timer in series with program timer may be used to adjust length of signal. When load contacts have capacity greater than 15 amp, it is desirable to use auxiliary actuating means. Usually a quick-release spring drive, electrically wound, to operate contacts. Otherwise timing mechanism is overloaded.	Used for daily automatic control of plant lighting, heating, and ventilating equipment, factory work signals, pumps, and compressors; also the heating, before the work day starts, of ovens and furnaces, lead and glue pots, dip tanks, soldering irons, molding press dies, and testing equipment. Primary advantages are savings of electric power and labor costs.

2. INTERVAL TIMERS

TYPE	DESCRIPTION	DIAGRAM	DESIGN DETAILS	APPLICATIONS
SPRING DRIVEN	Used to hold circuits open or closed for a predetermined interval and then return them to their original positions. Thus, they will control the duration of an operation or process.		Timing is started by turning the knob to the desired interval value. This winds the spring motor and closes the mercury load switch. At the end of the timed period, the unwinding spring returns the knob to its original position and the mercury switch opens. *Minneapolis-Honeywell Regulator Co.*	Used to control the operating time of plastic molding presses, die casting machines, machine tools, conveyors, centrifuges, and pumps. Also applied to bottle filling machines, photoprinters, mixers, bake ovens, resistance welding equipment, induction heaters, chemical feeders, x-ray equipment, and to cooking, sterilizing, distillation, rubber curing, washing, electroplating, and heat treating. Many interval timers can be used as time-delay relays by arranging contacts to operate at end of interval only, instead of at both beginning and end.
SYNCHRONOUS MOTOR DRIVEN			Initial position of control pin is set by adjusting knob with time-set pointer. This determines time interval. A second pointer rotates during timing to indicate time remaining. At end of interval, pin hits tripping arm to actuate the contact finger of a SPDT load switch. Solenoid clutch starts timing and permits spring reset to operate when it is deenergized. *Eagle Signal Corp.*	
OTHER TYPES			Electronic timers are used for short intervals; usually under 1 min. From 0.02 sec up, capacitor discharge or charge through a gas tube, which operates load contact relay, is usual measuring means. Rheostat in RC circuit is connected to calibrated dial. Gas tubes with heated cathodes require a few seconds to heat. Cold types are instantaneous, but less sensitive. For intervals from 10 microsec to 1 sec, cycle counters operating from frequency generators can be used for control purposes. Output pulses for operation of load contacts controls the number of counts. A series of switches, one for each decade stage, controls the number of counts. Output pulses for operation of load contacts are supplied at start and finish of each interval.	

3. TIME DELAY RELAYS

TYPE	DESCRIPTION	DIAGRAM	DESIGN DETAILS	APPLICATIONS
THERMAL	Electric, mechanical, or electromechanical contact making devices with a time lag between the energizing or deenergizing of the control circuit and the subsequent opening or closing of the load circuits.		Hermetically sealed relay suitable for controlling application of plate voltage in vacuum tube circuits. When power is applied, heater causes bimetal element to bend till it closes load contact. *Thomas A. Edison, Inc.*	Used to delay the startup, continuation, recycling, or shutdown of an operation until optimum conditions are reached. For example, in electronic equipment using thermionic tubes, time-delay relays are used to postpone the application of plate voltage until the cathodes have reached operating temperature.
IMMEDIATELY RECYCLING THERMAL	Where errors of 5 or 10 per cent are allowable, simple electromagnets with delayed armature movement created by copper slugs, capacitors, thermal devices, dashpots, and weights are typical.		Unlike most thermal timers, this unit can repeat its operation with reasonable (10 per cent) accuracy as soon as it has timed out. Differential expansion of two metal strips operates SPDT contacts, with a permanent magnet for snap action. Thermal relay contacts are in series with those of magnetic relay. When control circuit is closed, thermal relay opens its own contact as it heats and then energizes magnetic relay, which in turn de-energizes the heater. When cool, thermal contacts close and circuit is complete. Not suitable for brief delays because of time required for cooling. *Struthers-Dunn, Inc.*	Other applications include overload protection of electrical machinery, extended operation of alarm signals from momentary impulses, induction heating, plastic molding, mixing, and operation of machine tools. Relays with short delay periods are useful in electrical control circuits where chattering or other transient effects require sustained control contact. Also could be used with a gas-fired oven to delay re-ignition following a shutdown, allowing time for purging unburned gas.
MOTOR DRIVEN	Time delays are built in; and if adjustable, there is seldom any indication of the time values. Where accuracy and adjustability are important, calibrated motor-driven and electronic types are used.		More accurate with longer delay periods than thermal types. Dial indicates time setting and sets a stop. Stop adjusts delay time by limiting travel of motor-driven arm. Arm operates switch, and is reset by spring when motor is deenergized. *Haydon Mfg Co., Inc.*	
ELECTRONIC			Typical electronic time delay relay. Uses resistive-capacitive network with variable resistance for timing adjustment. *General Control Co.*	

212

4. TIME-CYCLE CONTROLLERS

TYPE	DESCRIPTION	DIAGRAM	DESIGN DETAILS	APPLICATIONS
SINGLE-SHAFT CONTROLLER	Opens or closes one or more circuits during a timed interval. May be called a program controller since it can control a predetermined series of related events for pre-selected intervals. Units are flexible because they must perform many functions. They may be either repeat cycle or stop-cycle and may have means for readily changing the sequences and duration of operations and the interval between operations, adding or subtracting operators, changing the over-all range, and changing the form and type of operator.		Series of cams on motor-driven shaft operate electric switches or air poppet valves in a specific sequence. Switches or valves are held open or closed for timed intervals, independent of one another. Any number of cams and load contacts can be added. *Automatic Temperature Control Co., Inc.*	Uses include the molding of tires, phonograph records, rubber goods, and grinding wheels; sequencing the starting of large motors, sequencing and timing a series of machine operations, thermocouple switching, automatic retort control, automatic solvent recovery control, fixed bed catalytic reforming and ash and soot removal systems. Time-cycle controllers, combined with auxiliary timers that control long intervals or process variable schedules, can be the control center of an automatic machine, process, or entire factory. They have been successfully used in controlling all operations on a machine tool. The operator has only to load and start the machine, and the controller, guided by a program punched on tape, directs the machine by moving the cutting tools in the right direction at the right time and at the desired speeds and feeds.
TWO-SHAFT CONTROLLER			Impulse-sequence type with separate drives for time measurement and control of operators. This permits more accurate timing. Operations are timed by punching notches in thin aluminum disc. Each time the roller hits notch an impulse causes the shaft carrying the cams to rotate between two adjacent pins of a series spaced around the index cam. Dogs on cam latch open or trip closed the load switches in this interval of rotation. Step operation at high camshaft speed means the dog settings can be anywhere within the index travel without appreciable effect on accuracy. Also the controller can be started by a momentary contact. A switch on camshaft can be adjusted to reset the timing disc to zero at any point. Resetting is effected by a solenoid clutch, through a high speed gear train. *The Bristol Co.*	
OTHER TYPES			Where individual adjustability is unimportant and the number of circuits is small, several load contacts can be operated from lobes of a single cam. Lobes may be detachable segments, able to be placed anywhere on the graduated periphery of the cam. The flexibility of the impulse-sequence type can be obtained with a combination timer using a drum or cams rotating at high speeds. For long dwells, the drum is stopped and timing is done by one or more interval timers. The interrupter is a simple form with a single cam that continually opens and closes a single contact. The portion of the rotation during which the contact is open or closed depends on the adjustable dwell time of the cam. This is often used to change the rate of another timer by interrupting its motor drive circuit. Variations of the interrupter, known as input controllers, are used to control the elements of heating devices. The "on" and "off" time can be set manually or controlled automatically from deviation contacts in a pyrometer. Either way the load contact is operated for timed periods, on a repeat cycle basis.	

5. TIME-SCHEDULE CONTROLLERS

TYPE	DESCRIPTION	DIAGRAM	DESIGN DETAILS	APPLICATIONS
GENERAL			Timers contain three parts: the automatic controller, the means for changing the set point, and the timing means. A simple example is an elapsed time controller consisting of a motor driven dial-type interval timer and automatic controller. The interval timer starts either as the controller starts or when the variable reaches the set point, depending on whether the controlled time is to include the rise of the variable to its set point. In either case variable rises at maximum rate to the set point, where it is held by controller for the duration. At this point timer's load contact shuts down controller and it resets. To move set point at controlled rates or to obtain different values on a time schedule, use: cam with directly-linked follower; cam-operated pneumatic transmitter; or motor drive with interrupter to control rate of change and a timer to control holding period.	Processes include air conditioning, canning, dyeing, cooking, pasteurizing, defrosting, plastic polymerization, wax-sweating, gas-pressure regulation, sulfate pulp digesting and rubber vulcanizing.
CAM OPERATED	Timers are essentially automatic controllers whose set point is automatically positioned for a pre-selected time interval. They may control a variable at a number of rates of change, as well as at different fixed values for a series of time intervals. Usually controls a critical variable in a batch process.		Thin metal cam is cut to the desired time-variable schedule. Cam motor-drive speed is such that cam revolves once in each process cycle. Friction clutch permits manual cam setting. The cam follower is linked to the set-point mechanism of the control unit. Controllers are available in non-recording type, single-case recording type, and two-case recording type (as shown). Cams can be cut to any desired schedule. Principal limitation is maximum rate of cam rise (due to pressure angle). Also, cam must be large and fine adjustments cannot be made without filing or recutting cam. A momentary contact can be used for starting; resetting at end of cycle can be automatic.	
STRIP-CHART POTENTIOMETER, CAMLESS TYPE			Strip-chart potentiometer adapted to highly flexible time-schedule controller. Separate motors drive the index upscale and down, each having change gears giving a basic number of speeds. Auxiliary switches can be adjusted to operate at various index settings. System is useful where schedule changes are required from batch to batch. Range of schedules is limited only by the number of auxiliary switches available for operating accessory timers. *Minneapolis-Honeywell Regulator Co.*	
CAMLESS TYPE			Recording pneumatic temperature controller with three interval timers and an interrupter, plus auxiliary setting knobs, switches, and signals. The interrupter brings the temperature to the set point at a controlled rate, where it is held by the holding timer. Other timers permit a timed interval at the initial setting, before interrupter takes over, to assure a uniform base temperature and mixture, and an overtime period after completion of the cycle if more processing is required.	

MECHANICAL TIMER FOR SHORT-CYCLE OPERATION

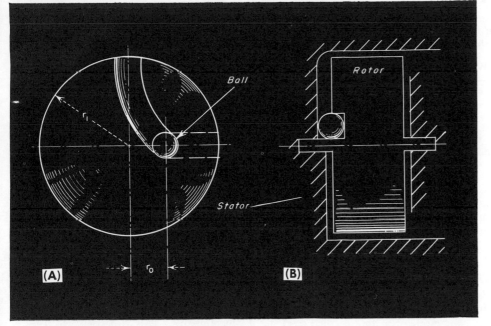

Fig. 1. Three basic components of this timing device are a stator with a radial groove, a rotor with a spiral groove, and a ball that rides in these grooves. When the mechanism rotates, the ball tends to move radially in the stator groove because of centrifugal force. As it does so, it is constrained by the spiral groove and thereby exerts a driving force on the rotor. With a constant rate spiral, curves in Fig. 2 give the time characteristics plotted against angular velocity.

THIS MECHANISM, shown in Fig. 1(A) and (B), is a simple means of obtaining a timing cycle inversely proportional to the rotational velocity of a member. The principal advantage of this unit is that the cycle is completed with the same angular displacement of the stator housing regardless of the value of the angular velocity of the housing. Thus, such a mechanism can be used to meter the distance travelled by a rotating body. At speeds of 1,000 to 100,000 rpm, it has a practical timing range of approximately 1/1,000 to 1.0 sec.

$$\frac{1}{t}\sqrt{\frac{I}{M}} = \frac{A\,\omega\,\sqrt{C}}{\text{arc cosh}\left(1 + \frac{A\theta}{r_0}\right)}$$

where

$$C = \frac{\left(1 - \frac{f}{\tan\phi}\right)}{1 + 2f\tan\phi}$$

$$A = \frac{r_1 - r_0}{\theta}$$

f—Coefficient of friction for ball in rotor-stator slot
F—Driving ball centrifugal force
I—Moment of inertia of rotor
m—Mass of driving ball
r_0—Initial spiral radius
r_1—Final spiral radius
t—Time
ϕ—Spiral angle
θ—Rotor face angle
ω—Angular velocity of mechanism

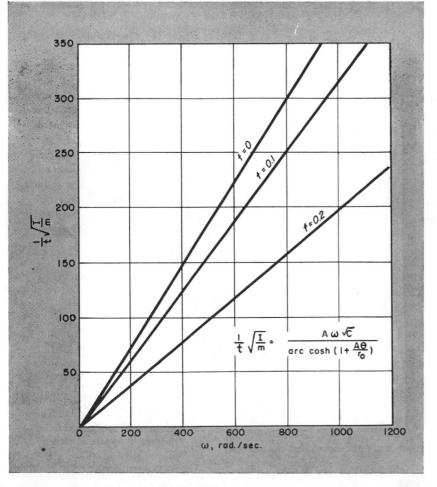

$$\frac{1}{t}\sqrt{\frac{I}{m}} = \frac{A\,\omega\,\sqrt{C}}{\text{arc cosh}\left(1 + \frac{A\theta}{r_0}\right)}$$

Fig. 2— Speed-time relationship plotted for three values of the coefficient of friction. Knowing ω, $\frac{1}{t}\sqrt{I/m}$ can be read from the appropriate f curve. Then, numerical values of I and m are chosen to get the desired value of time delay.

FIVE NEW TIMING DEVICES

1. Cam-Operated Device

2-PART CAM is heart of this timer. Lower disk can move through a short arc relative to the upper disk which is attached to the shaft, mainspring and friction clutch. When turned, the upper disk lifts the follower out of the slot, then the cam pin picks up the lower disk and carries it around with it. The upper disk is rotated for the desired time interval. When released the dual cams return to their original relative position and present a sharp-edged slot for the follower to snap into.

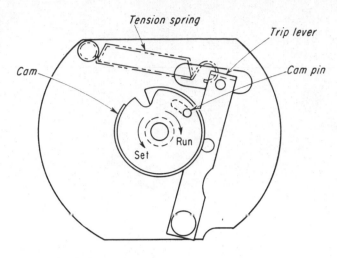

The time interval possible with mechanical timers is very flexible; it can be a few seconds or up to 12 hours. Most commercial applications have a range of either a few minutes or a few hours with any desired adjustability. Time intervals of a few seconds are achieved by attaching the cam mechanism to the "seconds" (high-speed) gear in the clock mechanism, which is omitted in timers that mark only minutes and hours. Similarly, intervals of more than 12 hours are clocked by attaching the cam mechanism to a still slower gear in the clock mechanism.

Accuracy is a function of workmanship and comparable to that of any watch mechanism. For most commercial applications, accuracy ranges from 0.5 to 5% of the time interval.

Automatic recycling of a mechanical timer is possible, but generally other timing devices are more suitable where manual resetting is objectionable. This is particularly true where programming of multiple automatic operations is needed. Mechanical timers may be reset by a solenoid. This can be just as effective as manual resetting, but may not be as economical as using timers more readily adapted to recycling.

2. Double-Operation Timers

Mechanical timers of commercial quality can also be adapted to timing of two sequential operations in one cycle. Usually this is done by arranging two cams in series with simple friction clutches, or a special gear segment and cam arrangement. Timing of the first operation is determined by the angular displacement of the gear segment. The second operation is performed as fast as the inertia of the load and the remaining energy in the spring will permit.

Sometimes, this second operation is used to trigger an auxiliary spring or mechanism, as in photo below. The multiple-operation timer that releases spring energy in more than two steps is generally considered impractical for conventional timing jobs.

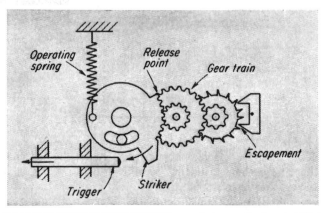

DOUBLE-OPERATION TIMER regulates a first operation for a predetermined time interval until striker contacts trigger. Then trigger is pushed with remaining spring energy.

3. Jaw Clutch

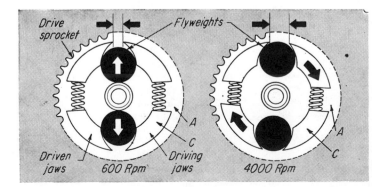

mounted on the fuel-injector drive has jaws separated by a pair of centrifugal weights. These move outward as engine speed increases, forcing the jaws apart against the clutch springs. Result is the driven member of the timer is advanced in relation to driving member (A).

The drive jaws are bolted to a chain-drive sprocket that operates the timer. The driven jaws (C) are bolted to the end of a camshaft that operates individual injection pumps. Torque is transmitted through the jaws by the flyweights inserted between them. Since the jaws are bolted to their backing plates they cannot move outward but have to rotate with respect to each other. This produces the required fuel-injection advance as engine speed increases.

4. Timers for Switching

Multi-switch program timers loaf along tripping switches surely but slowly. The longer the trip time the greater the spread in actual contact closure times. This spread can cause control and timing variations that spell trouble. To put the snap back in switching, Alkan and Sinay of Paris, France, use a drive that lets the motor run continuously but advances the switch cam shaft step-by-step. Idling for 9/10 of the revolution of its worm drive it advances in the last 1/10 through the same angle it would have made if it had been moving continuously. This reduces tripping and contact closure time by a factor of 10.

To obtain the long idle, rotation of the cam shaft by the worm is negated by a plate cam with a slope equal to the worm lead. As the worm is rotated by the drive pin, the cam follower lifts the worm a distance equal to 9/10 of one pitch distance and the cam drive gear, remains stationary.

Fast advance occurs when the roller follower passes the peak of the plate cam and drops to the starting position. The spring drives the worm down, moving the cam shaft spur gear

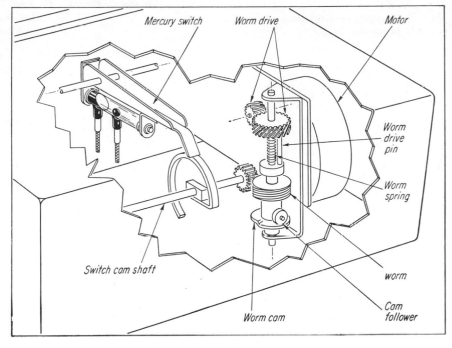

and the cam a distance equal to the worm lead.

The worm is not pinned to the shaft but is free to slide vertically. The pin drive makes possible the slight up-and-down movement of the worm without using expensive splines. The programmer is available with 3, 6, 10, 14, or 22 micro or mercury switches. Programming is achieved by inserting metal cam segments in the nylon cam hubs. Each hub has 36 slots 10 deg apart, cam segments are 10 or 20 deg.

5. Thermal Time-Delay from Australia

For on-off temperature and humidity controllers and other applications involving fairly long time-constants, the Commonwealth Scientific and Industrial Research Organization is developing a simple, effective dual transducer system.

The basic unit is a small copper bobbin on which a heater is wound and to which a thermistor is attached (see diagram). They are mounted in pairs on an aluminum frame and connected in a bridge circuit (to minimize effects of ambient temperature) to a printed circuit board.

Time constants can be varied by fitting suitable thermal masses (aluminum or copper weights) to the bobbin extension, and output characteristics by varying the percentage of the input signal fed to each unit.

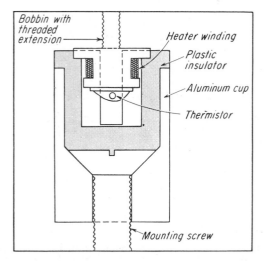

TRANSDUCER UNIT consists of bobbin and heater, mounted in plastic sleeve. Aluminum cup provides path for heat dissipation.

Unloaded units, says CSIR have a time constant of about 35 sec; but this may be extended to 10 min. using unlagged weights; and to over 30 min. if plastic-capped weights are used. The "caps" are foamed-plastic insulators.

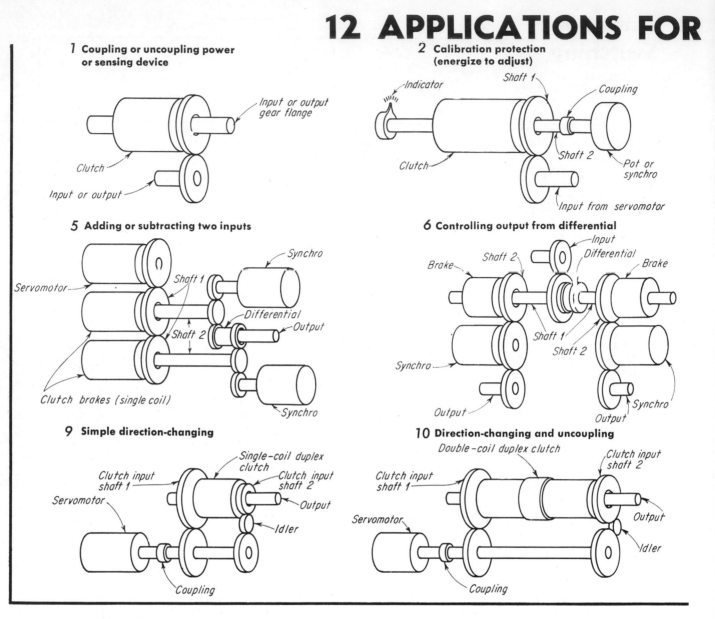

1 Coupling or uncoupling power or sensing device

Input or output gear flange

Clutch

Input or output

2 Calibration protection (energize to adjust)

Indicator

Shaft 1

Coupling

Clutch

Shaft 2

Pot or synchro

Input from servomotor

5 Adding or subtracting two inputs

Servomotor

Shaft 1

Synchro

Differential

Shaft 2

Output

Clutch brakes (single coil)

Synchro

6 Controlling output from differential

Input

Differential

Brake

Shaft 2

Brake

Shaft 1

Shaft 2

Synchro

Output

Output

Synchro

9 Simple direction-changing

Single-coil duplex clutch

Clutch input shaft 1

Clutch input shaft 2

Servomotor

Output

Idler

Coupling

10 Direction-changing and uncoupling

Double-coil duplex clutch

Clutch input shaft 2

Clutch input shaft 1

Servomotor

Output

Idler

Coupling

MAGNETIC FRICTION CLUTCHES

The most common type of electromagnetic control clutch—the simplest and most adaptable—is the magnetic friction clutch. It works on the same principle as a simple solenoid-operated electric relay with a spring return to normal. Like the relay, it is a straightforward automatic switch for controlling the flow of power (in this case, torque) through a circuit.

Rotating or fixed field?

This is a question primarily of magnetic design. Rotating-field clutches employ a rotating coil, energized through brushes and slip rings. Fixed-field units have a stationary coil. Rotating-field units are still the more common, but there has been marked trend toward the fixed-field design.

Generally speaking, a rotating-field clutch is a two-member unit, with the coil carried in the driving (input) member. It can be mounted directly on a motor or speed-reducer shaft without loading down the driving motor. In the smaller sizes, it offers a better ratio of size to rated output than the fixed-field type, although the rotating coil increases inertia in the larger models.

A fixed-field clutch, on the other hand, is a three-member unit, with rotating input and output members and a stationary coil housing. It eliminates the need for brushes and slip rings, but it demands additional bearing supports, and may require close tolerances in mounting.

PURELY MAGNETIC CLUTCHES

Probably less familiar than the friction types are hysteresis and eddy-current clutches, which operate on straight magnetic principles and do not depend upon mechanical contact between their members. The two styles are almost identical in construction, but the magnetic segments of the hysteresis clutch are electrically isolated and those of the eddy-current type are interconnected. The magnetic analogy of both styles is similar in that the flux path is passed between the two clutch members.

Hysteresis clutches

The hysteresis clutch is a proportional-torque control device which—as its name implies—exploits the hysteresis effect in a permanent-magnet rotor ring to produce a substantially constant torque that is almost completely independent of speed (except for slight, unavoidable secondary

ELECTROMAGNETIC CLUTCHES AND BRAKES

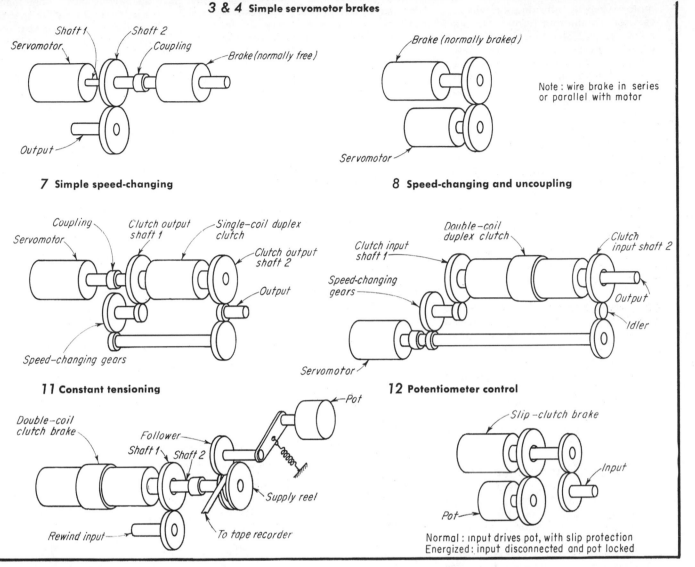

3 & 4 Simple servomotor brakes

Shaft 1 — Shaft 2 — Coupling

Servomotor — Brake (normally free)

Output

Brake (normally braked)

Servomotor

Note: wire brake in series or parallel with motor

7 Simple speed-changing

Coupling — Clutch output shaft 1 — Single-coil duplex clutch

Servomotor — Clutch output shaft 2 — Output

Speed-changing gears

8 Speed-changing and uncoupling

Double-coil duplex clutch — Clutch input shaft 2

Clutch input shaft 1 — Output — Idler

Speed-changing gears

Servomotor

11 Constant tensioning

Double-coil clutch brake — Pot

Follower

Shaft 1 — Shaft 2 — Supply reel

Rewind input — To tape recorder

12 Potentiometer control

Slip-clutch brake — Input

Pot

Normal: input drives pot, with slip protection
Energized: input disconnected and pot locked

---

eddy-current torques—which do not seriously reduce performance). It is capable of synchronous driving or continuous slip, with almost no torque variation at any slip differential for a given control current. Control-power requirement is small enough for vacuum-tube drive. Typical applications include wire or tape tensioning, servo-control actuation, and torque control in dynamometers.

Eddy-current clutches

Eddy-current clutches, on the other hand, are inherently speed-sensitive devices. They exhibit virtually no hysteresis, and develop torque by dissipating eddy currents through the electrical resistance of the rotor ring. This torque is almost a linear function of slip speed. These clutches are best used in speed-control applications, and as oscillation dampers.

PARTICLE AND FLUID MAGNETIC CLUTCHES

There is no real difference between magnetic-particle and magnetic-fluid clutches, except that the magnetic medium in the first is a dry powder and in the second it is a similar powder—but suspended in oil. In either type, the ferromagnetic medium is introduced into the airgap between the input and output faces, which do not actually contact one another. When the clutch coil is energized, the particles are excited in the magnetic field between the faces; as they shear against each other, they produce a drag torque between the clutch members.

Theoretically, these clutches can approach the proportional control characteristics of a hysteresis clutch within the small weight and size limits of a comparably rated miniature friction clutch. But in practice the service life of miniature magnetic-particle clutches has so far been too short for industrial usage.

OTHER MAGNETIC CLUTCHES

Two sophisticated concepts—neither of them yet developed to the point of practical application—may prove of great academic interest to anyone researching this field.

Electrostatic clutches, which use high voltages instead of magnetic field to create force-producing suspensions.

Magnetostrictive clutches using a magnetic force to change the dimenisons of a crystal or metal bar poised between two extremely precise faces.

Adjustable-speed drives

Variable-transformer drive. You dial motor speed by adjusting the winding ratio on an autotransformer. Its simplicity keeps costs lower than for most other drives, particularly in low power ranges from subfractional to 5 or 10 hp. A disadvantage is that an increase in load lowers motor speed as much as 25%, and the operator has to readjust the knob. This is no problem

Controlled - rectifier voltage - regulated drive. SCRs (silicon controlled rectifiers) are the heart of most of the new type voltage regulators, and any size dc motor from fractional hp and up can be controlled. Several manufacturers are developing drives with 400-hp and larger dc motors, using the heavy duty SCRs now available.

SCR voltage regulators are small and have no moving parts other than small potentiometers for setting speed. Simple feedback controls, based on IR compensation in the motor, keep speed droop very low (about 2%). Speed control range can exceed 200:1 using armature control for constant torque and field control for constant horsepower.

Response is rapid. Timed accelera-

VARIABLE TRANSFORMER DRIVE. An autotransformer connected across the line adjusts output voltage. Rectifiers convert this to dc, which drives a dc shunt motor. The system is fairly efficient, but motor speed is somewhat affected by the load. Typical speed drop from no load to full load is 25% to full speed. Graphs on following two pages define typical performance for several speed settings.

CONTROLLED-RECTIFIER REGULATOR DRIVE. Supply voltage is ac, converted to phase-controlled dc. The regulator can be a thyratron, an SCR, or a magnetic amplifier. In each case, output voltage is determined by the length of time that the current is permitted to pass. Control is achieved through the trigger, which initiates the current flow every cycle. The regulator output drives a dc shunt motor.

MG (WARD-LEONARD) DRIVE. The ac motor drives the dc generator. The generator field is adjusted to vary output voltage, driving a dc shunt motor. The field of the dc motor also can be varied: weakening the field will speed up the motor, strengthening the field will slow it down. A rotating dc exciter is pictured, but solid-state versions are available.

EDDY-CURRENT CLUTCH DRIVE. The ac motor drives the input drum of the clutch. The output half of the clutch is called the spider, and rotates inside the drum. In the simplest version, the field control windings are stationary. The spider becomes magnetized when those windings are energized with dc, inducing eddy currents in the drum. The interaction between the drum and spider develops the torque.

WOUND-ROTOR AC MOTOR. This is an induction motor with slip rings to connect the rotor windings to an external impedance, such as a rheostat. By varying the rotor resistance, motor speed can be varied over a 3:1 range. In some versions the electrical phase instead of the resistance of the rotor circuit is manipulated, thus adjusting impedance with fewer losses.

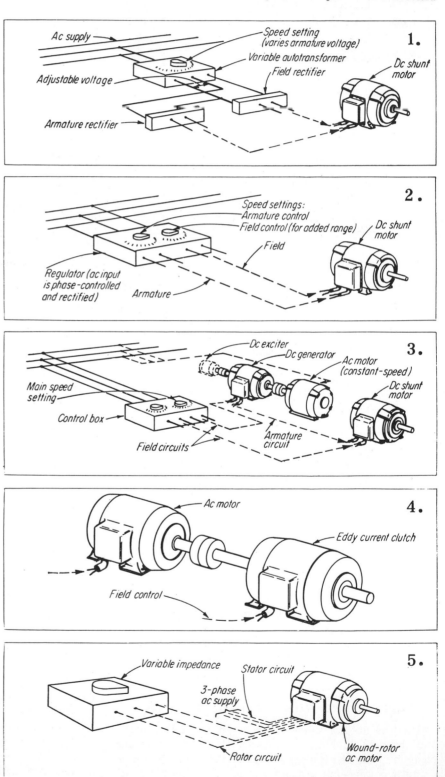

tion usually is provided to prevent too rapid speed changes which could be damaging to the motor and load. Reversible SCR drives have inherent regenerative braking. The latest reversible design operates from three-phase supply and is available in high hp ratings.

MG (Ward-Leonard) drive. Any size from 1 hp and up is available. The dc motor characteristics are similar to those in the SCR voltage-regulated drive. The drive can develop either constant torque or constant horsepower versus speed, depending on whether you adjust the armature or field voltage.

For constant-torque output, the typical speed range is 8:1. For constant horsepower, 1:4. In combination, a 16:1 speed range is typical. Normal speed droop is 8% between 25% and 100% load, and can be regulated much closer by adding speed-sensing feedback controls. For that matter, any type drive can be regulated closely if you add proper feedback.

An advantage of an MG drive is its inertial isolation from the power line. Line-voltage transients are mechanically and electrically damped by the rotating ac motor and dc generator. However, load transients are not damped very much by the ac motor and generator because the coupling is purely electrical. In fact, SCR-type drives stabilize load transients better than MG drives because the corrective action is quicker.

Another advantage of an MG set is its inherent regenerative braking—excellent for controlling overhauling loads.

Eddy-current clutch drive. The input shaft must always rotate faster than the output shaft, because torque is produced only when there is relative motion (slip) between the input drum and the output spider. The greatest efficiency is at maximum output speed and full load.

Maximum speed is about 90% of ac motor synchronous speed. For normal torques, minimum speed is generally 1/10 of top speed. For short times this low limit can be reduced to zero, but control will be jerky. The low-speed limit also can be reduced if load torque tends to diminish substantially with speed. About a 20:1 ratio is the maximum practical.

Torque is proportional to dc excitation of the field at a given slip. For a given torque, output speed can be lowered by reducing dc excitation. Overload torque is limited because it cannot exceed the normal 200% maximum torque of the ac motor.

Close speed regulation is possible only with speed-sensing feedback controls that adjust the field excitation. Then speed can be held within a few percent from 25 to 100% load.

Acceleration can be controlled by varying the rate of buildup of field-coil excitation. It functions best when load torque is constant. Logarithmic control is available. Controlled deceleration and braking are best handled by separate friction or eddy-current brakes, because the clutch itself is not adaptable to regenerative or dynamic braking.

Eddy-current drives are available from 1 hp to any size. The main limitation is the problem of dissipating the heat generated by clutch slip. This heat loss is proportional to torque times slip, and at low speeds, losses are very high. (see Energy Losses, p 148). The most economical operation is at constant torque for all speeds.

Wound rotor ac motor. The commonest version is a 3-phase slip-ring motor with adjustable external resistance in the rotor circuit. By adjusting the resistance, you can get maximum torque at any selected speed.

Power range is anything from 1 to hundreds of horsepower. Economical speed range is approximately 3:1, and speed regulation (droop), based on the slope of the torque-speed curve, is high.

Hydrostatic drives. In most hydrostatic drives, an electric motor drives a pump, and the pump supplies oil to a fluid motor. The only differences are in the way the oil flow is modulated.

The most inexpensive way is to use valves, such as the four-way valve shown in the sketch. However, because the pump handles full flow at all times, much of the energy is bypassed and wasted at low fluid-motor speeds.

The most efficient and versatile way to modulate flow is to control the displacement of either or both the pump and the fluid motor. Although more expensive than simple four-way valves, adjustable-displacement pumps and motors save horsepower by not moving the fluid when it is not needed.

Hydrostatic drives can be built in any size from fractional horsepower up.

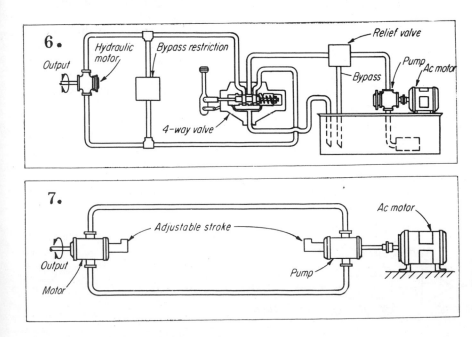

6. Output — Hydraulic motor — Bypass restriction — Relief valve — Pump — Ac motor — Bypass — 4-way valve

7. Output — Motor — Adjustable stroke — Pump — Ac motor

HYDROSTATIC DRIVE (VALVE CONTROL). A fixed-displacement pump running at constant speed drives a fixed displacement hydraulic motor. The four-way valve (or any other flow-control valve) throttles or bypasses pump flow to control speed of the hydraulic motor. This is the simplest hydrostatic drive, but is inefficient at low speeds due to wasted pump hp.

HYDROSTATIC DRIVE (PUMP AND MOTOR CONTROL). If the pump is the adjustable element, zero displacement results in zero flow and zero motor output speed. If the hydraulic motor is the adjustable element, minimum displacement represents maximum speed (actually, minimum displacement is limited to 25% of full stroke). If both pump and motor are adjustable, rpm range can exceed 72:1.

Analog and Digital Techniques Control Machine Member

MONTREAL, CANADA—A numerical machine tool control that represents a unique combination of analog and digital techniques has been developed by Sperry Gyroscope Company of Canada, Ltd. System incorporates highly accurate linear transducers, a tape reader that does not need a shift register or memory store, and a hydraulic valve that permits positioning accuracy at high travel speed.

The tape reader operates pneumatically, reading blocks of information instantaneously and obviating the need for a complex and costly shift register which would normally store information registered by sequential line-by-line readers. A block of information consists of 2 in. of tape and

contains all command details pertaining to one hole position, plus any other auxiliary functions.

The transducers consist of slabs of a glass mica compound with a coefficient of expansion closely approximating that of steel. The slabs have plated on them a series of fine lines in the shape of an elongated hairpin coil.

Two major components form the transducer: a stator, made up of sufficient sections aligned end to end, to cover the travel length of the controlled axis. And a slider, similar to a stator section, plated in a series of 25 separate coils, each coil about 0.25 in. The slider is rigidly linked to the moving machine member and rides above the stator. A clearance of a few

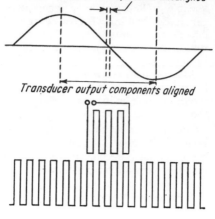

Transducer output components misaligned

Transducer output components aligned

thousandths separates the stator and slider, hence no mechanical wear is introduced.

Low frequency ac excitation of any one coil on the slider will induce an approximately sinusoidal signal in the stator coil. Signal will be at full amplitude when the turns in the energized slider coil are exactly aligned with the stator coil, and the signal will fall off to a null when the two coils are misaligned, above. By phase shifting, the 25 separate slider coils give 50 null positions.

The Sperry control system can operate satisfactorily with any conventional machine drive such as ac, dc or hydraulic motors. However, the development of the Sperry electro-hydraulic servo valve is ideally suited for use with hydraulic pistons in industrial applications.

The valve features high immunity to dirt in the hydraulic system and requires no destructive dither impulse for smooth and instantaneous operation. Essentially, it consists of a body containing four ports—two to each side of the piston—a spool and a torque motor. Use of four ports balances the fluid flow in the valve and locks the table when it reaches its index position.

This control system, according to B. W. King, Managing Director of Sperry Gyroscope of Canada, Ltd, is successfully applied to a wide variety of jig borers, turret drills, compound tables, and boring mills. ∎

Combination of analog and digital techniques . . .
controls table motion. Analog coarse data element brings machine member to about 0.050 in. of desired position. Electronic switching brings the digital fine measuring system into play to precisely position machine member to 0.001 in., with an accuracy of ± 0.0005 in. and a repeatability of ± 0.0001 in.

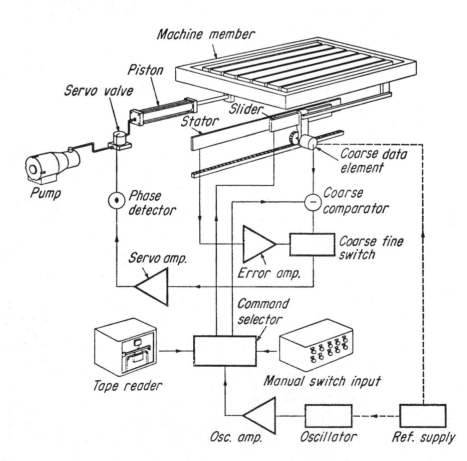

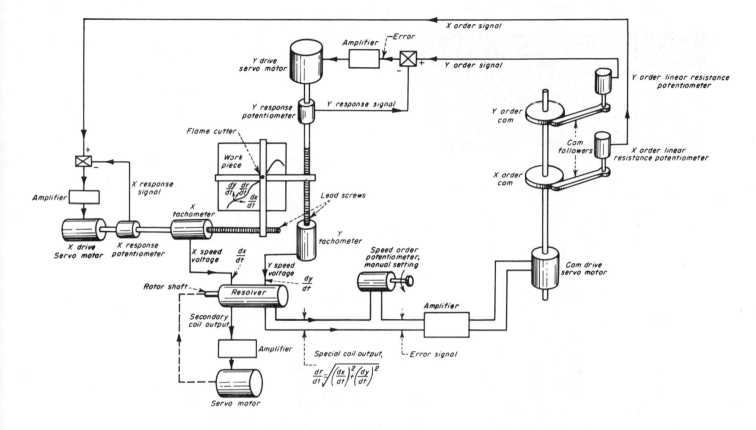

FLAME CUTTING CONTROL DEVICE. Arrangement for automatically cutting preset contours with a flame cutter. The system provides for cutting the proper contour and for maintaining constant cutting speed regardless of the shape of the contour. The control system can be divided into two parts in accordance with these functions.

The contour shaping system is controlled by two cams that contain the proper coordinate information to give the correct shape. The cam followers drive X and Y order linear resistance potentiometers which transmit signals to the X and Y lead screw drives. Each drive consists of a closed loop servo. The order signal is compared with a feedback voltage from the multi-turn response potentiometer and the difference or error is amplified. The drive motor is energized by the amplified signal and drives the lead screw and response potentiometer until the order signal equals the response signal.

In the cutting speed regulating circuit, the tachometers attached to the lead screws develop outputs proportional to the speed of rotation of the screws or to dx/dt and dy/dt in the coordinate system. These rate of change voltages are applied to the primary coils of a resolver. The output of the secondary resolver coils is amplified and used to drive a servo motor which positions the rotor (carrying the secondary coils) so as to reduce the resolver output to zero. Thus, this resolver servo loop simply positions the rotor in accordance with the dx/dt and dy/dt input signals. A special coil, with its axis perpendicular to the secondary coils, is wound on the rotor of the resolver. A voltage is induced in this special coil proportional to the vector sum of dx/dt and dy/dt, so that this voltage, $\frac{dr}{dt}$, is proportional to the instantaneous tangential cutting speed at any point on the contour. The signal, $\frac{dr}{dt}$, is compared with the voltage from a manually set speed order potentiometer, and the difference or error is amplified and used to energize the order cam servo motor. Thus, cutting speed can be maintained at any desired value by properly adjusting the speed order unit.

NEW SYSTEMS AND DEVICES FOR BRAKING

WASTE MOTION . . . It Brakes Saw

Switch off this power saw and its 3600-rpm blade
comes to standstill in five seconds, increasing safety and
saving time too. Electrical stage of braking system
draws off enough energy from spinning rotor to
let mechanical shoe finish the job.

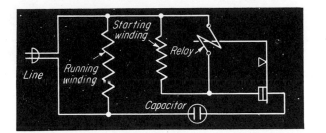

At power shutoff . . .

continued spinning of the rotor generates a voltage in the starting
winding. This loads the starting capacitor in conduit
box to quickly dissipate the momentum of the
rotor. At approximately 1200-1000 rpm, the residual flux and
regenerative braking drop off to a negligible value.

Below 1800 rpm, centrifugal force of the counterweights can no
longer overcome pressure of the tension springs. They pull the pivoted
counterweight inward, forcing the brake shoe against the
bearing support and stopping the motor.

The saw is started with brake applied, but with no other load at this
stage the rotor accelerates rapidly and disengages the brake.

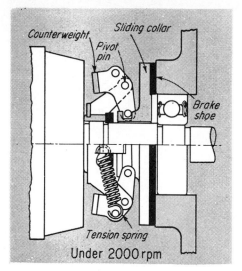

Under 2000 rpm

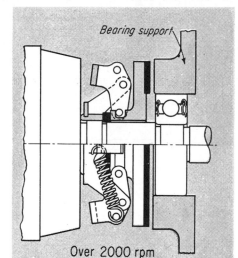

Over 2000 rpm

A better braking system for electric motors is claimed by ASEA, Vasteras, Sweden.
Essentially, it is a spring-applied, electromagnetically released braking mechanism
that uses flexible elements interposed between braking disk and motor shaft in
place of the usual direct spline connection. The result, says ASEA: much less
drag and therefore much less wear on the motor.

The flexible element may be simply a perforated spring-steel diaphragm
(see sketch), or it may be a set of leaf
springs or helical springs, or even a set
of rubber blocks. In any case, the flexible element is mounted on a carrier
splined to the motor shaft and is arranged
so that it can be displaced axially.

When the motor is in operation, an
armature is magnetically drawn to one
side, contacting the rotor. Then, when
power is shut off, the armature is released,

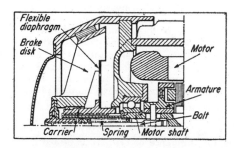

moving the bolt into the position shown and causing the disk to bear against the
motor housing. The braking torque so generated is transmitted to the shaft by
the flexible diaphragm and its carrier.

Speedy Tape Stops Fast Too

Though it handles 1000 characters per second this tape reader is braked to standstill within one punched hole. The brake generates its own high voltage for speedup action.

The machine handles 5-, 6-, 7- or 8-hole punched tape for highspeed computer operations. Phototransistors are connected to buffer amplifier for information or program feeding. The unit is manufactured by Associated Automation Ltd, subsidiary of Elliott-Automation, London, Eng.

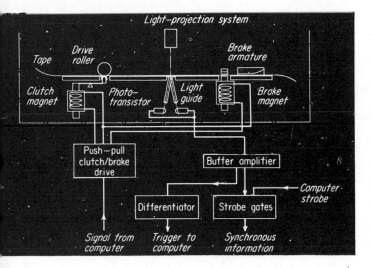

Pair of rollers . . .

provides rapid acceleration and deceleration of tape. Upper roller is mounted directly on the motor shaft. Lower (pinch) roller is mounted on pivoted armature and acts as a clutch when its electromagnet is activated.

Stopping within one punched hole is achieved by electromagnetic brake which clamps tape to brake pad. Brake is overriding control since clutch force is only ⅓ of brake force. Speed of brake operation (necessary to avoid losing characters on restart) is accomplished by using small armature displacement and high voltage generated in the inductance to produce a high potential across it. Coil is energized at 5 volts but has 1600 volts' measured potential. Push-pull circuit powers brake and releases roller with single signal.

Clear plastic guides provide accurate pickup and transmission of light from the punched hole in tape to light-sensitive transistors. Light is directed to tape surface by hooded prism projecting from front of reader housing. Release bar retracts the guide rollers and disconnects both magnetic coils for setup or positioning of tape.

Foot-Controlled Hydraulic Brake System Cushions Stop on Power Failure

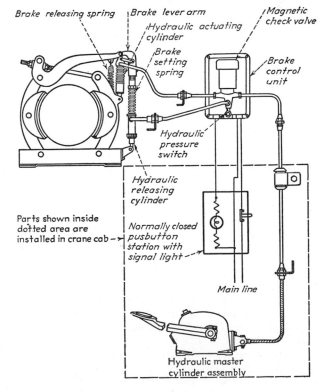

The crane braking system (right) operates when the main line switch closes. Full application of the master-cylinder foot-pedal compresses the brake-setting spring mounted on the hydraulic releasing cylinder. After the setting spring is fully compressed, the hydraulic pressure switch closes, completing the electric circuit and energizing the magnetic check valve. The setting spring remains compressed as long as the magnetic check valve is energized, since the check valve traps the fluid in the hydraulic releasing cylinder. Upon release of the foot pedal, brake lever arm is pulled down by the brake releasing spring, thus releasing the brake shoes.

High-speed counters

WILLIAM FOLEY, *Cramer Div, Giannini Controls Corp*

The electronic counter simply counts electrical pulses and gives a running display of accumulated pulses at any instant. Since the input is an electrical signal, generally a transducer is required to transform the nonelectrical signal into a usable input for the counter.

With a preset function on the counter, you can select any number within the count capacity of the device. Once the counter reaches the preset number, it can open or close the relay to control some operation. The counter will either reset automatically or stop. A dual unit permits continuous control over two different count sequence operations. Two sets of predetermining switches are usually mounted on the front panel of the counter, but they can be remote. If two different numbers are programmed into the counter, it will alternately count the two selected numbers. Multiple presets are also available, but at higher cost.

Besides performing two separate operations, a dual preset can control speeds as shown in Fig. 1. In the metal shearing operation run at high speed, one preset switch can be used to slow the material down at a given distance before the second preset actuates the shearing, then both automatically reset and start to measure again. The same presets could be used to alternately shear the material into two different lengths.

One area of measurement well adapted to high-speed counters is measuring continuous materials such as wire, rope, paper, textiles, or steel. Fig. 2 shows a coil-winding operation in which a counter stops the machine at a predetermined number of turns of wire.

Another application is shown in Fig 3 where magazines are counted as they run off a press. A photoelectric pickup senses the alternate light and dark lines formed by the shadow of the folded edge of each magazine. At the predetermined number, a knife edge, actuated by the counter, separates the magazines into exact batches.

A third application is machine-tool control. A preset counter can be used with a transducer or pulse generator mounted on the feed mechanism. It could, for example, convert revolutions of screw feed, hence displacement, into pulses to be fed into the counter. A feed of 0.129 in. might represent a count of 129 to the counter, which when preset at that number, could stop, advance, or reverse the feed mechanism.

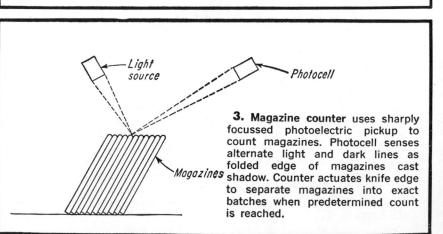

1. Dual preset function on high-speed counter controls high-speed shearing operation. If material is to be cut in 10-ft lengths and each pulse of electromagnetic pickup represents 0.1 ft, operator presets 100 into first input channel. Second input is set to 90. When 90 pulses are counted, second channel slows the material, then when counter reaches 100, first channel actuates shear. Both channels reset instantaneously and start next cycle.

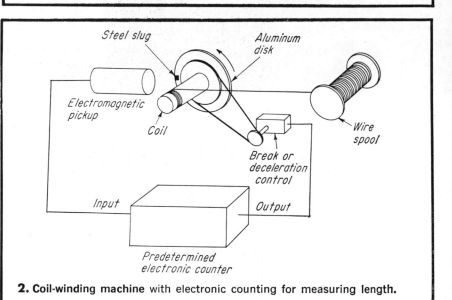

2. Coil-winding machine with electronic counting for measuring length.

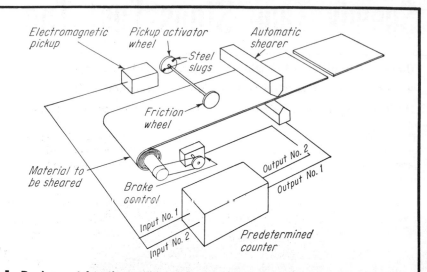

3. Magazine counter uses sharply focussed photoelectric pickup to count magazines. Photocell senses alternate light and dark lines as folded edge of magazines cast shadow. Counter actuates knife edge to separate magazines into exact batches when predetermined count is reached.

7

SWITCHING MECHANISMS AND MAGNETIC DEVICES

limit switches

E. L. RUDISILL, *Control Specialist, General Electric Co.*

FRANKLIN D. YEAPLE, *Associate Editor*

LIMIT SWITCHES can be defined as electric current switching devices that are operated by some type of mechanical motion. Limit switches find their greatest field of application on automatic machinery by controlling a complete operating cycle automatically by closing and opening electrical circuits in the proper sequence.

In addition to interlocking control circuits, limit switches have many other uses. For example, one of the most important is as safety devices to stop a machine, sound a warning signal, or illuminate a warning light when a dangerous operating condition develops. Thus, properly applied switches can both control highly efficient automatic electric machinery and protect it and the operator.

IN the broadest sense, limit switches are devices which make or break an electrical connection when a machine component or other mass approaches a selected position. These switches, including all presence and position detectors, fall into three categories: mechanical, interrupted beam, and proximity.

Mechanical: A rotary arm or push-rod on the switch housing is mechanically connected to the electrical switching element inside. The great majority of limit switches fall into this category. You can buy at least a million different configurations; there are dozens of standard contact arrangements, dozens of modes of contact motion, dozens of basic case configurations, and hundreds of ways to mount and operate the actuator arm. Besides these, there are many combinations of materials to permit operation in special environments.

Interrupted beam: A beam of light, a sound, or a jet of fluid is aimed across the path of the object to be detected. Interruption of the beam indicates presence of the object. The beams are usually of visible light or ultrahigh-frequency sound, but infrared beams and air jets are available.

Proximity: Presence of an object close to the sensor face disturbs an electrical or magnetic circuit and triggers the switch. Most available sensors are magnetic in principle—either ac or permanent magnet—but some work with capacitance, electrical conductivity, and thermal conductivity.

MECHANICAL LIMIT SWITCHES

There are two broad classes: linear and rotary. A linear switch has a lever or plunger that is actuated by an object moving in a straight line, whereas a rotary is actuated directly by a rotating shaft. Electrical problems are identical. In fact, linear and rotary limit switches often have the same basic switch inside.

Linear mechanical

By far the greatest number of limit switches sold are linear mechanical with a simple lever-arm actuator. The lever can be replaced with any of the special actuators shown

Typical limit switches: The variety can be comprehended best by comparing the sketches of housings, actuators, and contact designs throughout this article. The smallest designs are based on subminiature precision snap-acting switches smaller than a cube of sugar. Largest are heavy-duty traveling-crane limit switches, which interrupt 50 amp to reverse crane-trolley motors.

Some limit switches are designed from scratch to be limit switches only. The spring-loaded latch-type switches are the best examples.

The greatest variety of limit switches, however, are miniature precision snap-acting switches adapted to limit-switch application. They are available from many manufacturers in great profusion because the same basic switches are used almost everywhere there is electricity. There are about a half-dozen fundamental snap-action principles

Application tips:

- Don't use the limit switch body or arm as a mechanical stop.
- Don't smack the arm too fast going, or let it snap back returning.
- Don't hit the arm at a sidewise angle—it can't take it.
- Don't locate the switch where it will be sprayed, kicked, hammered on, burned, or forgotten.

Rotary mechanical

There are two subdivisions—rotary cam and geared rotary—and they differ greatly. A rotary-cam switch is

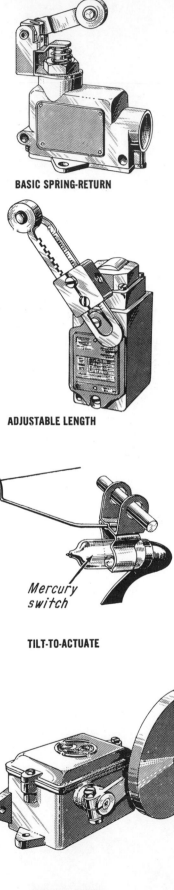

Actuator

BASIC SPRING-RETURN

ADJUSTABLE LENGTH

Mercury switch

TILT-TO-ACTUATE

OVERSIZE WHEEL

styles for linear mechanical switches

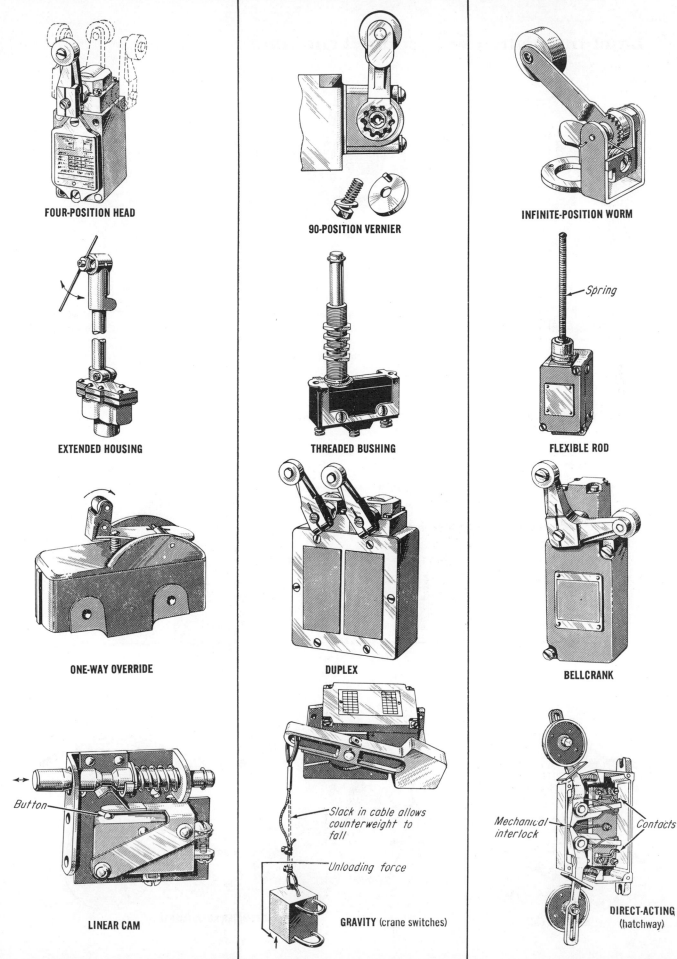

FOUR-POSITION HEAD

90-POSITION VERNIER

INFINITE-POSITION WORM

EXTENDED HOUSING

THREADED BUSHING

Spring

FLEXIBLE ROD

ONE-WAY OVERRIDE

DUPLEX

BELLCRANK

Button

LINEAR CAM

Slack in cable allows counterweight to fall

Unloading force

GRAVITY (crane switches)

Mechanical interlock

Contacts

DIRECT-ACTING (hatchway)

Latching switch with contact chamber

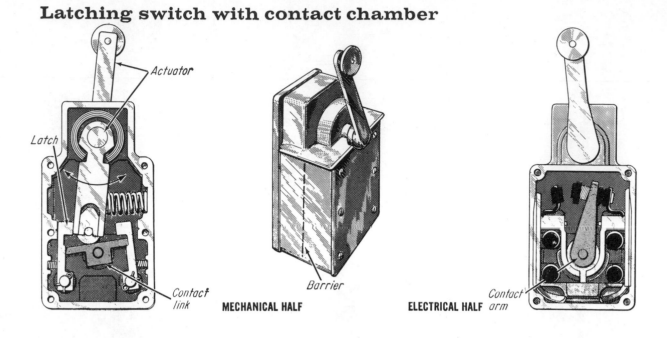

Actuator

Latch

Contact link

MECHANICAL HALF

Barrier

ELECTRICAL HALF

Contact arm

Rotary-cam limit switches

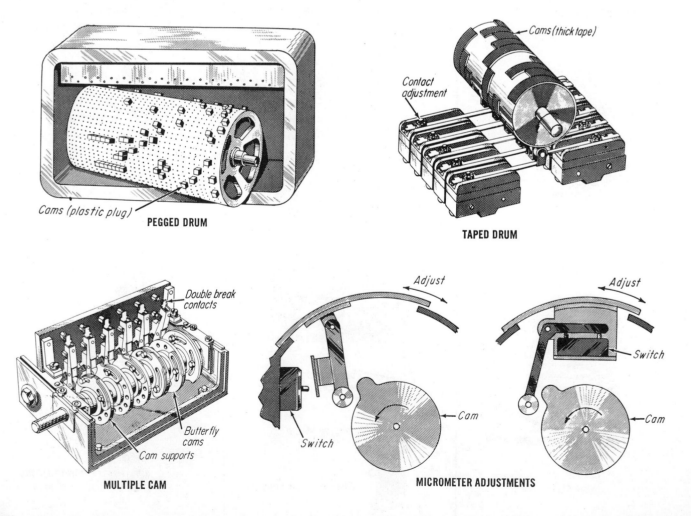

Cams (plastic plug)

PEGGED DRUM

Cams (thick tape)

Contact adjustment

TAPED DRUM

Double break contacts

Butterfly cams

Cam supports

MULTIPLE CAM

Adjust

Adjust

Switch

Cam

Switch

Cam

MICROMETER ADJUSTMENTS

hardly a limit switch because its major function is to control the sequence of events in one or more circuits. It makes only one revolution to complete its cycle and it actuates any number of switches, depending on the number of cams. A geared rotary switch is a true limit switch because it normally operates just once—when the input shaft has turned a predetermined number of revolutions. Its major application is on motorized garage doors, but it can be applied to any operation where a motor or shaft turns a fixed number of revolutions to complete an action.

Rotary-cam switch: The only complicated feature is the cam adjustment—made so because users want extreme accuracy and ease of adjustment.

Some cams cannot be adjusted directly and must be replaced with cams of different shapes to change the switch sequencing. Others have cams that can be rotated relative to the shaft and locked. Still others have cams fixed to the shaft, but with pre-etched tabs that can be broken off wherever desired to change the shape of the cam. The advantage here is that you don't have to know the desired cam settings until after the switch is installed.

One popular cam form—variously called a fanning cam, butterfly cam, or split cam—extends the operating lobe or dwell of the cam without changing cams. It is really two cams, side by side, and each one actuates the switch. If the two cams are positioned with the lobes together (superimposed), the switch will have the minimum actuating arc. If the lobes are spread (fanned), the actuating arc increases.

In some fanning-cam designs, each cam is fanned individually with a micrometer or vernier adjustment. The ratio of adjusting screw to cam rotation typically is about 8:1. Some units have as many as 24 circuits in a single housing.

Micrometer-type two-adjustment rotary-cam switches are also available.

Geared rotary limit switch: A true limit switch, this usually has one or sometimes more precision snap-acting switches that operate after the drive shaft has turned from 1 to 4000 revolutions (ratios from 1:1 to 4000:1 are available). Its major advantage over a linear limit switch is that it can be placed on the driving shaft a safe distance from the machine or part being driven. This might also be a disadvantage if there is appreciable slippage or wind-up in the machine transmission.

Geared rotary limit switches

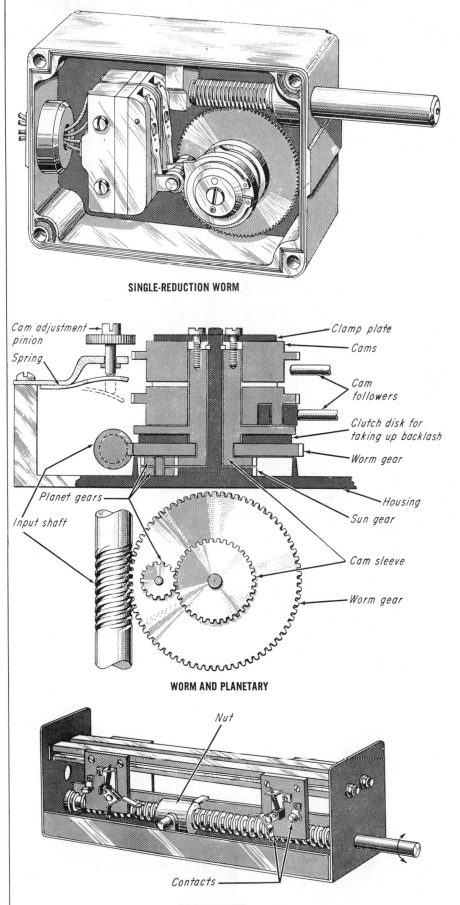

SINGLE-REDUCTION WORM

WORM AND PLANETARY

TRAVELING NUT

Limit switches, used to confine or restrain the travel or rotation of moving parts within certain predetermined points, are actuated by varying methods. Some of these, such as cams, rollers, push-rods, and traveling nuts, are described and illustrated below.

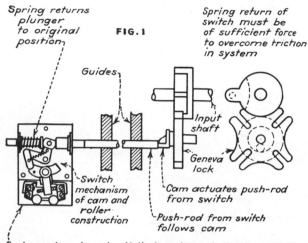

FIG. 1

Spring returns plunger to original position

Guides

Input shaft

Geneva lock

Switch mechanism of cam and roller construction

Cam actuates push-rod from switch

Push-rod from switch follows cam

Spring-return, two-circuit limit switch, stationary mounting
Allen-Bradley Co.

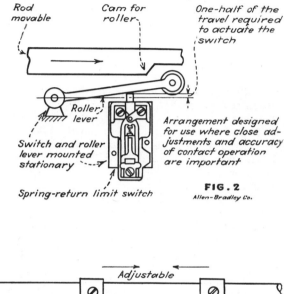

FIG. 2

Rod movable

Cam for roller

One-half of the travel required to actuate the switch

Roller lever

Switch and roller lever mounted stationary

Spring-return limit switch

Arrangement designed for use where close adjustments and accuracy of contact operation are important

Allen-Bradley Co.

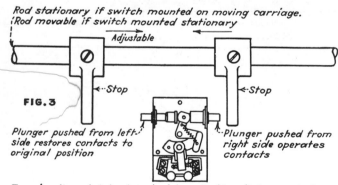

FIG. 3

Rod stationary if switch mounted on moving carriage. Rod movable if switch mounted stationary

Adjustable

Stop

Stop

Plunger pushed from left side restores contacts to original position

Plunger pushed from right side operates contacts

Two-circuit, maintained-contact type limit switch mounted stationary, or mounted on moving carriage

Allen-Bradley Co.

FIG. 4

Adjustable

Rod stationary if switch and linkage assembly mounted on moving carriage. Rod movable if switch and linkage mounted stationary

Coarse adjustment

Fine adjustment

Fixed point

Maintained-contact type, push lever operated limit switch

Sleeve

Switch and accompanying linkage mounted stationary, or mounted on moving carriage

Allen-Bradley Co.

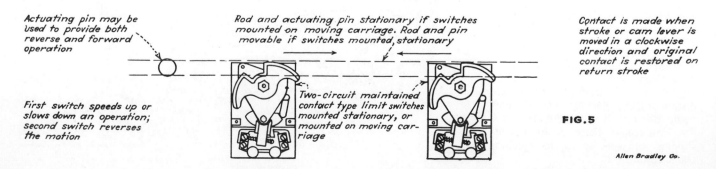

FIG. 5

Actuating pin may be used to provide both reverse and forward operation

First switch speeds up or slows down an operation; second switch reverses the motion

Rod and actuating pin stationary if switches mounted on moving carriage. Rod and pin movable if switches mounted stationary

Two-circuit maintained contact type limit switches mounted stationary, or mounted on moving carriage

Contact is made when stroke or cam lever is moved in a clockwise direction and original contact is restored on return stroke

Allen-Bradley Co.

MACHINERY MECHANISMS

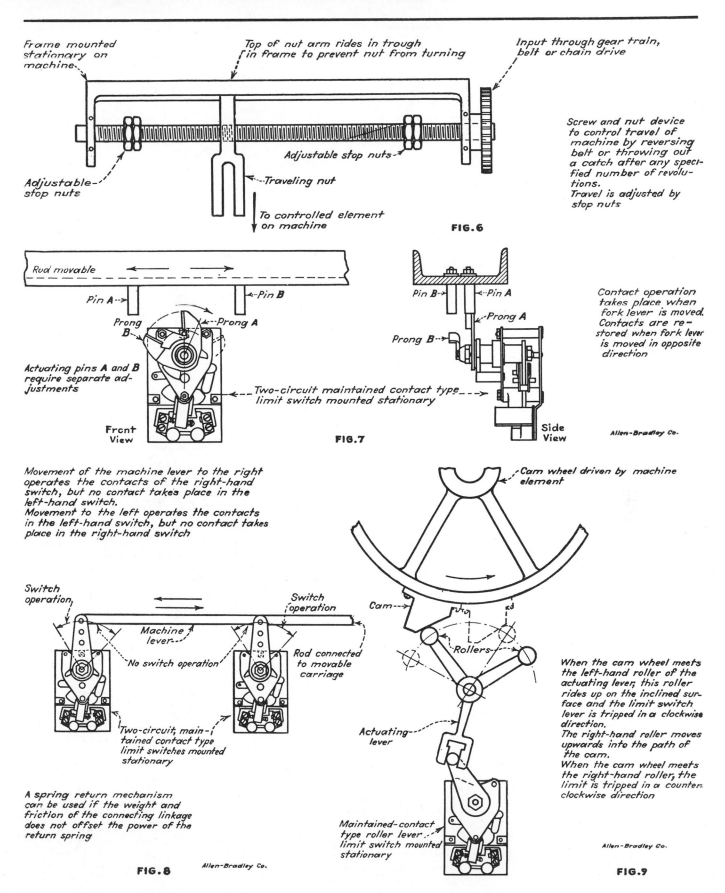

Frame mounted stationary on machine

Top of nut arm rides in trough in frame to prevent nut from turning

Input through gear train, belt or chain drive

Adjustable stop nuts

Adjustable stop nuts

Traveling nut

Screw and nut device to control travel of machine by reversing belt or throwing out a catch after any specified number of revolutions.
Travel is adjusted by stop nuts

To controlled element on machine

FIG.6

Rod movable

Pin A   Pin B

Pin B   Pin A

Prong B   Prong A

Prong A

Prong B

Actuating pins A and B require separate adjustments

Two-circuit maintained contact type limit switch mounted stationary

Contact operation takes place when fork lever is moved. Contacts are restored when fork lever is moved in opposite direction

Front View

Side View

Allen-Bradley Co.

FIG.7

Movement of the machine lever to the right operates the contacts of the right-hand switch, but no contact takes place in the left-hand switch.
Movement to the left operates the contacts in the left-hand switch, but no contact takes place in the right-hand switch

Cam wheel driven by machine element

Switch operation

Switch operation

Machine lever

No switch operation

Rod connected to movable carriage

Cam

Rollers

Actuating lever

Two-circuit, maintained contact type limit switches mounted stationary

A spring return mechanism can be used if the weight and friction of the connecting linkage does not offset the power of the return spring

Maintained-contact type roller lever limit switch mounted stationary

When the cam wheel meets the left-hand roller of the actuating lever, this roller rides up on the inclined surface and the limit switch lever is tripped in a clockwise direction.
The right-hand roller moves upwards into the path of the cam.
When the cam wheel meets the right-hand roller, the limit is tripped in a counterclockwise direction

FIG.8   Allen-Bradley Co.

Allen-Bradley Co.

FIG.9

233

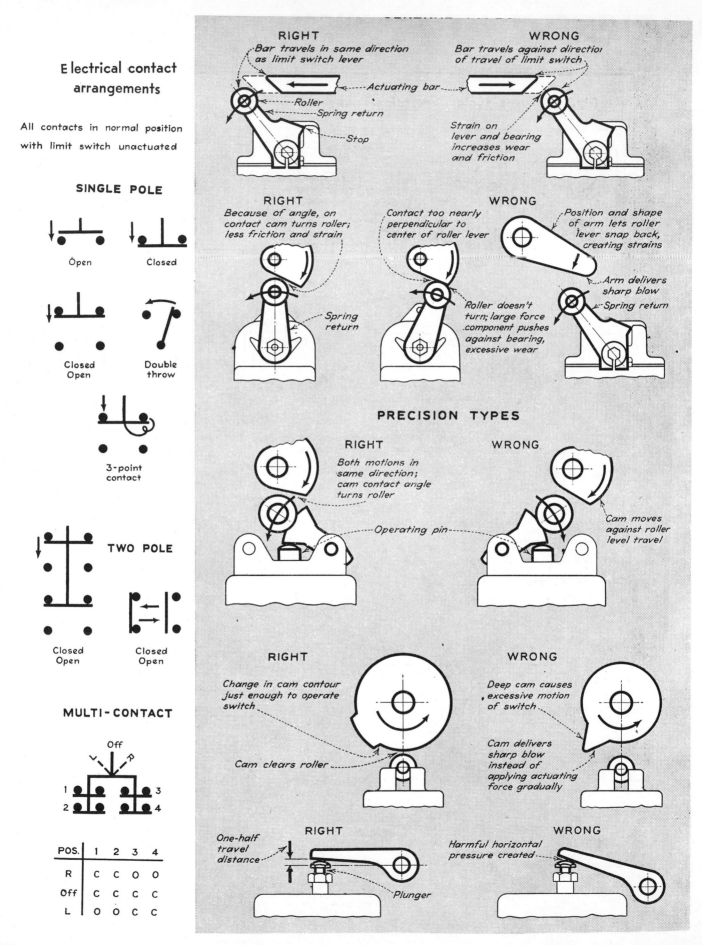

Electrical contact arrangements

All contacts in normal position with limit switch unactuated

SINGLE POLE

Open

Closed

Closed Open

Double throw

3-point contact

TWO POLE

Closed Open

Closed Open

MULTI-CONTACT

Off

L   R

1   3
2   4

POS.	1	2	3	4
R	C	C	O	O
Off	C	C	C	C
L	O	O	C	C

RIGHT — Bar travels in same direction as limit switch lever

Actuating bar — Roller — Spring return — Stop

WRONG — Bar travels against direction of travel of limit switch

Strain on lever and bearing increases wear and friction

RIGHT — Because of angle, on contact cam turns roller; less friction and strain

Spring return

WRONG — Contact too nearly perpendicular to center of roller lever

Roller doesn't turn; large force component pushes against bearing, excessive wear

Position and shape of arm lets roller lever snap back, creating strains

Arm delivers sharp blow — Spring return

PRECISION TYPES

RIGHT — Both motions in same direction; cam contact angle turns roller

Operating pin

WRONG

Cam moves against roller level travel

RIGHT — Change in cam contour just enough to operate switch

Cam clears roller

WRONG — Deep cam causes excessive motion of switch

Cam delivers sharp blow instead of applying actuating force gradually

RIGHT

One-half travel distance

Plunger

WRONG

Harmful horizontal pressure created

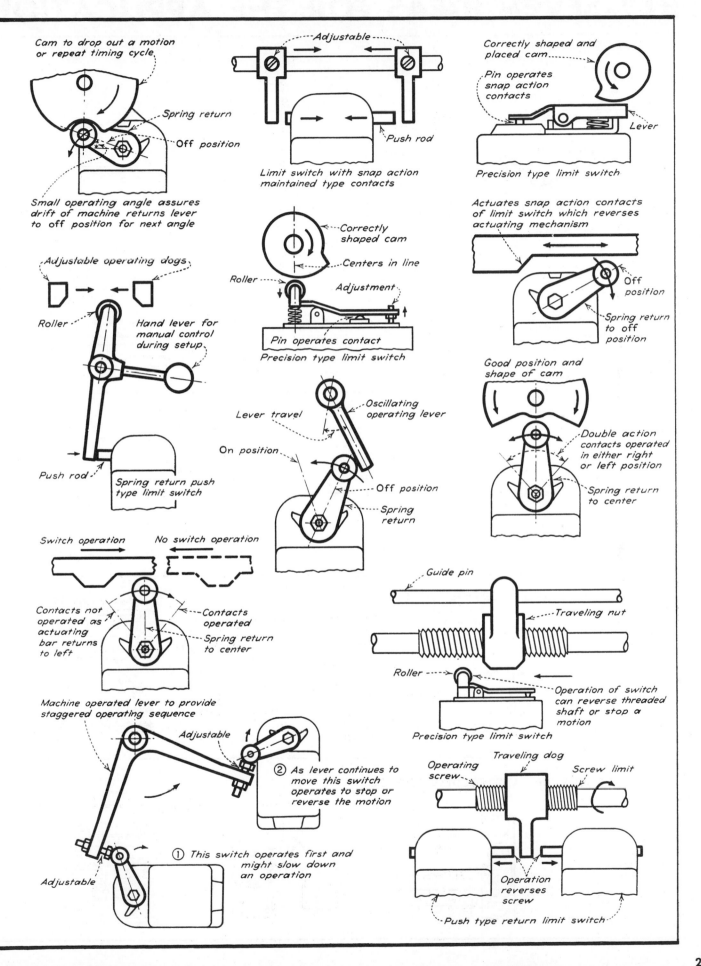

Cam to drop out a motion or repeat timing cycle

Spring return

Off position

Small operating angle assures drift of machine returns lever to off position for next angle

Adjustable

Push rod

Limit switch with snap action maintained type contacts

Correctly shaped and placed cam

Pin operates snap action contacts

Lever

Precision type limit switch

Adjustable operating dogs

Roller

Hand lever for manual control during setup

Push rod

Spring return push type limit switch

Correctly shaped cam

Centers in line

Roller

Adjustment

Pin operates contact

Precision type limit switch

Lever travel

Oscillating operating lever

On position

Off position

Spring return

Actuates snap action contacts of limit switch which reverses actuating mechanism

Off position

Spring return to off position

Good position and shape of cam

Double action contacts operated in either right or left position

Spring return to center

Switch operation

No switch operation

Contacts not operated as actuating bar returns to left

Contacts operated

Spring return to center

Guide pin

Traveling nut

Roller

Operation of switch can reverse threaded shaft or stop a motion

Precision type limit switch

Machine operated lever to provide staggered operating sequence

Adjustable

② As lever continues to move this switch operates to stop or reverse the motion

① This switch operates first and might slow down an operation

Adjustable

Traveling dog

Operating screw

Screw limit

Operation reverses screw

Push type return limit switch

THIRTY-SEVEN IDEAS FOR THE APPLICATION

PROCESS CONTROL

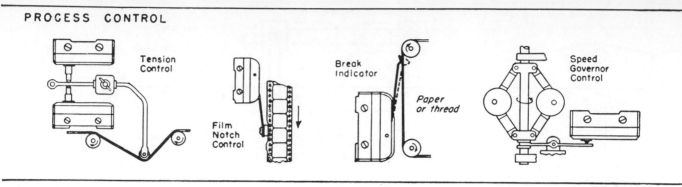

Tension Control

Film Notch Control

Break Indicator — Paper or thread

Speed Governor Control

MOTION CONTROL

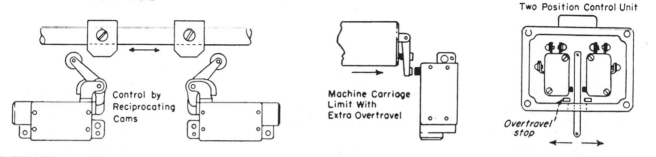

Control by Reciprocating Cams

Machine Carriage Limit With Extra Overtravel

Two Position Control Unit

Overtravel stop

ENCLOSURE PROTECTION

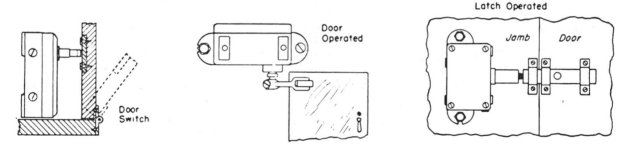

Door Switch

Door Operated

Latch Operated

Jamb   Door

THERMOSTATIC AND PRESSURE CONTROL

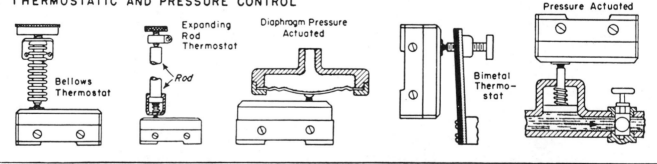

Bellows Thermostat

Expanding Rod Thermostat — Rod

Diaphragm Pressure Actuated

Bimetal Thermostat

Pressure Actuated

COUNTING, SORTING AND FEEDING DEVICES

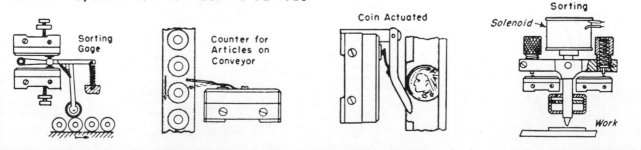

Sorting Gage

Counter for Articles on Conveyor

Coin Actuated

Sorting

Solenoid

Work

OF PRECISION SNAP-ACTION SWITCHES

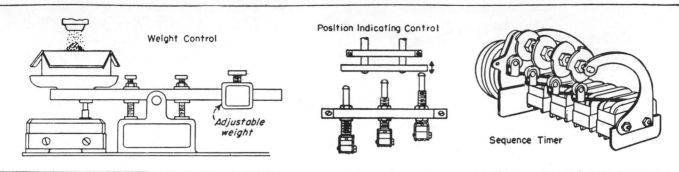

Weight Control

Adjustable weight

Position Indicating Control

Sequence Timer

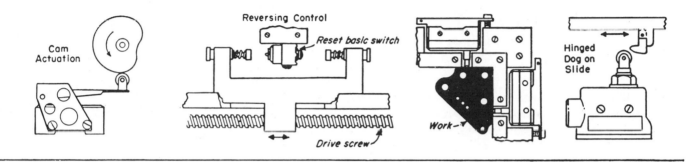

Cam Actuation

Reversing Control

Reset basic switch

Drive screw

Work

Hinged Dog on Slide

GAGING AND THICKNESS CONTROL

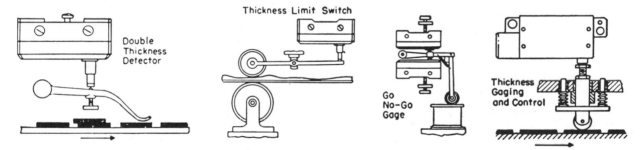

Double Thickness Detector

Thickness Limit Switch

Go No-Go Gage

Thickness Gaging and Control

LEVEL CONTROL

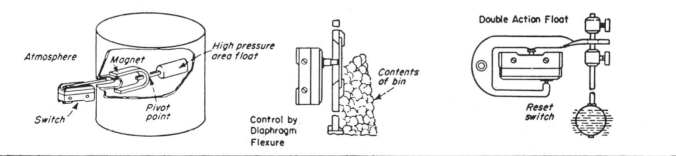

Atmosphere

Magnet

High pressure area float

Switch

Pivot point

Control by Diaphragm Flexure

Contents of bin

Double Action Float

Reset switch

MISCELLANEOUS

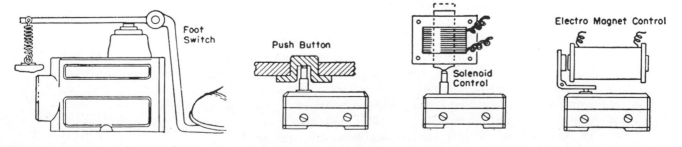

Foot Switch

Push Button

Solenoid Control

Electro Magnet Control

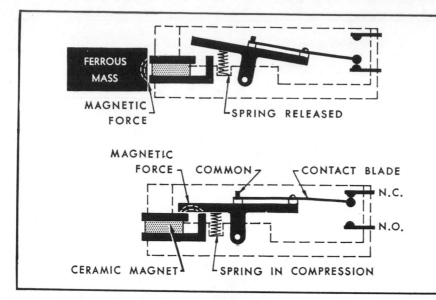

Change in path of magnetic flux operates proximity switch . . .
that has snap-action similar to standard limit switch and repeatability said to be within 0.001 in. In sensing position (top illustration) magnetic flux from ceramic magnet flows through steel plates and ferrous mass being sensed, enabling contact blade to close circuit. In absence of ferrous mass, flux flows through pivoted iron beam, which holds it in place against force of compressed spring keeping circuit open. Inert gas atmosphere in sealed housing (phenolic body in brass shell) prevents oxidation and corrosion. Switch can be actuated by objects traveling either axially or tangentially. Actuating device can also be a selected contour or oriented magnet, to permit switching across larger gap. Contacts are rated 6 amp current at 110 v resistive and 3 amp at 220 v for nominal life. Measures $1\frac{7}{8}$ x $2\frac{1}{2}$ in. long. *(Tann Corp., Detroit, Mich.)*

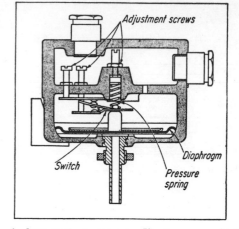

A low-cost, compact, diaphragm switch for fluid flow control is being made available through a British firm.

Designed in Switzerland, the unit has a minimum of parts (see diagram) and weighs only 9 oz. Diameter is 4 in.; height with spindle, 3¾ in.

The diaphragm serves as the actuating element, and the snap switch, which can be operated by very slight pressure, serves as the changeover contact.

(From Delbag Air Filters Ltd., London)

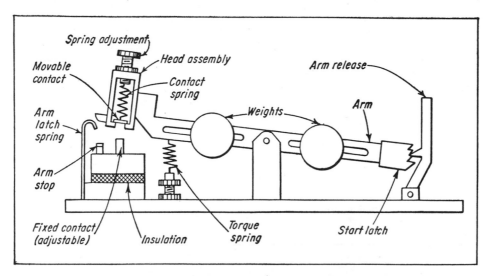

Better control of "contact bounce"—undesirable, rapid-fire opening and closing of electrical contacts that wears them out and interferes with performance of electrical controls—is promised by new studies at Price Electric.

A mechanism incorporating the essentials for controlling or eliminating contact bounce has now been designed. It consists of a contact actuating arm mounted on adjustable cone pivots, carrying a small movable contact member that has a provision for controlling stored force. Adjustable weights balance the arm and an adjustable coil spring attached to it provides a variable torque for rotating the arm to engage a fixed contact. The diagram shows it in open position.

IN SWITCHING DEVICES

A weightlessness switch—a switch that will respond to less-than-normal gravimetric conditions—has been designed for the Atomic Energy Commission. The operating principle is an interesting one, taking advantage of the effects of gravimetric changes on the surface tension and therefore the shape of a globule of a conducting liquid.

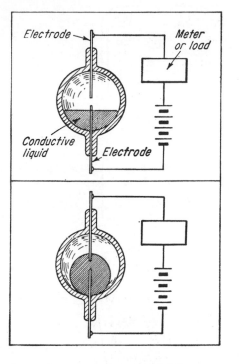

The switch consists of an insulated cavity filled with a conducting liquid such as mercury and containing a pair of electrodes. Under normal conditions (upper diagram), gravity forces the liquid against the cavity wall so it assumes a flat shape, pulled away from the contacts, and the switch is in an open-circuit condition. But, as the weight of the liquid approaches weightlessness or zero gravity the surface tension of the liquid forces it to assume a spherical shape so that it surrounds the electrodes and closes the circuit.

The amount of liquid placed in the cavity determines the point of weightlessness at which the circuit is closed. The remaining space may be filled with an inert gas. However, a time-delay feature may be introduced by using a viscous nonconducting fluid such as silicone oil as the filler. This functions to prevent the rapid change in shape of the conducting liquid, thus delaying the shorting of the conductors.

The device is available for royalty-free, non-exclusive licensing.

A switch which pulls itself closed and cleans its own contacts has been designed and patented in Britain by M & C Switchgear Ltd, Kirkintilloch, Glasgow.

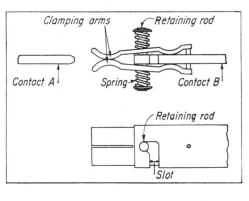

The switch consists of a pair of contact arms which enclose a rod-shaped conductor and are spring-biased so that the two arms serve as a clamp (see diagram). Movement of conductor A in and out of the contact arms exerts a wiping or cleaning action; and, under high-current conditions, the contact arms are magnetically attracted to each other, reducing contact resistance. A slot, provided in contact B, makes it possible to dissassemble the unit by disengaging the ends of the contacts from the retaining rod and sliding it out of the slot.

ELECTRIC SWITCH DEVICES

B. B. RAMEY
Chief Engineer
Black & Decker Manufacturing Company

FIG 1

Switch-Position
Indicator

ON — ON
OFF   OFF

Fig. 1—Trigger operated ratchet-type single pole switch, a design no longer in general use. An arrow stamped on the end of the shaft shows through a hole in the cover plate to indicate the position of the switch. Spring blades pressing on the faces of the square contact block give a snap action and hold the block in position.

Fig. 2—Ratchet-type switch with double pole for 3-phase. Can also be used for single phase. The word "on" is stamped on diametrically opposite points on the ratchet wheel. With switch in "on" position, the word shows through a hole in the cover plate. A spring level snaps into the star wheel, giving quick snap action. As in Figs. 1 and 3, to open the switch a definite movement of the trigger is required.

FIG. 2

OFF ON

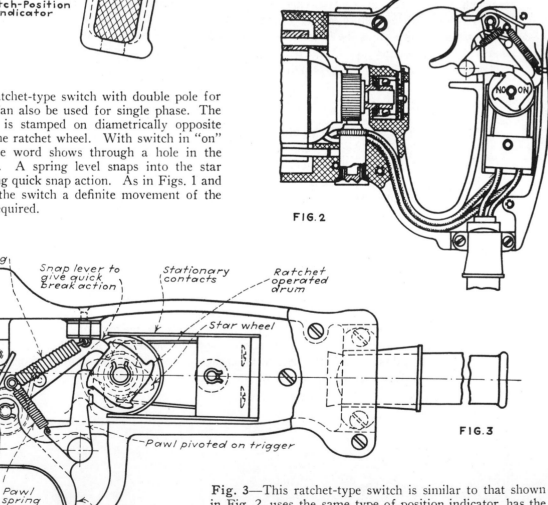

Snap lever spring

Snap lever to give quick break action

Stationary contacts

Ratchet operated drum

Trigger spring

Star wheel

Pawl pivoted on trigger

Pawl spring

Trigger

FIG. 3

Fig. 3—This ratchet-type switch is similar to that shown in Fig. 2, uses the same type of position indicator, has the same arrangement of pawl, snap lever, star wheel and round contact block. Only the type of handle is different.

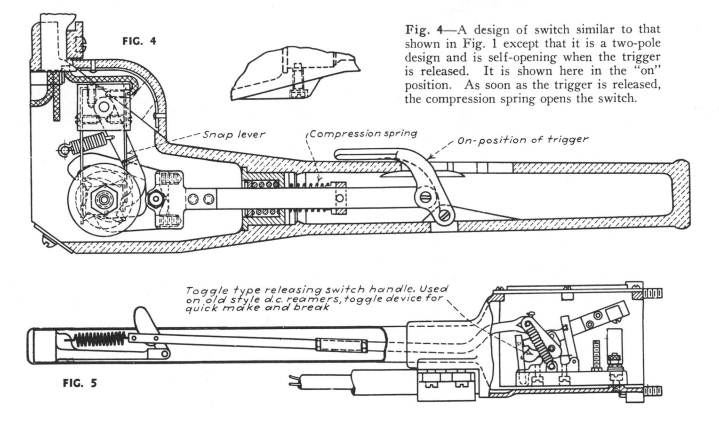

FIG. 4

Fig. 4—A design of switch similar to that shown in Fig. 1 except that it is a two-pole design and is self-opening when the trigger is released. It is shown here in the "on" position. As soon as the trigger is released, the compression spring opens the switch.

—Snap lever

(Compression spring

—On-position of trigger

Toggle type releasing switch handle. Used on old style d.c. reamers, toggle device for quick make and break

FIG. 5

Fig. 5—A toggle-type self-opening switch used on old style d.c. reamers. The tripper is pushed forward until the line of pull of the spring passes the dead center of the link to which it is attached. The spring then pulls the switch closed. Upon releasing the trigger the mechanism returns to the position shown, the switch snapping open when the toggle spring passes dead center.

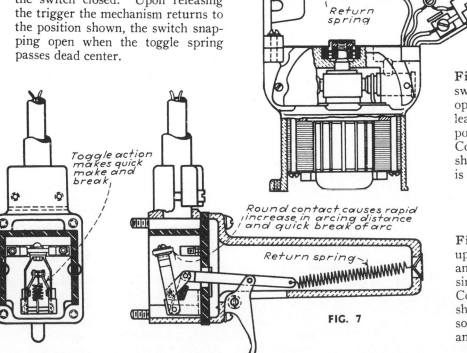

Return spring

FIG. 6

Fig. 6—A conventional type switch of old design which is self-opening when the trigger is released, but can be held in the closed position by means of a locking pin. Common to all of the switches shown in this group of designs, it is not dust-proof.

Toggle action makes quick make and break

Round contact causes rapid increase in arcing distance and quick break of arc

Return spring

FIG. 7

Fig. 7—A special design of built-up switch of the self-opening type and provided with a locking pin, similar to that shown in Fig. 5. Common to all of the designs shown here, the switch is now obsolete in favor of fully-inclosed and easily replaceable switch units.

ELECTRIC SWITCH DEVICES

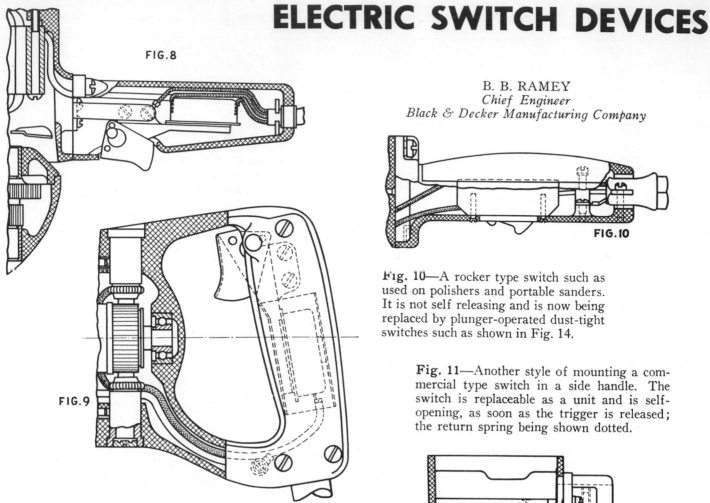

FIG.8

B. B. RAMEY
Chief Engineer
Black & Decker Manufacturing Company

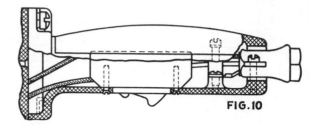

FIG.10

FIG.9

Fig. 10—A rocker type switch such as used on polishers and portable sanders. It is not self releasing and is now being replaced by plunger-operated dust-tight switches such as shown in Fig. 14.

Fig. 11—Another style of mounting a commercial type switch in a side handle. The switch is replaceable as a unit and is self-opening, as soon as the trigger is released; the return spring being shown dotted.

Fig. 8—A modern type commercial switch mounted in a side handle. Such switches are readily replaced as a unit, are inexpensive and sealed against the entrance of dirt. The switch opens as soon as the trigger is released unless the locking pin is set, in which case a slight pull on the trigger releases the locking pin and opens the switch.

Fig. 9—Another example of a modern commercial switch mounted as a unit in a grip type end handle.

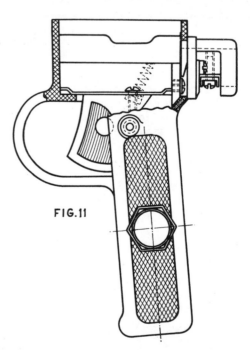

FIG.11

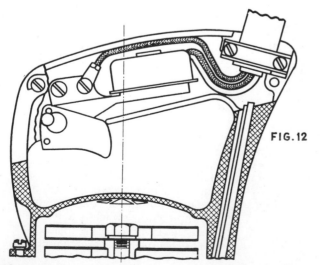

FIG.12

Fig. 12—In this switch mounting the trigger actuates the switch by means of a lift rod attached to the back of the trigger. A tension spring attached to the upper end of the lift rod and anchored to the lower end of the switch plate pulls the switch open as soon as the trigger is released. If the locking pin is depressed when the trigger is pulled back it passes through the hole in the trigger which then cannot return to the open position. As soon as the trigger is pressed the locking pin is released, snaps back and releases the trigger.

Fig. 13—A slider operated switch. The slider moves back and forth as indicated in the drawing. This switch is not provided with any release arrangement. It is used only on light model tools where no damage would be done if the tool were laid down with the power still on.

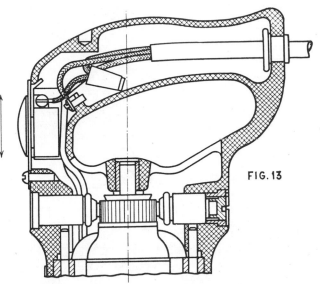

FIG. 13

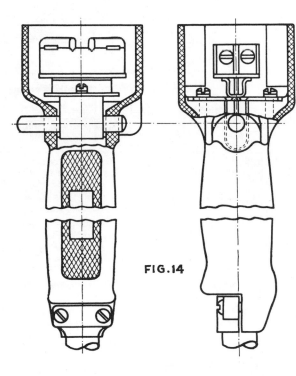

FIG. 14

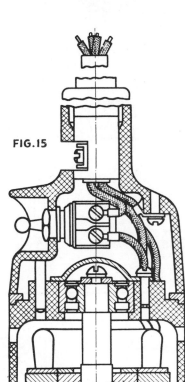

FIG. 15

Fig. 15—Latest design of switch arrangement for small die grinders and sanders. The toggle-operated switch unit is mounted in a dust-tight compartment and a dust-seal is provided where the toggle comes through the case. This type of switch does not have a release arrangement that opens it automatically.

Fig. 16—This switch is of the same type as shown in Fig. 11. It is mounted in a longer handle, being actuated by a remote trigger arrangement. It is provided with an additional return spring for quick action and also has a locking pin for holding the switch in the closed position when the trigger is released. A slight pull on the trigger releases the locking pin and opens the switch.

Fig. 14—Latest type switch handle for polishers, sanders, and portable grinders. The switch is in a dust-tight chamber and is operated by a plunger instead of a trigger, which eliminates the necessity of an opening such as is required when triggers or rockers are used. The plunger makes a close fit. Switch is not self-releasing, it being necessary to push the plunger for both on and off positions.

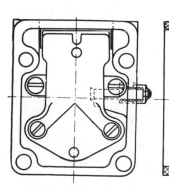

FIG. 16

ELECTRICALLY DRIVEN

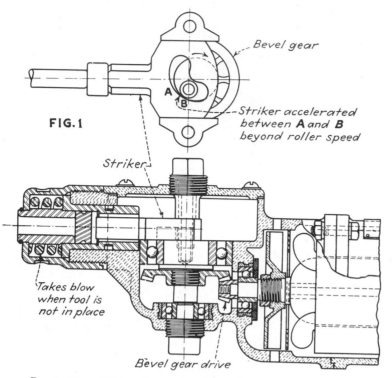

FIG.1

Bevel gear

Striker accelerated between **A** and **B** beyond roller speed

Striker

Takes blow when tool is not in place

Bevel gear drive

Fig. 1—Free driving *throw* of cam slotted striker is produced by eccentric stud roller during contact between points *A* and *B* of slot. This accelerates striker beyond tangential speed of roller for an instant before being picked up for return stroke

THE APPLICATION of controlled impact forces can as practical in specialized stationary machinery in the portable electric hammers shown here. Su mechanisms have been employed in vibrating co crete forms, in nailing machines and other spec machinery. In portable hammers they are efficie

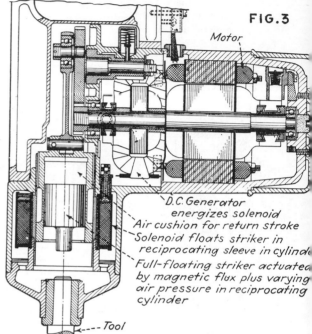

FIG.3

Motor

D.C. Generator energizes solenoid
Air cushion for return stroke
Solenoid floats striker in reciprocating sleeve in cylinde
Full-floating striker actuated by magnetic flux plus varying air pressure in reciprocating cylinder

Tool

Fig. 3—Striker has no mechanical connection wi reciprocating drive in this Speedway hammer

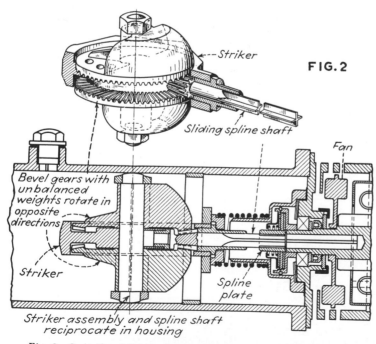

Striker

FIG.2

Sliding spline shaft

Fan

Bevel gears with unbalanced weights rotate in opposite directions

Striker

Spline plate

Striker assembly and spline shaft reciprocate in housing

Fig. 2—Centrifugal force of two oppositely rotating weights throw striker assembly of this Master hammer. Power connection is maintained by sliding splined shaft. Guide, not shown, prevents rotation of the striker assembly

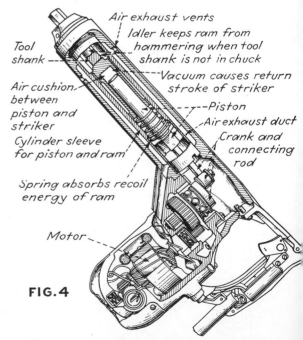

Air exhaust vents
Idler keeps ram from hammering when tool shank is not in chuck

Tool shank

Vacuum causes return stroke of striker

Air cushion between piston and striker

Piston

Air exhaust duct

Cylinder sleeve for piston and ram

Crank and connecting rod

Spring absorbs recoil energy of ram

Motor

FIG.4

Fig. 4—Combination of mechanical, pneumatic and spring action is used in this Van Dorn hammer

HAMMER MECHANISMS

In drilling, chiseling, digging, chipping. tamping, riveting and similar operations where quick concentrated blows are required. Striker mechanisms illustrated are operated by means of springs, cams, magnetic force, air and vacuum chambers, and centrifugal force. Drawings show only striking mechanism.

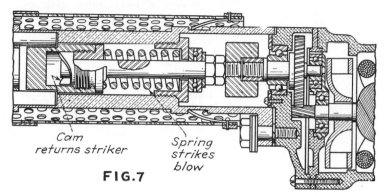

Fig. 7—Spring operated Milwaukee hammer employs shaft rotating in female cam to return striker

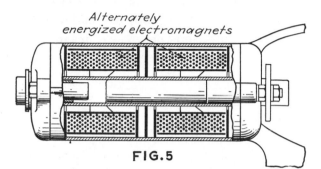

Fig. 5—Two electromagnets operate the Syntron hammer. Weight of blows may be controlled by varying electric current in coils or timing current reversals by air gap adjustment of the contacts

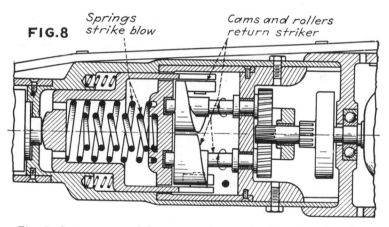

Fig. 8—Spring operated hammer with two fixed rotating barrel cams which return striker by means of two rollers on opposite sides of the striker sleeve. Auxiliary springs prevent striker from hitting the retaining cylinder. Means of rotating the tool, not shown, are also incorporated in this hammer

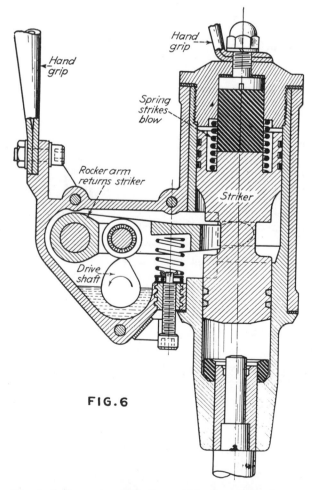

FIG. 6

Fig. 6—Spring operated hammer with cam and rocker for return stroke has screw adjustment of blow

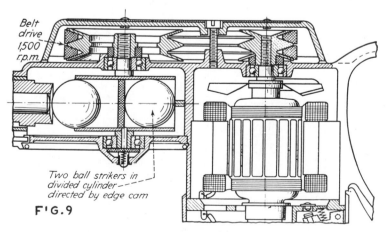

Fig. 9 Two steel balls rotated in a divided cylinder and steered by an edge cam develop centrifugal force to strike blows against tool holder. Collar is held clear of hammer by compression spring when no tool is in holder. A second spring cushions blows when motor is running but tool is not held against work

Permanent Magnet Mechanisms,

The potential utility of permanent magnets in various mechanisms has been greatly increased in recent years by the development of higher and higher strength magnetic materials. These materials are, of course, best known to the electrical industry in which they were developed and to electrical engineers who have made most use of them. Many uses can be made of strong magnets in purely mechanical devices where electro-magnets are impractical or undesirable. Many such uses have already been made, as shown by the accompanying mechanisms and devices, most of which were developed by engineers in the employ of well-known manufacturers. Undoubtedly there are many other ways of using permanent magnets.

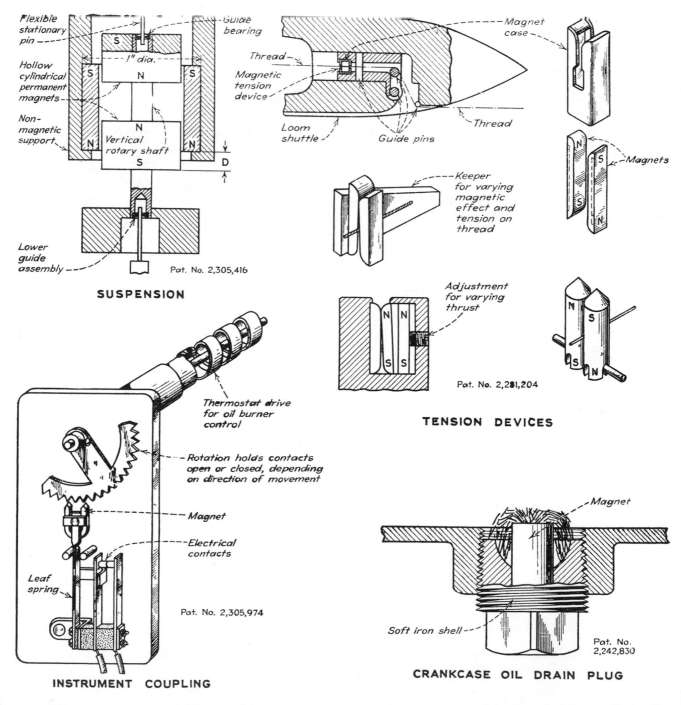

SUSPENSION

Pat. No. 2,305,416

TENSION DEVICES

Pat. No. 2,281,204

INSTRUMENT COUPLING

Pat. No. 2,305,974

CRANKCASE OIL DRAIN PLUG

Pat. No. 2,242,830

Their Design and Uses

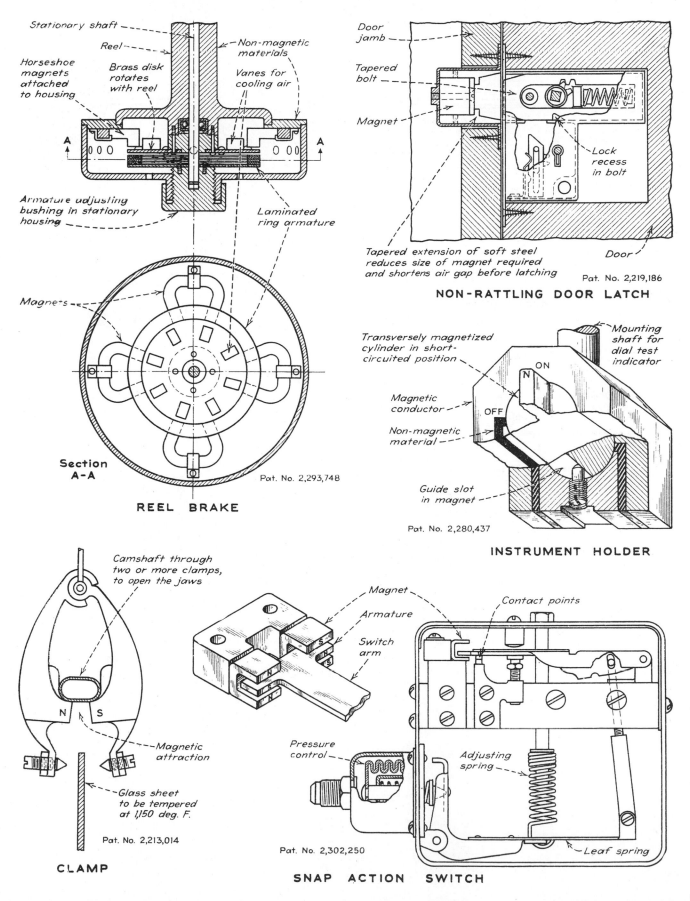

Stationary shaft —

Reel —

Non-magnetic materials

Horseshoe magnets attached to housing

Brass disk rotates with reel

Vanes for cooling air

A — — A

Armature adjusting bushing in stationary housing

Laminated ring armature

Magnets —

Section A-A

Pat. No. 2,293,748

REEL BRAKE

Door jamb

Tapered bolt —

Magnet —

Lock recess in bolt

Tapered extension of soft steel reduces size of magnet required and shortens air gap before latching

Door

Pat. No. 2,219,186

NON-RATTLING DOOR LATCH

Transversely magnetized cylinder in short-circuited position

Mounting shaft for dial test indicator

ON

N

Magnetic conductor —

OFF

Non-magnetic material — —

Guide slot in magnet

Pat. No. 2,280,437

INSTRUMENT HOLDER

Camshaft through two or more clamps, to open the jaws

Magnet

Armature

Switch arm

Contact points

Magnetic attraction

N   S

Pressure control

Adjusting spring

Glass sheet to be tempered at 1,150 deg. F.

Pat. No. 2,213,014

Pat. No. 2,302,250

Leaf spring

CLAMP

SNAP ACTION SWITCH

Permanent Magnet Mechanisms

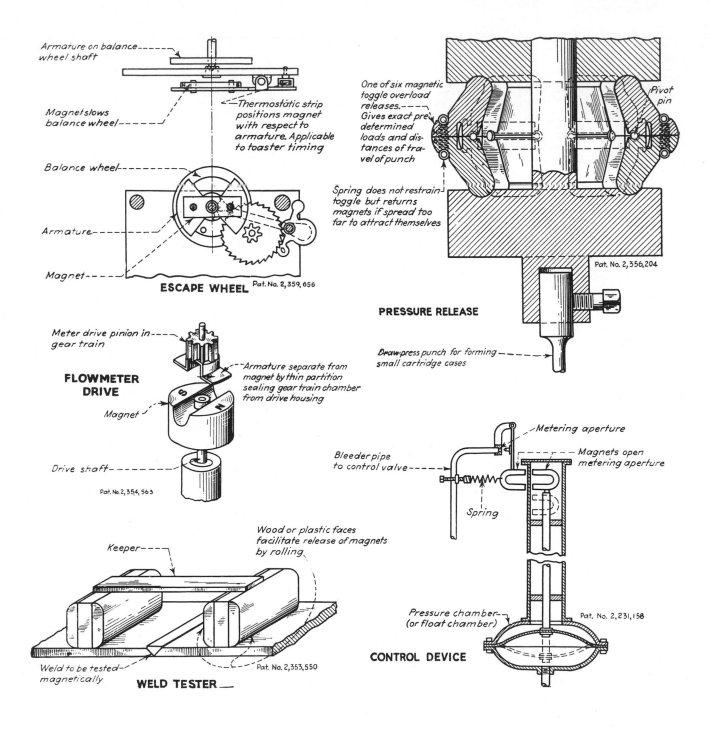

Armature on balance wheel shaft

Magnet slows balance wheel

Thermostatic strip positions magnet with respect to armature. Applicable to toaster timing

Balance wheel

Armature

Magnet

ESCAPE WHEEL Pat. No. 2,359,656

Meter drive pinion in gear train

FLOWMETER DRIVE

Armature separate from magnet by thin partition sealing gear train chamber from drive housing

Magnet

Drive shaft

Pat. No. 2,354,563

One of six magnetic toggle overload releases. Gives exact predetermined loads and distances of travel of punch

Pivot pin

Spring does not restrain toggle but returns magnets if spread too far to attract themselves

Pat. No. 2,356,204

PRESSURE RELEASE

Draw press punch for forming small cartridge cases

Keeper

Wood or plastic faces facilitate release of magnets by rolling

Weld to be tested magnetically

Pat. No. 2,353,550

WELD TESTER

Metering aperture

Magnets open metering aperture

Bleeder pipe to control valve

Spring

Pressure chamber (or float chamber)

Pat. No. 2,231,158

CONTROL DEVICE

And Their Applications

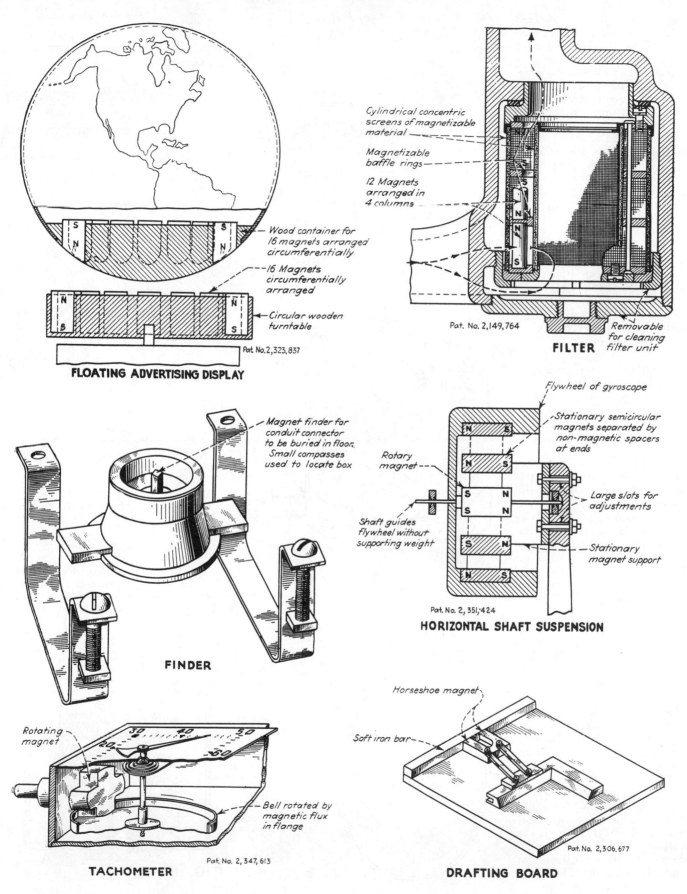

Cylindrical concentric screens of magnetizable material

Magnetizable baffle rings

12 Magnets arranged in 4 columns

Wood container for 16 magnets arranged circumferentially

16 Magnets circumferentially arranged

Circular wooden turntable

Pat. No. 2,323,837

Pat. No. 2,149,764

Removable for cleaning filter unit

FLOATING ADVERTISING DISPLAY

FILTER

Magnet finder for conduit connector to be buried in floor. Small compasses used to locate box

Flywheel of gyroscope

Stationary semicircular magnets separated by non-magnetic spacers at ends

Rotary magnet

Large slots for adjustments

Shaft guides flywheel without supporting weight

Stationary magnet support

Pat. No. 2, 351, 424

FINDER

HORIZONTAL SHAFT SUSPENSION

Rotating magnet

Bell rotated by magnetic flux in flange

Horseshoe magnet

Soft iron bar

Pat. No. 2, 347, 613

Pat. No. 2,306,677

TACHOMETER

DRAFTING BOARD

PERMANENT MAGNETS IN

Permanent magnets cast or sintered from high-coercive aluminum-nickel alloys often are the simplest and most effective means for performing mechanical operations. These illustrations show how they can be designed to replace springs, clamps, over-center mechanisms, to transmit motion, and to translate speed into torque. Several unique methods of mounting these hard-to-machine magnets are shown in addition to the common methods of welding, brazing, soldering, inserting in die-castings, and fastening by rivets, screws, through-bolts and clamps.

Fig. 1—Theft-proof electric light socket, of which mechanical principles only are shown, uses permanent magnet "key" which is cast in two halves pinned and magnetized so that one claw is north pole, the other south pole.

Fig. 2—A small cast permanent magnet placed in the cover of the die-cast raceway of this conduit system permits quick and easy location of outlet many years later. A compass-type finder does the trick.

Fig. 3—Magnets of aluminum-nickel alloy perform holding operation in this snap-action limit switch of General Electric Company. As operating dog shifts, spring tension builds up tending to shift yoke assembly which is held stationary by the magnet. When operating dog approaches end of travel, direct mechanical contact breaks yoke away from holding magnet. Spring then snaps yoke to opposite side.

Fig. 4—Unique application of small permanent magnets is in plastic letters of "Quixet" movie titler of Hamilton Dwight Company. Magnets hold letters in place on steel title sheet.

Fig. 5—Beauty shops find a use for permanent magnets in attractive hairpin pullers such as shown here. Magnet is inserted into hot Catalin case; shrinkage of plastic on cooling grips unit firmly.

Fig. 6—Two aluminum-nickel cast magnets are used in this Frantz FerroFilter for removing iron particles from lubricating systems. A soft lead core is cast in one magnet over which is flared a brass tube, and the other magnet is fastened by pressing on a brass band.

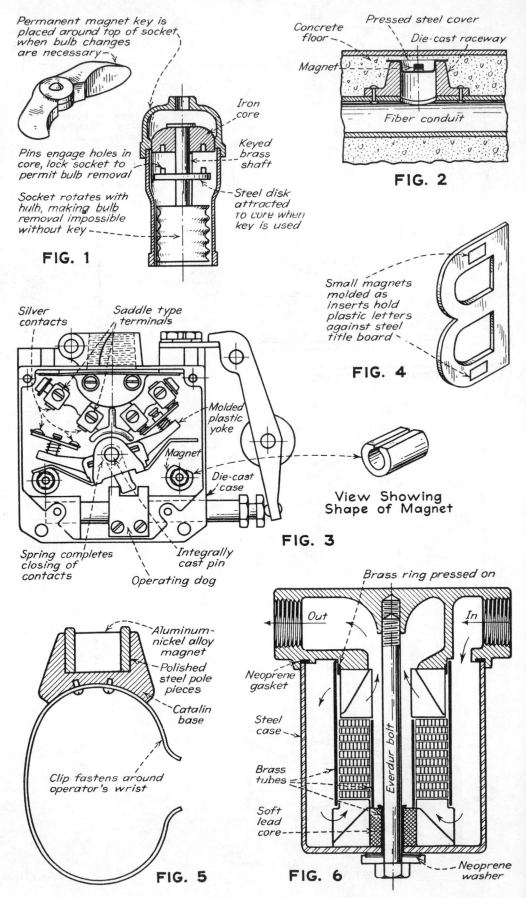

Permanent magnet key is placed around top of socket when bulb changes are necessary

Pins engage holes in core, lock socket to permit bulb removal

Socket rotates with bulb, making bulb removal impossible without key

Iron core

Keyed brass shaft

Steel disk attracted to core when key is used

FIG. 1

Concrete floor

Pressed steel cover

Die-cast raceway

Magnet

Fiber conduit

FIG. 2

Small magnets molded as inserts hold plastic letters against steel title board

FIG. 4

Silver contacts

Saddle type terminals

Molded plastic yoke

Magnet

Die-cast case

Spring completes closing of contacts

Integrally cast pin

Operating dog

View Showing Shape of Magnet

FIG. 3

Aluminum-nickel alloy magnet

Polished steel pole pieces

Catalin base

Clip fastens around operator's wrist

FIG. 5

Brass ring pressed on

Out

In

Neoprene gasket

Steel case

Brass tubes

Soft lead core

Everdur bolt

Neoprene washer

FIG. 6

MECHANICAL APPLICATIONS

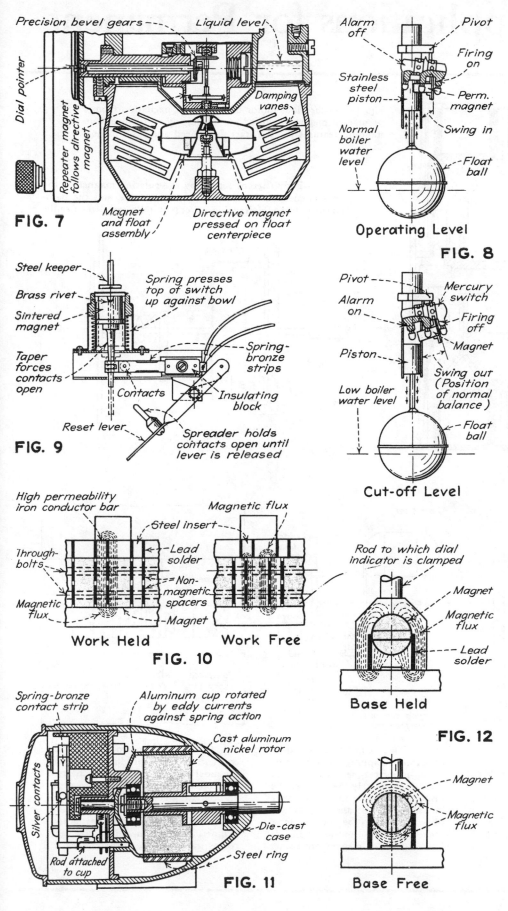

FIG. 7

Precision bevel gears
Liquid level
Dial pointer
Repeater magnet follows directive magnet
Damping vanes
Magnet and float assembly
Directive magnet pressed on float centerpiece

FIG. 9

Steel keeper
Brass rivet
Sintered magnet
Taper forces contacts open
Spring presses top of switch up against bowl
Spring-bronze strips
Contacts
Insulating block
Reset lever
Spreader holds contacts open until lever is released

Work Held   Work Free
FIG. 10

High permeability iron conductor bar
Magnetic flux
Steel insert
Lead solder
Through-bolts
Non-magnetic spacers
Magnetic flux
Magnet

FIG. 11

Spring-bronze contact strip
Aluminum cup rotated by eddy currents against spring action
Cast aluminum nickel rotor
Silver contacts
Die-cast case
Steel ring
Rod attached to cup

Alarm off
Pivot
Firing on
Stainless steel piston
Perm. magnet
Swing in
Normal boiler water level
Float ball

Operating Level

FIG. 8

Pivot
Mercury switch
Alarm on
Firing off
Magnet
Piston
Swing out (Position of normal balance)
Low boiler water level
Float ball

Cut-off Level

Rod to which dial indicator is clamped
Magnet
Magnetic flux
Lead solder

Base Held

FIG. 12

Magnet
Magnetic flux

Base Free

Fig. 7—Sintered magnet in the float of this Kollsman direction indicator transmits its rotary motion to the cobalt-steel follower magnet located on the other side of the aluminum wall of the float case, and thence through bevel gears to the dial pointer shaft. Magnetic couplings of this type are often used to transmit motion through solid partitions.

Fig. 8—Magnet cast of aluminum-nickel alloy in this Schaub Magnetrol operates mercury switch to control boiler water level. For applications where the float is free to slide up and down the rod between limits, a magnetic clutch (not shown) holds rod and cylinder in the up position until the float reaches lower limit stop.

Fig. 9—Magnetic switch on General Electric glass coffee maker automatically shuts off heating element when upper bowl fills. With current "on" magnet is held up by a steel keeper mounted at the end of a rod in upper bowl stem. When the last cup or so of water rises through the stem, turbulence against a disk on upper end of keeper rod lifts keeper from bottom of bowl, releasing magnet which opens contacts.

Fig. 10—Brown & Sharpe magnetic chucks illustrate design of shunts to turn permanent magnet holding devices on and off. Chuck consists of a pack of rectangular-shaped aluminum-nickel magnets and soft steel conductor bars separated by non-magnetic spacers. Pack slides between face plate and bottom plate by means of crank and eccentric. Positions of pack when "on" and "off" and paths of magnetic flux are shown in the diagram. All joints between component parts are ground to close fits to reduce reluctance.

Fig. 11—Plugging relay of General Electric Company is operated by eddy currents set up in aluminum cup by rotor of aluminum-nickel magnet alloy. Magnetic reaction produced turns the cup through its limited rotation, closing contacts against spring action. As rotor slows down, a definite point is reached where spring force overcomes magnetic force, at which point the contacts trip open.

Fig. 12—Magnetic dial indicator base can be turned on and off by 90-deg. rotation of hand knob on end of cylindrical magnet. Principle of operation is similar to Fig. 10.

Applications for Permanent

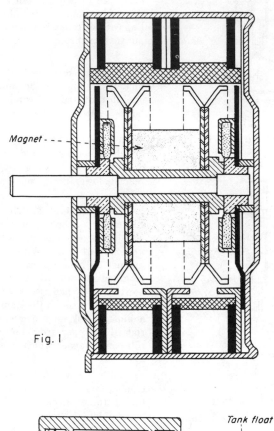

Fig. 1—Synchronous motor derives its d-c excitation from a permanent magnet mounted within the rotor structure. Outstanding features are self-start, low-speed and high torque.

Fig. 2—Eddy current set up by the rotating magnets is the only connection between speedometer cable and the dashboard pointer. Hairspring on cup spindle stabilizes needle.

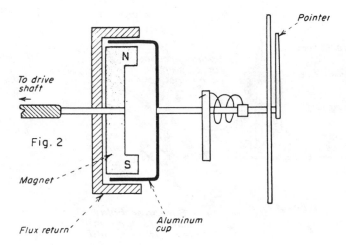

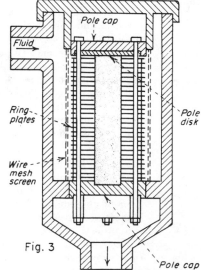

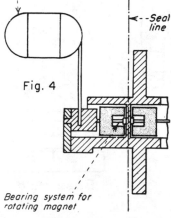

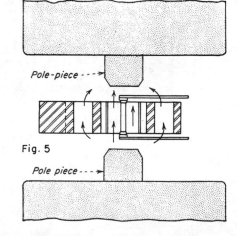

Fig. 3—Magnet filter, designed to remove minute ferrous particles from a liquid or gaseous medium by having a magnetic field of force across a multiplicity of air gaps.

Fig. 4—Two magnets, separated by aluminum diaphragm, function as a leak-proof magnetic coupling to indicate accurately the level of the insulating liquid in transformer tanks. Portion of assembly at left of seal line can be located in a tank—magnet on outside then follows motion of magnet on inside.

Fig. 5—In a Magnetron, a strongly concentrated field produces forces on the moving electrons between the two pole pieces in such a manner to cause an oscillating condition, creating electro-magnetic field energy. These pole pieces collect flux from permanent magnets several times their size, and concentrate it between their faces.

Magnets

Carboloy Department
General Electric Company

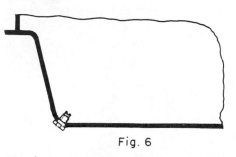

Fig. 6—Magnetic drain plug attracts and removes ferrous particles from a circulating oil or lubricant stream. The plug also helps to remove the particles that normally settle out.

Fig. 7—Permanent magnet switching device in a telephone. When handset is removed from instrument base, spring clips return to normal position, bringing contacts together and closing the circuit.

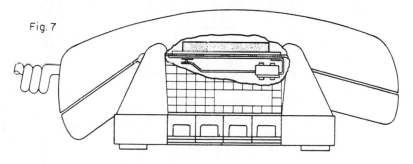

Fig. 8—Device uses magnets to provide smooth frictionless torque that is constant with speed. Torque is controlled by increasing or decreasing the distance between two magnets and a hysteresis ring also of permanent magnet material.

Fig. 9—Lamp socket and reflector is mounted on adjustable rod attached to magnetic base. Unit can be securely attached to a variety of metallic machine surfaces.

Fig. 10—Ring-section magnets mounted inside a conveyor drum. Ferrous contaminants are held in place until they pass barrier and drop down a disposal chute.

Fig. 11—Magnetic assembly acts as valve and holding agent. Working opposite to spring force, assembly moves to the right. When near the steel ring, it snaps against it and remains until mechanical component of the valve forces it away.

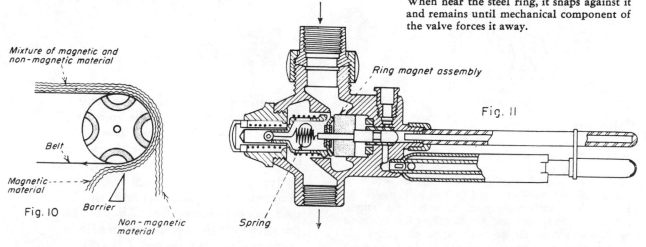

Chip Removal

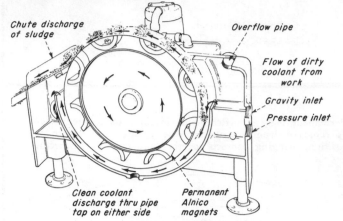

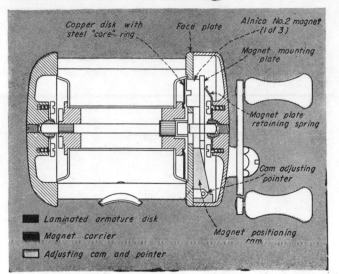

Permanent magnets remove chips from coolant in magnetic separator produced by Barnes Drill Co. Cross sectional view shows flow channel, arrangement of magnets and construction details.

Controlled Braking

THREE SMALL Alnico magnets are mounted inside one end cap of the Electromatic fishing reel so that a copper disk attached to the adjacent spool flange rotates in their magnetic field. The spool is therefore braked during the first few seconds of a cast, thus retarding movement of the spool and preventing the line from kinking.

BRAKING EFFECT is varied to suit casting conditions by moving the magnets in relation to the disk. Magnets and disk are separated by moving the pointer, which wedges the tapered cam between face plate and magnet plate. Retaining spring forces the magnet plate toward the copper disk when the cam is retracted.

Magnetic Chuck

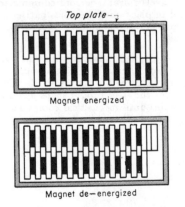

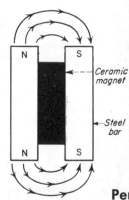

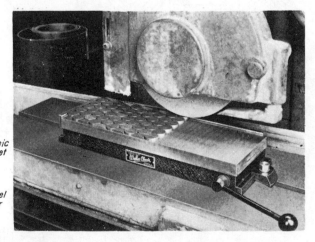

Poles are on faces . . .

of ceramic magnets, not on edges, making them extremely useful for compact but powerful magnetic circuits. Inside the chuck, top-magnet section has rows of $\frac{5}{8}$-by-1-in magnets between the alternating north and south pole bars. Magnets of bottom section are $\frac{3}{4}$ by 1 in. All magnets are $\frac{1}{4}$ in thick. Chuck is energized when top and bottom sections are positioned with like poles aligned, de-energized by shifting bottom section until unlike poles align and retain flux in magnet assembly. Shifting is done with crank and cam-link which pry, then slide the bottom section.

Permanent magnets, formed by sandwiching flat ceramic magnets between steel bars, are the pole pieces of a new magnetic chuck made by O. S. Walker Co., Worcester, Mass. Its top plate has alternate bars of magnetic and nonmagnetic steel, and can be ground flat. Chuck is thinner and half the weight of previous designs — yet has greater holding power.

Stepping-Off Tube Lengths

A pair of electromagnets are now stepping off tube lengths in an extremely ingenious arrangement. The magnets are placed on 1-ft centers about $\frac{1}{32}$ in. above the tube OD and aligned with it (sketch). One magnet is the *write* head, the other the *read* head.

As the tube moves past the heads, a magnetic spot is imprinted on the tube surface by a short electrical pulse through the write head. When the spot reaches the read head an electric current is generated in the head windings. This triggers the next pulse of the write head to imprint a second magnetic spot, which is picked up by the read head to repeat the sequence. Once started, the system is self-sustaining.

The magnetic "imprinter" has been added to a conveyor at the Tube Investment Ltd plant in Walsall, Staffordshire, England. The box-shaped carrier arm is hinged to the conveyor structure. The arm is raised and lowered by an air cylinder which operates against two damping springs on the down stroke. This ensures gentle contact between the *fractional measuring contact wheel,* which holds the read and write heads, and the tube. The measuring wheel has a 1-ft circumference to give accurate fractional measurement.

System was developed by the Steel Tube Development Engineering Dept of the company, which reports that the spots are counted when imprinted to record tube length in feet.

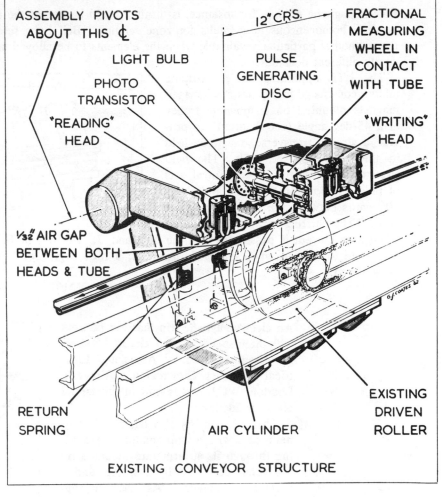

ASSEMBLY PIVOTS ABOUT THIS ℄

LIGHT BULB

PHOTO TRANSISTOR

"READING" HEAD

12" CRS.

PULSE GENERATING DISC

FRACTIONAL MEASURING WHEEL IN CONTACT WITH TUBE

"WRITING" HEAD

$\frac{1}{32}$" AIR GAP BETWEEN BOTH HEADS & TUBE

RETURN SPRING

AIR CYLINDER

EXISTING DRIVEN ROLLER

EXISTING CONVEYOR STRUCTURE

New Magnetic Principle

A liquid magnet built at MIT shows real promise for practical application.

Instead of the conventional iron core, the magnet has an electrically conductive liquid that circulates between two coaxial cylinders in an axial magnetic field.

As shown in the sketch, the liquid conductor is forced inward through the cylindrical space. The axial magnetic field B is generated in this space by external exciting coils, and the tangential current I in the liquid conductor induces a magnetic field in the same direction as the initial applied field. The magnetic field resulting from this azimuthal current adds to the initial applied field so that, A. H. Kolm of MIT says, the hydromagnet in effect represents a self-exciting, internally short-circuited homopolar generator. With an exciting field of 100 k gauss and a flow rate of 100 gpm, a magnet with an ID of 1 in. and OD of 12 in., using a liquid sodium-potassium alloy as the conductor, will generate a 124 k gauss field.

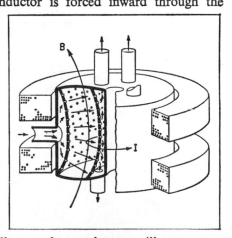

Electromagnetic mixing, for instance, is turning out to be one of the best ways to produce homogeneous alloy melts for zone refining. Bell Labs researchers say the method is particularly valuable when the elements to be alloyed are of significantly different densities.

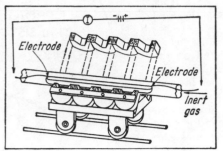

The BTL apparatus for electrostatic mixing consists of four pairs of U-shaped magnets mounted on a movable trolley at a 45-deg angle (see diagram) to provide a strong, transverse, magnetic field in the region of the melt. The field strength between the three central sets of poles is about 1000 gauss, and about 500 gauss between the two end pairs of poles. The stirring action takes place when a dc current is passed through the melt and, J. J. Schott of Bell Labs says in a note to *Review of Scientific Instruments*, a high degree of uniformity can be achieved.

An electromagnetic trip that can be used with high-speed latched circuit breakers has been designed by Associated Electrical Industries, Crown House, Aldwych, London, WC2, and is now in substantial pilot production.

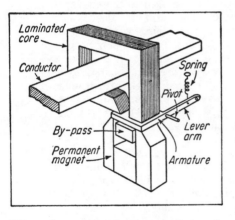

The unit consists of a laminated magnetic core with a strip conductor extending through it, an armature mounted on a pivoted arm held by a spring, and a permanent magnet. As the diagram shows, the armature is positioned between the laminated core and the permanent magnet so it can move toward either one. When the current in the conductor is in the direction that reinforces the flux in the armature created by the permanent magnet, the armature is held in contact with the poles of the permanent magnet. When the direction of current is reversed, the flux of the laminated core overcomes that of the permanent magnet; and, at a predetermined value, the armature moves toward the core. The action takes place at high speed, with the permanent magnet flux being diverted to the bypass member.

By varying the strength of the magnetic field and the configuration of the elements, AEI says, operation of the unit can be adjusted for varying currents.

8

THERMO-, PYRO-, AND PHOTO-ACTUATED DEVICES

THERMOSTATIC MECHANISMS

Sensitivity or change in deflection for a given temperature change depends upon the combination of metals selected as well as the dimensions of the bimetal element. Sensitivity increases with the square of the length and inversely with the thickness. The force developed for a given temperature change also depends on the type of bimetal, whereas the allowable working load for the thermostatic strip increases with the width and the square of the thickness. Thus, the design of bimetal elements depends upon the relative importance of sensitivity and working load.

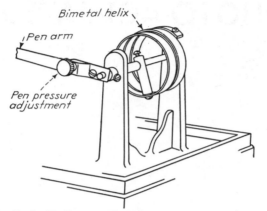

Fig. 1—In the Taylor recording thermometer, a pen is moved vertically across a revolving chart by a brass-invar bimetal element. To obtain sensitivity, the long movement of the pen requires a long strip of bimetal, which is coiled into a helix to save space. For accuracy, a relatively large cross section gives stiffness, although the large thickness requires increased length to obtain the desired sensitivity.

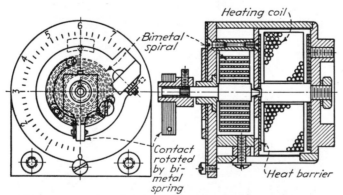

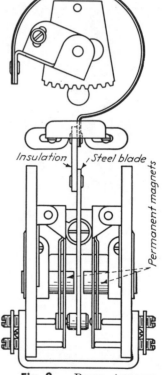

Fig. 2 —Room temperatures in summer as well as winter are controlled over a wide range by a single large-diameter coil of brass-invar in the Friez thermometer. To prevent chattering, a small permanent magnet is mounted on each side of the steel contact blade. The magnetic attraction on the blade, increasing inversely with the square of the distance from the magnet, gives a snap action to the contacts.

Fig. 3 —In this Westinghouse overload relay for large motors, a portion of the motor current is passed through a heating coil within the relay. Heat from the coil raises the temperature of a bimetal spiral which rotates a shaft carrying an electrical contact. To withstand the operating temperature, a heat-resistant bimetal is used, coiled into the spiral form for compactness. Because of the large deflection needed, the spiral is long and thin, whereas the width is made large to provide the required contact pressure.

By the use of heat barriers between the bimetal spiral and the heating coil, temperature rise of the bimetal can be made to follow closely the increase in temperature within the motor. Thus, momentary overloads do not cause sufficient heating to close the contacts, whereas a continued overload will in time cause the bimetal to rotate the contact arm around to the adjustable stationary contact, causing a relay to shut down the motor.

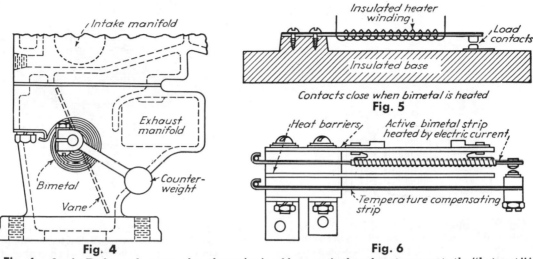

Fig. 4

Fig. 5

Fig. 6

Fig. 4 —On the Dodge carburetor, when the engine is cold, a vane in the exhaust passage to the "hot spot" is held open by a bimetal spring against the force of a small counterweight. When the thermostatic spiral is heated by the outside air or by the warm air stream from the radiator, the spring coils up and allows the weight to close the vane. Since high accuracy is not needed, a thin, flexible cross section is used with a long length to give the desired sensitivity.

Fig. 5 —In the Friez relay, a constant current through an electrical heating coil around a straight bimetal strip gives a time-delay action. Since the temperature range is relatively large, high sensitivity is not necessary, hence a short straight strip of bimetal is suitable. Because of the relatively heavy thickness used, the strip is sufficiently stiff to close the contact firmly without chattering.

Fig. 6 —A similar type of bimetal element is used in the Ward Leonard time-delay relay for mercury-vapor rectifiers. This relay closes the potential circuit to the mercury tube only after the filament has had time to reach its normal operating temperature. To eliminate the effect of changes in room temperature on the length of the contact gap, and therefore the time interval, the stationary contact is carried by a second bimetal strip similar to the heated element. Barriers of laminated plastic on both sides of the active bimetal strip shield the compensating strip and prevent air currents from affecting the heating rate. The relatively high temperature range allows the use of a straight thick strip, whereas the addition of the compensating strip makes accurate timing possible with a short travel.

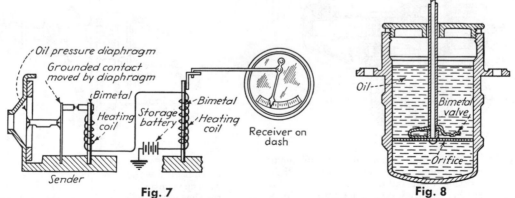

Fig. 7

Fig. 8

Fig. 7—Oil pressure, engine temperature, or gasoline level are indicated electrically on automobile dashboard instruments built by King-Seeley in which a bimetal element is used in both the sender and receiver. A grounded contact at the sender completes an electric circuit through heaters around two similar bimetal strips. Since the same current flows around the two bimetal elements, their deflections are the same. But the sender element when heated will bend away from the grounded contact until the circuit is broken. Upon cooling, the bimetal again makes contact and the cycle continues, allowing the bimetal to follow the movement of the grounded contact. For the oil-pressure gage, the grounded contact is attached to a diaphragm; for the temperature indicator, the contact is carried by another thermostatic bimetal strip; in the gasoline-level device, the contact is shifted by a cam on a shaft rotated by a float. Deflections of the receiving bimetal are amplified through a linkage that operates a pointer over the scale of the receiving instrument. Since only small deflections are needed, the bimetal element is in the form of a short stiff strip.

Fig. 8—Oil dashpots used in heavy-capacity Toledo scales have a thermostatic control to compensate for changes in oil viscosity with temperature. A rectangular orifice in the plunger is covered by a swaged projection on the bimetal element. With a decrease in oil temperature, the oil viscosity increases, tending to increase the damping effect; but the bimetal deflects upward, enlarging the orifice enough to keep the damping force constant. A wide bimetal strip is used for stiffness so that the orifice will not be altered by the force of the flowing oil.

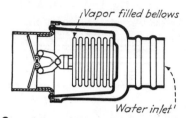

Fig. 9 —Automobile cooling water temperature is controlled by a self-contained bellows in the thermostat made by the Bridgeport Brass Company. As in the radiator air valve, the bellows itself is subjected to the temperature to be controlled. As the temperature of the water increases to about 140°F., the valve starts to open; at approximately 180°F., free flow is permitted. At intermediate temperatures, the valve opening is in proportion to the temperature.

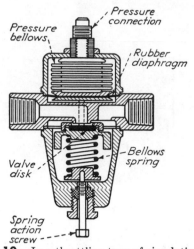

Fig. 10 —In a throttling type of circulating water control valve made by C. J. Tagliabue Manufacturing Company for use in refrigeration plants, the valve opening varies with the pressure on the bellows. This valve controls the rate of flow of the cooling water through the condenser, a greater amount of water being required when the temperature, and therefore the pressure, increases. The pressure in the condenser is transmitted through a pipe to the valve bellows thereby adjusting the flow of cooling water. The bronze bellows is protected from contact with the water by a rubber diaphragm.

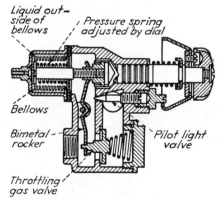

Fig. 11 —An automatic gas-range control made by the Wilcolator Company has a sealed thermostatic element consisting of a bulb, capillary tube, and bellows. As food is often placed near the bulb, a nontoxic liquid, chlorinated diphenyl, is used in the liquid expansion system. The liquid is also noninflammable and has no corrosive effect upon the phosphor bronze bellows. By placing the liquid outside instead of inside the bellows, the working stresses are maximum at normal temperatures when the bellows bottoms on the cup. At elevated working temperatures, the expansion of the liquid compresses the bellows against the action of the extended spring which, in turn, is adjusted by the knob. Changes in calibration caused by variations in ambient temperature are compensated by making the rocker arm of bimetal suitable for high-temperature service.

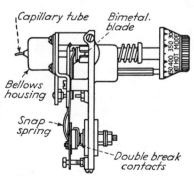

Fig. 12 —For electric ranges, the Wilcolator thermostat has the same bellows unit as is used on the gas-type control. But, instead of a throttling action, the thermostat opens and closes the electrical contacts with a snap action. To obtain sufficient force for the snap action, the control requires a temperature difference between "on" and "off" positions. For a control range from room temperature to 550°F., the differential in this device is plus or minus 10°F.; with a smaller control range, the differential is proportionately less. The snap-action switch is made of beryllium copper, giving high strength, better snap action, and longer life than obtainable with phosphor bronze, and because of its corrosion resistance the beryllium-copper blade requires no protective finish.

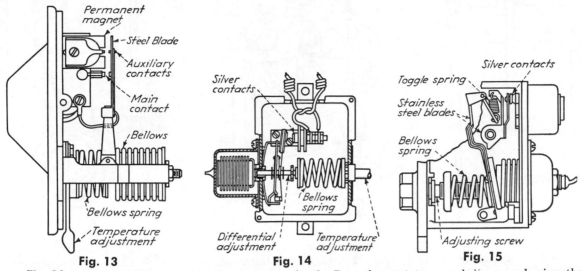

Fig. 13   **Fig. 14**   **Fig. 15**

Fig. 13 —For heavy-duty room-temperature controls, the Penn thermostat uses a bellows mechanism that develops a high force with small changes in temperature. The bellows is partly filled with liquid butane, which at room temperatures is a gas having a large change in vapor pressure for small temperature differentials. Snap action of the electrical contact is obtained from a small permanent magnet that pulls the steel contact blade into firm contact when the bellows cools. Because of the firm contact, the device is rated at 20 amp. for noninductive loads. To avoid chattering or bounce under the impact delivered by the rapid magnetic closing action, small auxiliary contacts are carried on light spring blades. With the large force developed by the bellows, a temperature differential of only 2°F. is obtained.

Fig. 14 —Snap action in the Tagliabue refrigerator control is obtained from a bowed flat spring. The silver contacts carried on an extended end of the spring open or close rapidly when movement of the bellows actuates the spring. With this snap action, the contacts can control an alternating-current motor as large as 1½ hp. without the use of auxiliary relays. Temperature differential is adjusted by changing the spacing between two collars on the bellows shaft passing through the contact spring. For temperatures used in freezing ice, the bellows system is partly filled with butane.

Fig. 15 —In the General Electric refrigerator control, the necessary snap action is obtained from a toggle spring supported from a long arm moved by the bellows. With this type of toggle action, the contact pressure is a maximum at the instant the contacts start to open. Thermostatic action is obtained from a vapor-filled system using sulphur dioxide for usual refrigerating service or methyl chloride where lower temperatures are required. To reduce friction, the bellows makes point contact with the bellows cup. Operating temperature is adjusted by changing the initial compression in the bellows spring. For resistance to corrosion, levers and blades are stainless steel with bronze pin bearings.

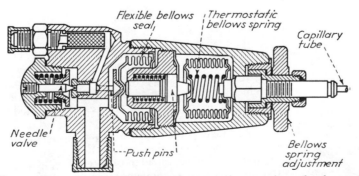

Fig. 16 —Two bellows units are used in the Fedders thermostatic expansion valve for controlling large refrigeration systems. A removable power bellows unit is operated by vapor pressure in a bulb attached to the evaporator output line. The second bellows serves as a flexible, gastight seal for the gas valve. A stainless steel spring holds the valve closed until opened by pressure transmitted from the thermostatic bellows through a molded push pin.

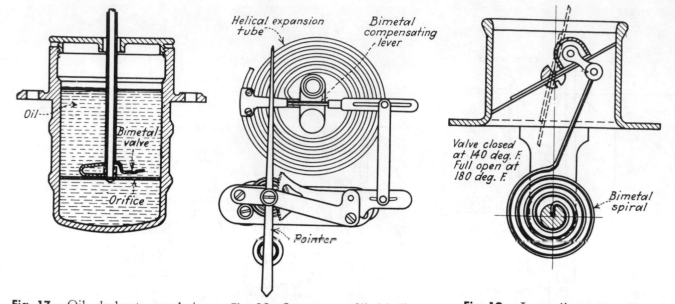

Fig. 17 —Oil dashpots used in heavy capacity Toledo scales have a thermostatic control to compensate for changes in oil viscosity with temperature. A rectangular orifice in the plunger is covered by a swaged projection on the bimetal element. With a decrease in oil temperature, the oil viscosity increases, tending to increase the damping effect; but the bimetal deflects upward, enlarging the orifice enough to keep the damping force constant. A wide bimetal strip is used for stiffness so that the orifice will not be altered by the force of the flowing oil.

Fig. 18 —In mercury-filled indicating thermometers, expansion of the mercury in a bulb at the end of a capillary line causes the spiral tube in the gage to uncoil, moving the dial pointer by means of a linkage. However, changes in the temperature of the mercury in the capillary and spiral also affect the movement of the linkage introducing an error in the reading. In the Taylor indicating thermometer, compensation for changes in gage temperature is obtained by a flat bimetal strip that forms a part of the pointer linkage. The strip is designed so that its deflections are equal but opposite to the effect caused by changes in gage temperature. Since little load is imposed on the thermostatic strip, the compensating action can be obtained with high accuracy.

Fig. 19 —In cooling-water thermostats for automobile engines, the water flow imposes a load on the bimetal spiral, and in addition the over-travel caused by continued cooling after the valve is closed sets up stresses which increase as the temperature decreases. Sufficient strength and cross-section to safely withstand these stresses without permanent deformation requires a long flexible element. High accuracy is not obtainable, but in this application a relatively large variation in operating temperature is permissible. In the Chase thermostat, the bimetal element is in the form of a tapered spiral spring which is connected to a rotating valve by a simple linkage. To stabilize the bimetal element, it is subjected to a series of hot and cold treatments at temperatures beyond the normal temperature range.

Fig. 20 —Toggle action, without separate springs, is obtained in the Spencer disk thermostat. The disk is a saucer-shaped piece of bimetal sheet which snaps itself from a concave to a convex shape at a predetermined temperature. Both the amount of movement and the temperature differential between opening and closing temperature depend on the design of the disk. For greater sensitivity, smaller differential and a larger movement than can be obtained with the plain disk, the bimetal disk is corrugated.

Since the disk is small and stores but little heat, it warms or cools rapidly.

When used as an electrical control device, insulated silver contacts are mounted on the bimetal disk. In the cold position shown, each of the contacts bridges a gap in insulated plates connected to the heavy terminals. When heated, the disk snaps to a convex shape, opening the circuit through the device at three points.

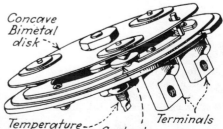

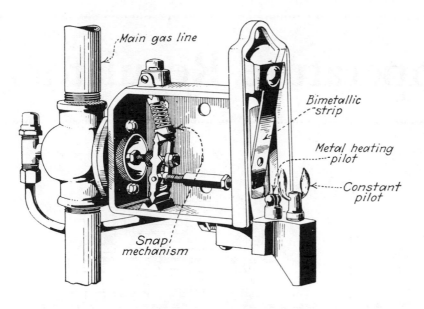

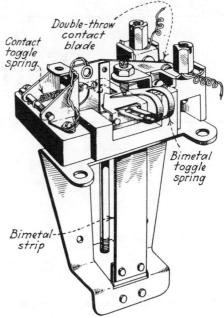

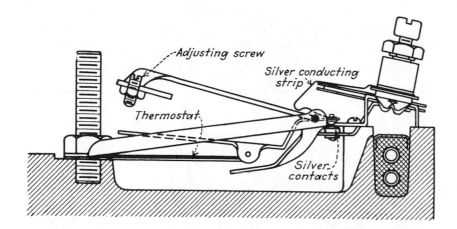

Fig. 21 —When the bimetal element in a gas pilot-light control is placed near the pilot flame, the bimetal is subjected to a temperature near its maximum operating range, and in service over long periods of time the valve may become corroded and fail to function when an emergency arises. In the pilot control made by the Patrol Valve Company, operating temperature of the bimetal is reduced and distortion from overheating is prevented by a dual pilot construction. The constant-burning pilot ignites a second pilot

which heats the bimetal strip when the thermostatic control calls for heat. The bimetal strip upon heating opens the toggle-operated main burner valve, which, by means of a double-seat construction, reduces the supply of gas to the second pilot, leaving just enough flame to keep the bimetal from closing the valve. Since relatively wide limits for temperature of operation are permissible, the bimetal element is designed to develop sufficient force to operate the toggle spring without the use of high working stresses.

Fig. 22 —In the Westinghouse thermostat for electric hot water heaters, a small range of temperature difference between on and off is needed, and to eliminate the necessity for an intermediate relay, the contacts must break a relatively heavy current. These conflicting requirements are met by using a double-toggle mechanism. A light toggle spring on the contact blade keeps the contacts firmly seated until the stronger toggle on the bimetal strip comes into operation.

The bimetal blade is free to move nearly to the dead center position thereby storing energy in its toggle spring before any pressure is applied to the contact blade. Energy released by the toggle spring, when the bimetal blade passes dead center, delivers an impact to the contact blade, breaking loose any slight welding that may have occurred during the previous operation. This thermostat is used as a current-limiting switch, disconnecting one heater as another is connected. Because of the double-toggle design the thermostat contacts will safely interrupt 5 kw. at 220 volts a.c. with a temperature differential of 5 deg. F. or less.

Fig. 23 —Electric irons require a convenient adjustment for the temperature at which the bimetal element opens the circuit. In the mechanism designed by Proctor & Schwartz, a double lever not only permits adjustment of the operating temperature, but also relieves the bimetal strip of any restriction when it cools to room temperature.

Since the operating temperature range is high, a heat resisting bimetal material is used in the form of a short, stiff strip. Current is conducted to the bimetal contact through a flexible silver ribbon, eliminating the effect of heat caused by current passing through the bimetal strip.

Temperature Regulators

L. C. BLAUVELT

Hoffman LaRoche

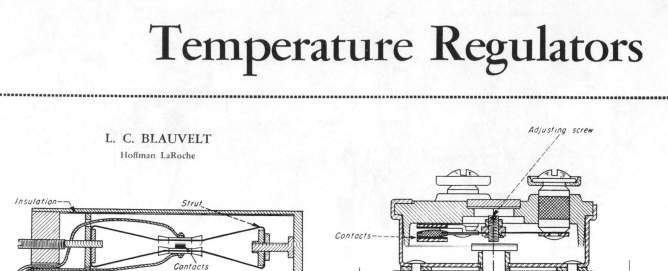

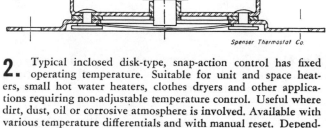

1. Bimetallic device is simple, compact and precise. Contacts mounted on low-expansion struts determine slow make-and-break action. Shell contracts or expands with temperature changes, opening or closing the electrical circuit that controls a heating or cooling unit. Adjustable and resistant to shock and vibration. Range: —100 to 1,500 F. Accuracy: Operates on less than 0.5 deg. temperature change.

2. Typical inclosed disk-type, snap-action control has fixed operating temperature. Suitable for unit and space heaters, small hot water heaters, clothes dryers and other applications requiring non-adjustable temperature control. Useful where dirt, dust, oil or corrosive atmosphere is involved. Available with various temperature differentials and with manual reset. Depending on model, temperature setting range is from —10 to 550F and minimum differential may be 10, 20, 30, 40 or 50F.

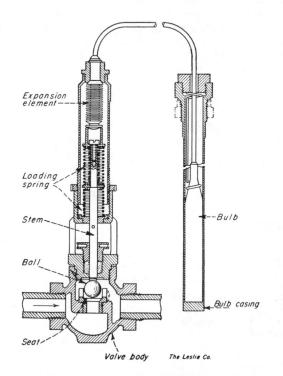

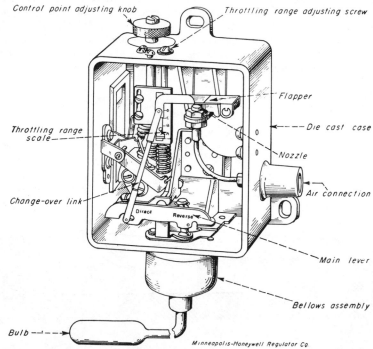

5. Self-contained regulator is actuated by expansion or contraction of liquid or gas in temperature sensitive bulb which is immersed in medium being controlled. Signal is transmitted from bulb to sealed expansion element which opens or closes the ball-valve. Range: 20 to 270 F. Accuracy: ±1 deg. Max. press. 100 psi. for dead end service, 200 psi continuous flow.

6. Remote bulb, non-indicating regulator uses a bellows assembly to operate a flapper. This allows air pressure in the control system to build up or bleed depending upon the position of the change-over link. Unit can be direct or reverse acting. Control knob adjusts the setting and the throttling range adjustment determines the percentage of the control range in which full output pressure (3-15 psi) is obtained. Range: 0-700 F. Accuracy: About ±0.5 percent of full scale range depending upon installation factors.

Temperature regulators are either of the on-off or throttling type. The characteristics of the process determine which should be used. Within each group, selection of a device is governed by the accuracy required, space limitations, simplicity and cost.

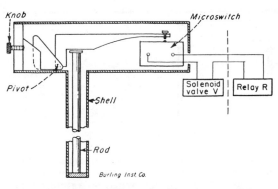

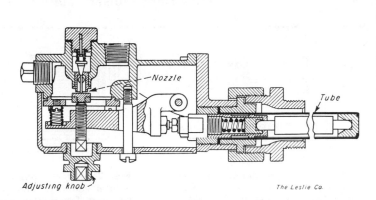

3. Bimetallic unit has rod with a low coefficient of expansion and a shell with a high coefficient. Microswitch gives snap action to the electrical control circuit. Current can be large enough to operate a solenoid valve or relay directly. Set point is adjusted by knob which moves the pivot point of the lever. Range: —20 to 1,750 F. Accuracy: 0.25 to 0.50 degrees.

4. Bimetallic actuated, air piloted control. Expansion of rod causes air signal (3-15 psi) to be transmitted to a heating or cooling pneumatic valve. Position of pneumatic valve depends upon the amount of air bled through the pilot valve of the control. This produces a throttling type of temperature control as contrasted to the on-off characteristic that is obtained with the three units described previously. Range: 32 to 600 F. Accuracy: ± 1 to ±3 F depending upon the range.

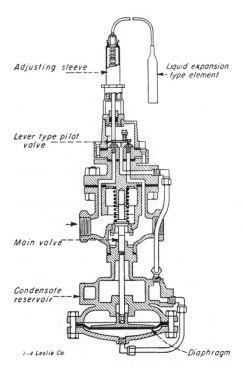

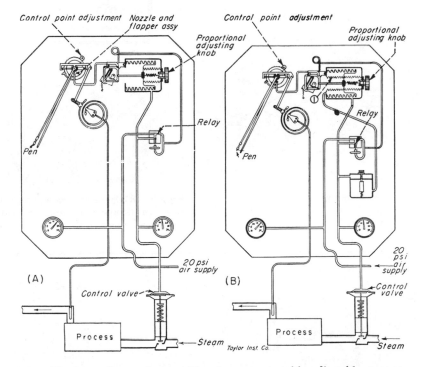

7. Lever-type pilot valve is actuated by temperature sensitive bulb. Motion of lever causes water or steam being controlled to exert pressure on a diaphragm which opens or closes the main valve. Range: 20 to 270 F. Accuracy: ±1 to 4 degrees. Pressure: 5-125 psi, steam; 5-175 psi, water.

8. Two recording and controlling instruments with adjustable proportional ranges. In both, air supply is divided by a relay valve. A small part goes through nozzle and flapper assembly. The main part goes to the control valve. Unit B has an extra bellows for automatic resetting. It is designed for systems with continuously changing control points and can be used where both heating and cooling are required for one process. Both A and B are easily changed from direct to reverse acting. Accuracy: One percent of range of —40 to 800 F.

Typical Industrial Uses of

Industrial heating applications can be divided into four categories: contact; immersion; radiant; and air. For these purposes a wide variety of types

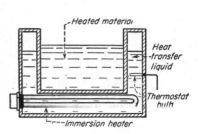

Fig. 1—Indirect immersion heating with tubular type unit located in a transfer medium. Useful for adhesives or other materials that are easily damaged by overheating.

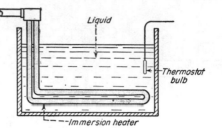

Fig. 2—Direct immersion heating with portable tubular heaters. Can be used for molten salt, oil tempering baths, melting lead, solder, and stereo-type metal (not zinc).

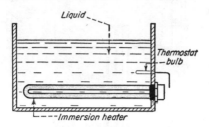

Fig. 3—Direct immersion heating with permanently mounted tubular heater. When operating temperature is high, heaters with low watt densities must be used.

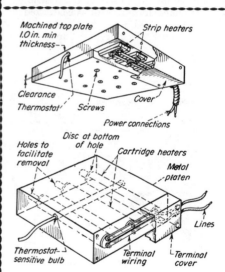

Fig. 6—Moving platens and dies can be heated with strip heaters or with cartridge type units.

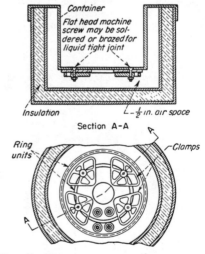

Fig. 7—Ring units are commonly used in thin-walled tanks or containers as shown in the sketch above.

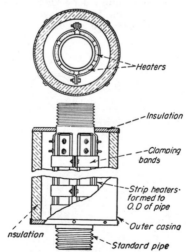

Fig. 8—Strip heaters curved to conform with tank or pipe. Inside radii can be as small as 1 3/16 inch.

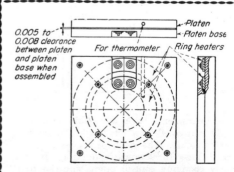

Fig. 11—Ring type heaters can also be used as shown above in parts such as platens, dies and molds.

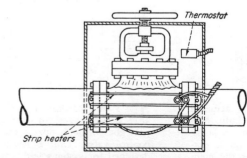

Fig. 12—Strip heaters and thermostat are mounted in sheet metal casing to prevent valves freezing.

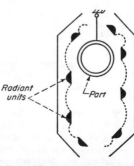

Fig. 13—Radiant heaters for degreasing or for paint baking oven. Grease is removed by vaporizing.

Electric Heating Elements

and sizes of units have been developed. These sketches, which illustrate typical applications of each, were supplied by the Edwin L. Wiegand Company.

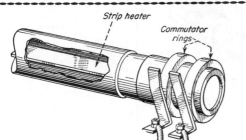

Fig. 4—Strip heater used on machine parts in motion such as revolving rolls. One or more units can be placed within the roll, connected to commutator rings. Brushes wired to power supply contact the rings.

Fig. 5—Six thermostatically controlled tubular heaters are used in conjunction with the cartridge units as shown to provide flexibly controlled zones of heat. Each set of cartridge units is separately controlled. Thus, heat and temperature can be regulated closely.

Fig. 9 — Immersion heater screwed into standard tee fitting for heating liquids.

Fig. 10—Two types of heaters for forced air duct installations. Tubular type (*B*) is recommended for higher temperature uses than finned-units in (*A*). Operating temperatures can be over 1,000 F at air velocities of 6 ft per second.

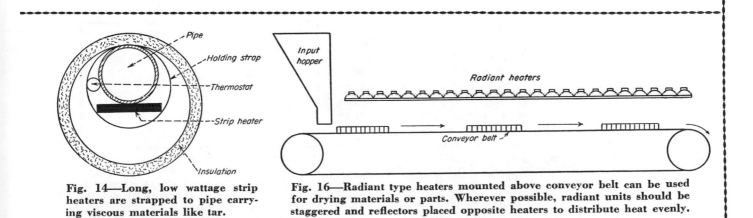

Fig. 14—Long, low wattage strip heaters are strapped to pipe carrying viscous materials like tar.

Fig. 16—Radiant type heaters mounted above conveyor belt can be used for drying materials or parts. Wherever possible, radiant units should be staggered and reflectors placed opposite heaters to distribute heat evenly.

NEW HEAT-ACTUATED DEVICES

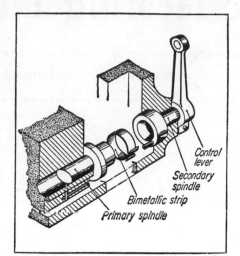

Two spindles and a bimetallic strip form a new temperature-compensation control for hydraulic systems. One spindle, which fits into the orifice through which the oil flows, has a slightly eccentric shape. One end is machined at a small angle to its axis so that its rotation will vary the effective area of the orifice. The other spindle, in line with the first, carries a control lever. Connecting the two, and immersed in the hydraulic fluid, is the bimetallic strip. Since the strip is sensitive to changes in temperature and responds by changing its shape, any change in temperature will make the eccentric spindle rotate with respect to the secondary spindle. This rotation adjusts the size of the orifice and compensates for viscosity changes so that control pressure remains constant.

The unit was originally designed by engineers at Simms Motor Units Ltd, Oak Lane, London N2, England, for a hydraulic speed governor, but they believe the basic principle can be applied to many other systems where the control pressure is determined by the flow of oil through a nozzle or orifice.

Melting point controls oven temperature

A constant-temperature oven with a novel means for turning itself on and off has been designed by D. J. Fewings of Marconi's Wireless Telegraph.

The basic principle is simple: The component to be maintained at a constant temperature, and a heater coil, are embedded in a material which expands as it melts and activates a switch that turns the heater on and off.

As long as heat input is less than or equal to heat loss, current flows to the heater. When input exceeds output, and the system temperature begins to rise, the solid melts, expands, compresses the bellows and hits the switch.

In the unit pictured, naphthalene (melting point, 175 F) is the active material. It meets the temperature requirements for the crystal oscillator and has the advantage of "adjustability" (adding anthracene can vary its melting point by about 6 deg) and a rather large change in volume on melting—over 10%. However, other compounds can be used.

Fewings says the change of internal temperature can now be held to about 1/173 of the change in external temperature, and it can be improved.

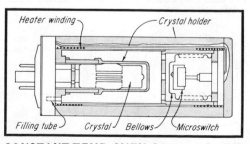

CONSTANT-TEMP OVEN for crystal oscillator is pictured above, with crystal and crystal holder. Diagram shows oven construction. Naphthalene surrounds crystal holder, presses against bellows chamber as it expands and activates the switch.

New machine to perforate plastics and fabrics

A novel method for producing perforated plastic sheeting and also providing heat-sealable areas has been devised by Kendall Co engineers. It's a process which turns prescribed areas of crystalline plastics—Mylar, Saran, Kel-F —into amorphous regions that melt at lower temperature, can be heat-sealed, and are readily perforated.

A stream of hot fluid (liquid or air) is directed across the sheet while it's supported on a perforated, heat-conducting base. In the areas where the sheeting

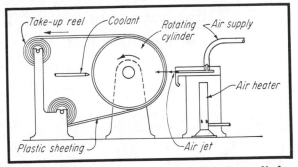

SHEET PERFORATOR consists of rotating cylinder with perforated surface which serves as film support, plus reels and jets. Here, air is the hot fluid. Process may be applied to fibrous materials as well as film.

touches the conductive material, the plastic is kept cool and retains its crystalline structure. But in the unsupported areas, it heats, softens or melts, and holes are made.

Best results are obtained with jets at between 500 to 1700 F and film speeds from 12 to 100 fpm (depending on type of film and whether it is to be softened or melted).

SENSORS
For inaccessible places

At work. Action of the radiation pyrometer depends on the fact that for a smooth surface, the sum of emissivity and reflectivity is always unity. Radiation from the surface under test and radiation reflected at the surface from a reference heater in the measuring head (see schematic) are focused on an infrared detector. The intensity of these combined radiations is compared with the direct radiation from the back of the heater, effected by the alternate chopping of the two beams.

By adjusting the temperature of the heater the two beams can be made equal in intensity and the temperature of the heater is then proportional to that of the surface under test. A resistance thermometer is wound on the heater and forms one arm of a bridge circuit. The off-balance current in the bridge indicates changes in heater temperature and a microammeter indicating this current is calibrated in terms of surface temperature. This calibration is made during the initial setting up and covers all surface emissivities.

Controls. Heater current is controlled by the signal from a photocell through a solid state relay. This specially developed control circuit includes an automatic gain control operated by the second harmonic content of the photocell output, which thus maintains control of the gain when the radiation beams are balanced and the fundamental ac signal is zero.

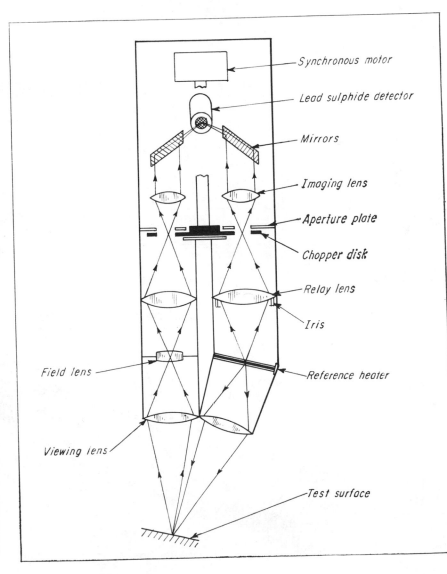

Instant muscle with

Cartridge-actuated devices generate a punch that cuts cable and pipe, shears bolts for fast release, and provides emergency thrust

ARMOND W. SCHELLMAN, President, Arlind Company, West Caldwell, NJ

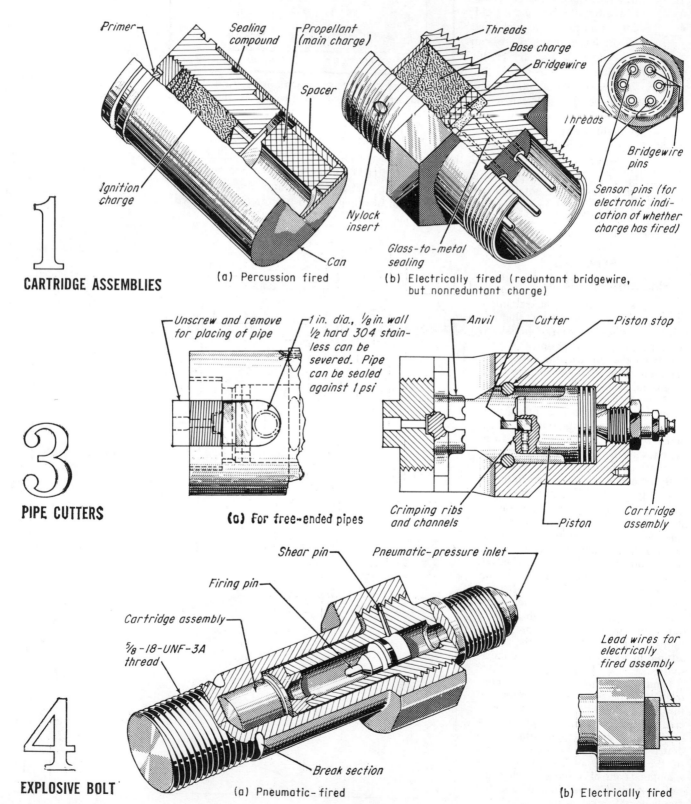

1 CARTRIDGE ASSEMBLIES

Primer — Sealing compound — Propellant (main charge) — Spacer — Ignition charge — Nylock insert — Can

(a) Percussion fired

Threads — Base charge — Bridgewire — Threads — Bridgewire pins — Sensor pins (for electronic indication of whether charge has fired) — Glass-to-metal sealing

(b) Electrically fired (reduntant bridgewire, but nonreduntant charge)

3 PIPE CUTTERS

Unscrew and remove for placing of pipe — 1 in. dia., ⅛ in. wall ½ hard 304 stainless can be severed. Pipe can be sealed against 1 psi

(a) For free-ended pipes

Anvil — Cutter — Piston stop — Crimping ribs and channels — Piston — Cartridge assembly

4 EXPLOSIVE BOLT

Cartridge assembly — Firing pin — Shear pin — Pneumatic-pressure inlet — ⅝-18-UNF-3A thread — Break section

(a) Pneumatic-fired

Lead wires for electrically fired assembly

(b) Electrically fired

pyrotechnic power

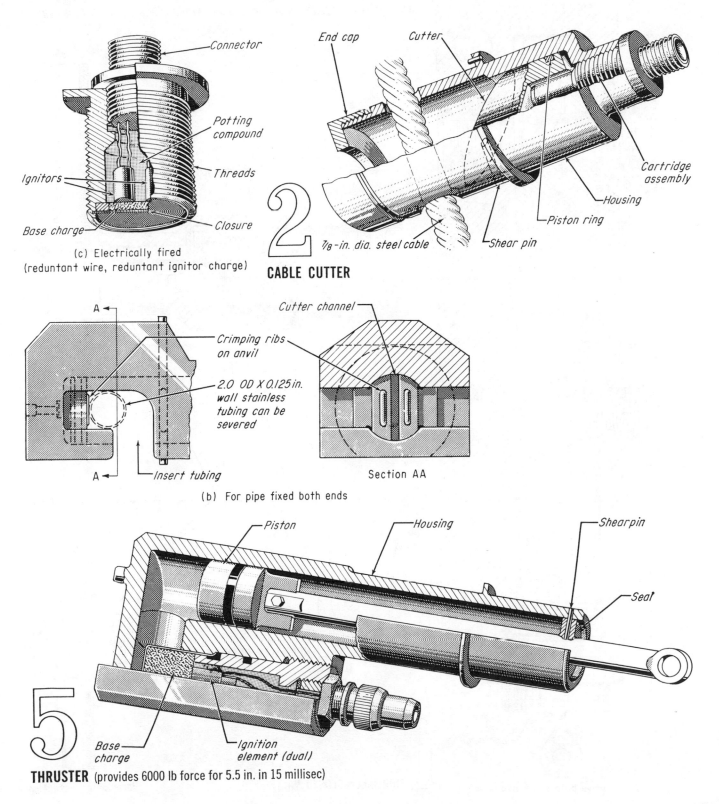

Connector

Potting compound

Threads

Ignitors

Closure

Base charge

(c) Electrically fired
(reduntant wire, reduntant ignitor charge)

End cap

Cutter

Cartridge assembly

Housing

Piston ring

Shear pin

⅞-in. dia. steel cable

2 CABLE CUTTER

Cutter channel

Crimping ribs on anvil

2.0 OD X 0.125 in. wall stainless tubing can be severed

Insert tubing

Section AA

(b) For pipe fixed both ends

Piston

Housing

Shearpin

Seal

Base charge

Ignition element (dual)

5 THRUSTER (provides 6000 lb force for 5.5 in. in 15 millisec)

Gas pressure from

They open and close valves, provide reserve pressure, and generate high-pressure gas for remote actuation. Cartridges can be fired electrically, pneumatically or manually

ARMOND W. SCHELLMAN, President, Arlind Company, West Caldwell, NJ

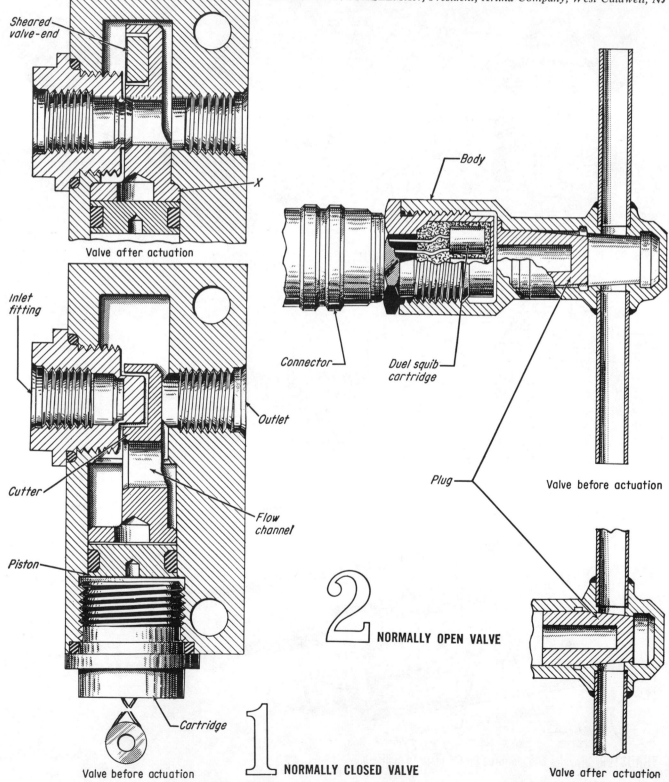

Sheared valve-end

Valve after actuation

Inlet fitting

Outlet

Cutter

Flow channel

Piston

Cartridge

Valve before actuation

1 NORMALLY CLOSED VALVE

X

Body

Connector

Duel squib cartridge

Plug

Valve before actuation

2 NORMALLY OPEN VALVE

Valve after actuation

pyrotechnic devices

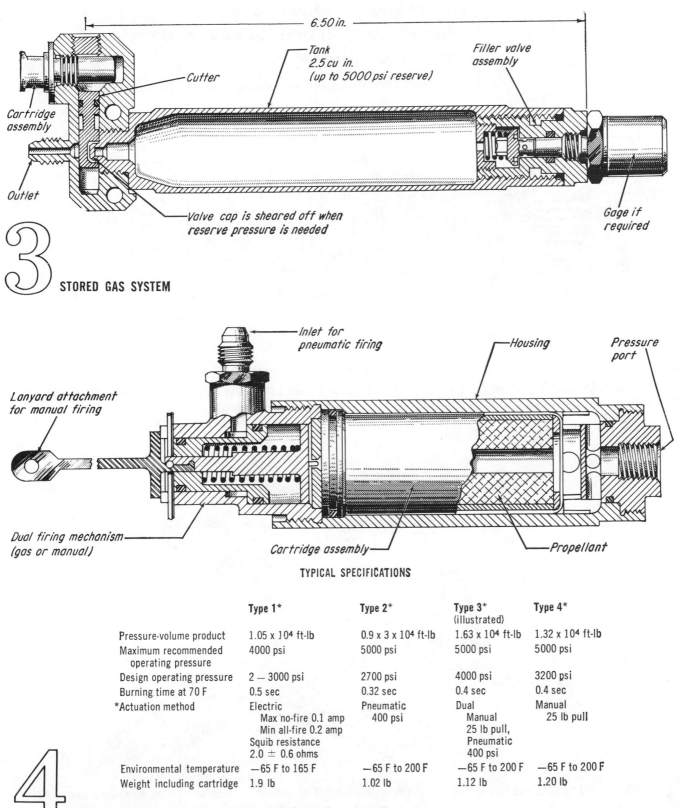

6.50 in.

Tank
2.5 cu in.
(up to 5000 psi reserve)

Filler valve
assembly

Cutter

Cartridge
assembly

Outlet

Valve cap is sheared off when
reserve pressure is needed

Gage if
required

3 STORED GAS SYSTEM

Inlet for
pneumatic firing

Housing

Pressure
port

Lanyard attachment
for manual firing

Dual firing mechanism
(gas or manual)

Cartridge assembly

Propellant

TYPICAL SPECIFICATIONS

	Type 1*	Type 2*	Type 3* (illustrated)	Type 4*
Pressure-volume product	1.05×10^4 ft-lb	$0.9 \times 3 \times 10^4$ ft-lb	1.63×10^4 ft-lb	1.32×10^4 ft-lb
Maximum recommended operating pressure	4000 psi	5000 psi	5000 psi	5000 psi
Design operating pressure	2 — 3000 psi	2700 psi	4000 psi	3200 psi
Burning time at 70 F	0.5 sec	0.32 sec	0.4 sec	0.4 sec
*Actuation method	Electric Max no-fire 0.1 amp Min all-fire 0.2 amp Squib resistance 2.0 ± 0.6 ohms	Pneumatic 400 psi	Dual Manual 25 lb pull, Pneumatic 400 psi	Manual 25 lb pull
Environmental temperature	—65 F to 165 F	—65 F to 200 F	—65 F to 200 F	—65 F to 200 F
Weight including cartridge	1.9 lb	1.02 lb	1.12 lb	1.20 lb

4 GAS GENERATOR (usually remote from device to be actuated)

8 cartridge-actuated

These compact devices pierce diaphragms, cut large holes or thick cable, lift heavy loads, extend thrust rods, release hooked or pinned loads in emergency, and provide dual valving.

G. C. STICHLING, President, Cartridge Actuated Devices Inc, Fairfield, NJ

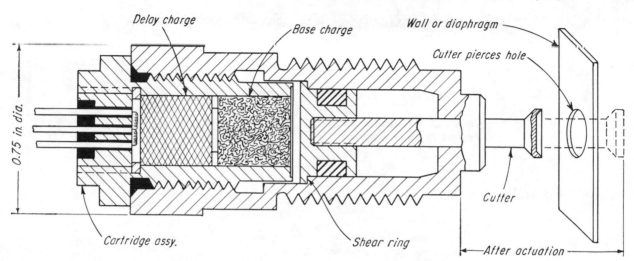

1 "PIN MOTORS" pack a powerful punch for their size and are ideal when holes must be pierced in sheetmetal at locations where other power sources or punching means are either unavailable or impractical.

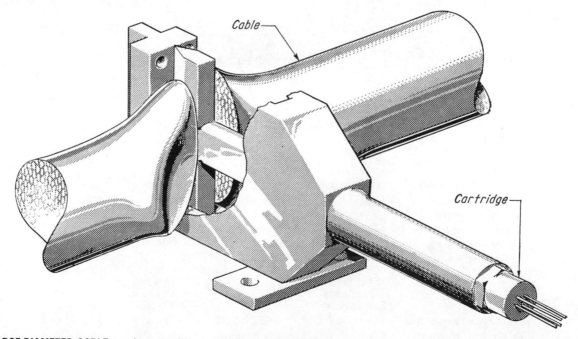

3 LARGE-DIAMETER CABLE can be cut with a relatively small cartridge mechanism — anvil and cutter framework are large but not costly.

mechanisms

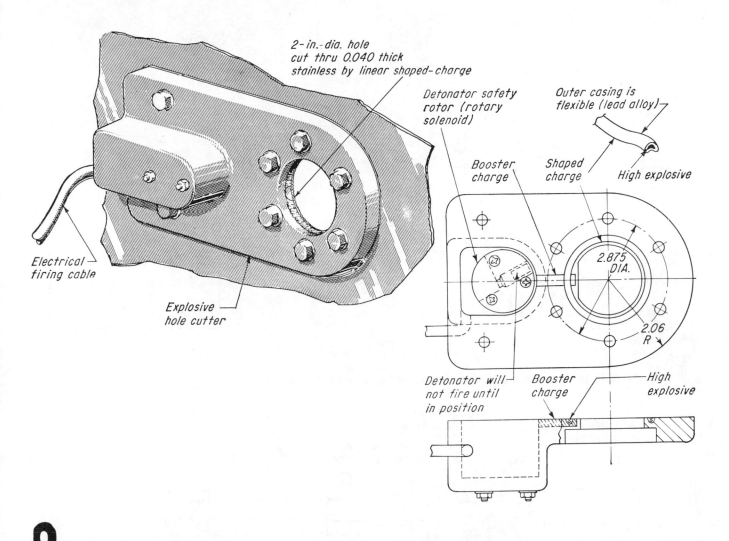

2-in.-dia. hole cut thru 0.040 thick stainless by linear shaped-charge

Detonator safety rotor (rotary solenoid)

Outer casing is flexible (lead alloy)

Booster charge

Shaped charge

High explosive

Electrical firing cable

Explosive hole cutter

2.875 DIA.

2.06 R

Detonator will not fire until in position

Booster charge

High explosive

2 EXPLOSIVE HOLE CUTTER relies on a shaped charge, enclosed in a flexible lead casing and assembled to blast a peripheral cut, which need not necessarily be circular.

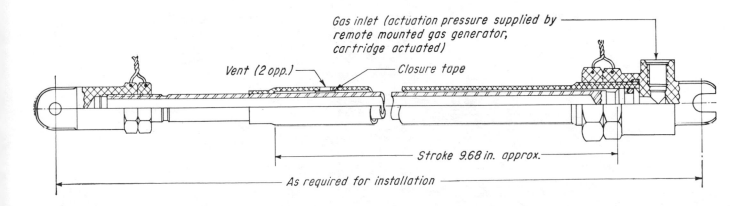

Gas inlet (actuation pressure supplied by remote mounted gas generator, cartridge actuated)

Vent (2 opp.)

Closure tape

Stroke 9.68 in. approx.

As required for installation

4 THRUSTER BAR is actuated by gas pressure generated by a cartridge at a remote location. Thrust force can be as high as necessary, within structural and practical limits. (Typically, it is from 100 to 10,000 psi.)

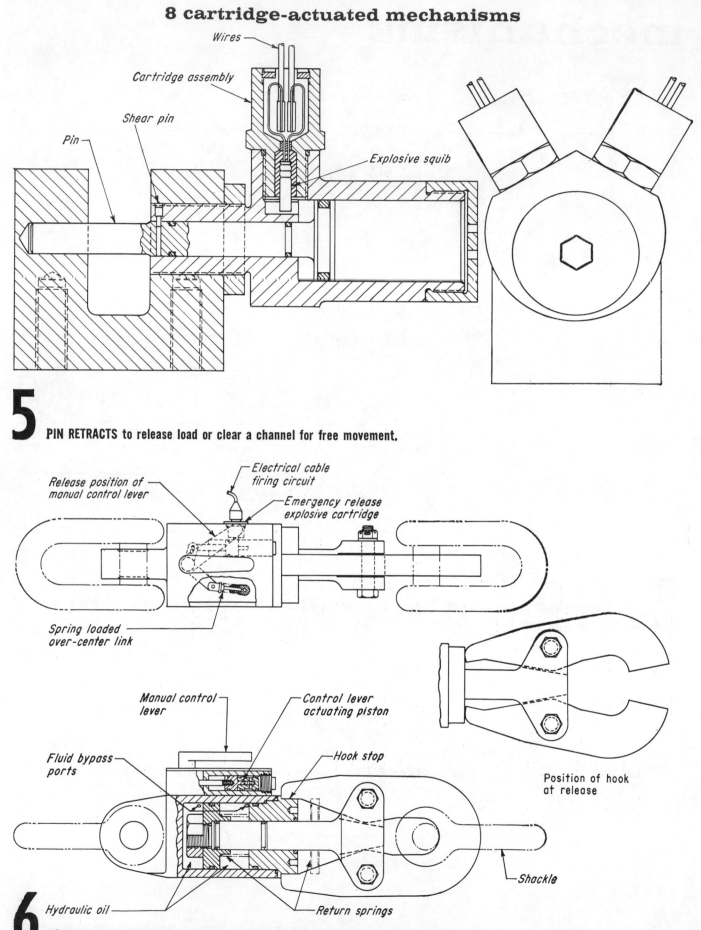

Wires

Cartridge assembly

Shear pin

Pin

Explosive squib

5 PIN RETRACTS to release load or clear a channel for free movement.

Release position of manual control lever

Electrical cable firing circuit

Emergency release explosive cartridge

Spring loaded over-center link

Manual control lever

Control lever actuating piston

Hook stop

Fluid bypass ports

Position of hook at release

Hydraulic oil

Return springs

Shackle

6 EMERGENCY HOOK RELEASE lets loads be jettisoned at any time. Hook is designed to release automatically if overloaded.

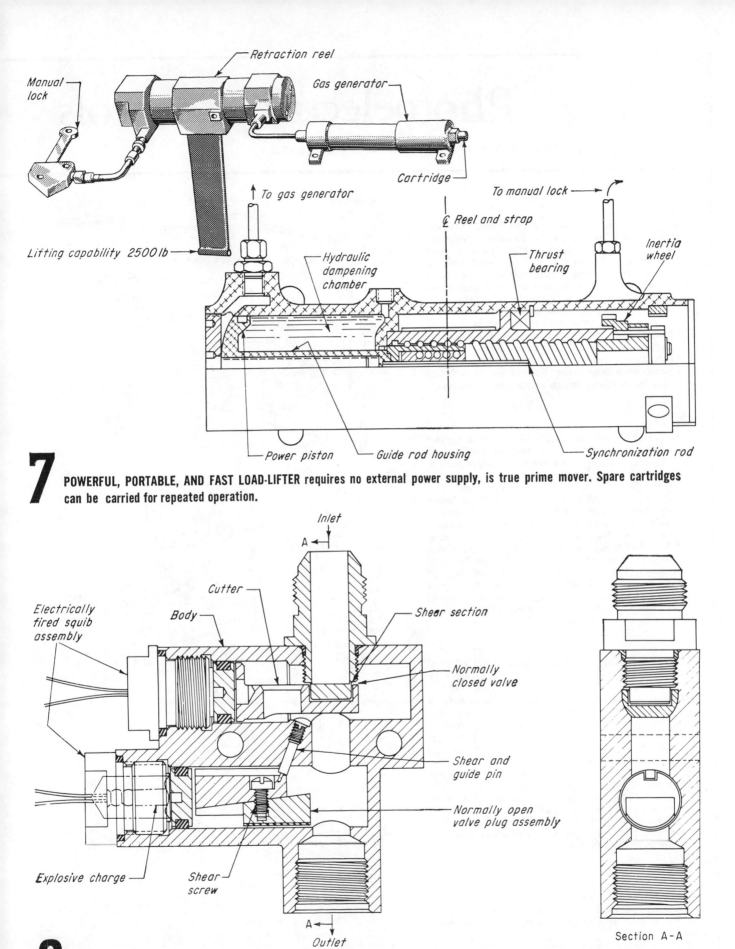

7 **POWERFUL, PORTABLE, AND FAST LOAD-LIFTER** requires no external power supply, is true prime mover. Spare cartridges can be carried for repeated operation.

8 **DUAL VALVE** is so designed to let flow be started and stopped by same unit. Firing one squib starts flow; firing the other squib stops flow.

Photoelectric Controls

PHOTOSWITCH DIVISION, ELECTRONICS CORPORATION OF AMERICA

FIG. 1—Automatic weighing and filling. Problem is to fill each box with exact quantity of products such as screws. Electric feeder vibrates parts through chute and into box on small balance. Photoelectric control is mounted at rear of scale. Light beam is restricted to very small dimensions by optical slit. Control is positioned so that light is interrupted by balanced cantilever arm attached to scale when proper box weight is reached. Photoelectric control then stops flow of parts by de-energizing feeder. Simultaneously, indexing mechanism is activated to remove filled box and replace with empty one. Completion of indexing re-energizes feeder which starts flow of screws.

FIG. 2—Operator safeguard. Most presses operate by foot pedal leaving hands free for loading and unloading operations. This creates a safety hazard. Use of mechanical gate systems reduce production speeds. With photoelectric controls, curtain of light is set up with multiple series of photoelectric scanners and light sources. When light is broken at any point by operator's hand, control energizes a locking mechanism which prevents punch press drive from being energized. Wiring is such that power or tube failure causes control to function as though light beam was broken. In addition, the light is frequently used as the actuating control since clutch is thrown as soon as operator removes his hand from the die on the press table.

FIG. 3—Sorting cartons of three types of electronic tubes. Since cartons containing one type differ widely as to size, it is not feasible to sort by carton size and shape. Solution: small strip of reflecting tape is placed on cartons by a packer during assembly. For one type of tube, strip is placed along one edge of bottom and extends almost to the middle. For second type, strip is located along same edge but from middle to opposite side. No tape is used for third type. Cartons are placed on conveyor so that tape is at right angle to direction of travel. Photoelectric controls, shown in *A*, "see" the reflecting tape pass and operate pusher bar mechanism, shown in *B*, which pushes carton on to proper distribution conveyor. Cartons without tape pass through.

FIG. 4—Cut-off machine uses photoelectric control for strip material which does not have sufficient mass to operate a mechanical limit switch satisfac-

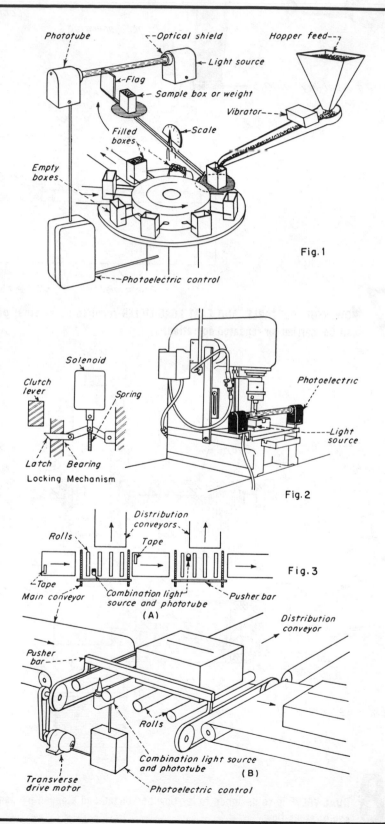

Fig. 1

Fig. 2

Fig. 3

(A)

(B)

Some typical applications for reducing production costs and increasing operator safeguards by precisely and automatically controlling the feed, transfer or inspection of products from one process stage to another.

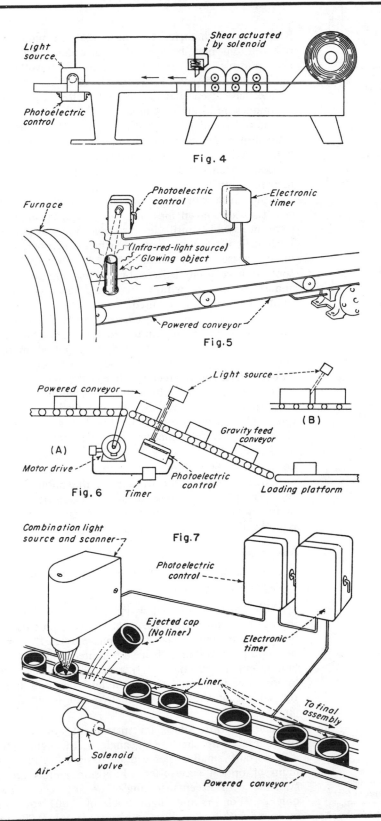

Fig. 4

Fig. 5

Fig. 6

Fig. 7

torily. Forward end of strip breaks light beam thus actuating the cut-off operation. Light source and control is mounted on adjustable stand at end of machine to vary length of finished stock.

FIG. 5—Heat-treating conveyor uses electronic timer in conjunction with photoelectric control to carry parts emerging from furnace at 2300 F. Problem is to operate conveyor only when a part is placed on it and only for distance required to reach next process stage. Parts are ejected on to conveyor at varying rates. High temperatures caused failures when mechanical switches were used. Glowing white-hot part radiates infra-red rays which actuates photoelectric control as soon as part comes in view. Control operates conveyor which carries part away from furnace and simultaneously starts timer. Conveyor is kept running by timer for pre-determined length of time required to position part for next operation.

FIG. 6—Jam detector. Cartons jamming on conveyor cause loss of production time and damage to cartons, products and conveyors. Detection is accomplished with a photoelectric control using a timer as shown in (A). Each time a carton passes light source, control beam is broken which starts timing interval in the timer. Timing circuit is reset without relay action each time beam is restored before preset timing interval has elapsed. If jam occurs causing cartons to butt one against the other, light beam cannot reach control. Timing circuit will then time out, opening load circuit which stops conveyor motor. By locating light source at an angle to conveyor, as shown in (B), power conveyor can be delayed if cartons are not butting but are too close to each other.

FIG. 7—Automatic inspection. As steel caps are conveyed to final assembly, they pass intermediate stage where an assembler inserts insulation liner into cap. Inspection point for missing liners has reflection-type photoelectric scanner which incorporates both light source and phototube with common lens system to instantly recognize difference in reflection between dark liner and light steel cap. When it detects a cap without a liner, a relay operates ejector device composed of air blast controlled by solenoid valve. Start and duration of air blast is accurately controlled by timer so that no other caps are displaced.

For better light-actuated mechanisms

THE PHOTOCONDUCTIVE CELL

ROBERT A FARRALL
Instrument dept
General Electric Co

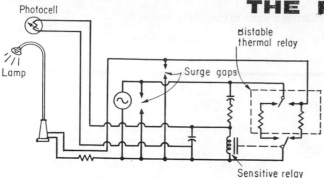

AUTOMATIC STREET-LIGHT SWITCH. Circuit is shown in the daytime (OFF) position. When light has diminished to a predetermined level, cell resistance rises and the relay is energized, in turn energizing the left heater. Light goes on when the heater has caused the bistable relay to trip. The same relay disconnects the heater as it turns on the lamp. At dawn the operation is reversed.

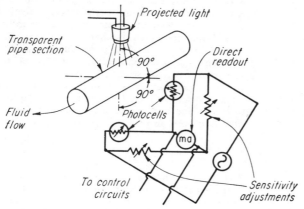

A TURBIDIMETER. Two photocells are located at right angles to each other on the outside of a transparent pipe carrying the liquid to be measured. A light source is projected directly at one cell and at 90° to the other. Cell 1 measures light transmitted through the liquid; cell 2 measures light scattered by the liquid. As the liquid becomes more turbid, cell 2 will receive more light. The cells' outputs are initially adjusted to balance the bridge circuit when liquid turbidity is some known value. Any deviation from the standard will unbalance the circuit.

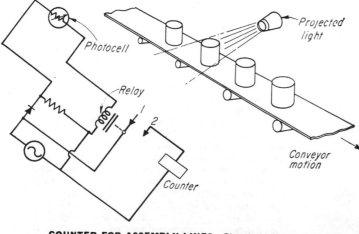

COUNTER FOR ASSEMBLY LINES. Circuit is shown in normal position with photocell resistance low and relay energized, preventing current flow to counter. When an object passes between lamp and photocell, cell resistance increases, dropping out the relay and (position 2) energizing the counter. After the object has passed the circuit returns to normal. Cells are capable of counting light pulses up to 100 cps.

Its improved characteristics mean that the photoconductive cell can now be applied to a wider range of jobs than possible with the more common photovoltaic cells. Many of the properties of this cell, which had prohibited its use, have been changed through better manufacturing techniques, resulting in a more versatile light detector.

The cell is not self-generating, as are other light-sensing cells; rather, its resistance changes when it is exposed to light. As light intensity increases, cell resistance decreases: current through the cell becomes a function of light intensity.

Although the operating principle of the photoconductive cell has been known for some time, practical applications were impossible until designs were improved recently. Early cells used silver contacts, which did not give good ohmic contact in low-voltage ranges. Now that the silver contacts have been replaced by indium and tin contacts, almost any voltage within the dissipation and insulation limits of the cell can be used.

Stability has been improved by hermetically sealing the cells in glass enclosures similar to those used for vacuum tubes. Previously, the cells had been potted in plastic, which water vapor and other toxic agents could penetrate and so attack the photoconductive material.

Poor sensitivity, for which the photoconductive cell had been known, is now remedied by improved doping techniques. Cells now have good light-to-dark ratios and sensitivity. For example, one type has a dark-resistance of 500 megohms, while at 0.05 ft-candles, its resistance goes down to 200,000 ohms.

A further look at the features of the photoconductive cell may point up some areas in which it can most profitably be used. A summary of the characteristics of a typical cell can be seen in the table.

Advantages

Characteristics of the photoconductive cell that are advantageous in applications are:

Ability to respond to low light levels—attributable to the nearly unlimited sensitivity of the cell, plus its ability to operate at high voltage (300 volts plus). By contrast, selenium photovoltaic cells have a limited sensitivity. Obtaining milliampere outputs from a selenium cell requires hundreds or thousands of footcandles. The only limit on the output of the photoconductive cell is its designed power rating.

Small size—this allows for instrument miniaturization. In devices where the viewing angle of the light detector is important, small angles can be designed with a minimum of optical accessories. Exposure meters are now available with acceptance angles or angles of view of only 2°. For example, light levels of 0.001 ft-c can be measured with a cell whose active area is only 0.004 sq in.

NEW DEVELOPMENTS IN PHOTOELECTRIC DEVICES

A photoelectric control for street lighting, introduced by Tung-Sol Electric, shows how simple design for photocell operation can be. The unit has only four major components (lightning arrestor, snap switch, photocell, and resistors) and operates on the same principle as an automobile signal flasher. When the light intensity is above 2 ft-candelas, current flows into the heater coil, warming the restraining wire and keeping it elongated. But when the ambient light drops below 2 ft-candelas, the photocell's resistance increases, cutting down the current and allowing the wire to contract so the contacts snap closed and the light goes on.

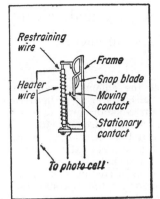

A photoelectric metering device that can be coded to deliver the exact desired scale weight of one or more compounds has been designed by Soviet engineers.

The device consists of a coded drum, mounted to a standard weighing head and containing a series of holes corresponding to the balance scale markings. An electromagnetic coupling connects the drum to the balance-pointer axle. Germanium photodiodes are placed inside the drum and a lamp outside (see diagram). To ensure precise cutoff of the feed, two sets of diodes and lamps are used. Set *A* reduces the feeder flow; set *B* shuts it off.

For multicomponent batching, there is a returning device which brings the drum

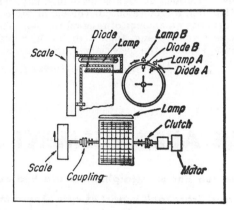

A photoelectric pulse counter for humans demonstrates the unusual versatility of today's light-sensing devices. Designed by two Army engineers, the pulse-counter does its work by sensing changes in the intensity of light transmitted through a vascular (blood cell) area. Since these changes are dependent on the heart beat (pulse rate), it thus provides an indication by which pulse rate can be measured. Its advantages: The measurement is independent of extraneous noise and is not affected by the motion of the test subject.

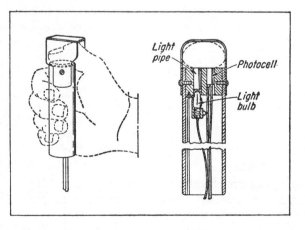

Variations in light transmission owing to changes in the amount of oxygen in the patient's blood are readily eliminated by using a photocell sensitive in the 7100 to 7500 A range, a wavelength whose transmission seems unaffected by the amount of oxygen in the blood.

PHOTOCELL ADJUSTS MAGNETIC CLUTCH IN TAPE RECORDER

Tape in this recorder is kept under constant tension by light-sensitive unit—it matches the torque driving the supply and takeup reels to the amount of tape on each.

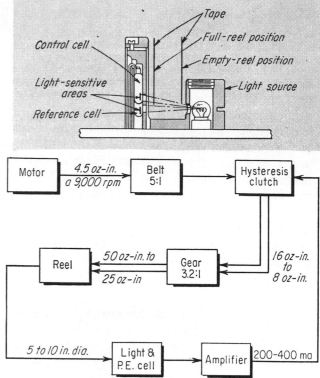

PHOTOCELL CONTROLS sense the amount of tape on supply and takeup reels, and adjust coupling force in drive clutches accordingly. To maintain constant tape tension, the torque driving each reel must vary directly with the diameter of the tape-pack. Normal tape tension is 10 oz. Tape-pack diameter varies from 5 to 10 in., so the required torque varies from 25 to 50 oz-in. at each reel.

The sensing units, one per reel, each contain two photocells. As a reel fills up, the section of tape passing the sensing unit moves closer to the photocells, reducing the amount of light striking the upper (control) cell. The lower (reference) cell remains exposed at all times, correcting for any variations in light-source intensity. The degree of shading and, therefore output voltage of the control photocell, depends on amount of tape on the reel. This output voltage is amplified and applied to the hysteresis clutch which then supplies the necessary coupling force.

(Tape Recorder by Ampex Corp.)

MIRROR ARRANGEMENT FOR TUBE STRAIGHTENER

The tubes are gun barrels straightened in a hydraulic press. The mirror-faced "ram rod" is part of optical system that permits checking the bore for alignment—without need to remove tube from press.

Primarily designed for rifle and machine gun barrels, straighteners can handle tubes from 5/8 to 1¾ in. dia. Between 20 and 25 lengths of tube can be finished per hour. Produced by Berlin-Luebecker Maschinenfabrik, Lubeck, Ger.

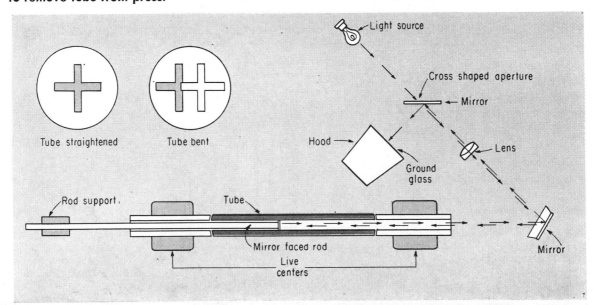

Mirror-faced plunger . . .
is inserted into bore of tube mounted between live centers. Light source behind press is projected through a cross-shaped aperture in the mirror. Using externally mounted mirror and the mirror-faced plunger, the light pattern is reflected back to the hooded ground-glass screen. When cross-like images coincide, tube under test is perfectly straight.

LIGHT SCANS THICKNESS OF MATERIAL

Optical-type gage doesn't actually contact the material being checked, so is unaffected by its speed or properties. The instrument is sensitive to variations of 0.0001-in. thickness of sheet, foil or webbing.

Single or multiple installations may be used to check thickness at one or more points across the width. Warning lights or audible signals can be incorporated, or connections made to thickness or coating controls for fully automatic operation. Mark N Thickness Gage is produced by Mark N Laboratory, Bethel, Conn.

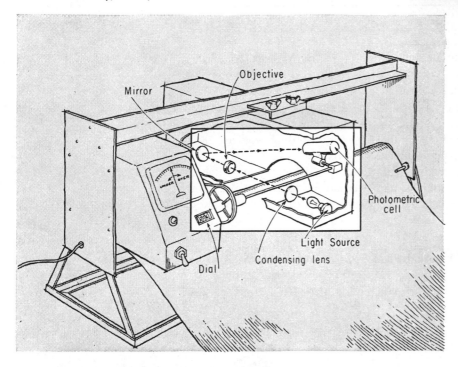

Optical principle . . .

is key to operational flexibility of gage. Light passes through condensing lens, across material being tested, through objective lens—then is reflected from mirror to photometric cell. Changes in thickness of the material being tested vary the amount of light reaching photometric cell and are indicated on the meter after passing through a balancing circuit. Motor-drive moves photometric cell back and forth by means of an inclined screw drive to alter its elevation and give the desired thickness setting.

Properties such as dielectric constant, conductivity, absorption of radiation are not involved in the measurement, therefore the gage measures stock of any type without modification. Opacity does not influence measurement because the material is tangentially illuminated. Gage is particularly suited to quality control of coating processes where variations in electrical or absorption characteristics eliminate usual methods.

ASPECT SENSOR

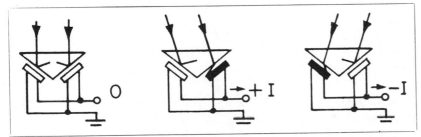

Sensor consisting of two photocells and an isosceles prism cut at any one of a number of critical angles (depending on light source) was originally developed for use in aerospace vehicles. At null position rays from light source are essentially totally reflected; light movement to right or left causes refraction of light onto one or another opposing silicon photocells, generating plus or minus output. Peak output at 25 deg from null, 4.4 micro amp. Range, more than 90 deg, plus or minus. Weighs 1 gm. HH Controls Inc, 69 Pearl St, Cambridge 39, Mass.

PHOTORECORDING SYSTEM

A photologging system that can take the place of standard impact-marking data-recording techniques has been devised by Eastman Kodak Co and will be made available to interested manufacturers for machine development. The system can, says Eastman, "provide a hard-copy printed record of data, monitored by appropriate sensing units, from all types of industrial processes or operations."

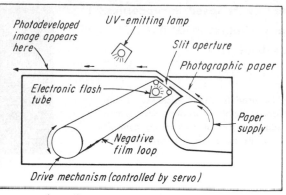

The logger works from a continuous film loop (16, 35, or 70 mm), containing negative images of all the characters, words, or digits to be used in recording. This loop passes under a slit aperture and is positioned, via a drive sprocket and servomechanism from the process being controlled, so the desired image to be recorded appears in front of the slit. Above the slit, the photologging paper unrolls (see diagram). An electronic flash tube provides the light for recording, and an ultraviolet lamp develops the image, making it immediately visible.

The 6-in. photographic paper provides five recording columns, giving time in minutes, time in seconds, name of variables, and two data columns, one providing for four digits, the other for five; and the paper moves at 9 in./min with a printout rate of one step every 3 sec.

PHOTOCHROMIC DEVICES

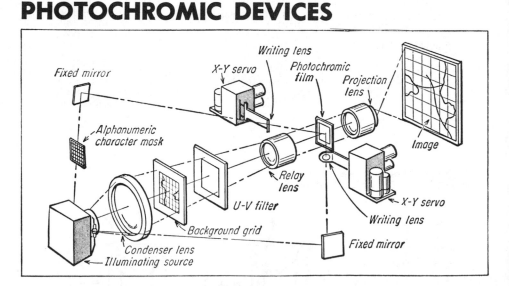

The information-display system is being developed by National Cash Register. L. J. Hines of NCR's Electronics Div says the Photochromic devices will be rugged, reliable, and versatile and will encompass the entire range from a simple analog X-Y plotter to a multi-color, multi-channel, real-time plotter with display of alphanumeric information.

As Hines points out, Photochromic films behave like photographic films but don't need a chemical developer. Pictures become visible immediately when Photochromic films are exposed to ultraviolet light. The films have no grain, and pictures can be displayed and erased repeatedly. Either light or heat can be used to erase the image and light-sensitive and heat-sensitive components can be combined to provide controlled persistence.

9

FLUID-POWER CONTROL AND ACTUATING DEVICES

HYDRAULIC CIRCUITS are but combinations of pumps and valves designed to apply pressure at regulated intervals. There are countless possible combinations of pumps and valves for controlling such pressure to the operating cylinders.

Hydraulic transmissions in machine tools may include slides, clamps, interlock and safety devices, all properly timed with relation to each other.

The circuit also consists of combinations of stop valves, reversing valves,

pilot valves for controlling larger valves such as the main reversing valve, throttling or dwell valves for slowing motion or delaying action, sequence valves to hold back certain motions until others are completed, and relief valves to maintain a uniform pressure in the system.

Where required oil pressure is not high, or where lightweight machine parts are to be accelerated and decelerated, constant-volume pumps such as gear and vane pumps are used.

The variable-volume system is used where there must be close control, where the pump delivers a variable and metered volume of oil, and where heavy machine parts and work are to be accelerated or decelerated without shock. It uses a plunger pump in which the length of stroke can be controlled.

Data and illustrations of hydraulically controlled machine tools supplied from Socony-Vacuum Oil Company publication "Hydraulic Systems."

Fig. 1—Circuit of a vertical broaching machine using a variable-volume pump. Difference between areas on top and bottom faces of piston gives slow down stroke and rapid return for a given pump discharge. Check valve allows additional oil required on the down stroke to be drawn from the reservoir. At the end of the down stroke, a slide engages an adjustable stop and controls the reversing valve in the pump. On up stroke, relief valve permits excess oil to enter reservoir.

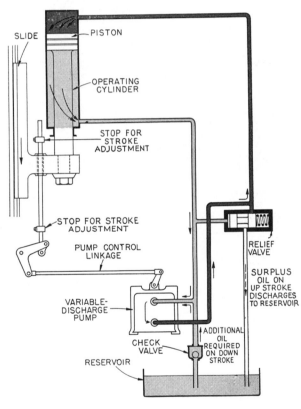

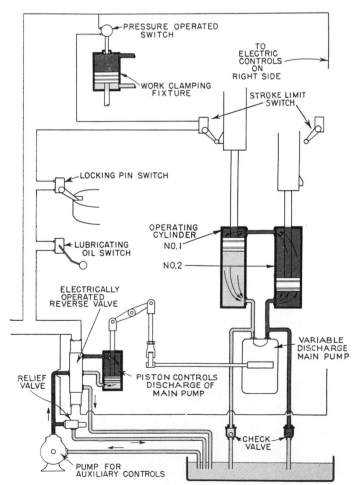

Fig. 2—Variable-volume hydraulic system of a double broaching machine. Two interconnected operating cylinders can be supplied with oil in either direction. As No. 2 piston moves up, the oil moves to the top of No. 1, pushing No. 1 piston down, and expelling oil to the pump suction. If, due to leakage above pistons, the operating cylinders get out of step, there are valves and connections, not shown, for manually refilling upper ends of cylinders. Oil flow to main pump control is regulated by an electrically operated reversing valve the solenoid of which is in series with the lubricating oil switch, locking pin switch, stroke limit switch, and the pressure switch on the work clamping fixture.

MACHINE TOOLS – I

CUTTER

WORK

TABLE

RETURN

CUTTING OR WORKING STROKE

OPERATING CYLINDER

METERING PUMP

REVERSING VALVE

RELIEF VALVE

BOOSTER PUMP

LOW PRESSURE GEAR PUMP

RESERVOIR

STRAINER

Fig. 3—Lock feed hydraulic system of a milling machine. Table travel speed is controlled by a variable discharge metering pump which removes measured amounts of oil from the front of the advancing piston. The positive flow of oil to and from the operating cylinder accurately controls working piston motion. When the reversing valve is thrown to the position shown by the dotted lines, the booster pump discharges entirely through the relief valve, and the gear pump supplies low-pressure oil for a quick return stroke.

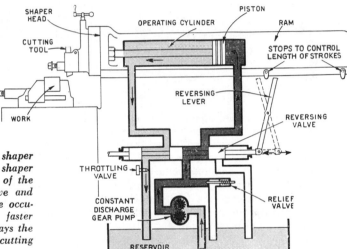

SHAPER HEAD

CUTTING TOOL

WORK

OPERATING CYLINDER

PISTON

RAM

STOPS TO CONTROL LENGTH OF STROKES

REVERSING LEVER

REVERSING VALVE

THROTTLING VALVE

CONSTANT DISCHARGE GEAR PUMP

RELIEF VALVE

RESERVOIR

Fig. 4—Constant-volume hydraulic circuit for a shaper drive. Forward motion of the piston moves the shaper head forward for the cutting stroke. At the end of the working stroke, a stop throws the reversing valve and the shaper head starts on the return stroke. Space occupied by the piston rod makes the return stroke faster than the working stroke. The return stroke is always the same for a given pump discharge rate but the cutting stroke can be adjusted by the throttling valve.

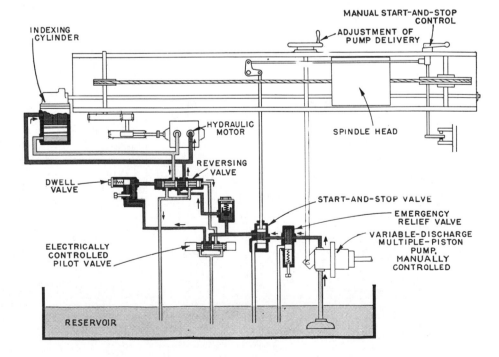

INDEXING CYLINDER

MANUAL START-AND-STOP CONTROL

ADJUSTMENT OF PUMP DELIVERY

HYDRAULIC MOTOR

SPINDLE HEAD

REVERSING VALVE

DWELL VALVE

START-AND-STOP VALVE

EMERGENCY RELIEF VALVE

VARIABLE-DISCHARGE MULTIPLE-PISTON PUMP, MANUALLY CONTROLLED

ELECTRICALLY CONTROLLED PILOT VALVE

RESERVOIR

Fig. 5—Hydraulic system of a horizontal honing machine. When start and stop valve is in start position, oil is sent to either end of a reversing valve. Electrical contact points are set for the desired spindle head travel. A hydraulic motor, through gears and a cable, reciprocates the spindle head. Dwell valve between pilot and reversing valve, causes dwell at end of working stroke. A hydraulic indexing cylinder and ratchet mechanism advances spindle each time the hydraulic motor reverses for a working stroke.

HYDRAULIC CONTROL OF

JAMES A. LEONARD, *Hydraulic Machinery Inc.*

Hydraulic operation of machines, sequencing of processing operations, and pressure testing have been developed to meet a wide range of conditions, often with interlocked timing of several operations. Automatic operation is often produced by electric solenoids activated by switches whose contacts are opened and closed by moving machine elements. Such operation is possible hydraulically also as shown in Fig. 4.

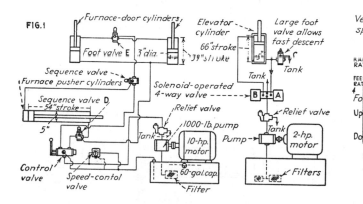

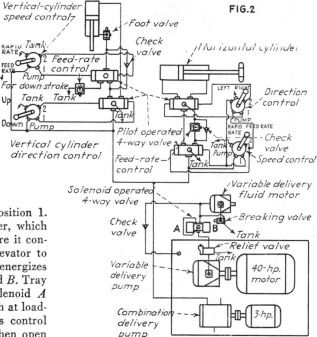

Fig. 1—Furnace doors are opened when control valve is at position 1. Pressure build-up then opens sequence valve to pusher cylinder, which pushes new tray into furnace and heated tray onto elevator where it contacts a limit switch that energizes solenoid A. This causes elevator to lower tray into quench tank and contact a limit switch that de-energizes solenoid A and starts a timer, which eventually energizes solenoid B. Tray moving off elevator contacts a limit switch that energizes solenoid A thus lowering elevator for loading unless held at C. A limit switch at loading position de-energizes solenoid A. During these operations control valve is put in position 2, causing pusher cylinder to retract, then open sequence valve D to close furnace door unless held by foot valve E.

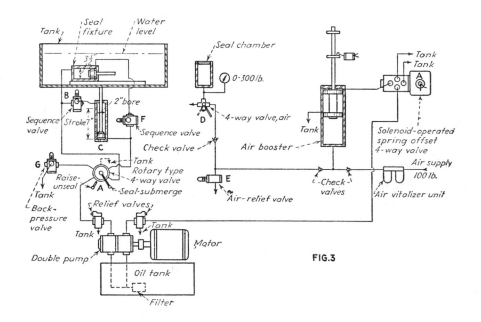

Fig. 2—Fluid motor on boring mill runs when solenoid A is energized and solenoid B is de-energized, and stops when the reverse is true. Push-buttons on panel control speed. Horizontal and vertical cylinder direction and speed are controlled by four 2-position pilot valves. Feed rate is regulated by a control valve.

Fig. 3—End of part to be pressure tested is held in seal chamber by seal fixture when rotary valve A is in position shown. Pressure build-up opens sequence valve B, causing cylinder C to submerge test set-up. Air is admitted by moving valve lever D to position shown. Energizing solenoid A builds pressure in booster cylinder from 100 to 250 lb. Air pressure is released by reversing lever D and test set-up is raised by reversing valve A. Pressure build-up opens sequence valve F, thus releasing seal fixture.

MACHINE TOOLS — II

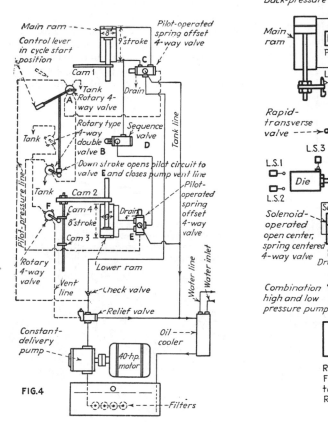

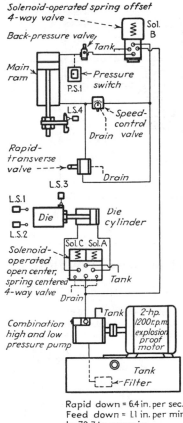

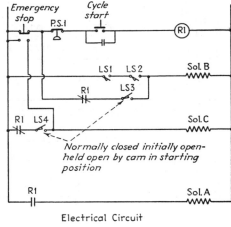

Electrical Circuit

FIG.5

FIG.4

Rapid down = 6.4 in. per sec.
Feed down = 1.1 in. per min.
to 70.7 in. per min.
Rapid up = 8.1 in. per sec.

Fig. 4—Main ram of press is started downward by moving lever of valve *A* to position shown, causing pilot pressure to shift valve *C*. Cam 1 reverses valve *A*, thus retracting ram and opening sequence valve *D* to valve *E*, which causes lower ram to eject work from die until cam 2 reverses valve *B* and cam 3 reverses valve *F*. Valve *F*, reversed slightly before *B*, keeps vent line closed. Valve *B* removes pressure from valve *E*, which allows lower ram to retract until valve *F* is reversed by cam 4, thus opening vent line to tank.

Fig. 5—Start button energizes solenoid *A*, causing die piston to close and contact switches P.S. 1 and 2. This energizes solenoid *B* through L.S. 3, which closed when cam moved with die, and causes main ram of press to move down on work until oil pressure opens P.S. 1, de-energizing solenoid *A* and energizing solenoid *C*. This causes die to retract, opening L.S. 3 and thus de-energizing solenoid *B*, which causes main ram to rise. Opening of L.S. 4 by ram de-energizes solenoid *C*, venting pump to the oil storage tank.

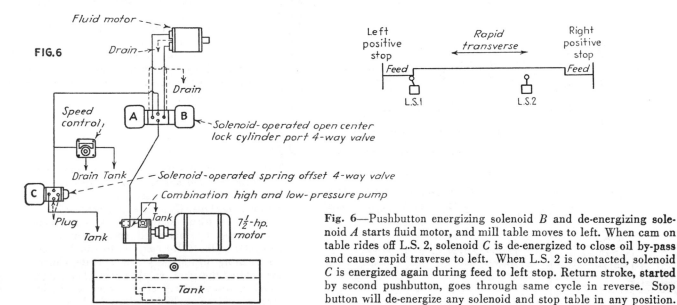

Fig. 6—Pushbutton energizing solenoid *B* and de-energizing solenoid *A* starts fluid motor, and mill table moves to left. When cam on table rides off L.S. 2, solenoid *C* is de-energized to close oil by-pass and cause rapid traverse to left. When L.S. 2 is contacted, solenoid *C* is energized again during feed to left stop. Return stroke, started by second pushbutton, goes through same cycle in reverse. Stop button will de-energize any solenoid and stop table in any position.

HYDRAULIC CONTROL OF

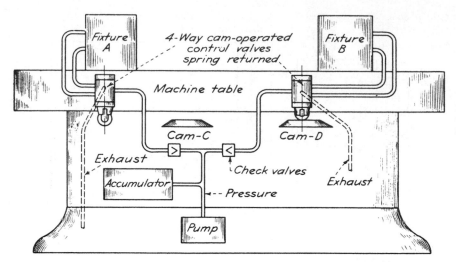

AUTOMATIC CONTROL OF FIXTURES ON MILLING MACHINE

Fig. 1—Simple circuit automatically controlling clamping action of two fixtures on milling machine. Four-way cam-operated control valves attached to the reciprocating table clamp work when roller passes over stationary cams, then release pressure when roller drops free. Spring returns valve to normal position. Accumulator holds supply of oil under pressure, permitting instantaneous action and use of smaller pump.

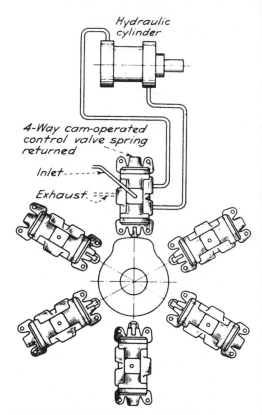

MULTIPLE VALVES CONTROLLED BY SINGLE ROTATING CAM

Fig. 2—Multiple valves operated by a single rotating cam give sequence control over cylinders for successive operations. The operation of each individual cylinder circuit can be varied by using reducing valves, by-pass valves or feed control valves.

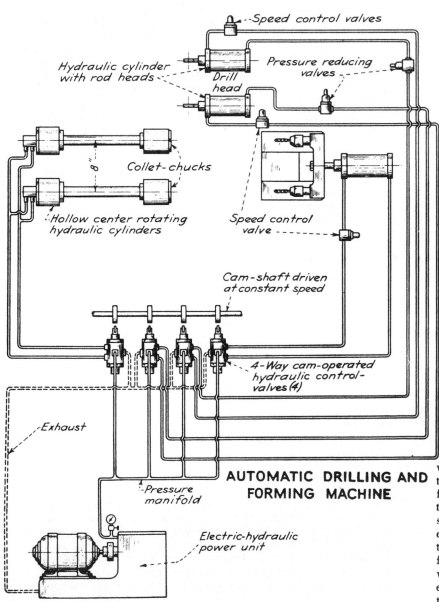

AUTOMATIC DRILLING AND FORMING MACHINE

Fig. 3—Arrangement of cam shaft and four-way cam-operated spring return valves to control operation of an automatic drilling and forming machine. Cams are arranged on shaft to time operations, shaft being driven at constant speed by motorized speed reducer or equivalent. One valve controls two hollow-center rotating cylinders which operate chucks for holding the work, another controls cylinder which moves two drill heads, other two valves each control one cylinder which feeds forming tools into and out of the work.

MACHINE TOOLS – III

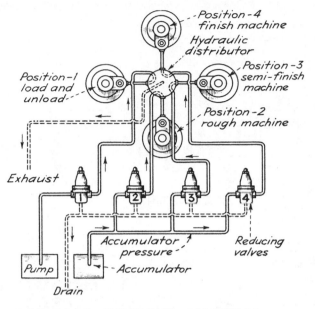

- Position-4 finish machine
- Hydraulic distributor
- Position-1 load and unload
- Position-3 semi-finish machine
- Position-2 rough machine
- Exhaust
- Accumulator pressure
- Reducing valves
- Pump
- Accumulator
- Drain

4-SPINDLE CHUCKING MACHINE

J. C. COTNER
Logansport Machine, Incorporated

Fig. 4—Used on automatic multiple spindle chucking machines, this arrangement permits individual pressure control to control valve on each operating cylinder. Operating pressure is controlled through reducing valves for varying chucking pressures for different work positions. Accumulator pressure is applied to position 2, 3, and 4, to insure proper chucking conditions. Position 1 is supplied with oil under pressure directly from the pump to operate chucking cylinder for unloading and loading.

Fig. 5—Cams driven at the desired speed by an electric motor-driven speed reducer tilt five mercury switches, causing three solenoid valves to operate in proper sequence. Cycle of operation of this machine for molding powder into hard cakes: 1. Pressure to *A*, exhaust *C*, block *B* and *D*, causing top ram to move down; 2. Pressure to *A*, exhaust *C* and *B*, block *D*, causing lower ram to move up and pressing powder between rams; 3. Block *A*, and *C*, exhaust *B*, pressure to *D*, both rams move up to unload position; 4. Exhaust *A*, pressure to *C*, and *B*, block *D*, lower ram moves down to loading position. Time cycle controller automatically shuts off, completing cycle.

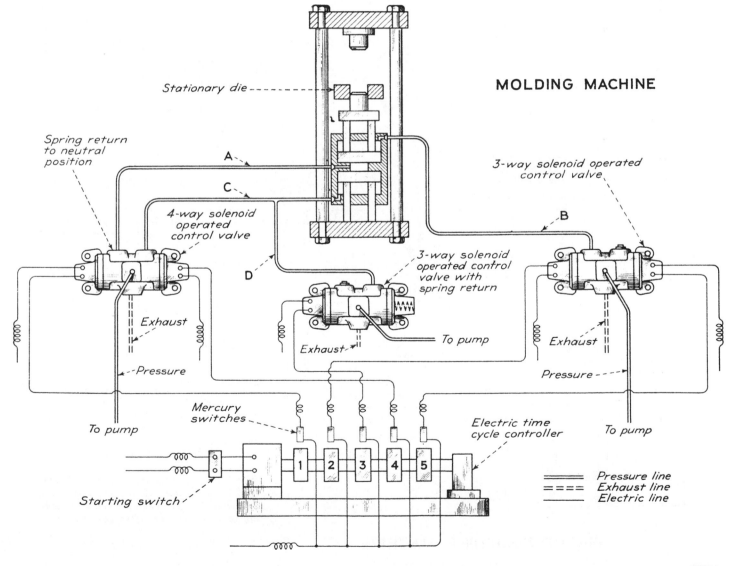

MOLDING MACHINE

- Stationary die
- Spring return to neutral position
- 3-way solenoid operated control valve
- 4-way solenoid operated control valve
- A
- C
- B
- D
- 3-way solenoid operated control valve with spring return
- Exhaust
- Pressure
- Exhaust
- To pump
- Exhaust
- Pressure
- To pump
- Mercury switches
- To pump
- Electric time cycle controller
- Starting switch

Pressure line
Exhaust line
Electric line

Fig. 6 —Four-way solenoid valves controlled by limit switches give the following automatic operating cycle of a press: Closing the starting switch actuates solenoid valve causing die to move under press ram. At end of stroke the die strikes limit switch, causing other solenoid valve to operate and apply pressure to ram which comes down and remains there until pressure builds up in line to a predetermined point. Pressure switch then acts to reverse solenoid valve, returning ram to original position. Time relay, normally closed, breaks current to solenoid so that valve is free to operate when the pressure switch energizes opposite solenoid. Swing cam on ram trips another limit switch which reverses solenoid valve to return die to loading position.

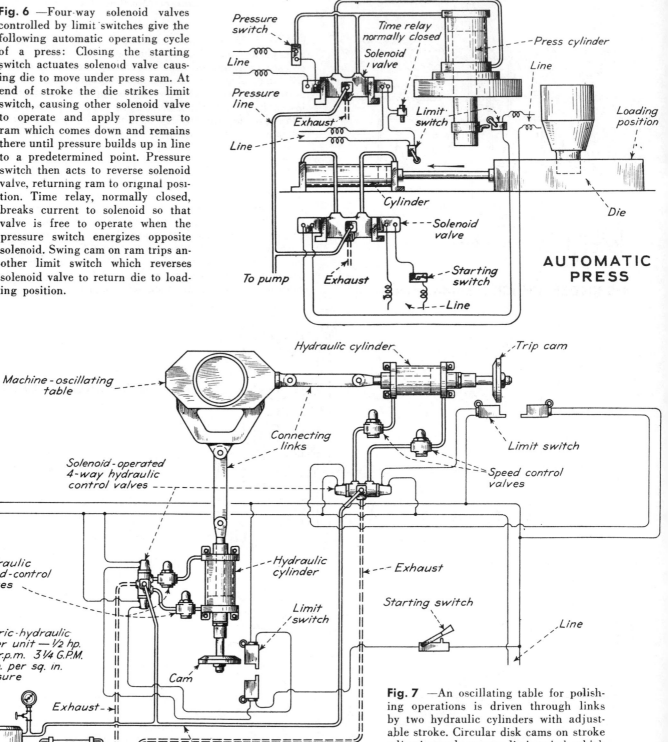

AUTOMATIC PRESS

Fig. 7 —An oscillating table for polishing operations is driven through links by two hydraulic cylinders with adjustable stroke. Circular disk cams on stroke adjusting rods operate limit switch which controls solenoid valves. Speed control valves used on lines from each end of cylinders are adjusted to give proper oscillatory motion. Cylinders start from back position and each advances according to speed control valve adjustment.

MIRROR POLISHING MACHINE

J. C. COTNER
Logansport Machine, Incorporated

Fig. 8 —Hydraulic operation of this special forming machine is set in motion by a four-way hand-operated valve which actuates chucking cylinder, and operates valve *B*, causing facing tool feed cylinder 2 to rapid advance until cam contacts speed control valve *E*. Cylinder then feeds for facing operation. When facing is completed, cams shift pilot valves *H* and *I*, operating control valves *B* and *C*; cylinder 2 returns rapidly and cylinder 3 advances. When forming operation is completed, cam shifts pilot operating valve *J*, operating valves *C* and *D*. Cylinder 3 then rapidly returns to starting position and cylinder 4 is placed into cut-off operation. At the finish of cut-off, cam shifts pilot operating valve *K*, operating control valve *D*. Cylinder 4 rapidly returns to starting position. Operator then places valve handle of control valve *A* into position 2 which releases work in collect chuck. Cam-operated speed control valves control the feed by metering exhaust oil from the cylinder.

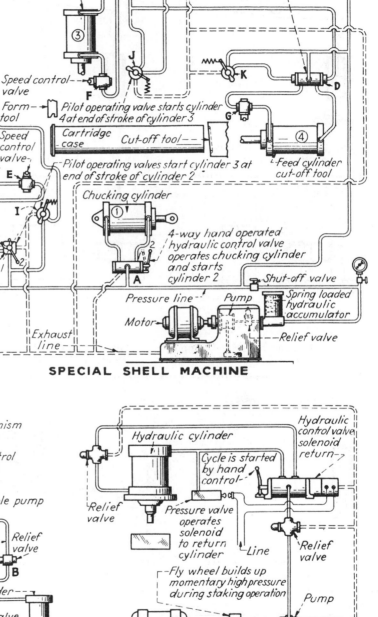

SPECIAL SHELL MACHINE

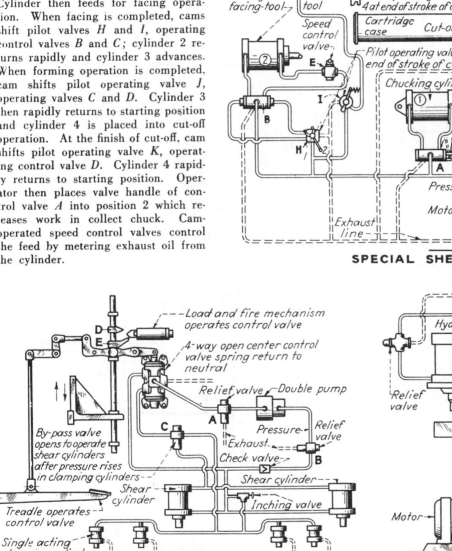

HYDRAULIC SHEAR

STAKING MACHINE

Fig. 9 —Foot treadle and load and fire mechanism operate a four-way valve which controls a shear. Double pump is used to supply hydraulic power, the smaller having a low delivery to keep shearing cylinders up and off work during loading or standby period. In the working position oil is applied first to clamping cylinders and when predetermined pressure has been reached, by-pass valve will open and operate shear cylinders. Inching of shear can be obtained without operating treadle by bleeding off pressure from small pump through inching valve.

Fig. 10 —Flywheel in assembly provides energy for momentary high pressure needed for staking operations with a small motor. Cycle is started by hand control. When pressure in ram reaches desired point, pressure switch closes circuit of solenoid which reverses control valve causing cylinder to return. Relief valve on return line is set at pressure just sufficient for ram return. During standby period, oil from pump flows through valve at reduced pressure eliminating heating.

Mechanisms Actuated by Air or

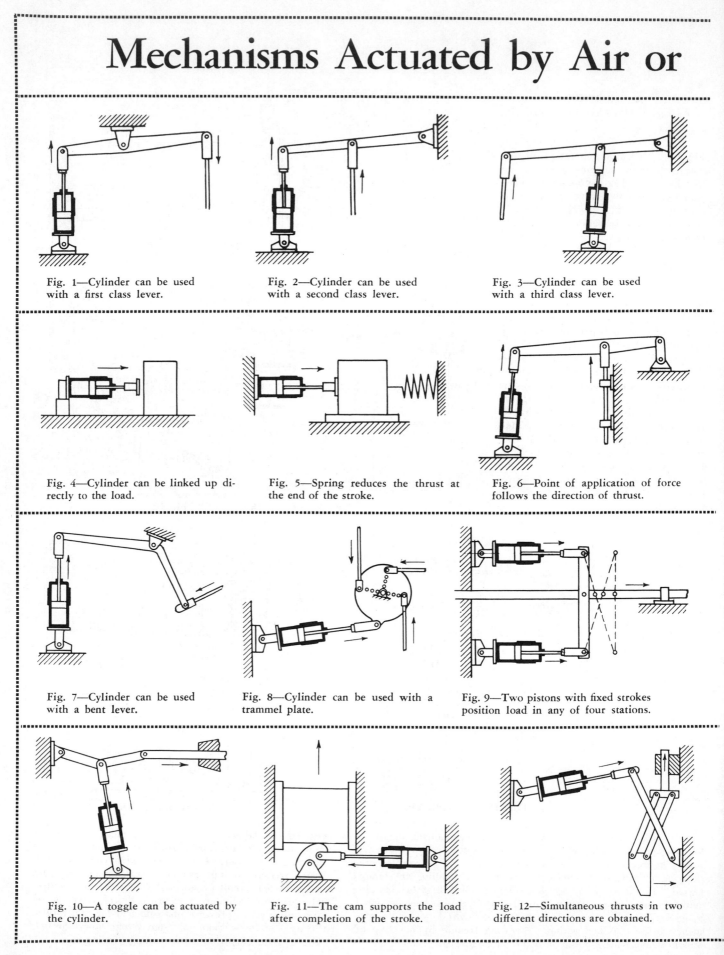

Fig. 1—Cylinder can be used with a first class lever.

Fig. 2—Cylinder can be used with a second class lever.

Fig. 3—Cylinder can be used with a third class lever.

Fig. 4—Cylinder can be linked up directly to the load.

Fig. 5—Spring reduces the thrust at the end of the stroke.

Fig. 6—Point of application of force follows the direction of thrust.

Fig. 7—Cylinder can be used with a bent lever.

Fig. 8—Cylinder can be used with a trammel plate.

Fig. 9—Two pistons with fixed strokes position load in any of four stations.

Fig. 10—A toggle can be actuated by the cylinder.

Fig. 11—The cam supports the load after completion of the stroke.

Fig. 12—Simultaneous thrusts in two different directions are obtained.

Hydraulic Cylinders

Acknowledgment is made to Adel Precision Product Corporation, Blackhawk Manufacturing Company, Hydraulic Equipment Company, Mead Specialties Company, Westinghouse Air Brake Co., and especially to Hanna Engineering Works.

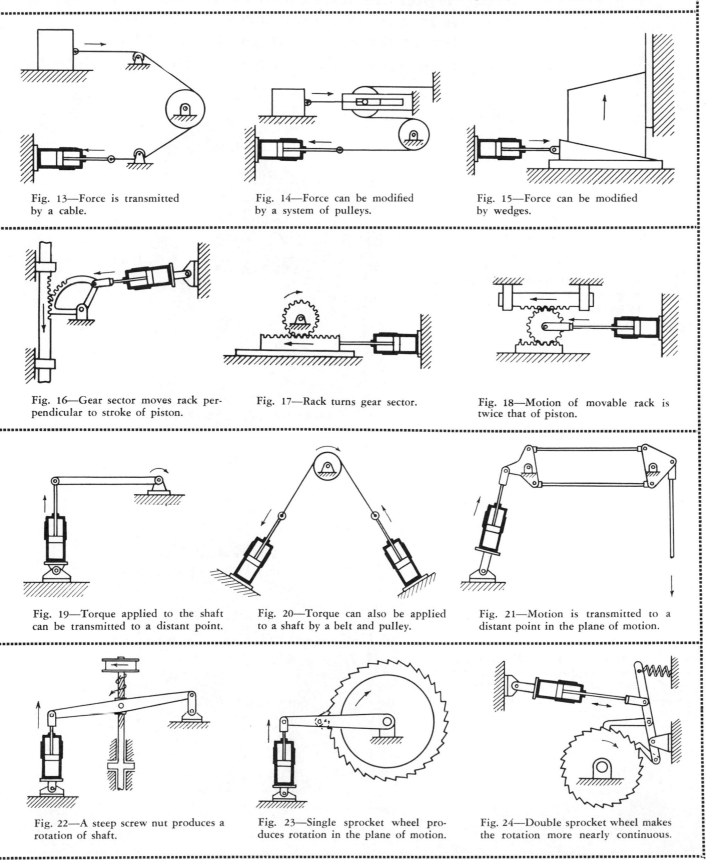

Fig. 13—Force is transmitted by a cable.

Fig. 14—Force can be modified by a system of pulleys.

Fig. 15—Force can be modified by wedges.

Fig. 16—Gear sector moves rack perpendicular to stroke of piston.

Fig. 17—Rack turns gear sector.

Fig. 18—Motion of movable rack is twice that of piston.

Fig. 19—Torque applied to the shaft can be transmitted to a distant point.

Fig. 20—Torque can also be applied to a shaft by a belt and pulley.

Fig. 21—Motion is transmitted to a distant point in the plane of motion.

Fig. 22—A steep screw nut produces a rotation of shaft.

Fig. 23—Single sprocket wheel produces rotation in the plane of motion.

Fig. 24—Double sprocket wheel makes the rotation more nearly continuous.

6 fluid-power force

When the actuator in these amplifiers
is in position, input force is balanced
by feedback force from the actuator.

GERALD BLOOM, Project Engineer, Simmonds Precision Products Inc, Tarrytown, NY

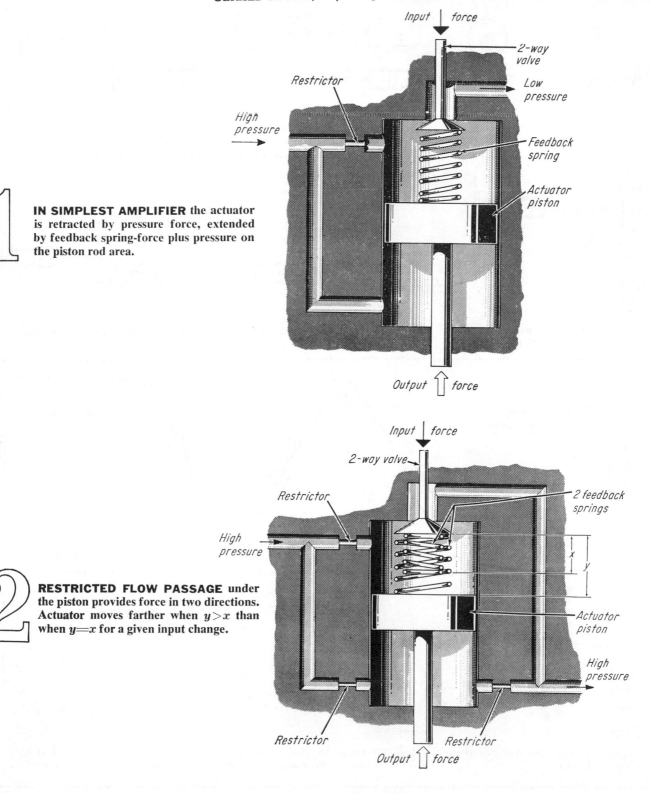

1 **IN SIMPLEST AMPLIFIER** the actuator
is retracted by pressure force, extended
by feedback spring-force plus pressure on
the piston rod area.

2 **RESTRICTED FLOW PASSAGE** under
the piston provides force in two directions.
Actuator moves farther when $y > x$ than
when $y = x$ for a given input change.

amplifiers

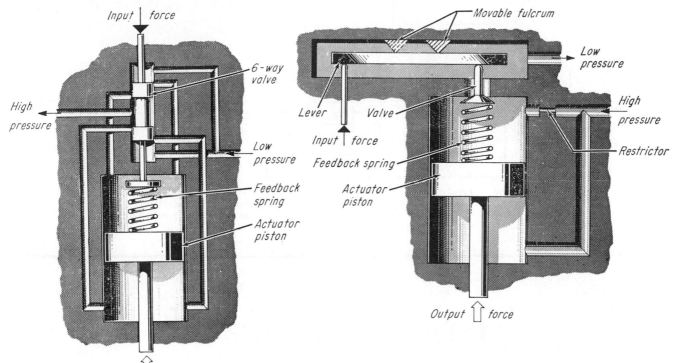

Input force

6-way valve

High pressure

Low pressure

Feedback spring

Actuator piston

Output force

Movable fulcrum

Low pressure

Lever

Valve

Input force

Feedback spring

Actuator piston

High pressure

Restrictor

Output force

3 **MULTI-PORT VALVE** gives full pressure actuation in both directions; therefore it provides high force and fast response for a given pressure level.

4 **LEVER-ACTUATED VALVE** may be advantageous in some applications. Here input force can be adjusted by changing the position of the fulcrum.

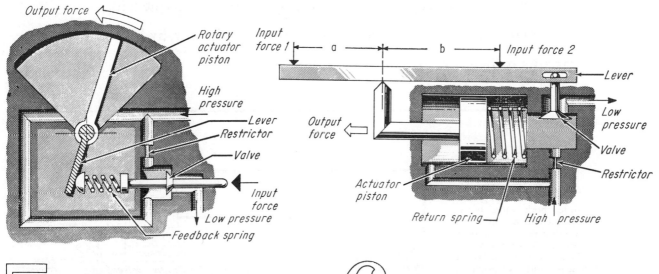

Output force

Rotary actuator piston

High pressure

Lever

Restrictor

Valve

Input force

Low pressure

Feedback spring

Input force 1

a

b

Input force 2

Lever

Output force

Low pressure

Valve

Restrictor

Actuator piston

Return spring

High pressure

5 **ROTARY OUTPUT** for large or multiple rotations, including those greater than 360 deg, uses fluid motor as actuator, with feedback through a torsion spring.

6 **FULCRUM ON ACTUATOR** moves until input forces balance. This amplifier, therefore, is useful for dividing forces so that Input $1 \times a =$ Input $2 \times b$.

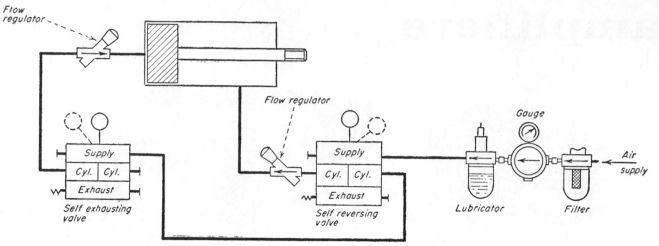

Fig. 1—Bi-manual control of a cylinder. Valve levers must be held in position for piston to operate. Release of both valves automatically returns piston. Release of self-reversing valve returns the piston; release of self-exhausting valve vents both sides of piston to exhaust.

From: The Machinist

Fundamentals of
PNEUMATIC CONTROL

R. COOPER
Lang Pneumatic, Ltd.

Typical air circuits using different types of pneumatic valves. Function of circuit dependent on valve operation and sequencing. Pneumatic circuits can be combined with electrical or hydraulic circuits to perform specific operations.

Fig. 2—Spring loaded locking piston. To activate cylinder both valve levers must be positioned. Once piston is set release of self-centering valve locks position of positive valve. To withdraw the piston both valves must be activated. Used for air-vices and air-powered clamps on machine tools.

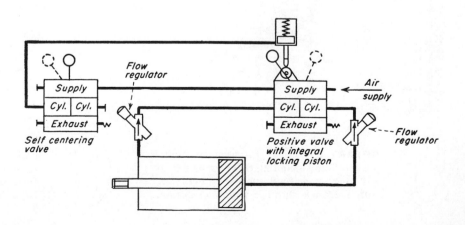

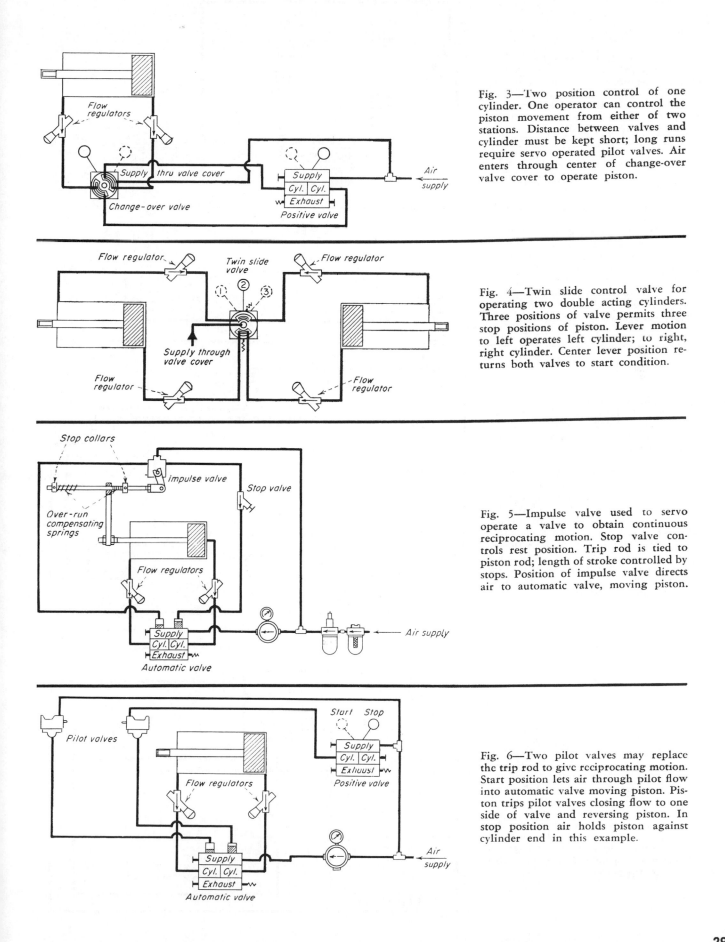

Fig. 3—Two position control of one cylinder. One operator can control the piston movement from either of two stations. Distance between valves and cylinder must be kept short; long runs require servo operated pilot valves. Air enters through center of change-over valve cover to operate piston.

Fig. 4—Twin slide control valve for operating two double acting cylinders. Three positions of valve permits three stop positions of piston. Lever motion to left operates left cylinder; to right, right cylinder. Center lever position returns both valves to start condition.

Fig. 5—Impulse valve used to servo operate a valve to obtain continuous reciprocating motion. Stop valve controls rest position. Trip rod is tied to piston rod; length of stroke controlled by stops. Position of impulse valve directs air to automatic valve, moving piston.

Fig. 6—Two pilot valves may replace the trip rod to give reciprocating motion. Start position lets air through pilot flow into automatic valve moving piston. Piston trips pilot valves closing flow to one side of valve and reversing piston. In stop position air holds piston against cylinder end in this example.

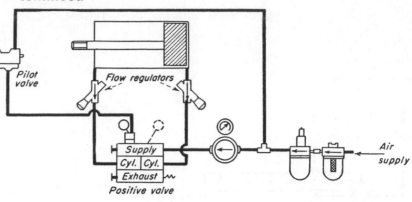

Fig. 7—Semi-automatic control of cylinder is obtained using one pilot valve. Manual operation of valve moves piston until pilot valve is depressed. Operating piston of main valve reverses, returning piston. To reactivate manual operation of valve is again required.

Fig. 8—Unloader valve gives semi-automatic operation. At end of stroke, build-up in cylinder of supply pressure from working pressure causes unloader valve to open. Unloader is set to open at pressure above working but slightly below supply. Two unloader valves give continuous reciprocation.

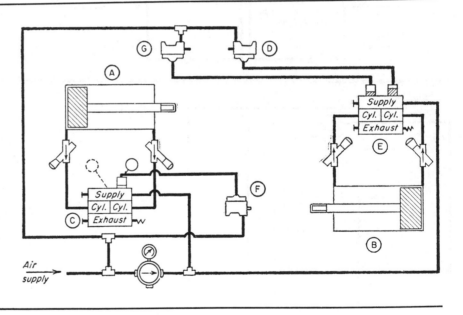

Fig. 9—Single-cycle automatic sequence with two cylinders. Valve C moves piston A forward which depresses pilot valve D, thus reversing automatic valve E which actuates piston B. When B completes its stroke, pilot valve F operates to reverse C, returning piston A. Piston A at the end of its stroke depresses pilot valve G, which reverses E returning piston B. Cycle is completed and can be reactivated only by valve C being manually operated. Cycle may be made automatic by replacing valve C with an automatic valve and an additional pilot valve which would be depressed by the return stroke of B to initiate the next cycle of automatic operation.

Fig. 10—Selector valve to operate two cylinders. Cycle is initiated by depressing valve C which reverses automatic valves D and E. E supplies air to pilot valve F, and D permits piston A to move forward. At end of stroke valve F is depressed reversing automatic valve G sending piston B forward. Piston B depresses pilot valve H which reverses the two automatic valves G and E. E sends air from F to pilot valve J. G lets piston B return and operates J to reverse valve D and return piston A to recycle.

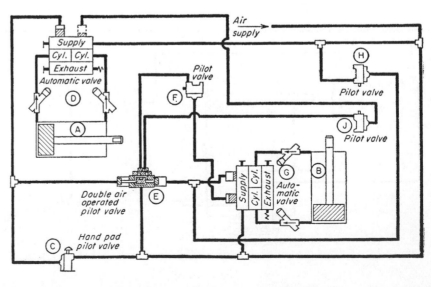

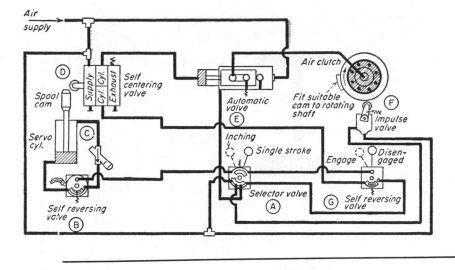

Fig. 11—Circuit using an air-operated clutch. To obtain single stroke operation, selector valve A is set in position. Depression of foot valve B moves servo cylinder C forward to trip control valve D, sending air to reverse valve E and to engage clutch. After one clutch revolution, valve F is tripped which reverses valve E through selector valve A. To actuate circuit, valve B must be released and again depressed. For inching, valve A is positioned to isolate valves F and h. Valve E is controlled by hand operated valve G to inch the clutch.

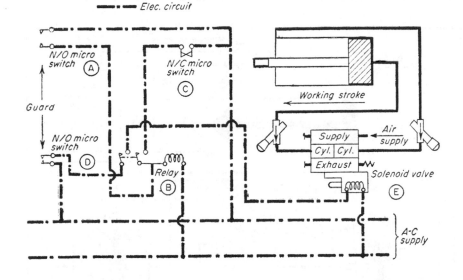

Fig. 12 — Electro-pneumatic circuit. Opening and closing guard actuates the press. Guard in up position causes small limit switch A to energize the relay B. As the guard is lowered, relay B is held energized by normally closed limit switch C. Depressing of limit switch D by closing guard, actuates solenoid operated valve E. Air forces piston to move and at end of stroke opens the normally closed limit switch C, de-energizing relay B. Electrical supply to solenoid valve E is interrupted returning valve and piston to original position. System cannot be re-engaged until guard is lifted closing switch A and priming relay B for next operation of the circuit.

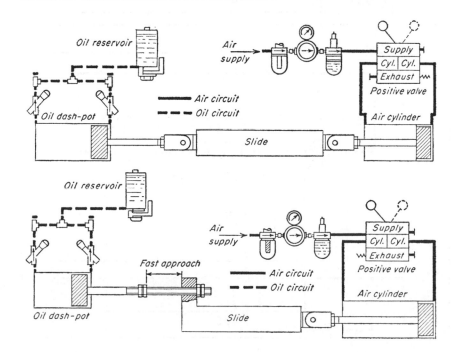

Fig. 13—Hydraulic-pneumatic circuit. (Upper) Simple hand controlled arrangement that provides constant speed to a slide under varying load by opposing an oil dash pot to the air cylinder. Damper pre-loads the air cylinder and governs the speed so that air cylinder will not slow down or speed up because of load changes and the compressibility of air. (Lower) Same system but by decreasing the oil cylinder size and extending the piston rod a fast approach stroke of the air cylinder is possible. Lock nuts adjust the length of the fast stroke.

301

HIGH-SPEED PNEUMATIC CONTROL

1 Drop forging hammer is controlled by pilot operated close-coupled valves. When the foot treadle is depressed, the pilot valve supplies air through valve 2 to the head of valve 3. Operation of valve 3 allows the hammer to drop by cutting off air and opening the bottom of the cylinder to exhaust. The hammer strikes valve 4, which does not affect the circuit at this time. Continuing downward, the hammer hits pilot valve 5, which supplies air to the head of valve 2. The shifting of valve 2 opens the head of valve 3 to exhaust. Valve 3 reverses and causes the hammer to be lifted. In its upward travel, the hammer hits valve 5 again (with no effect this time) and then strikes valve 4. This exhausts the air in the head of valve 2, reversing this valve which in turn shifts valve 3 again. Then, the hammer will drop again.

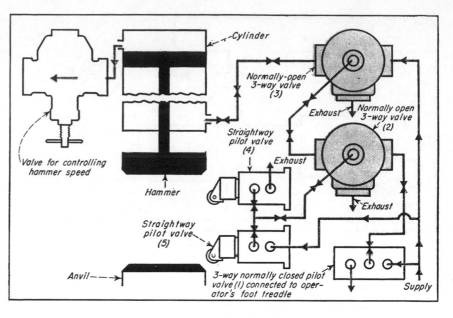

2 Tube forming machine bends the tube, reams the tube end, withdraws the ream and then releases the tube. Momentary operation of the valve 1 supplies air to the head of valve 2. Air flows past the ball check above the head of the operating spool, immediately reversing this valve. This action supplies air to the cylinder, advancing the piston against the tube. Note that the air supplied to the cylinder is also teed off to the head of valve 3 so that valve 3 is reversed by the action of valve 2, permitting piston to advance. The piston bends the tube against the block until it trips the limit switch 4, which starts operation of the motor driven reamer. The reamer reams the tube and withdraws. After a time delay, determined by the setting of the needle in its head, valve 2 reverses, shifting valve 3 and withdrawing the bending rod.

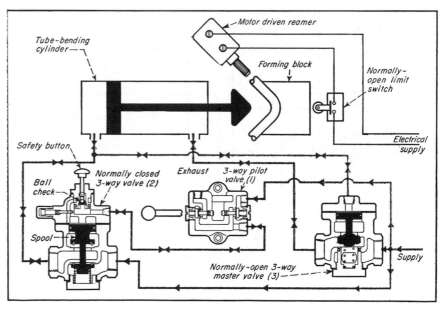

3 A circuit for alternate clockwise or counter-clockwise rotation of an air motor with positive stop. In this circuit, if the selector switch is returned to the right, the straightway normally-closed valve 2 is energized, supplying air to the air motor. At the same time, the normally-closed valve 3 is energized allowing the air supplied by valve 2 to exhaust through the motor. If the selector switch is thrown to the left, then normally-closed valves 1 and 3 are energized, supplying air to the motor and opening exhaust of the motor. If the selector switch is returned to the neutral position, all three normally-closed valves are closed and the air motor will be motionless. Note that in this case the operating valves are actuated by means of solenoids. The control switch may be located remotely from the valves. All valves are close-coupled to the air motor to assure fast response to control.

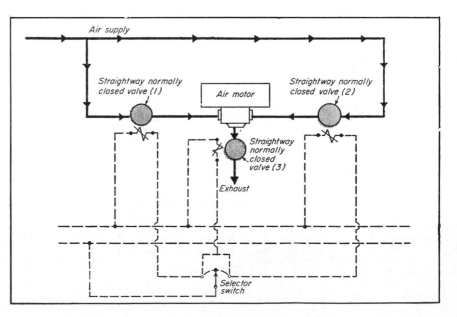

OF MACHINES

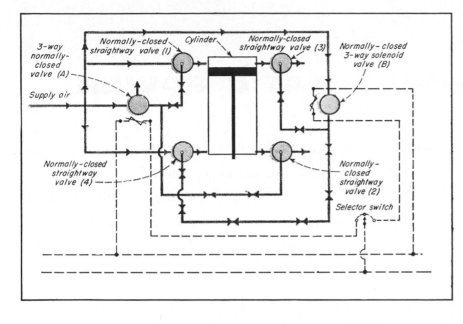

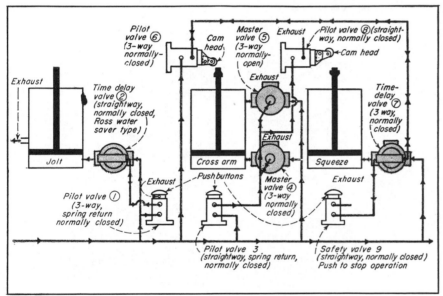

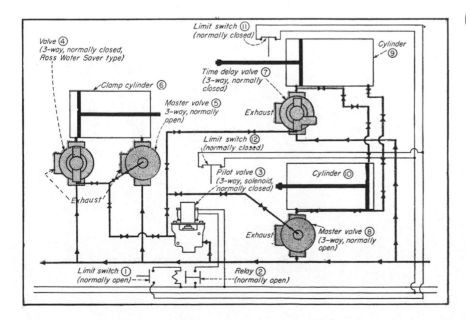

4 Circuit using pilot operated, close-coupled valves to duplicate the action of a 3-position, 4-way double solenoid valve. In the neutral position, the operating piston is locked by air trapped in the cylinder. When selector switch is thrown to the right, valve B is reversed, providing air to the heads of master valves 3 and 4. This supplies air to the lower end of the cylinder and exhausts air from the upper end, causing the piston rod to retract. The return of the selector switch to the neutral position de-engerizes the solenoid of valve B, exhausting the heads of valves 3 and 4 and closing them. This traps the air in the cylinder. Throwing the selector switch to the left energizes the solenoid of the valve A, which provides air to the heads of master valves 1 and 2 reversing them and extending the piston rod.

5 Jolt circuit of this foundry machine is started with the momentary operation of valve 1, which supplies air to the head of valve 2. This valve immediately opens, causing air to flow behind the jolt piston. The oscillation will continue for the number of cycles pre-set by the needle adjustment in the head of valve 2. The cross arm squeeze circuit is initiated by the depression of valve 3, which supplies air to the heads of valves 4 and 5. This reverses the cross arm cylinder, causing the piston to advance and trip valve 6. This momentarily supplies air to the head of valve 7, which reverses causing the squeeze cylinder rod to advance, overriding the cam of valve 8. After a time delay, valve 7 reverses, causing the squeeze rod to withdraw and tripping valve 8. This exhausts the heads of valves 4 and 5, retracting the cross arm rod.

6 Circuit for operation of a tube bending fixture. Momentary closing of limit switch 1 actuates valve 3 through relay 2. This admits air to the heads of valves 4, 5, 7 and 8. Valves 4, 5 and 8 reverse immediately, causing the clamping rod to advance and exhausting air from the rod end of cylinder 10 and the blank end of cylinder 9. After a time lag, valve 7 also reverses, causing the rod of cylinder 9 to retract and the rod of cylinder 10 to advance. When piston of cylinder 9 retracts, it opens limit switch 11. When the rod of cylinder 10 advances, it opens limit switch 12. These act to de-energize relay 2 and pilot valve 3. (Limit switches 11 and 12 are interlocked.) This exhausts the pilot circuit, immediately reversing valves 5, 7 and 8, causing piston 9 to advance and piston 10 to retract. Valve 4 reverses after a time lag and causes the rod of the clamping cylinder to retract.

15 JOBS for PNEUMATIC POWER

Here's how suction can be employed to feed, hold, position and lift parts, form plastic sheet, sample gases, test for leaks, convey solids, and de-aerate liquids; and compressed air can convey materials, atomize and agitate liquids, speed heat transfer, support combustion and protect cable.

REFERENCE:
Air Motor Applications. Published by Gast Manufacturing Corporation, Benton Harbor, Michigan.

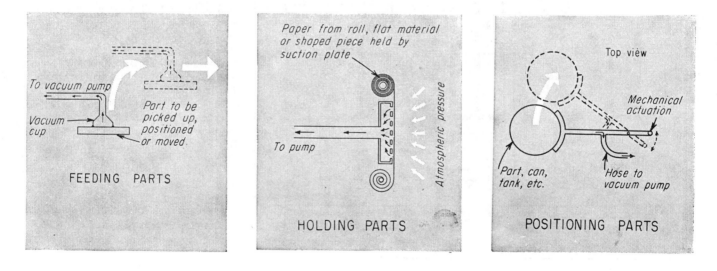

FEEDING PARTS

HOLDING PARTS

POSITIONING PARTS

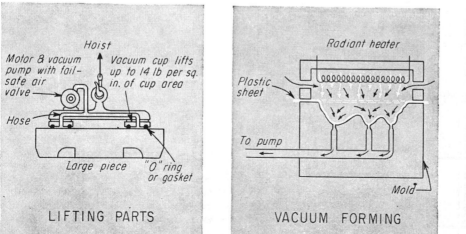

LIFTING PARTS

VACUUM FORMING

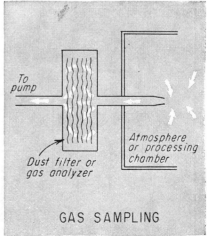

GAS SAMPLING

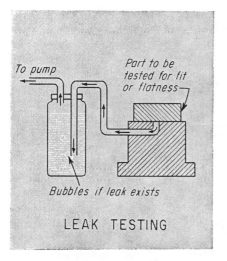

To pump

Part to be tested for fit or flatness

Bubbles if leak exists

LEAK TESTING

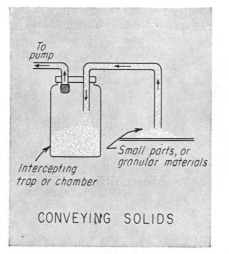

To pump

Intercepting trap or chamber

Small parts, or granular materials

CONVEYING SOLIDS

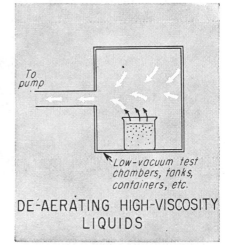

To pump

Low-vacuum test chambers, tanks, containers, etc.

DE-AERATING HIGH-VISCOSITY LIQUIDS

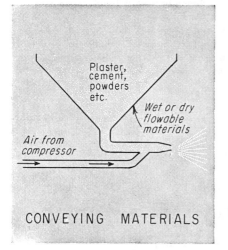

Plaster, cement, powders etc.

Wet or dry flowable materials

Air from compressor

CONVEYING MATERIALS

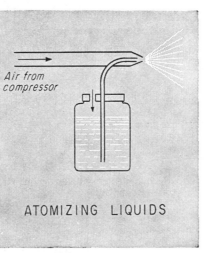

Air from compressor

ATOMIZING LIQUIDS

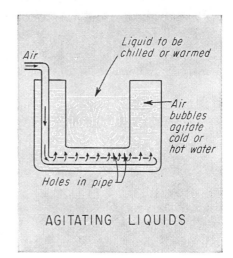

Air

Liquid to be chilled or warmed

Air bubbles agitate cold or hot water

Holes in pipe

AGITATING LIQUIDS

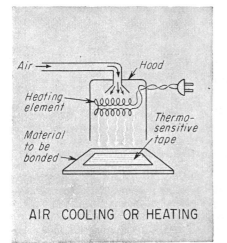

Air

Hood

Heating element

Thermo-sensitive tape

Material to be bonded

AIR COOLING OR HEATING

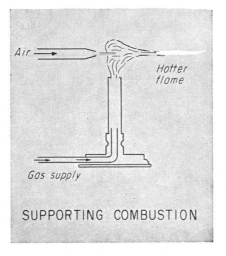

Air

Hotter flame

Gas supply

SUPPORTING COMBUSTION

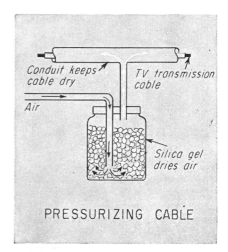

Conduit keeps cable dry

TV transmission cable

Air

Silica gel dries air

PRESSURIZING CABLE

LIFT TRUCK STEERS HYDRAULICALLY

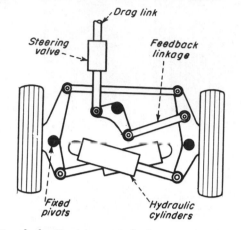

Hydraulically steered rear wheels are featured on a 35,000-lb-capacity fork truck designed for heavy outdoor lifting and tiering work by the Industrial Truck Division of Clark Equipment Co., Battle Creek, Mich. The power steering made it feasible to place driver and controls over fender of left front wheel. This position gives the driver increased visibility when raising and placing loads.

Extended pitman arm shaft . . .

offsets the steering column from the centrally mounted pitman arm and drag links which carry steering action to rear of truck. Control valve is mounted in the final drag link and is spring centered. Dual hydraulic cylinders equalize turning effort in each direction, make possible a 70° turning angle and prevent mechanism from locking in either extreme position. Truck is called the CY-350.

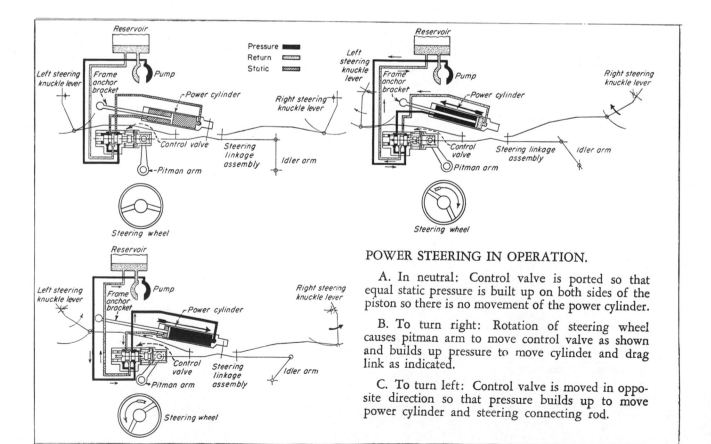

POWER STEERING IN OPERATION.

A. In neutral: Control valve is ported so that equal static pressure is built up on both sides of the piston so there is no movement of the power cylinder.

B. To turn right: Rotation of steering wheel causes pitman arm to move control valve as shown and builds up pressure to move cylinder and drag link as indicated.

C. To turn left: Control valve is moved in opposite direction so that pressure builds up to move power cylinder and steering connecting rod.

HYDRAULIC POWER ACTUATES CLUTCH, BRAKE AND STEERING IN INTERNATIONAL HARVESTER 300 HP DIESEL TRACTOR

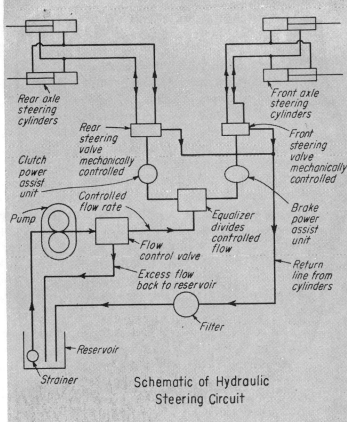

Schematic of Hydraulic Steering Circuit

Hydraulic power for operating brakes, clutch and steering is supplied by an engine-driven pump delivering 55 gpm at 1200 psi. System is designed to give 15-gpm preference to the steering system. Steering drive to each wheel is mechanical for synchronization, with mechanical selection of front-wheel, four-wheel or crab steering hookup; hydraulic power amplifies manual steering effort.

Transmissions available lacked the wide speed range needed; creeping speeds, closely grouped series in the working range, and high speeds for road travel. A new transmission was developed with ratios giving 6 forward speeds in the range of 3.5 to 7.5 mph, and 14 and 23 mph (with engine governed at 2100 rpm) plus four reverse speeds of 2.7, 3.2, 3.7 and 11.3 mph. A torque converter reduces shock loads on gearing and provides torque amplification, but can be locked out if desirable.

For operator comfort, cab is dust-tight, positive-pressure ventilated by a blower and dry filter, and provided with a heater and an air conditioner.

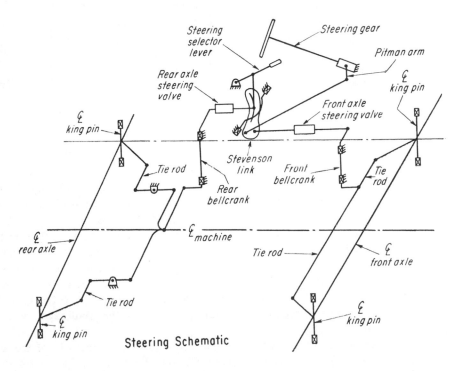

Steering Schematic

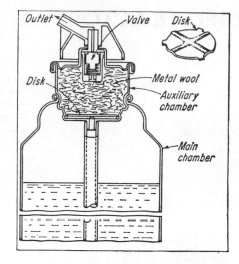

A hot shave, right from the can—and perhaps also aerosol-sprayed hot-dip coatings and foams—may stem from research now under way by aerosol producers and marketers. Gillette Co has already patented a system that provides for heating a small charge of the aerosol liquid before dispensing. An auxiliary chamber filled with steel wool or some other heat-conductive material is fitted to the top of the aerosol can, separated from it by a baffle or disk. This disk fits over the inlet port of the main chamber and serves to segregate the charge and to direct the flow of the liquid toward the heated walls of the chamber (see diagram). For heating, an external source is needed; but the heat source might simply be the hot water tap. Holding the can under the faucet for a moment will do.

Cans that carry their own heat source are, however, being developed. Aerosol Techniques Inc reportedly has an aerosol system in which the soap solution is pumped past a series of heating elements in the can. Other approaches being explored include exothermic compounds and thermoelectric heaters.

A fluid amplifier that's first cousin to the muscle engine has been designed at the Laboratory for the Study of Sensory Systems (Tucson, Ariz).

Key element in the system is a thin expandable rubber tube, reinforced longitudinally with nonelastic fibers so it can expand and contract radially, but not axially. This is placed in a rigid conduit (see diagram).

As pressure is introduced into the system by action of the sensing device (in

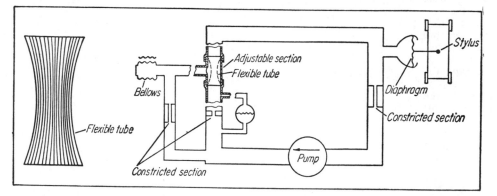

this case, the bellows), pressure builds up between the conduit wall and the flexible element, so that the latter constricts at its center, closing the orifice and restricting the flow of fluid through the system. This action of the flexible element is much like that of the tricuspid valve of the heart.

In the system diagrammed the pressure variations, as amplified by the flexible tube, are fed to the diaphragm at the right, which operates the stylus arm.

As pressure against the flexible tube increases in response to the signal from the bellows, and the flow of fluid through the tube decreases, pressure on the recorder diaphragm is also reduced, and the stylus moves to the left. A decrease in the bellows signal increases the pressure on the diaphragm and moves the stylus to the right.

Constrictions in the conduits help to increase the sensitivity of the system, and the small bypass chamber with its flexible diaphragm helps to smooth out any pulsations from the pump.

Automatic positioning system . .

uses a direct-dialing analog programmer for point-to-point machine setup on short production runs in operations such as punching, drilling, inserting. System is said to be time-saving in programming for repetitive and symmetrical motion patterns. Variations can be made by resetting dials. Positioning is by electrohydraulic servo systems, capable of positioning speed of 0.2 sec per basic motion with positioning accuracy of 1 part in 1000. Modulated signal permits adjustment for longitudinal and transverse axis movements.

CDC Control Services, Inc, 792 S. Warminster Rd, Hatboro, Penna.

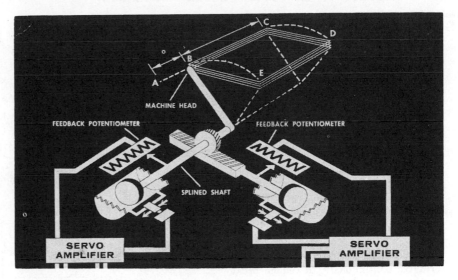

Pneumatic actuator provides choice of speeds with one control

A door-actuating system in which a single pressure control, adjustable for different speeds in each direction, serves for both opening and closing, is being introduced by Establissements L. Faiveley of France. The company claims it's less expensive than other systems devised for similar purposes, and has a built-in, thrust-limiting safety device.

The device consists of an actuator cylinder containing a differential piston and rod, checkvalve, needle valve, and an electromagnetically operated control valve (see diagram). Full line pressure

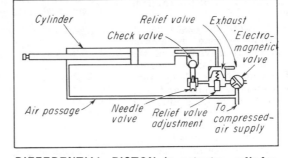

DIFFERENTIAL PISTON in actuator cylinder is so arranged that left half of chamber is supplied directly through lower air passage from compressed-air supply; inflow and outflow of air in right half is controlled by needle and relief valve.

is applied to the rod end of the cylinder at all times. The needle valve regulates the speed of emergence of the rod by throttling air through the checkvalve to the head end of the cylinder. Retraction of the rod is regulated by the outflow of air, controlled by the spring-operated relief valve, thus providing for independent adjustment of speed in each direction.

Electrohydraulic drive combines fast action with positive positioning

To provide precise positioning over a limited range, and high-speed positioning over a long range, a newly patented drive combines electrical and hydraulic elements.

Primary aim of the device is to provide a drive for nuclear reactor control-rod elements which must be moved only slightly by specified amounts during normal operation; but must be "scrammed" or jammed home in the event of accident.

During precise positioning, a reversible motor turns the lead screw to advance and retract control rods; while the hydraulic system, operated by pressurized water (the reactor coolant and fluid) from the reactor itself, takes over under emergency conditions.

In the normal condition, as shown, the fluid acts against both sides of the piston. When an emergency occurs a "scram valve" opens, bleeding pressure from the lower side of the piston, and the piston pushes the control rod "home."

This device (#2,937,984) is one of a number being released by the Atomic Energy Commission for royalty-free licensing.

FEED PROPORTIONAL TO SPEED

The lathes are produced by Ernault Batignolles, Paris, France.

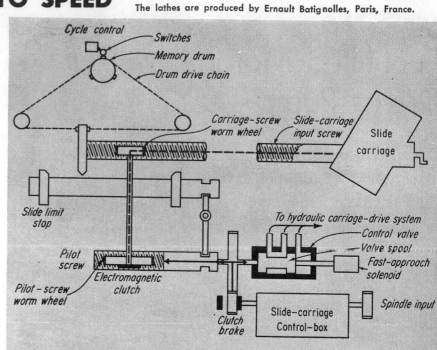

HYDRAULIC CIRCUIT CONTROL is mechanically interlocked to keep longitudinal speed proportional to spindle speed. During feed cycles, input screw for the slide carriage functions as a rack that feeds carriage speed and position data to control valve. Control valve in the feed circuit is also connected through gearing to the spindle.

Input from spindle feeds through the control box to the valve spool, rotating both it and the pilot screw. Pilot screw, in turn, drives the pilot-screw worm wheel. An electromagnetic clutch locks this worm wheel to a worm gear meshed with the slide-carriage input screw. The valve spool rotates continuously, to reduce break-away friction, but remains in the same longitudinal position in its sleeve as long as pilot-screw rotation matches longitudinal movement of the carriage input screw.

If the tool meets increased resistance, the slide carriage is slowed down; longitudinal movement of the input screw no longer matches rotational movement of the pilot screw, which then begins to "climb" and pulls the valve spool out of its equilibrium position. This displacement increases hydraulic pressure on the slide-carriage feed cylinder and speeds it up. When the carriage returns to normal speed, the forces between the carriage and pilot-screw wheels are again balanced and valve spool returns to original position.

When both spindle and carriage are stopped, the slide-carriage screw can be turned by a hand crank. This causes a similar displacement of the valve spool, so the carriage moves until the spool returns to equilibrium position. The operator can now position the slide carriage with very little effort—just by turning the crank.

The feed-advance control system also provides the means for carrying out automatic cycles. To start or stop the carriage, an electromagnetic clutch-brake is energized or deenergized. During machining pass, advance can be changed from "normal" to "fine"—or direction of advance changed —by electromagnetic clutches in the control box.

For fast return, the electromagnetic clutch on the pilot-screw worm gear is deenergized disconnecting the pilot screw and its worm wheel. Since there is no restraining force from the carriage-screw worm wheel, the hydraulically loaded valve spool shifts to fast-return position. For fast approach, a solenoid attached to the valve spool is energized to overcome the hydraulic loading and move the spool in opposite direction. The limit stops are tied into the valve-control mechanism. When the lug on the end of the carriage screw runs up against a stop, the stop-bar motion is transmitted to the control valve.

INFINITELY VARIABLE SPEED AND EASE OF CONVERSION

. . . to automatic control are two advantages claimed by Specken AG, Zurich, Switzerland, for the hydro-pneumatic machine-tool system diagrammed here.

By using compressed air as the primary power source, and a secondary hydraulic system to increase the pressure, Specken says it is possible to produce "an infinite variety of speed-stroke characteristics for the feed of any tool carriage, and convert almost any manually controlled machine tool into an automatic one."

The system consists of two major units: an operating cylinder A and a pressure converter B.

The operating cylinder is so designed that a control rod moving with the piston actuates valves a, b, c and d which, in turn, control its travel in both directions. The piston itself may be connected directly to the tool carriage; or, by means of a rack mechanism, to the feed pinion of the machine.

The pressure converter is, essentially, a dual piston; one surface being larger than the other. Air is fed in above the larger one (at the top) and oil is contained beneath the smaller one (at the bottom). Size is chosen so oil pressure will be approximately

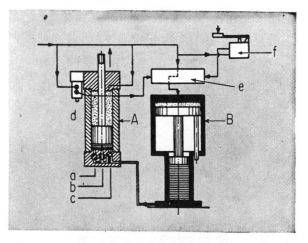

4 times the air pressure. By controlling the initial air pressure (with valve systems e and f), the company says, it is possible to provide for automatic stopping at either end of the stroke or in between, automatic reversal, high-speed return, and retarded reversal. It is also possible to interconnect several tool carriage drives for successive or phased operation.

SELF-POWERED HATCH COVER

Lewis Welding & Engineering Corp,

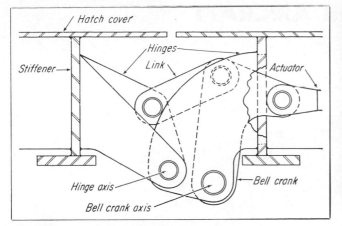

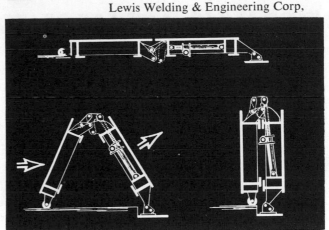

A unique hinge linkage actuated by a screw jack makes it possible for a single operator to open or close holds—in minutes

When the drive motor is energized the actuators extend, pivoting the bell-crank counterclockwise. Connected to the outer panel by the link, the bell-crank forces the panels to pivot on the hinge axis. The panels, supported by rollers on their outer ends, break upward as the screw jacks continue to extend. Function of the bellcrank and link is to swing the outer panels 180 deg without imposing bending moments on the screw jack.

Drive. A single electric motor in each pair of panels is connected to the jacks by line shafts. V-belt, timing belt, or a right-angle gear reducer drive can be specified to connect the motor to the line shaft; with the right-angle reducer drive an opening permits the panels to be articulated with a portable air wrench in case of electric power failure. Nyon couplings permit the shafts to flex, during opening and closing, when the jack screws pivot. Maintenance-free, the nylon flex couplings were selected because of their resistance to the corrosive conditions met by marine equipment.

HYDRAULIC DUMPERS AND LOADERS

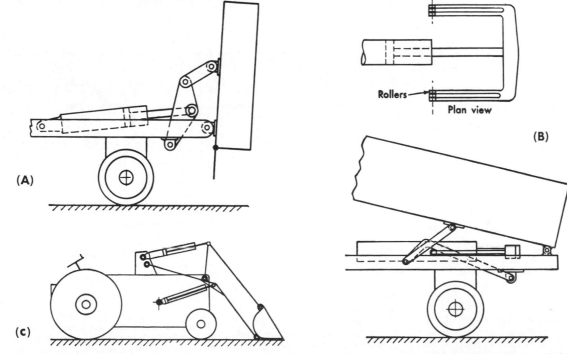

Dump motion in (A) is obtained by means of two four-bar linkages in series. Cam rollers in (B) help start heavy loads. Top cylinder in (C) lifts bucket while second dumps load. From J. S. Beggs, *Mechanisms*, McGraw-Hill Book Co.

HYDRAULIC ACTUATOR FOR AIRCRAFT

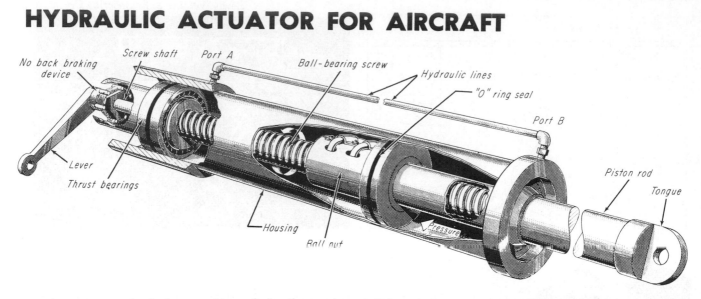

Accurate control of piston position in hydraulic actuator for aircraft has ball-bearing screw mounted directly to piston by means of threaded nut. Piston rod is actuated linearly by means of hydraulic pressure applied to ball nut through port A or B. Linear movement produces rotary motion in screw which is attached to no-back braking device Piston rod, therefore, can be stopped by any linear position by actuating the lever of braking device. Attaching gear train and rotary dial to screw shaft will give direct reading of linear position of piston rod. *Allison Div of General Motors*

ACTUATOR ACCEPTS ELECTRICAL DIGITAL CONTROL SIGNALS DIRECTLY—ELIMINATES DIGITAL-TO-ANALOG CONVERTERS

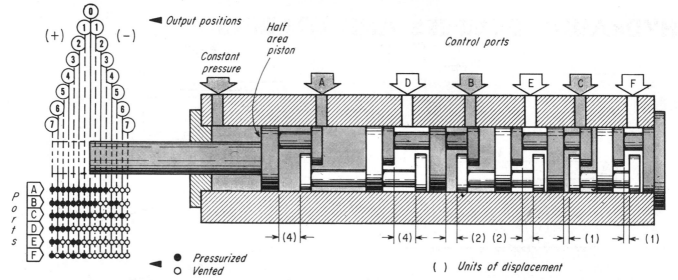

ACTUATOR output is produced by fluid pressure on a series of linked pistons in a cylinder. Precise positioning is accomplished by the mechanical links or interlocks, which determine the distance between adjacent pistons. When fluid pressure is applied between a pair of pistons they are forced apart to the limit of their interlocks. When the pressure is released the contact pressure on the half-area piston (far left) forces the pistons together until their interlocks bottom.

Maximum actuator extension is achieved when all control ports are pressurized. To obtain other actuator extensions different combinations of control ports are pressurized or vented by solenoid-operated, three-way transfer valves. For example, with pressure applied to port B alone, pistons 2 and 3 are forced apart until their interlocks limit further motion. The other two interlocks are held in contact with adjacent pistons by the pressure on the half-area piston. Venting all three ports, ABC, allows pressure on the half-area piston face to return the actuator rod to the zero position,

The number of output positions available from the actuator is equal to 2^n when n is equal to the number of ports or pistons. By adding one more piston to an actuator, the total number of output positions is doubled.

10
PUMP AND VALVE MECHANISMS

13 Rotary-Pump

SIGMUND RAPPAPORT *Project Supervisor, Ford Instrument Company Adjunct Professor of Kinematics,*

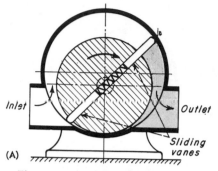

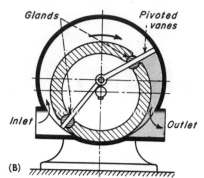

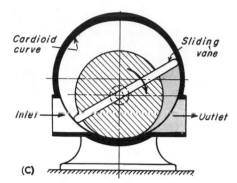

Fig. 1—(A) Ramelli pump with spring-loaded vanes to insure contact with wall; vane ends rounded for line contact. (B) Two vanes pivot in

housing and are driven by eccentrically mounted disk; vanes slide in glands and are always radial to housing, thus providing surface contact.

(C) Housing with cardioid curve allows single vane to be used, because opposing points on housing in line with disk center are equidistant.

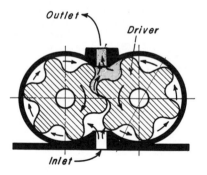

Fig. 5—Gear pump transports liquid between tooth spaces and housing wall. Circular tooth shape has only one tooth making contact and is more efficient than an involute shape which may enclose a pocket between two adjoining teeth, recirculating part of liquid. Helical teeth are also used.

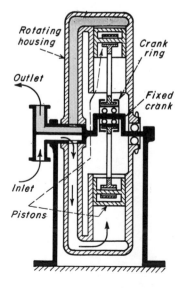

Fig. 8—Housing of Hele-Shaw-Beacham pump rotates round cranked shaft. Connecting rods attached to crank ring cause pistons to oscillate as housing rotates. No valves necessary since fixed hollow shaft, divided by wall, has suction and compression sides always in correct register with inlet and outlet ports.

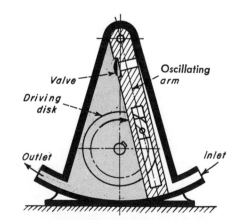

Fig. 9—Disk drives oscillating arm which acts as piston. Velocity of arm varies because of quick-return type mechanism. Liquid slowly sucked in and expelled during clockwise rotation of arm; return stroke transfers liquid rapidly.

Data based on material and sketches in AWF und VDMA Getrieblaetter, published by Ausschuss fuer Getriebe beim Ausschuss fuer Wirtschaftliche Fertigung, Leipzig, Germany.

Mechanisms

Polytechnic Institute of Brooklyn

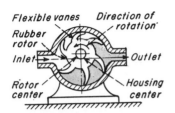

Fig. 2—Flexible vanes on eccentric rubber rotor displace liquid as in sliding-vane pumps. Instead of vanes sliding in and out, they bend against casing to pump.

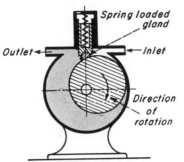

Fig. 3—Disk mounted eccentrically on drive shaft displaces liquid in continuous flow. Spring-loaded gland separates inlet from outlet except when disk is at top of stroke.

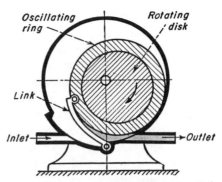

Fig. 4—Rotary compressor pump has link separating suction and compression sides. Link is hinged to ring which oscillates while driven by disk. Oscillating action pumps liquid in continuous flow.

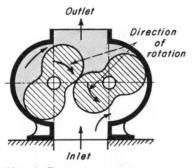

Fig. 6—Roots compressor uses two identical impellers with specially shaped teeth. Shafts connected by external gearing to insure constant contact between impellers.

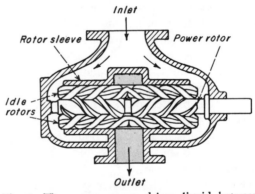

Fig. 7—Three-screw pump drives liquid between screw threads along axis of screws. Two idle rotors are driven by fluid pressure, not by metallic contact with power rotor.

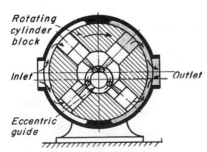

Fig. 10—Rotating cylinder block mounted concentrically in housing. Connecting-rod ends slide around eccentric guide as cylinders rotate and cause pistons to reciprocate. Housing divided into suction and compression compartments.

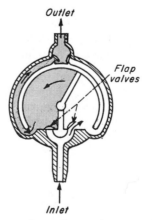

Fig. 11—Rotary-reciprocating pump usually operated manually to pump high-viscosity liquids such as oil,

NEW PUMP PRINCIPLES

Two new pumps are en route from Britain: One is an all-plastic, glandless, valveless pump for handling corrosive liquids. The other is a micrometering unit for handling very small flows.

The all-plastic pump, introduced by Watson-Marlow Air Pump Co, Buckinghamshire, England, is a rotary ("orbital lobe") unit that has only one major moving part—a ball-topped flange or lobe that serves to direct the fluid (see diagram). As the lobe orbits in the pump chamber, it increases the volume on one side, creating suction, and decreases it on the other, exerting pressure. A bellows seals the motor drive shaft and its eccentric and takes up the small orbital motion without stress and with minimum wear. Initially the pump will be made in TFE fluorocarbon plastic in sizes to 360 gpm. Larger models are now being designed, and US distribution is being arranged for the full line.

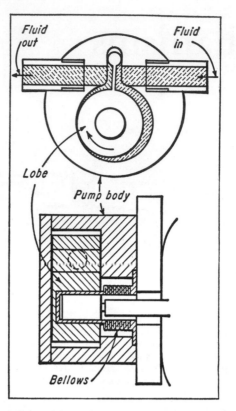

The micrometering pump, designed to control flow of low-viscosity liquids at rates down to 0.1 ml/min, is being developed by Cambridge Instrument Ltd (London).

An eccentric on the drive shaft moves a piston in the cylinder block and also transmits a semi-rotary oscillation, 90° out of phase with the piston movement, to the pivoted block. This makes the port in the block move between inlet and outlet ports in the main body, causing them to open and close in correct sequence (see diagram).

The pump is driven by a gearmotor running at 68 rpm and, Cambridge says, "operation is proportional to, but practically independent of head." The basic principle is not new, but Cambridge believes this is its first successful application in a pump this size, and plans are being made for commercial production and applications in equipment development.

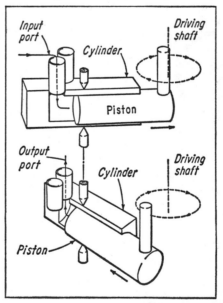

246-gph squeegee pump . . .

is threaded from side to ease tubing change and eliminate drip. Said to handle corrosive and sterile solutions, and abrasive slurries, virtually without maintenance. A single, continuous, flexible tube provides both inlet and outlet for pump, which completely isolates fluid from all moving parts. Solutions are squeezed through tube by a double-end ball-bearing motor. Randolph Co, 1018 Rosine St, Houston.

FLOATING VANE PUMP HAS NEW TYPE ACTION

The new "Cleco" pump features a pumping action resembling that of a square piston traveling smoothly and continuously in a square cylinder of infinite length. This action gives the features of a turbine having positive displacement. The pump will handle liquids, gases or air.

Chicago Laboratory & Engineering Co., N. Kedzie Ave., Chicago 18, Ill.

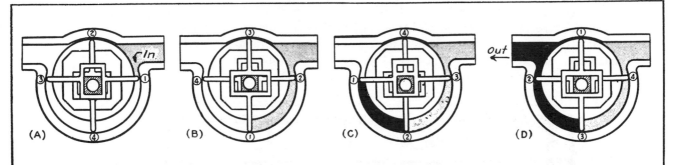

UNIQUE off center pin and yoke-crosshead give positive displacement. In (A), above, vane 1 creates a vacuum behind it as it is pushed out of the rotor and into the pumping chamber. In (B), vane 1 has been pushed out its maximum stroke and has filled the chamber between it and vane 2. In (C), vane 1 is being withdrawn into the rotor to allow fluid to discharge. Vaue 2 acts as a square piston. In (D), vane 1 is completely withdrawn, and vane 2 has started its withdrawal.

HAND PUMP WITH DOUBLE ACTING PISTON

While a diaphragm-type hand pump requires less manual effort for a given rate of flow, a double-acting piston pump is basically easier to manufacture. Objective behind the development of this new pump by John Wood Co., Muskegon, Mich., was to design a piston pump requiring less manual effort, without sacrificing cost and ease of manufacture.

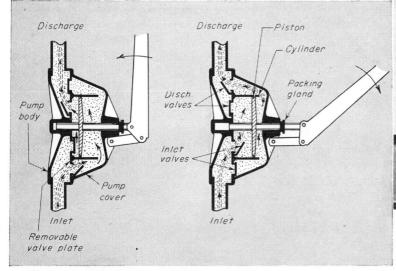

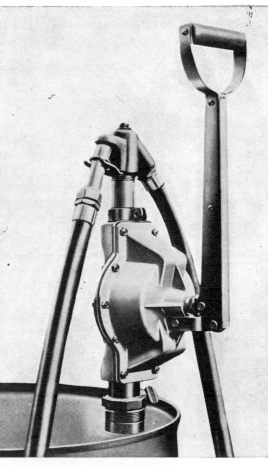

FLOW DIAGRAM illustrates simplicity of pump design reducing manufacturing costs. Cylinder is used to guide flow path, obviating any additional walling. Lower inlet valve and upper discharge valve are part of 1-piece assembly—the valve plate.

TO OVERCOME relatively sluggish response of double acting piston pump, the bore-to-stroke ratio was increased to 3-to-1, and handle lever given 16-to-1 ratio. Effectively, for given rate of delivery, same amount of effort is required to operate double-acting pump as conventional diaphragm pump. Pump can deliver up to 20 gal per minute.

A return to water power for factory operations is predicted by British engineers as a new variable-output water-hydraulic pump system goes into operation.

The prime mover is an electric motor, which drives a variable-output swashplate pump. This in turn supplies high-pressure oil to operate an opposed-piston system (see diagram) controlled by a simple spool valve. The central section thus becomes an oil motor, the two ends being the water pumps.

Tangyes Ltd, Birmingham, England, which makes the pump, says a single unit of this type can take the place of several of conventional design. In a test installation one 7½-gal pump replaces a three-pump system operating 250 presses. Admittedly, for most purposes a second pump would be needed, if only for insurance. But the system does prove that a single pump can do the job.

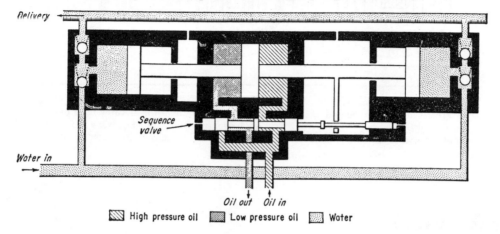

High pressure oil   Low pressure oil   Water

Rotary pump design has been simplified by Danish engineers in an attempt to provide a single-vane pump that requires virtually no machining.

The pump consists of a hollow, slotted cylindrical shaft, a vane that slides in the slot, and a housing that includes a cylindrical pumping chamber at one end. The pumping chamber is located eccentrically with respect to the shaft and is closed by an end plate having a semicircular bulge. It is so arranged that when the shaft rotates, the tapering region of the pumping chamber (its compression side) registers with the bulge so that the liquid delivered to it can flow out through the reservoir chamber on the axis.

Danfoss A/S, Nordborg, Denmark, which designed the pump (and has patented it in Denmark, Germany, and Britain), says the size of the reservoir is unimportant; the shaft can be adjusted axially without affecting the working

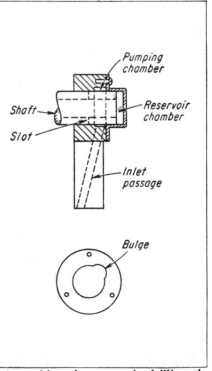

tolerances, and the only machining required in making the pump is drilling the pumping chamber and the bearing for the shaft.

NEW FAN AND BLOWER PRINCIPLES

A fan that uses wire mesh instead of blades and gets its job done with remarkable efficiency is claimed by Heat Pump & Refrigeration Ltd, London SE 7, England.

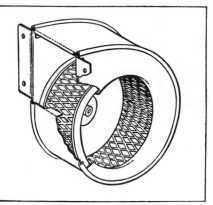

It's a centrifugal unit in which a cylindrical mesh cage—providing, in effect, hundreds of tiny inclined blades—substitutes for the usual impeller (see sketch). HP&R says a unit with a 3⅜-in. cage handling an intake volume of 50 cfm at about 2350 rpm requires a motor current of little more than 0.39 amp (240 v ac). Overall dimensions are 6⅛ by 5¼; weight, less than 2 lb. The cage is expanded aluminum, the housing aluminum or plastic. A shaded-pole, skeleton-frame motor is used.

The unit will first be employed in ventilation but is also being tested for conveyors and other equipment.

A variable-pitch fan for cars, a fan that will adjust its performance to cooling needs and minimize waste of power, is being introduced by Serck Radiator Services Limited, 39/43 Park Royal Road, London NW 10, England.

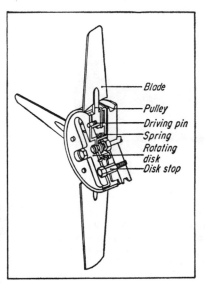

The fan is a four-bladed, pulley-driven unit which operates conventionally when the engine is running at low speed. But the blades are mounted on pivoted pins attached to a spring-biased disk (see diagram). As engine speed and torque increase, this disk rotates, overcoming the force of the spring, and the fan blades roll around so the blade angle is reduced and the air is spilled. At full speed, they are completely feathered.

Spring tension can be adjusted so the blade pitch will change at any desired speed. But normally, the first adjustment comes at half speed (about 2500 rpm).

SINGLE CONTROL KNOB operates all functions of a window power ventilator developed by Industrial Designer, Charles Davies, for United States Air Conditioning Corporation.

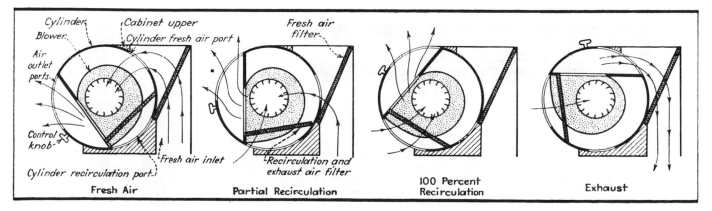

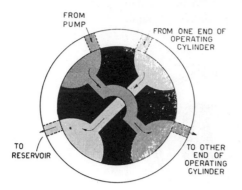

Valves are the nerve center of hydraulic circuits. In machine tools, they provide reversal of motion, dwell and throttling action, sequence control, and relief of oil pressure. Some of the common forms of these valves are illustrated.

Fig. 1—Schematic diagram of rotary reversing valve. Oilways in an oscillating cylindrical plug register with ports which connect both the main oil line from the pump and the discharge line to the reservoir with either end of the operating cylinder. When oil is directed from the pump to one end of the operating cylinder, oil in the other end of the cylinder is discharged through the reversing valve to the reservoir. One position of the reversing valve shown.

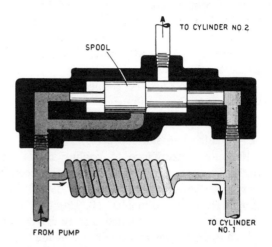

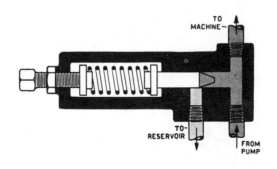

Fig. 2—Sequence control valve. Some machines are designed so that one series of motions must be completed before another series can start. This type valve prevents the flow of oil to No. 2 operating cylinder until the motion in No. 1 cylinder has been completed. Both ends of the freely floating spool are under oil pressure. The end exposed to pump pressure is smaller than the end exposed to pressure from No. 1 cylinder. From the pump, oil flows through a coil of tubing which slightly restricts the oil flow.

Pressure in No. 1 cylinder and on No. 1 end of the valve spool is less than the pump pressure, and this difference on the ends of the valve shifts the spool towards the low pressure side. Flow of oil to No. 2 cylinder is prevented. When motion in No. 1 cylinder is completed, oil no longer flows through the coil. Pressure on both sides of the valve is equalized. Full pump pressure now acts on the large end of the spool, and the spool shifts to admit oil to No. 2 cylinder.

Fig. 3—Spring-loaded relief valve. This valve is placed in the pump discharge line to permit oil to escape from the line to the reservoir when the amount of oil delivered by a constant-discharge pump is more than is needed. High pressure overcomes the compression of the spring, lifts the valve from its seat, and by-passes the oil until the pressure drops below the compression adjustment of the spring.

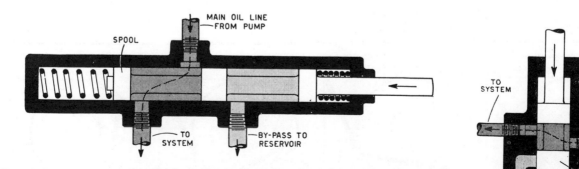

Fig. 4—Stop valves usually placed in the main oil line from the pump are operated manually or by cams. They are designed to stop the machine at a predetermined point. When the spool is shifted to a stop position, the flow of oil is interrupted and machine motion halted. While the machine is idling, the oil is by-passed at low pressure to the reservoir thereby reducing power costs. The machine is restarted either manually by the operator, or by cams which move the valve to a new position.

HYDRAULIC TRANSMISSIONS

Fig. 5—Reversing valve. This valve directs oil flow in and out of either end of an operating cylinder. A separate pilot valve, Fig. 6, controls the oil pressure. The reversing-valve spool maintains a central position and floats between two springs. Pilot valve action moves the spool. When the spool is at one end of the valve, oil under pressure flows from the pump through the valve into one end of the operating cylinder, and at the same time, oil in the other end of the operating cylinder is discharged into the reservoir.

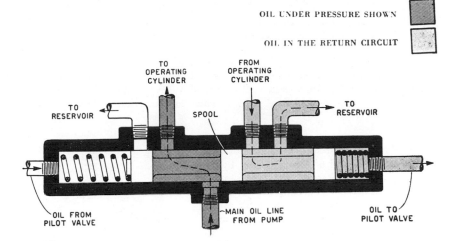

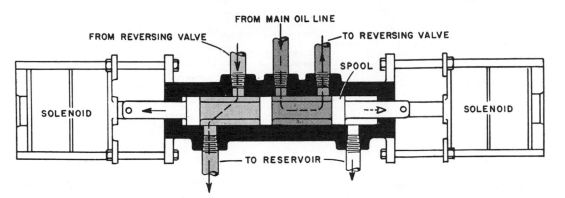

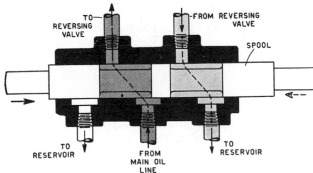

Fig. 6—Pilot valve. (above and left) Spools of these valves are thrown by cams or dogs, or may be moved magnetically by solenoids. Oil pressure from the pump is directed alternately to both ends by means of a reversing valve, Fig. 5.

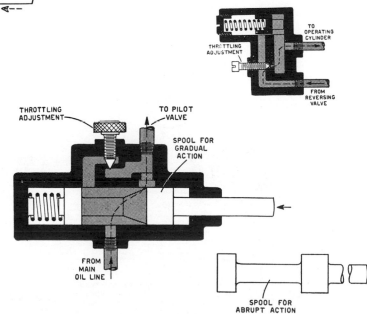

Figs. 7 and 8—Dwell and throttling valves. These spring-loaded valves are actuated by cams or oil pressure. Cam action moves the spool and shuts off this free oil delivery, permitting only a restricted oil flow through throttling adjustment. In the pilot valve line, this valve delays action of the reversing valve and permits a period of dwell at the end of the stroke of the operating piston. The change from free to restricted flow may be abrupt or gradual, depending upon the spool employed. In pressure actuated valves, Fig. 8, the valve is normally held closed by the spring. Delivery of oil is restricted by a throttling adjustment as long as the valve is closed. When flow is reversed, oil pressure lifts the valve and permits free delivery of the oil.

VALVE FOLLOWER MECHANISMS

ANY power-operated positioning mechanism, wherein the power controlled element is caused to move to a position corresponding to that to which the manually-operated control lever or wheel has been shifted, must incorporate a valve follower mechanism. The purpose of the valve follower mechanism is to automatically return the control valve of the power or servo unit to its neutral position when the controlled element reaches the position corresponding to that to which the control lever has been shifted.

Mechanical follower mechanisms are of one of the following basic types: (1) Screw and nut, (2) wedges, (3) floating levers, (4) epicyclic gearing, (5) flexible cord and pulleys. Electrical and electronic circuits and devices are also possibilities that might be considered for certain applications.

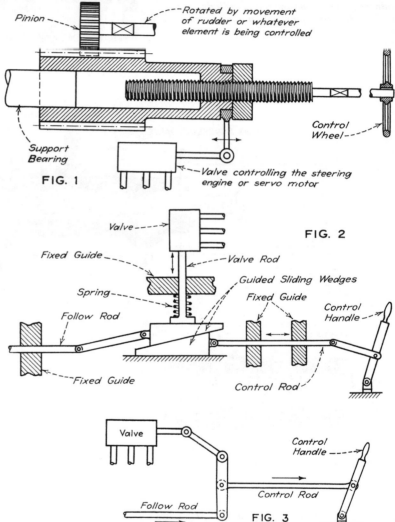

Fig. 1—Schematic of screw-and-nut follower mechanism. Rotation of control wheel by the operator causes axial movement of the nut in one direction. thereby actuating the valve controlling the servo motor. Servo motor moves the rudder, motion of which causes rotation of pinion in such a direction as to cause opposite axial travel of the nut, thereby returning the valve to neutral position. This is an old mechanism used for steering ships. The servo motor can be a steam engine, hydraulic or pneumatic cylinder or engine or an electric motor. For the last type, the valve is replaced by an electric control switch.

Fig. 2—A screw thread can be thought of as a modified inclined plane. Moving the control handle displaces the valve from its neutral position. causing servo motor to move the element being controlled. This last movement causes the follow rod to move in the same direction in which the control rod was moved, thereby returning valve to its neutral position.

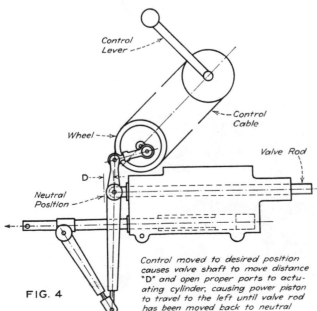

Control moved to desired position causes valve shaft to move distance "D" and open proper ports to actuating cylinder, causing power piston to travel to the left until valve rod has been moved back to neutral

Fig. 3—The floating lever is the most commonly used type of follower mechanism. Movement of control handle opens valve, causing servo motor to operate the desired element, movement of which causes follow rod to move in same direction as movement of control rod. This brings valve back to neutral position.

Fig. 4—Application of the floating lever principle to the design of a follower mechanism developed by Curtiss-Wright Aircraft Corporation. The valve and servo power cylinder are a unit.

FOR SERVO CONTROLS

Fig. 5—Modified form of floating lever principle applied to another Curtiss-Wright design. One advantage is the compact design made possible.

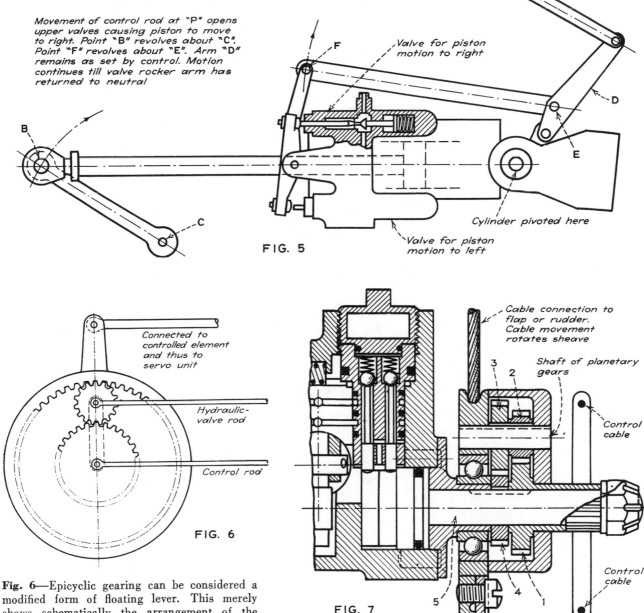

Movement of control rod at "P" opens upper valves causing piston to move to right. Point "B" revolves about "C". Point "F" revolves about "E". Arm "D" remains as set by control. Motion continues till valve rocker arm has returned to neutral

Valve for piston motion to right

Cylinder pivoted here

Valve for piston motion to left

FIG. 5

Connected to controlled element and thus to servo unit

Hydraulic-valve rod

Control rod

FIG. 6

Fig. 6—Epicyclic gearing can be considered a modified form of floating lever. This merely shows schematically the arrangement of the gears. The rod labeled "Hydraulic-valve rod" can actuate an electric rheostat or switch, pneumatic control valve, or any other device for the control of a power unit.

Cable connection to flap or rudder. Cable movement rotates sheave

Shaft of planetary gears

Control cable

Control cable

FIG. 7

Fig. 7—Epicyclic follower mechanism is built into this "position control valve" developed by Adel Precision Products Company. Movement of control cable rotates gear *1*. Shaft of planetary gears remains stationary, hence angular rotation of gear *1* is transmitted to gear 4 keyed to valve shaft, thus operating the valve and causing the servo to move the flap, rudder or whatever the part may be. Movement of flap rotates the sheave and with it, the shafts of the planetary gears. Gear *1* remains stationary and planetaries roll on it. This causes rotation of valve shaft back to its neutral position.

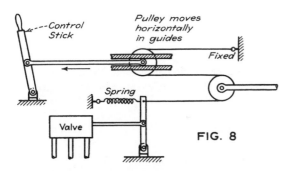

Control Stick

Pulley moves horizontally in guides

Fixed

Spring

Valve

FIG. 8

Fig. 8—Flexible metal tape running over pulleys can be used for follower mechanisms. This type mechanism is specially suited where a greater number of movements are involved as it is merely necessary to increase the number of pulleys.

LINKAGE ARRANGEMENTS FOR ENGINE VALVES

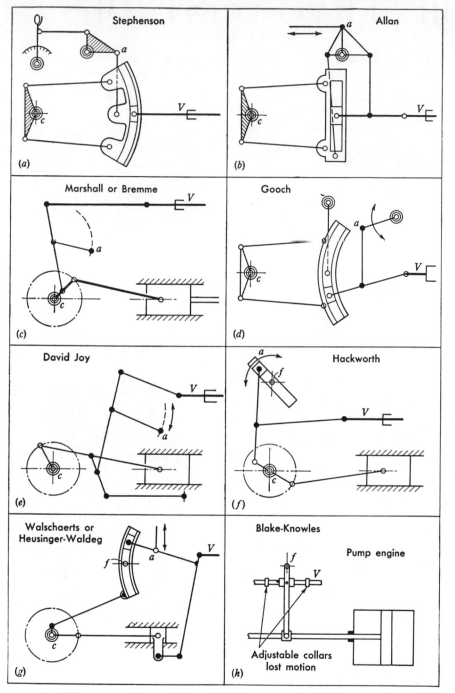

(a) Stephenson *(b)* Allan *(c)* Marshall or Bremme *(d)* Gooch *(e)* David Joy *(f)* Hackworth *(g)* Walschaerts or Heusinger-Waldeg *(h)* Blake-Knowles — Pump engine — Adjustable collars lost motion

Valve gears.   Some of these classical movements date back over 100 years. They are of general interest because of the possibility of modifying them for other purposes.   The following notation is used: *f* denotes a pivot fixed in the frame. *a* denotes an adjustable pivot for reversing or for changing cutoff. *c* denotes crankshaft center.   *V* denotes valve rod.

(From *Mechanisms* by J. S. Beggs)

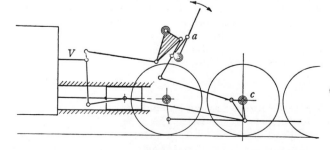

The Baker valve gear applied to a New York Central (fast freight) locomotive.   This gear is popular because of the absence of slides exposed to dirt.   (*The Pilliod Company.*)

11

MEASURING AND METERING DEVICES

From: Control Engineering

Measuring mass flow

GEORGE T. GEBHARDT, Boeing Airplane Co.

Industrial applications require accurate, reliable flowmeters.
These representative flowmeters employ many interesting principles,
some—the axial-flow and gyroscopic types—yielding true mass flow,
and others—the venturi, acoustic velocity, and turbine types—measuring
volumetric flow and requiring density compensation to yield mass flow.

TRUE MASS FLOWMETER

Angular Momentum Principle—Axial-Flow Types—The axial-flow type of true mass flowmeter works on the principle of conservation of angular momentum. The General Electric, Avien, and Control Engineering Corp. flowmeters work on this principle. An impeller driven at a constant angular velocity imparts angular momentum to the fluid being measured. The fluid's rate of change of angular momentum as it leaves the impeller is proportional to the impeller's velocity and to the mass rate of fluid flow. A torque-sensing wheel, located adjacent to and down-stream of the impeller, removes the angular momentum from the fluid at the same rate the fluid gains momentum from the impeller. If the impeller's angular velocity remains constant, the torque on the sensing wheel is proportional to mass rate of fluid flow through the flowmeter.

Control Engineering Corp. flowmeter (A), operates on the conservation of momentum principle. The flowmeter resembles a gyroscope and its operation is most readily explained in gyroscopic terms. In (B), the *C* axis is equivalent to a gryoscope's spin axis, fluid motion in the pipe section perpendicular to the *C* axis replacing the spinning wheel. The entire pipe assembly is rotated about the *A* axis, which corresponds to the precession axis of a gyro. The mass flow rate produces a corresponding torque about the *B* axis. The pipe loop parallel to the *C* axis corrects for centrifugal force produced when deflection occurs about the torque axis.

Flexure pivots connect the pipe elements to the sensing element. Sensing element deflection, proportional to torque or mass flow rate, is picked up by an electromagnetic rotary transducer, whose signal is carried by slip rings to an amplifier, and from there to a flow rate meter and to a photoelectric pulse former and counter to yield total flow.

This instrument has been highly developed for industrial uses, even for nonhomogeneous fluids. However, its intrinsic configuration makes it bulky in larger pipe sizes.

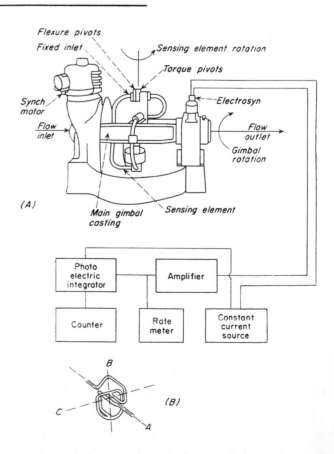

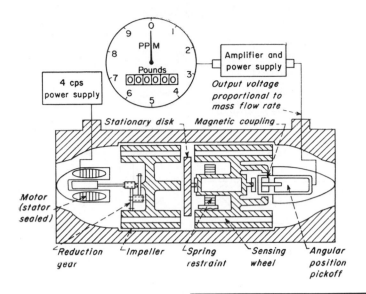

The General Electric flowmeter, a regulated motor-generated power supply drives the impeller at a constant frequency. The down-stream sensing wheel is spring-restrained and magnetically coupled to an angular-position pickoff. A stationary disk reduces viscous coupling between the impeller and sensing wheel at zero flow. The pickoff's output voltage, proportional to mass flow rate, feeds into a servo amplifier, a rate meter, and an integrator-counter.

Inaccurate at low flow rates, due to extraneous torques; the flowmeter can measure flow in only one direction, and cannot measure rapid changes in flow.

The Avien flowmeter, contains two impellers driven in opposite directions and at a speed proportional to line frequency. This arrangement permits measurement in either direction of flow in a pipe but causes a higher pressure drop. A sensing wheel, restrained by an electromechanical torquer, removes the angular momentum from the fluid. The torque motor providing the restraint receives an amplified potentiometer signal proportional to the angular position of the sensing wheel, and thus proportional to the mass flow rate times the angular velocity of the impeller.

To make the flowmeter output dependent only on the mass flow rate requires a constant angular velocity. But the angular velocity, being proportional to line frequency, varies with changes in line frequency. Such variations can be compensated by feeding the transducer output signal into a line-frequency correcting network and using the resulting output to drive a servo amplifier-recorder. When the line frequency varies from nominal the attenuation of the correcting network changes in the proper direction to

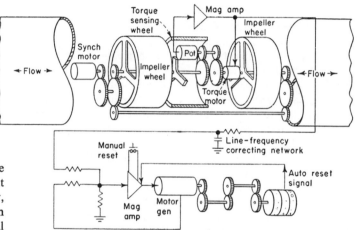

compensate for the change in impeller angular velocity. Mass flow rate can be indicated by using a drag-cup meter.

VENTURI-TYPE FLOWMETER

The Bendix flowmeter uses a venturi as the sensing element. Since mass flow is equal to the square root of the product of density times Δp measured at the venturi, it is necessary to use a densitometer and also to correct for the square-root function. To do this, a Δp diaphragm operates against a spring with stiffness proportional to displacement squared, thus creating a displacement of the transducer core proportional to the square root of Δp. The excitation voltage for the transducer comes from the densitometer, that yields a square root-of-density voltage depending on the number of density-sensitive float-switches operated. Because the transducer output voltage is the product of the core displacement and the excitation voltage, it is proportional to the mass flow rate. Output voltage feeds an amplifier, drives a motor at a speed proportional to mass flow rate, operates a magnetic drag-cup rate indicator, and totalizes flow on a counter.

The small pressure drop in the venturi and the absence

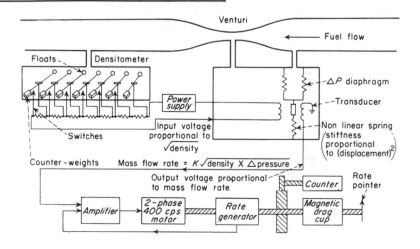

of mechanical components in the flow stream are desirable characteristics of this system. Undesirable characteristics include: nonlinear output, small contact pressures in the densitometer switches, and the step-type densitometer output possibly giving insufficient resolution.

327

ACOUSTIC VELOCITY FLOWMETER

The Maxson flowmeter measures the velocity of fluid flow with acoustic wavetrains. It is essentially a volumetric flowmeter and therefore requires a densitometer to measure mass flow rate. Two sets of crystals (each set a transmitter and a receiver), one angled upstream and the other downstream, transmit and receive acoustic wave-trains. Each crystal set operates as follows: a short train of 10-mc oscillations from a generator is converted into acoustic energy to the transmitter, projected through the fluid, and picked up by the receiver across the tube. After being amplified, the received signal retriggers the generator and another energy train is repeated around the loop. The repetition frequency depends on the time it takes for the energy to cross the tube and on whether the signal is sent at an upstream or downstream angle to the direction of fluid flow.

The upstream repetition frequency is $f_1 = (v + V \cos \theta)/2d$ and the downstream repetition frequency is $f_2 = (v - V \cos \theta)/2d$; where v is the acoustic velocity, V the fluid velocity, d the distance between the transmitter and receiver, and θ the angle between the signal direction and the fluid flow direction. The beat frequency $f_1 - f_2$ equals $V \cos \theta/d$, and is therefore proportional to the fluid velocity but independent of the acoustic velocity.

Another crystal, placed in contact with the fluid, determines the density. This crystal, in series with an inductance, forms a tuned circuit, so that the voltage across it is directly proportional to the product of the density and the acoustic velocity. Dividing this product by a voltage proportional to acoustic velocity (obtained from one of the oscillating loops in which the voltage, for the fluid velocities normally encountered, is proportional to the acoustic velocity) yields a density signal.

A computer multiplies the beat frequency (velocity) signal and the density signal, so that the computer output is proportional to mass flow rate. The computer also contains an integrator. Thus, the flowmeter yields both mass flow rate and total flow of the fluid.

No additional pressure drop is introduced in the flow system and the flowmeter can measure a wide variety of liquids. However, the liquids must not contain solids or air bubbles comparable in size to the wavelength of the acoustic wave. The electronic equipment complexity may be a limitation for some industrial applications.

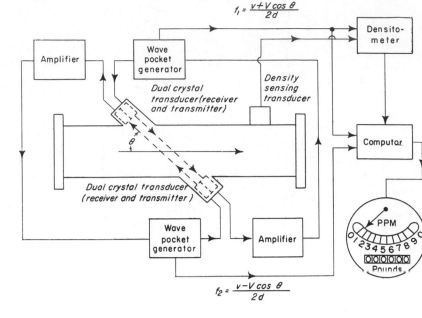

TURBINE-TYPE FLOWMETER

The Potter mass flowmeter consists of the familiar turbine-type volumetric flowmeter, in conjunction with a simple float densitometer, giving a mass flow reading. A permanent magnet in the rotor generates an ac current in a coil located in the external housing. The generated frequency is proportional to the volumetric flow rate. An electronic converter changes the frequency signal into a dc voltage proportional to volumetric flow rate. A separate float positions an angular transducer, which produces a dc output voltage proportional to fluid density. The signals from the densitometer and frequency converter are fed to a computer, whose output is the product of density and velocity, or mass flow rate. Computer output can operate a flow rate meter or can be integrated to record total flow on a counter.

The sensing element is available in many ranges and for many fluids. Against this advantage is the fact that the conversion of the frequency signal to dc (as required for compatibility with the dc densitometer signal) precludes direct use of the frequency signal for accurate counting.

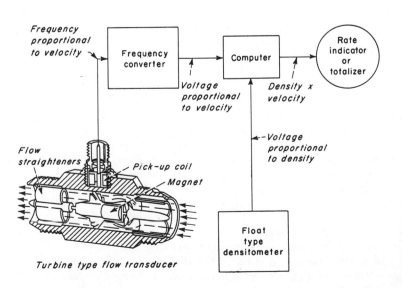

Turbine type flow transducer

328

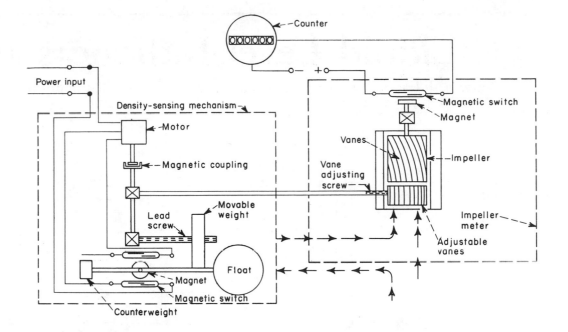

ADJUSTABLE-VANE DENSITOMETER

The Revere densitometer provides mass flow rate measurements in conjunction with a turbine-type volumetric flowmeter. The densitometer consists essentially of a float balanced by an on-off servo-controlled movable weight. To increase sensitivity, the movable weight attached to the float is designed to hunt about the balance position determined by the density. For example, when a change in density causes the float to drop, the lower magnetic switch closes and operates the motor and lead screw to move the weight to the left. This automatic weight balancing simultaneously drives a vane-adjusting screw so that the position of vanes upstream of the turbine's impeller is determined by the density of the fluid flowing through the meter.

Without the vanes the turbine is a volumetric flowmeter. The vanes introduce a swirl to the fluid just before it reaches the turbine, thereby reducing rotational speed of the turbine as a linear function of vane position. Since vane position is proportional to density, the output of the turbine becomes proportional to mass flow rate.

A six-pole magnet driven by the turbine opens and closes a magnetic switch which operates into a counter. The count is directly proportional to total mass flow, while the count per unit time indicates the mass flow rate. This simple recording technique is the main advantage of the flowmeter. The adjustable vane, in the fluid path, increases pressure drop across the flowmeter and is correction-limited to plus or minus 15 per cent of density change.

CLOSED-LOOP SERVO FLOAT DENSITOMETER

In United Control's flowmeter the impeller, whose speed is proportional to volumetric flow, generates a two-phase signal which (after amplification) drives a synchronous motor. The motor speed, a facsimile of impeller speed, then becomes proportional to volumetric flow rate. The motor operates rate and total flow indicators through variable-ratio drives. To obtain mass flow readings at these indicators, the densitometer adjusts the ratio by means of a differential transformer, so that the output of the drives is proportional to the product of volumetric flow rate and density.

Floats in the densitometer position a differential transformer as a function of density. A density change produces an error signal, which, after amplification, drives an induction motor. This motor positions a second differential transformer until the error reduces to zero and also adjusts the variable-ratio coupling to the indicators. A drag-cup indicator shows mass flow rate, while a counter pulsed from the commutator shows total flow. Pulse counting improves accuracy of total flow measurement. The closed-loop limits errors in the densitometer; however, drifts in transformer outputs could increase them.

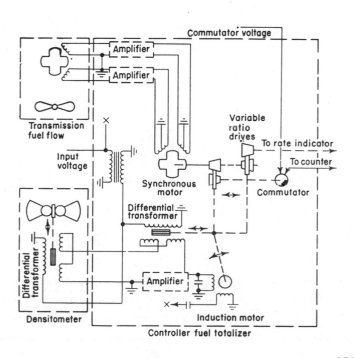

Liquid Level Indicators and

Thirteen different systems of operation are shown.   Each one represents at least

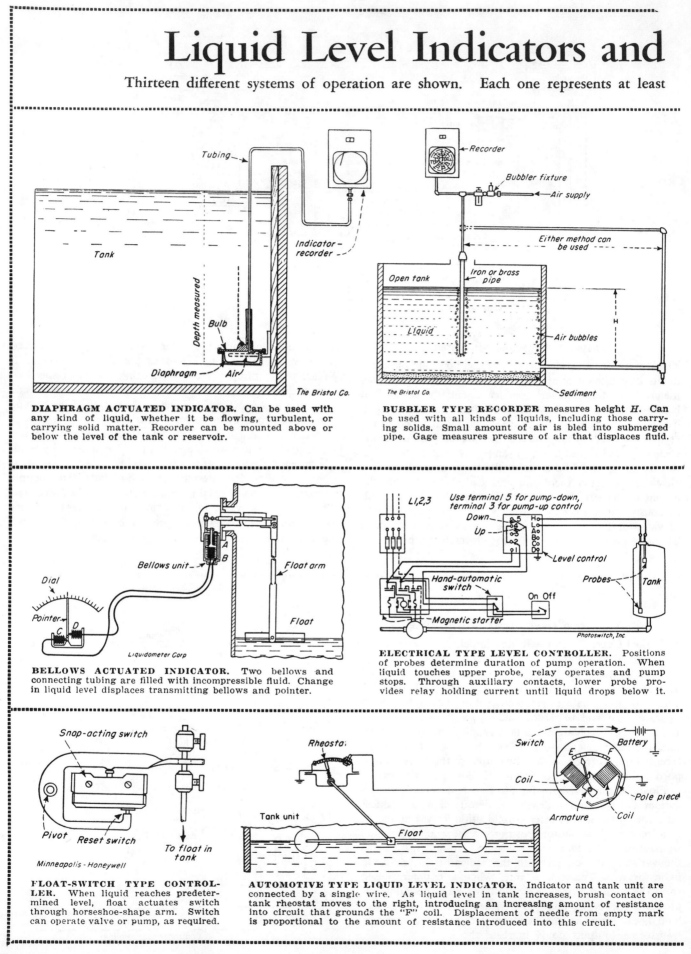

DIAPHRAGM ACTUATED INDICATOR. Can be used with any kind of liquid, whether it be flowing, turbulent, or carrying solid matter. Recorder can be mounted above or below the level of the tank or reservoir.

BUBBLER TYPE RECORDER measures height H. Can be used with all kinds of liquids, including those carrying solids. Small amount of air is bled into submerged pipe. Gage measures pressure of air that displaces fluid.

BELLOWS ACTUATED INDICATOR. Two bellows and connecting tubing are filled with incompressible fluid. Change in liquid level displaces transmitting bellows and pointer.

ELECTRICAL TYPE LEVEL CONTROLLER. Positions of probes determine duration of pump operation. When liquid touches upper probe, relay operates and pump stops. Through auxiliary contacts, lower probe provides relay holding current until liquid drops below it.

FLOAT-SWITCH TYPE CONTROLLER. When liquid reaches predetermined level, float actuates switch through horseshoe-shape arm. Switch can operate valve or pump, as required.

AUTOMOTIVE TYPE LIQUID LEVEL INDICATOR. Indicator and tank unit are connected by a single wire. As liquid level in tank increases, brush contact on tank rheostat moves to the right, introducing an increasing amount of resistance into circuit that grounds the "F" coil. Displacement of needle from empty mark is proportional to the amount of resistance introduced into this circuit.

Controllers

H. W. HAMM

one commercial instrument.   Some of them are available in several modified forms.

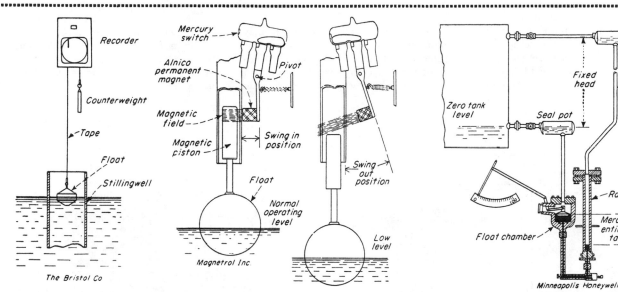

FLOAT TYPE RECORDER. Pointer can be attached to a calibrated float tape to give an approximate instantaneous indication of fluid level.

MAGNETIC LIQUID LEVEL CONTROLLER. When liquid level is normal, common-to-right leg circuit of mercury switch is closed. When level drops to predetermined level, magnetic piston is drawn below the magnetic field.

DIFFERENTIAL PRESSURE SYSTEM. Applicable to liquids under pressure. Measuring element is mercury manometer. Mechanical or electric meter body can be used. Seal pots protect meter body.

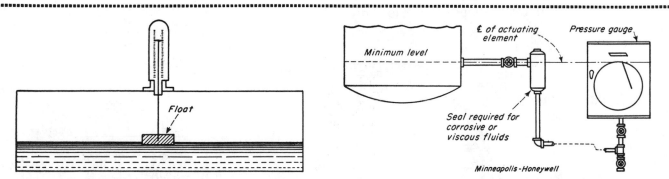

DIRECT READING FLOAT TYPE GAGE. Inexpensive, direct-reading gage has dial calibrated to tank volume. Comparable type as far as simplicity is concerned has needle connected through a right-angle arm to float. As liquid level drops, float rotates the arm and the needle.

PRESSURE GAGE INDICATOR for open vessels. Pressure of liquid head is imposed directly upon actuating element of pressure gage. Center line of the actuating element must coincide with the minimum level line, if the gage is to read zero when the liquid reaches the minimum level.

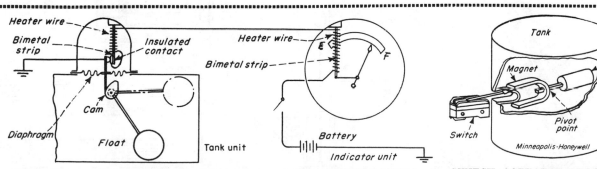

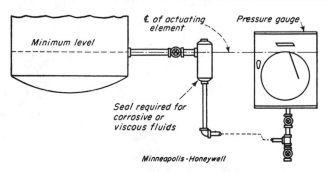

BIMETALLIC TYPE INDICATOR. When tank is empty, contacts in tank unit just touch. With switch closed, heaters cause both bimetallic strips to bend. This opens contacts in tank and bimetals cool, closing circuit again. Cycle repeats about once per sec. As liquid level increases, float forces cam to bend tank bimetal. Action is similar to previous case, but current and needle displacement are increased.

SWITCH ACTUATED LEVEL CONTROLLER. Pump is actuated by switch. Float pivots magnet so that upper pole attracts switch contact. Tank wall serves as other contact.

Means of determining liquid level, detection of changes in liquid level, transmission of indicated levels, or warnings of changes beyond set limits; and means of using level changes for level control, or control of other conditions such as temperature and pressure, have been accomplished by numerous mechanisms. The most popular

devices employ floats or pressure measurement with instruments such as the U-tube manometer, bourdon tube, and bellows.

The methods shown here are largely indicating methods or simple devices for automatic control of liquid level although they can conceivably be applied to control other conditions such as tem-

perature and pressure. Methods using electric resistance of a column of liquid and measurement of pressure changes by means of piezo-electric crystals are not shown. Patent No. 2,162,180 describes a method involving determination of change in air pressure when a measured volume of air is introduced into a tank.

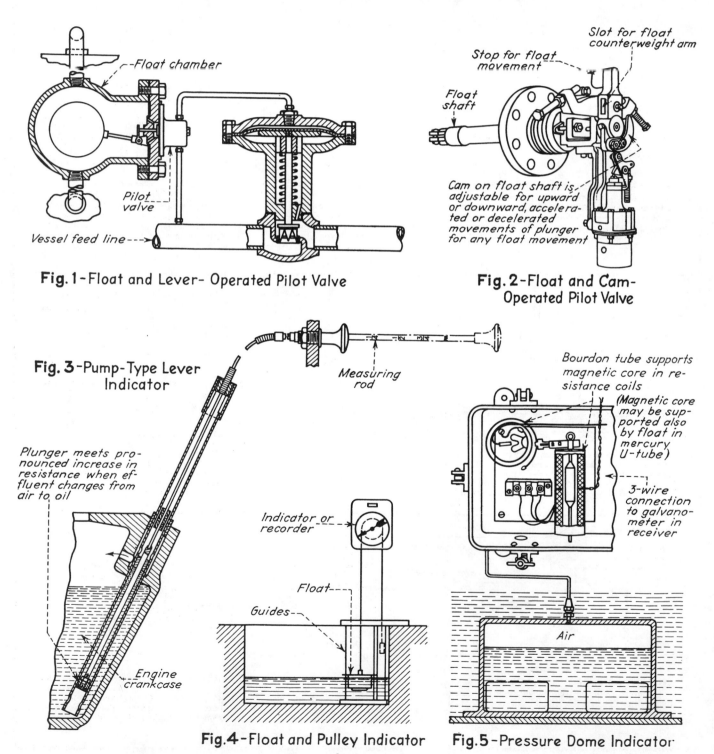

Fig. 1-Float and Lever- Operated Pilot Valve

Fig. 2-Float and Cam- Operated Pilot Valve

Fig. 3-Pump-Type Lever Indicator

Fig.4-Float and Pulley Indicator

Fig.5-Pressure Dome Indicator

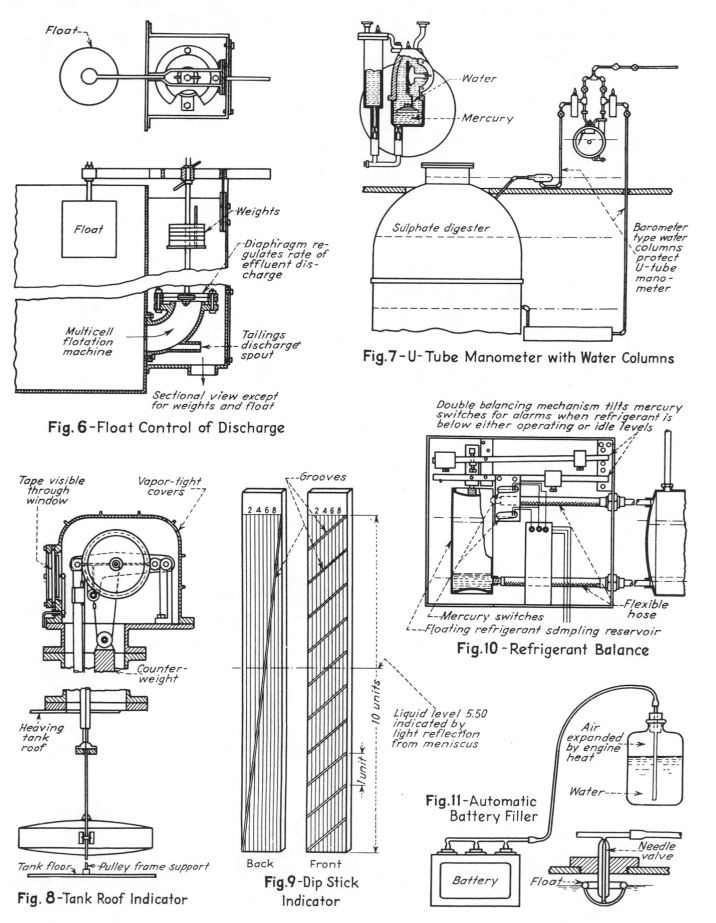

Float

Float

Weights

Diaphragm regulates rate of effluent discharge

Multicell flotation machine

Tailings discharge spout

Sectional view except for weights and float

Fig. 6-Float Control of Discharge

Water

Mercury

Sulphate digester

Barometer type water columns protect U-tube manometer

Fig.7-U-Tube Manometer with Water Columns

Tape visible through window

Vapor-tight covers

Counterweight

Heaving tank roof

Tank floor — Pulley frame support

Fig. 8-Tank Roof Indicator

Grooves

2 4 6 8

2 4 6 8

10 units

1 unit

Liquid level 5.50 indicated by light reflection from meniscus

Back   Front

Fig.9-Dip Stick Indicator

Double balancing mechanism tilts mercury switches for alarms when refrigerant is below either operating or idle levels

Mercury switches

Floating refrigerant sampling reservoir

Flexible hose

Fig.10-Refrigerant Balance

Air expanded by engine heat

Water

Fig.11-Automatic Battery Filler

Needle valve

Battery

Float

333

NOVEL LIQUID-LEVEL MECHANISMS

Control valve balances hydrostatic head in standpipe against that of fluid rising in tank. Near equilibrium, valve gradually closes, stopping inflow at preset level.

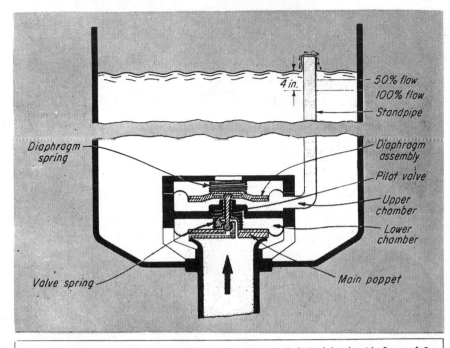

PS . . . Valve controls final shutoff level to ± 0.1 in. of desired level, with flows of 0 to 200 gpm and dead-head pressures of 10 to 50 psi. Maximum inlet pressure during closure was 61 psi when valve was tested with a dead-head pressure of 50 psi. For valve shown, cracking pressure and pressure drop for flows up to 150 gpm need not exceed 0.5 psi with a pilot head of 50 ft. Floatless level-control valve is produced by Whittaker Controls Div, Telecomputer Corp, Los Angeles.

INITIAL PRESSURE at valve inlet opens the main poppet which closes again as pressure rises in lower chamber. Then liquid enters the upper chamber through the pilot valve and fills the standpipe, producing hydrostatic pressure in both chambers. This pressure raises the diaphragm assembly in the upper chamber, compressing the diaphragm spring. Starting with the valve empty, as during initial operation, this takes about 10 seconds.

As the diaphragm assembly rises, it lifts the pilot valve off its seat, closing the upper passage to inlet pressure and allowing the liquid in the lower chamber to escape to the tank. With the pressure in the lower chamber reduced, inlet pressure again raises the main poppet and fills the tank.

As the tank fills, hydrostatic pressure on the upper side of the diaphragm assembly rises. When the fluid is within approximately 4 in. of the desired level, the hydrostatic head and spring force on the upper diaphragm are in equilibrium with the hydrostatic head in the standpipe. Further filling increases the pressure on the top of the diaphragm, allowing the diaphragm spring to reposition the pilot valve. The main poppet follows position of the pilot valve as it gradually closes. This continues until the main poppet is completely closed—which occurs when the liquid level is approximately 2 in. below the upper end of standpipe.

WATER-LEVEL SWITCH shuts off water by deenergizing solenoid valve. As water rises, it compresses air inside air tube which extends into sump. Air pressure flexes diaphragm and breaks circuit to solenoid. (The Maytag Co, Newton, Iowa)

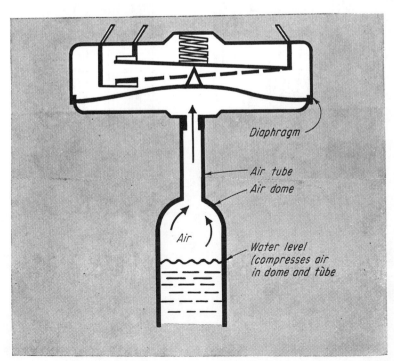

Oil-level detector uses photo-transistor, plastic light-guide

A level-detector which uses the total internal reflection in a light-guide made of acrylic plastic to indicate the level of oil in a tank is said to be unaffected by ambient temperature and simple in construction. It's part of an oil-flow calibrating rig developed at Britain's National Engineering Laboratory, East Kilbride, Glasgow. Key to its operation is the thin plastic light-guide—so thin that, when in contact with the oil being monitored, its light ceases to be reflected internally and, instead, passes into and through the oil, in effect cutting off the light to the transistor (see diagram) and indicating that the liquid has reached the preset check point.

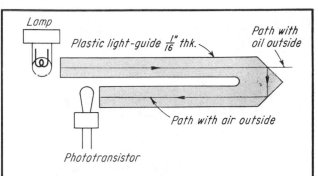

PLASTIC LIGHT-GUIDE is key element in new liquid level detector. When immersed in oil, light goes straight through upper arm of guide; does not reach photo-transistor. When the guide is above oil level, internal reflection carries light around the U, illuminates transistor, and provides monitor signal.

Harvester Stays Level

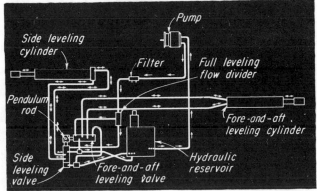

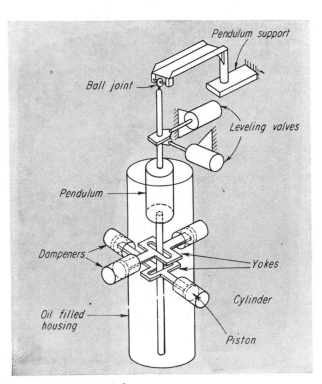

Hydraulic power . . .

for leveling is provided by engine-driven pump supplied from a central reservoir. Displaced pendulum rod moves the leveling valves to actuate the leveling cylinders. When thresher platform is leveled, pendulum is centered and valves closed.

The pendulum's job . . .

is to serve as vertical reference line and actuator that levels the combine platform no matter whether a hill goes up and down, or sideways. Two leveling valves connected to the pendulum-suspension rod are activated when the combine tilts. Oil pressure through these valves is directed to the appropriate leveling cylinder. This cylinder then levels the work surfaces, centers the pendulum, and closes the leveling valves.

Four pistons, in an oil-filled dashpot below the pendulum bob, provide damping in two planes. They are worked by an extension of the pendulum rod, which swings with the bob. Simple yokes allow the pendulum assembly to move in any direction and provide proportional displacement of both leveling valves for various tilt conditions.

DESIGN
fixes the Flush Toilet

Here is a ball cock valve that gives a positive shutoff. Instead of fighting against pressure in the water line, it turns that pressure around and uses it for a tight seal.

The flush tank was one of the first automatic servants to enter the home. For years it has been a candidate for redesign because of the shutoff trouble it frequently gives at both the refill and outlets. Here, in Fluid-master Model 400, a manufacturer offers something quite different from the conventional combination of air-tight float and mechanical linkage to shut off incoming water. In addition, there is extensive use of plastics and stainless steel to eliminate corrosion troubles. The mechanism is applicable to a wide variety of valve applications needing positive control of fluid level. Produced by Fluidmaster Inc, Anaheim, Calif.

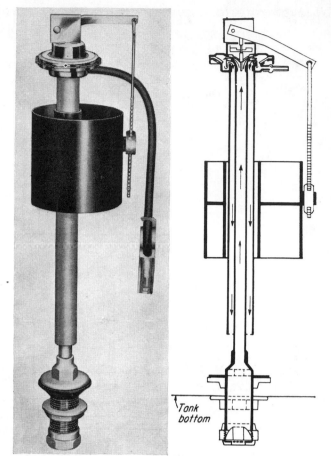

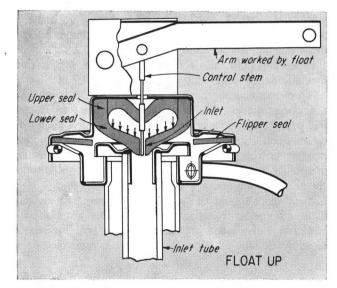

FLOAT UP

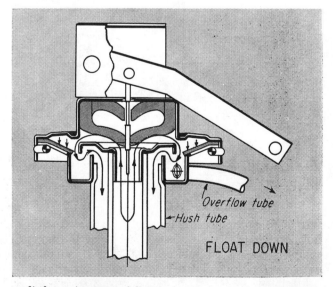

FLOAT DOWN

Positive shutoff . . .
is assured, when float goes up, by water pressure entering the opening between raised control stem and the lower seal. Heart-shaped valve chamber has 9 times the effective area of the valve seat, therefore provides 9 times the opposing force. In this stage, upper seal is closed by widened-diameter portion of the control stem.

When toilet is flushed, drop in water level lowers the float and control stem. Now, larger diameter of the control stem plugs entrance to the lower seal, at the boss, and in sequence opens the upper seal. This permits the heart-shaped chamber

to discharge its water; full line pressure now acts on the outside of the lower seal, lifting it to full flow position. Flipper seal is a suction breaker to prevent reverse siphon action should line pressure drop below atmospheric pressure.

With the exception of the red brass inlet tube required by plumbing codes, all metal parts are stainless steel. The hush tube is rigid, polyvinyl chloride; the refill tube, neoprene; the float, polyethelene. The only frictional contact is between the rubber seal and the stainless control stem. Waterflow between these elements provides adequate lubrication and continuous flushing to remove any foreign particles.

A flowmeter that compensates for variations in density . . .

. . . caused by temperature changes, is being developed by Armstrong Whitworth Equipment, Gloucester, Eng.

The device has an impeller and torque-measuring turbine that first impart angular momentum to the fluid being measured and then remove it—the torque needed to do the job being proportional to the mass flow. And, says A-W, it's accurate to within 1%.

The impeller, a tubular unit with vanes parallel to the direction of flow, is driven by a constant-speed dc motor from a rectified 115-v, 400-cps supply. The impeller is magnetically coupled to the motor drive and runs at a steady 100 rpm.

The turbine, similar in design to the impeller, is spring-restrained so that the turbine will rotate until spring and fluid torque balance.

An induction pickoff converts the angular deflection into an ac voltage output which is fed, through a rectifier, to a ratemeter and also into an ac integrating counter.

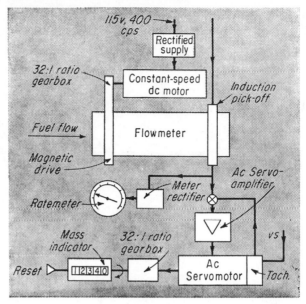

A thermoelectric flow-measuring device . . .

. . . that can detect small and rapid changes in flow rate has been designed in Sweden. It takes advantage of the fact that the amount of heat conducted away from a heated junction immersed in a fluid is affected by variations in the rate of flow of the fluid. Measuring fluctuations in heat transmission therefore indicates variations in fluid flow.

Central element of the new device, says Claes Allander of Stockholm, is a copper thermocouple, energized by a high-frequency oscillator. Dc generated by the thermocouple is fed through a low-pass filter, converted, amplified and then fed back to control the h-f current and keep the hot-junction temperature constant. This holds the hot junction at a temperature about 40 F above that of the cold junction which is at the same temperature as the fluid being monitored.

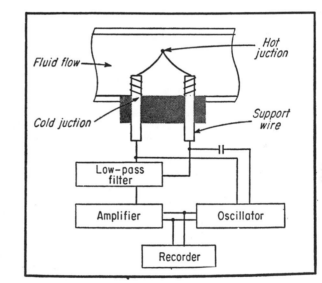

Sound waves may provide a new route to control of pure fluid devices, particularly digital units used to perform logic functions. Until now, most fluid systems of this type have been pneumatically controlled. But, Army Capt R. N. Gottron of Harry Diamond Laboratories says there is good evidence that acoustic energy can be used to switch digital units, and will require less power than the pneumatic systems. They may pave the way for new electropneumatic transducers, too.

Sound impinging on a jet produces a series of vortices at the exit of the jet,

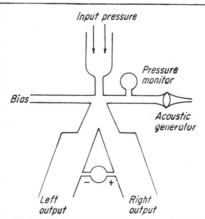

causing its flow parameters to change. This change, coupled with the second-order effects of acoustic streaming and radiation pressure, can make the jet of a digital amplifier switch from one output to the other (see diagram).

17 Ways to Measure Acceleration

HORTON B. SABIN
Arma Division
American Bosch Arma Corp.

Accelerometers measure the force needed to prevent a so-called proof mass from being accelerated relative to the case within which it is mounted. Force and acceleration are proportional and of necessity in the same direction. The simplest instruments, in concept at least, involve restraint of linear motion of the proof mass. This restraint may be by spring extension, viscous shear, linear magnetic force motors, or some other such force inducer. A second class of accelerometers consists of pendulum-type devices in which a pivot converts linear motion to angular motion within the instrument. Similar restraint mechanisms are used, this time acting about the pivot. Although modifications of the simple pendulum are widely used, the pendulum and its instrumentation are not as well understood as the linear accelerometer.

The most sensitive accelerometers in the world are the gravimeters used in geodetic measurements of the earth's gravity field. Here sensitivities of one 10-millionth of the value of g are common, though rarely exceeded. Navigational accelerometers seldom display sensitivities even one-hundredth as good, while linearity is at least another order of magnitude poorer again. But navigational accelerometers cover a range of about 100,000 to 1, while gravimeters have a range of about 100 to 1. Thus the ultimate performance of accelerometers in general involves a tradeoff between sensitivity and linearity on one hand and range on the other.

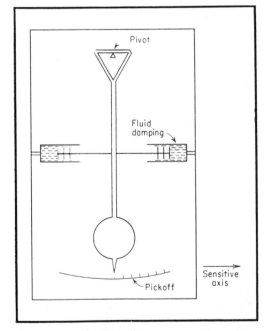

1 SIMPLE PENDULUM points to or oscillates about the net acceleration vector, indicating direction of acceleration but not magnitude. Where horizontal acceleration only is to be measured, the tilt of the pendulum is significant since this tilt angle is related to the ratio of horizontal acceleration to gravity. Thus, gravity provides a calibrated spring restraint for measuring horizontal acceleration, but the direction of gravity must be remembered if the tilt angle is to be measured. Viscous damping is commonly used.

2 COMPOUND PENDULUM differs from the simple pendulum only in having a different unbalance-mass to inertia ratio. The common instrumentation shown uses a feedback torquer amplifier to supply the spring restraint. This effective spring is so stiff that only small displacements occur and cross-coupling spring effects such as gravity are all but negligible. A flotation fluid minimizes pivot loading and also supplies damping adequate to make the float inertia term negligible and instrument response essentially first order. At the same time the damping coefficient to spring restraint time constant is small enough for present day vertical tracking systems. High precision requirements call for the viscous restraint to be Newtonian in character and nonvarying in time.

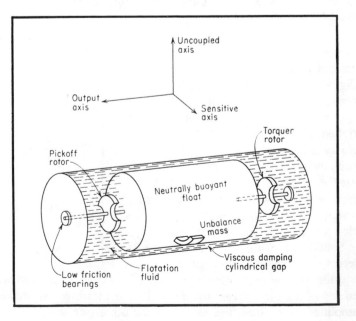

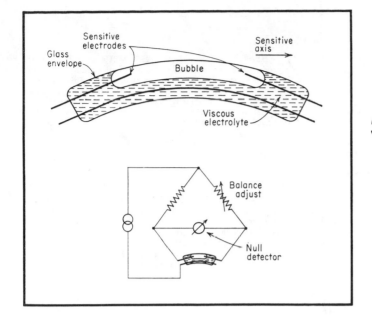

3   SINGLE AXIS BUBBLE LEVELS can detect tilt angles of a minute of arc or less. Gravity plays the same role as in the simple pendulum, while damping depends on liquid viscosity. Inertia effects are negligible. The liquid used is an electrolyte, and varying interelectrode conductances depend on the relative lengths of electrode uncovered by the liquid. A three-terminal network serves as two legs of a Wheatstone bridge, and a galvanometer null indicates verticality of the bubble vial. Current unbalance near null is an indication of horizontal acceleration.

4   CIRCULAR BUBBLE LEVELS are sensitive to horizontal accelerations in two directions but are not as linear as the single axis type. Both single axis and circular bubble levels require a known acceleration bias such as gravity and must remember the direction of gravity. This memory is provided by gyroscopes in all devices that are carried in moving vehicles.

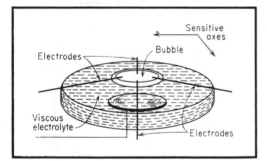

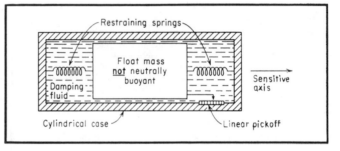

5   LINEAR CYLINDRICAL ACCELEROMETER with spring restraint has a displacement proportional to acceleration. The spring constant provides calibration, and the signal generator is usually one of a variety of forms of E-pickoff. Often partial flotation is obtained by immersing the proof mass in a damping fluid.

6   LINEAR CYLINDRICAL ACCELEROMETER in a different form uses a linear thrust motor acting in a servo loop to keep the pickoff at null. Acceleration is then proportional to some function of the excitation current supplied to the motor. Linearity is almost entirely dependent on the linearity of the thrust motor. The alignment rod restricts sideways motion of the proof mass.

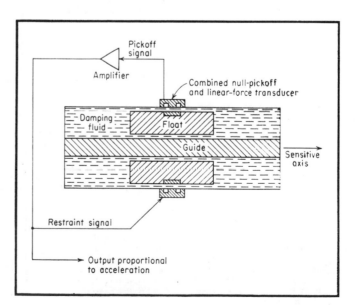

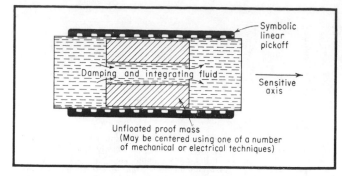

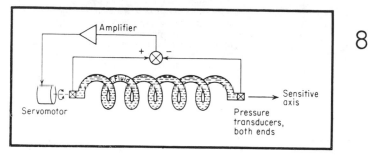

7 LINEAR CYLINDRICAL ACCELEROMETER in still another form uses the viscous restraint of the damping fluid to balance the force of acceleration. This process leads to integration, and devices of this type are often referred to as velocity meters. A linearly calibrated or corrected pickoff running the full length of the proof mass' freedom is necessary for precision instrumentation.

8 HYDROSTATIC SPIRAL TUBE ACCELEROMETER depends on angular acceleration to null the pressure difference between opposite ends of the tube. Linear acceleration along the spin axis creates the pressure difference, and the angular acceleration imparted by the servomotor nulls it out. Motor speed is proportional to instrument velocity, and the number of revolutions is proportional to distance traveled.

9 VIBRATING STRING ACCELEROMETER is sensitive to accelerations along the string axis. Tension differences result, and the natural frequencies of the two supporting strings vary accordingly. Even though elaborate instrumentation is required to obtain insensitivity to cross-axis accelerations, high caliber accelerometers have been constructed.

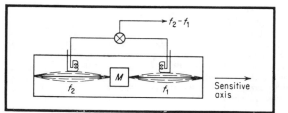

10 ONE-DEGREE-OF-FREEDOM PENDULUM uses gyroscopic torque to null the torque generated by linear acceleration. Instrument rotation about the table axis forces the gyro to precess, resulting in a torque about the pendulum pivot axis. A high gain amplifier drives the motor at a speed proportional to the deviation signal from the pickoff on the pendulum pivot axis. The integrating property of the gyro makes it possible to measure velocity with this instrument. Changes in velocity are proportional to turntable displacement.

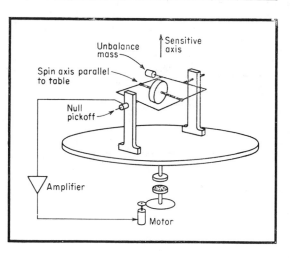

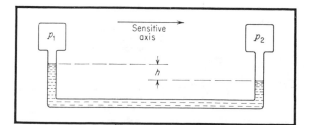

11 SIMPLE GAS PRESSURE ACCELEROMETER depends on acceleration of a horizontal column of liquid. As in a pendulum, this instrument is sensitive to accelerations normal to the gravity field. No integration is provided with this arrangement, although manipulating pressures P_1 and P_2 could conceivably modify the operation of this device.

12 TORSION PENDULUM modified to be insensitive to lateral accelerations is another form of linear accelerometer. Rotation of the pendulous mass rather than its translatory motion is the basic measured output.

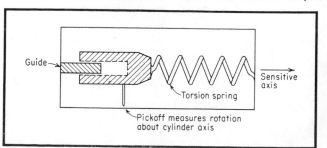

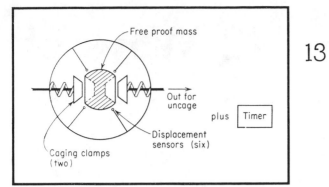

Free proof mass

Out for uncage

plus Timer

Caging clamps (two)

Displacement sensors (six)

13 TRANSIT-TIME ACCELEROMETER measures the time interval between release of a free-falling proof mass and its contact with the containing cavity. Thereafter it is recaged and rereleased and another interval or transit time measured: only periodic acceleration measurements are possible. Assuming constant acceleration through an interval, acceleration is proportional to the inverse square of the time interval. The actual measured quantity is the change in velocity during an interval. A possible continuous scheme might use multiple and overlapping measurements.

14 DOUBLE-INTEGRATING ACCELEROMETER, also known as the distance meter, uses the inertia reaction of an electrically driven rotor to balance the torque of a pendulum. The rotor is enclosed within an unbalanced but floated cylinder. Bearing friction is overcome by the electric drive while speed changes alone react, through the motor, against the float. The speed changes are a measure of changes in linear displacement.

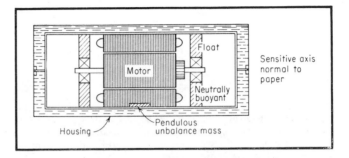

Float

Motor

Sensitive axis normal to paper

Neutrally buoyant

Housing

Pendulous unbalance mass

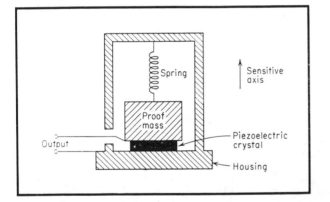

Spring

Sensitive axis

Proof mass

Output

Piezoelectric crystal

Housing

15 SELF-GENERATING ACCELEROMETER uses piezoelectric crystal in compression to self-generate an output voltage proportional to acceleration. In the spring-mass system consisting of a weight pressed against the top of the crystal, a highly compressed soft spring reduces creep instability. Linearity is good over a wide range of accelerations.

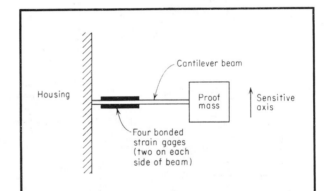

Housing

Cantilever beam

Proof mass

Sensitive axis

Four bonded strain gages (two on each side of beam)

16 CANTILEVER BEAM ACCELEROMETER has four strain gages bonded to the beam and is sensitive to acceleration perpendicular to the beam in the bending plane of the beam. Gages are connected as four legs of a Wheatstone bridge, yielding an output proportional to acceleration. In actual instruments the housing containing the beam and proof mass is often filled with a damping fluid. Piezoelectric elements such as barium titanate can be bonded to the beam as well as conventional wire strain gages.

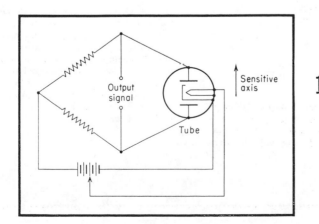

Output signal

Sensitive axis

Tube

17 VACUUM TUBE ACCELEROMETER uses special tube in which two flexible plates deflect under acceleration forces. This is a special case of the cantilever beam accelerometer. The current output of the bridge is directly proportional to tube acceleration.

KIRK CARLSTEN, Chief Engineer
and KARSTEN HELLEBUST
Metron Instrument Company

12 Ways of

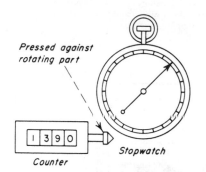

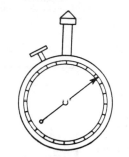

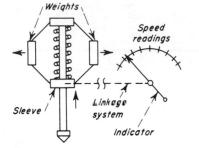

Fig. 1—Simple counter and separate stop watch: Requires dexterity since counter is held with one hand—stop watch with other hand. Average speed measured during one minute interval by noting the counter readings at beginning and end of the time interval.

Fig. 2—Combination counter and stop watch: Counter starts when button is pressed and then watch automatically stops counter hand at end of a given time (say six seconds). Dial is calibrated to read in rpm. Measures average speed.

Fig. 3—Centrifugal tachometers: Centrifugal governor type mechanisms with weights which move outwardly from shaft as speed increases causing sleeve to move up. Sleeve through linkage moves indicator pointer in proportion to speed. Care must be taken to avoid overspeeding.

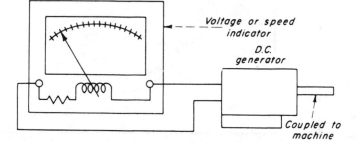

Fig. 4—D.C. Generator tachometers: D.C. voltage generated in proportion to speed and displayed on D.C. indicator or recorder. System does not use gearing and is usually limited to 150-2000 rpm at full scale. Generator matched with a particular indicator because voltage not exactly linear with speed.

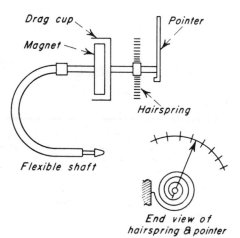

Fig. 6—Drag cup tachometers: Flexible shaft drives small permanent magnet in drag cup. Motion of magnet sets up eddy currents in wall of drag cup. Resulting rotary force causes drag cup to follow. Hair spring balanced to produce a pointer deflection proportional to speed. System simple and inexpensive, but with limited accuracy and speed range.

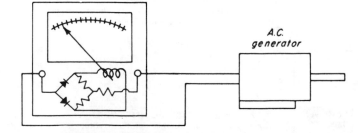

Fig. 5—A.C. Generator tachometers: A.C. voltage generated in proportion to speed and displayed on an A.C. indicator. System does not use gearing. Usually limited to full scale readings of 500 rpm minimum and 5000 rpm maximum. Not as accurate as D.C. systems, but covers wider speed range and does not require brushes.

Measuring Speed

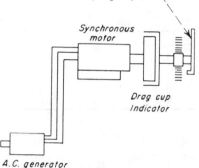

Fig. 7—Drag cup indicator driven by synchronous motor whose speed in controlled by remote A.C. generator. Synchronous motor drives small permanent magnet in drag cup similar to arrangement shown in Fig. 6. System expensive but without need for long and cumbersome flexible shafting.

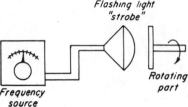

Fig. 8—Stroboscopic tachometers: Very fast flashing light used to view rotating part. Frequency of flashing adjusted until rotating part appears to stand still. Frequency reading corresponds to rpm of rotating part. Requires no accessible shaft and absorbs no power from rotating part. However, system requires constant adjustment if speed changes.

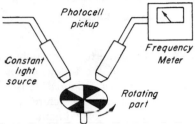

Fig. 9—Photo electric tachometers: Constant light source focused to shine on rotating disc; light reflects into photocell pickup. Intensity of light modulated by dark and light spots on rotating part. Frequency of modulations proportional to rotating speed and measured by frequency meter. Speeds up to 3,000,000 rpm can be measured but expensive equipment required.

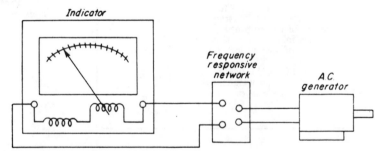

Fig. 11—A.C. frequency responsive tachometers: Similar to A.C. generator tachometers but measures generated frequency (not voltage). Range: 500 to 80,000 rpm with good accuracy. Expensive.

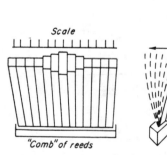

Fig. 10—Vibrating reed tachometers: "Comb" made up of a set of accurately tuned steel reeds: Comb held against any part of rotating machine, such as against case of motor. Vibration of machine vibrates only reeds "in tune" with machine's frequency. This speed, or frequency, read directly on a scale above the comb. Requires no access to a rotating shaft. Range is from 800 to 12,500 rpm with an accuracy within 50 rpm for individual reeds when new.

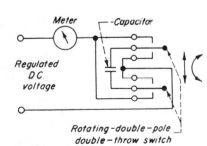

Fig. 12—Commutated capacitor tachometers: Rotating double pole, double throw switch charges and discharges capacitor. Resulting average D.C. current linear with speed. Current indicated on a D.C. microammeter as rpm. System very accurate. Linearity allows multiple range indicators and rotating switches are interchangeable.

8 simple methods measure . . .
MOMENT OF INERTIA

Oscillating and "falling weight" setups combine with simple formulas to give accurate answers for complex shapes.

BERNARD BRENNER, *staff engineer*
Ampex Corp, Redwood City, Calif

Moment of inertia is generally difficult to find when one or more of the following conditions exist: Body shape is irregular; material density is unknown; parts must be disassembled before precise dimensions can be found. The experimental methods shown here handle all such cases with sufficient accuracy for most engineering work. Only requirements: measurements of weight and time; and simple dimensions.

SYMBOLS

D = dia, in.
d = distance, in.
f = friction torque, oz-in.
g = gravity, in./sec²
J = inertia of test body about symmetry axis, oz-in.-sec²
J_r = reference inertia, oz-in.-sec²
k = torsional spring constant, oz-in./radians
L = length of pendulum, in.
R = radius, in.
T = period of oscillation (or time of weight fall), sec
W = weight of test body, oz
W_c = connecting-rod weight, oz
W_r = reference weight, oz

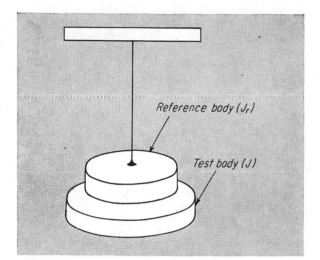

2—Torsional Pendulum (k is unknown)
T_1 is period with J_r only
T_2 is period with J_r and J together

$$J = J_r \left[\left(\frac{T_2}{T_1} \right)^2 - 1 \right]$$

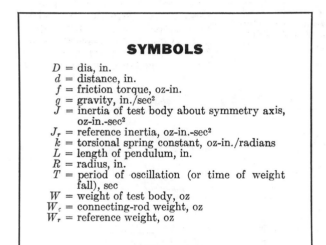

1—Torsional Pendulum (when k is known)

$$J = \frac{k T^2}{4 \pi^2}$$

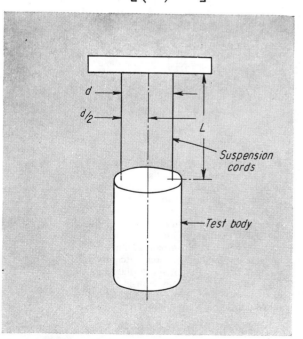

3—Bifilar Suspension (suspension cords must be highly flexible)

$$J = \frac{W d^2 T^2}{16 \pi^2 L}$$

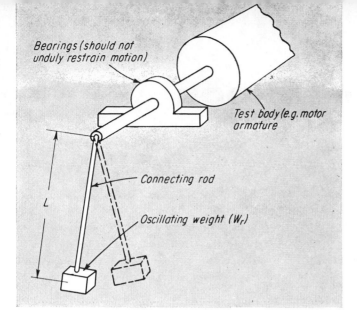

4—Pendulum (connecting-rod weight relatively light)

$$J = W_r L \left(\frac{T^2}{4\,\pi^2} - \frac{L}{g} \right)$$

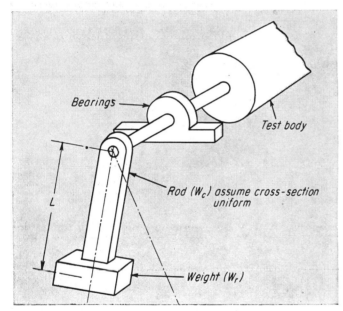

5—Pendulum (connecting-rod weight appreciable)

$$J = L \left[\frac{T^2}{4\,\pi^2} \left(W_r + \frac{W_c}{2} \right) - \frac{L}{g} \left(W_r + \frac{W_c}{3} \right) \right]$$

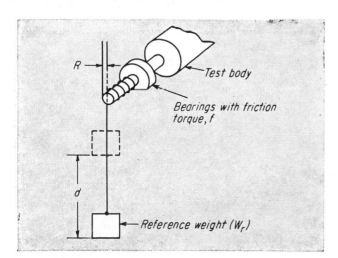

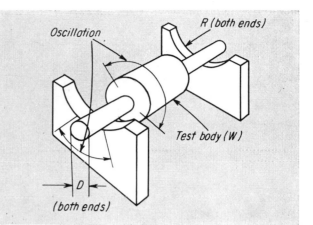

6—Rocker

$$J = \frac{W D^2 T^2}{16\,\pi^2\,R}$$

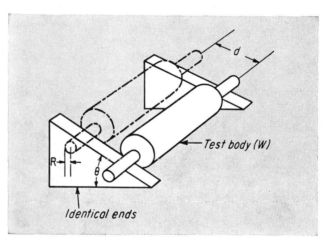

7—Inclined Plane

Body rolls d in. from rest (without slipping) in t seconds.

$$J = \frac{W R^2 t^2}{2d} \sin\theta$$

8—Falling Weight

Weight W_r starts from rest and travels d in. in T sec. Frictionless:

$$J = W_r R^2 \left(\frac{T^2}{2d} - \frac{1}{g} \right)$$

With shaft friction f:

$$J = W_r R^2 \left(\frac{T^2}{2d} - \frac{1}{g} \right) - \frac{R T^2 f}{2d}$$

10 X-RAY METHODS

VERN W PALEN
Philips Electronic Instruments
Mount Vernon, N. Y.

Diagrams of x-ray setups for inspecting, measuring and analyzing.

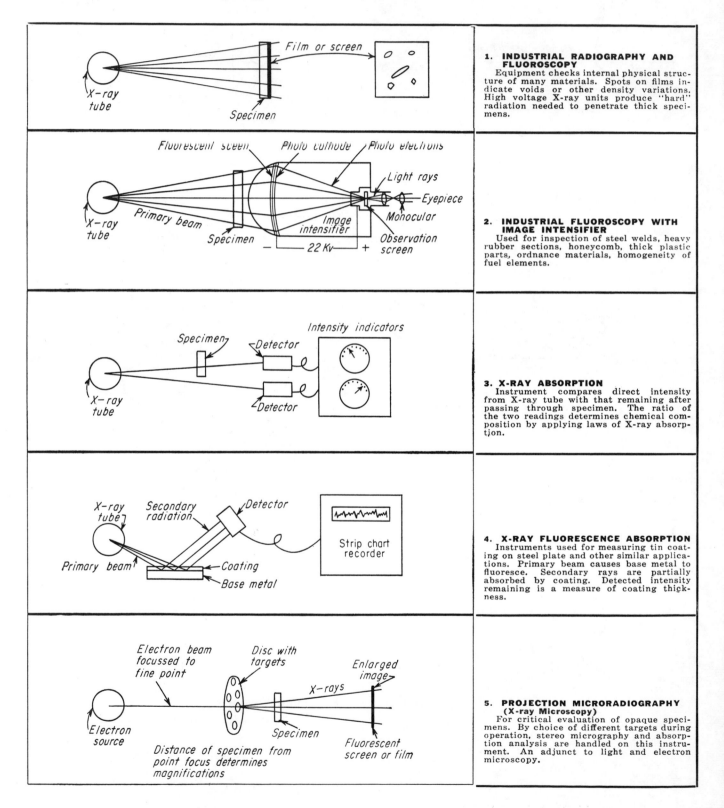

1. INDUSTRIAL RADIOGRAPHY AND FLUOROSCOPY
Equipment checks internal physical structure of many materials. Spots on films indicate voids or other density variations. High voltage X-ray units produce "hard" radiation needed to penetrate thick specimens.

2. INDUSTRIAL FLUOROSCOPY WITH IMAGE INTENSIFIER
Used for inspection of steel welds, heavy rubber sections, honeycomb, thick plastic parts, ordnance materials, homogeneity of fuel elements.

3. X-RAY ABSORPTION
Instrument compares direct intensity from X-ray tube with that remaining after passing through specimen. The ratio of the two readings determines chemical composition by applying laws of X-ray absorption.

4. X-RAY FLUORESCENCE ABSORPTION
Instruments used for measuring tin coating on steel plate and other similar applications. Primary beam causes base metal to fluoresce. Secondary rays are partially absorbed by coating. Detected intensity remaining is a measure of coating thickness.

5. PROJECTION MICRORADIOGRAPHY
(X-ray Microscopy)
For critical evaluation of opaque specimens. By choice of different targets during operation, stereo micrography and absorption analysis are handled on this instrument. An adjunct to light and electron microscopy.

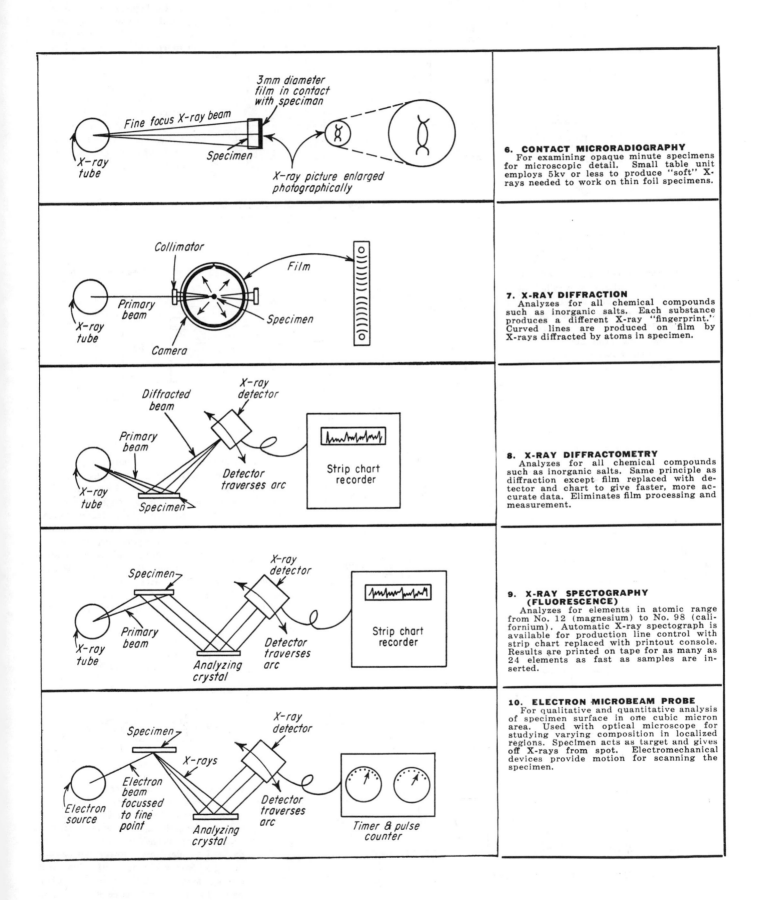

6. CONTACT MICRORADIOGRAPHY
For examining opaque minute specimens for microscopic detail. Small table unit employs 5kv or less to produce "soft" X-rays needed to work on thin foil specimens.

7. X-RAY DIFFRACTION
Analyzes for all chemical compounds such as inorganic salts. Each substance produces a different X-ray "fingerprint." Curved lines are produced on film by X-rays diffracted by atoms in specimen.

8. X-RAY DIFFRACTOMETRY
Analyzes for all chemical compounds such as inorganic salts. Same principle as diffraction except film replaced with detector and chart to give faster, more accurate data. Eliminates film processing and measurement.

9. X-RAY SPECTOGRAPHY (FLUORESCENCE)
Analyzes for elements in atomic range from No. 12 (magnesium) to No. 98 (californium). Automatic X-ray spectograph is available for production line control with strip chart replaced with printout console. Results are printed on tape for as many as 24 elements as fast as samples are inserted.

10. ELECTRON MICROBEAM PROBE
For qualitative and quantitative analysis of specimen surface in one cubic micron area. Used with optical microscope for studying varying composition in localized regions. Specimen acts as target and gives off X-rays from spot. Electromechanical devices provide motion for scanning the specimen.

Recording instruments for

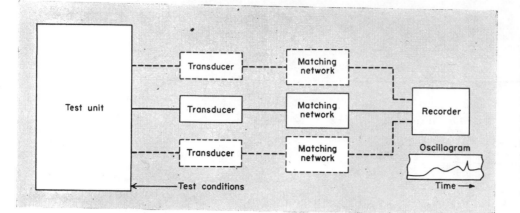

Fig. 1—Typical setup for a dynamic measuring system. Transducer gives a signal proportional to the physical event being measured. Matching network transforms the output signal from the transducer to a value sufficient to drive the recorder. Recorder converts the incoming signal to a record of the phenomena with respect to time.

Fig. 2—Self-balancing potentiometer. Input signal voltage to the recorder is compared against the slide wire voltage. Difference, or error, voltage is applied to a nulling amplifier which drives a balancing motor. Motor repositions the slide to tap off a voltage equal to the input. Time base is obtained by constant-speed driving of the chart paper over the rolls.

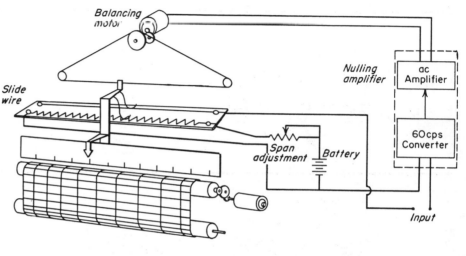

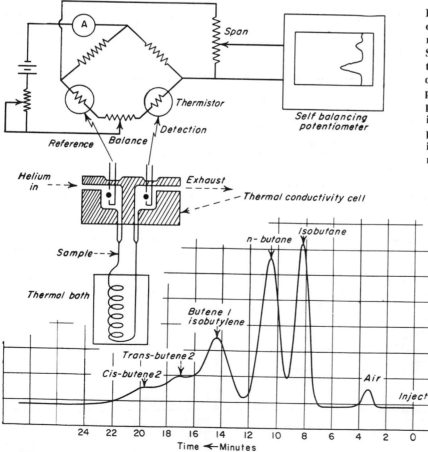

Fig. 3—Application of self-balancing potentiometer. (Upper left) Helium gas passes over a reference thermistor and enters the thermal bath. Sample gas is injected and carried by the helium through the thermal bath where decomposition occurs. Helium and sample gas composition products passing over the detector thermistor produces bridge unbalances caused by changes in thermal conductivity. (Lower left) Record produced shows a gas mixture of butane and C4 isomers. Identification of the gas products is made by their position on the time axis.

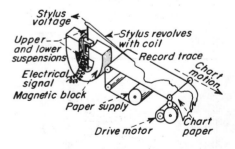

Fig. 4—Pen motor recorder. Galvanometer coil is driven in response to input current. Motor action causes the coil to revolve, and turning torque is balanced by restraining torque set up by the upper and lower suspension springs. Stylus turns with the coil, tracing signal variations on the chart paper for future reference and analysis.

dynamic measurements

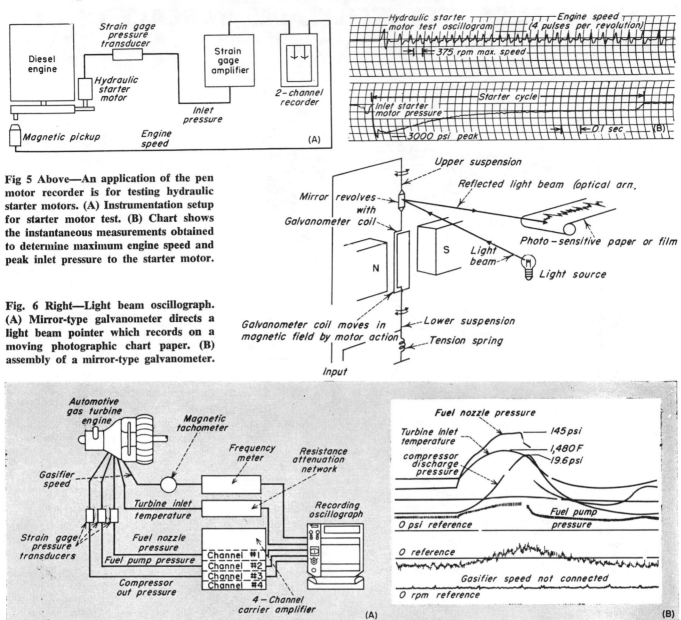

Fig 5 Above—An application of the pen motor recorder is for testing hydraulic starter motors. (A) Instrumentation setup for starter motor test. (B) Chart shows the instantaneous measurements obtained to determine maximum engine speed and peak inlet pressure to the starter motor.

Fig. 6 Right—Light beam oscillograph. (A) Mirror-type galvanometer directs a light beam pointer which records on a moving photographic chart paper. (B) assembly of a mirror-type galvanometer.

Fig. 7—Application of oscillograph. (A) Instrumentation for testing a gas turbine engine. (B) Vertical timing lines on the record are spaced **0.1 seconds apart. Breaks in data traces are for analysis identification of the various trace components.**

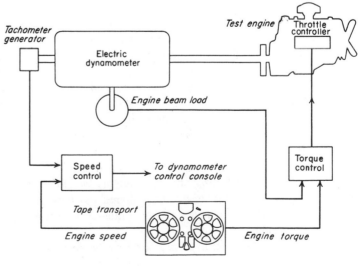

Fig. 8 Right—Dynamometer programming using tape recorder. Dynamometer subjects the engine to speed and torque conditions which have been recorded previously on tape in actual traffic situations.

JOHN L. HARNED, General Motors Research Staff

NOVEL WEIGHING SYSTEMS

INDUSTRIAL SLIDE USES STEEL TAPES IN PLACE OF RACK AND PINION. HOWE SCALE CO.

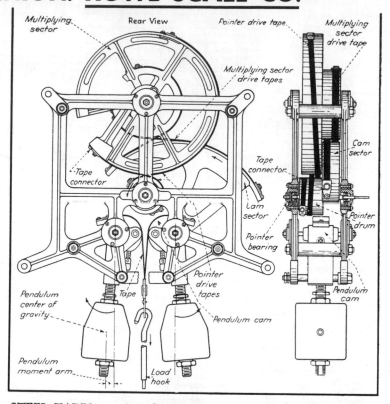

STEEL TAPES translate downward pull of hook into rotation of dial pointer. When a force is applied at the hook, the pendulums move upward until their countermoment has increased sufficiently to balance the hook force. Maximum load handled by head mechanism is 20 lb, which is sufficient to pull pendulums through 36 deg arcs and rotate pointer 360 degrees.

A friction-free weigh balance that senses weight with an air gage and uses a friction-free air bearing and a frictionless magnetic counterbalance to support the load has been designed for the Atomic Energy Commission. Its designers say the system is unusually compact, rugged, and low in cost. It can be equipped with remote indicating means, and is especially adaptable for go-no-go weighing.

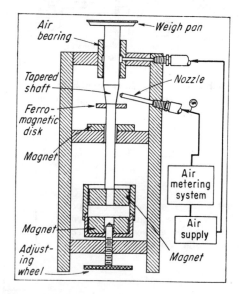

The weigh pan is supported on an aluminum shaft which rests on a magnet assembly, the magnets being installed so that like poles repel each other with sufficient force to support the shaft.

The air gage is the measuring device. It is installed so air is directed against the tapered portion of the supporting shaft. As the shaft moves down, under the weight of the object in the pan, the distance between the nozzle and the tapered portion decreases, and internal back pressure increases in the gage. The gage thus senses distance; but it can be calibrated to read in weight.

The device is available for royalty-free, non-exclusive licensing.

HYDRO-ELECTRIC WEIGHING SYSTEM

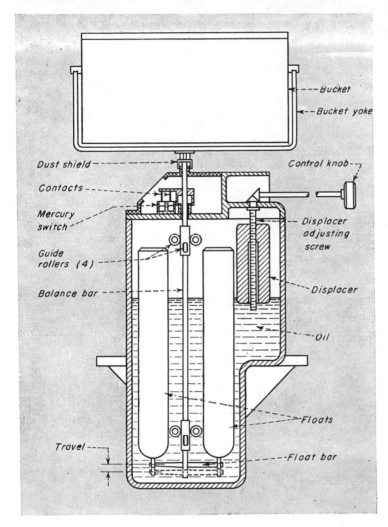

MATERIAL TO BE WEIGHED is delivered to the vibrator feed chute of the weigher by a variable speed conveyor system. Since the speed of the weigher is determined by the volume of material that is supplied, means for regulating the speed is provided. The vibrator feed smooths out the flow of material such that it falls into the machine at a high rate of speed but approximately one unit at a time. Vibration magnitude is adjustable and is controlled by a small dial mounted on the front of the weigher cabinet. As the material leaves the feed chute, it falls onto a bucket at rest on the weighing unit. When the charge of material is within $\frac{1}{2}$ oz of the desired weight, the charge and the weighing assembly on the vertical shaft leaves the pre-loading position and is supported only by floats, the shaft being guided by an anti-friction rollers. As the flow of material continues, the floats sink deeper into the liquid until the desired weight is reached. At this time, contacts of the mercury pot complete the electrical circuit and release the mechanism which removes the full bucket from the weighing unit and dumps it while simultaneously placing the empty bucket in position for the next charge.

To obtain the utmost accuracy, a special traveling shield protects the full bucket and directs any falling material to the empty one. The weighed charge then slides down the chute into the container held by the operator.

To change from one weight to another it is only necessary to turn a knurled knob on the front of the machine. This raises or lowers a displacement body in the flotation chamber with a corresponding change in the supporting action of the liquid. This change can be accomplished while the machine remains in operation.

MECHANICAL WEIGHING SYSTEM measures stress exerted on the specimen. There are two load balancing pendulums. The pendulum for the low range is linked directly to the main lever. An arm projecting from the pendulum carries a roller that lifts the cam and aluminum tube to actuate the dial pointer and drawing pen. For loads over 1,000 lb, the heavier pendulum is connected to the weighing system by the latch lever. The load must then balance the combined moment of both pendulums. To obtain the strain coordinates, a chain transmits the motion of the crosshead to the platen gear train. A rack and pinion arrangement slides the recorder platen transversely beneath the pen point. As the lever system deflects, the weighing platform moves downward slightly. To prevent this movement from affecting the curve, the drive chain sheave is mounted on the weighing platform.

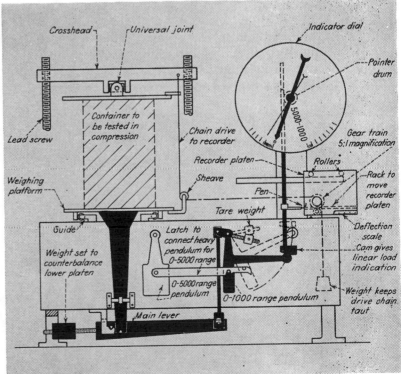

NOVEL MEASURING AND DETECTING DEVICES

To measure the output of very small motors...

. . . Politecnico dil Milano, Italy, has a unit that combines a spring-type torquemeter with a stroboscopic speedometer. It's said to overcome the problems caused by resistance and inertia in other devices of this type.

In the new unit (see diagram), the motor whose output is to be measured drives a resistive dynamo through a shaft, bearing, and pivot arrangement. As the motor turns, a spring attached to the driving shaft is twisted through an angle that corresponds to the torque transmitted, and this angle, in turn, can be read from the dial with a stroboscope.

To minimize friction, the indicator is sealed in the evacuated space between the face plate and the dial disk, and the spring is made slightly larger in diameter than the shaft around which it is wound, and considerably smaller than its housing.

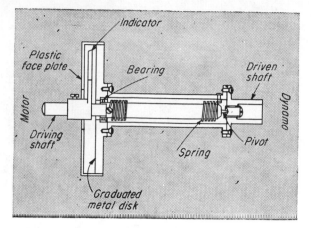

Spring-type torquemeter couples motor (installed at left) to dynamo with device diagrammed here.

In instrumentation, there are novel systems for measuring everything from the torque on a shaft to the speed of a bullet.

The system for measuring torque is based on the indication of torsional twist under dynamic loads. Dawe Instruments of England developed it as an outgrowth of research on its own transistor phase meter—an instrument that measures phase shift in electrical networks. The idea is to obtain two out-of-phase signals and compare them. This is done by a photocell system that takes its cue from white lines marked on the device being measured or half-white disks attached to it (see sketch).

Twin photocells pick up signals from the marks and feed the signals to a phase meter. As load is applied and the shaft twists, the amount of twist is indicated directly in angular degrees. Then, from the geometry of the shaft and the elastic modulus of the material, the applied torque can be derived.

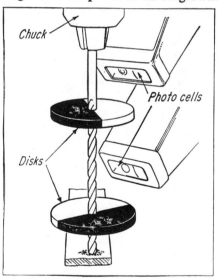

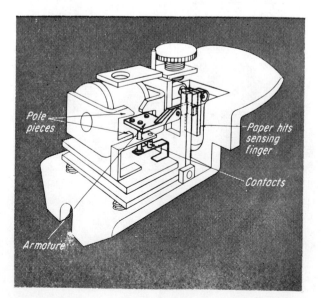

This electrical sensing system stops the printing press automatically whenever a sheet of incoming paper isn't fed in far enough for correct registry.

Correctly fed sheet . . .

hits sensing finger and raises armature above centerline of space between poles. When coil is energized at end of feed cycle, armature is pulled to upper pole of electromagnet and interlock contacts remain closed. If a sheet feeds short, armature is pulled to lower pole, opening contacts to operate alarm and stop press. Developed by AB Inventing Co., Stockholm, Sweden, device gives register accurate within 0.007 in.

ROTATING MIRRORS SPOT FLAWS

An electro-optical system for detecting flaws in moving sheet materials during processing has been designed in Canada; and, its maker says, it not only operates without contact on materials moving at speeds to 90,000 fpm; but actually gives stronger signals for smaller flaws than for big ones.

The unit consists of a pair of phototubes, with fixed and rotating mirrors to direct light beams to and from them.

Flaw signals are produced by changes in reflected or transmitted light; and the scanning system is arranged so the entire area of the moving web is covered (lower diagram). Since signal strength depends on rate of signal change, minimum flow size produces maximum signal strength.

The *Inspectasort* system can be hooked up to an alarm system or to a "memory wheel" mounted on the machine to cut off and divert material that is rejected.

Electronic Associates, Ltd, Ontario, is producing the unit, with initial installations going into Canadian paper mills.

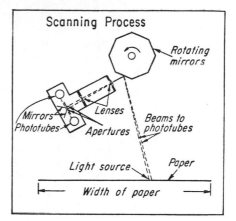

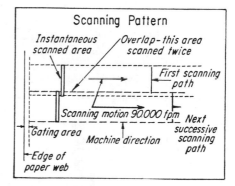

New *instrument gives remote measurement of tube thickness*

An eccentricity-gaging system that uses the metal wall of the tube being measured as a screen between two coils that form a current transformer has been designed at Tube Investments Ltd, England.

As the diagram shows, two pairs of coils are used. As long as the thickness at the two sides of the tube remains constant, the circuit stays in balance. Any eccentricity, however, will unbalance the circuit, providing an output signal to a meter calibrated for direct reading.

B. E. Noltingk of Tube Investments points out that the system is much simpler than ultrasonic and radioisotope gaging, and more adaptable to moving materials than magnetic systems. Furthermore, the system can be applied to nonferrous as well as ferrous metals; and, using a flexible rod to carry the internal coils, to tubing of almost any size and length.

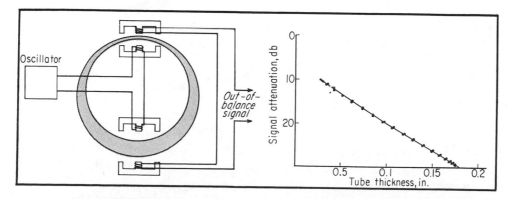

TUBE THICKNESS controls output of transformer circuits, so variations between the two areas being monitored provide a measurable output signal that indicates eccentricity. As chart shows, signal attenuation varies almost linearly with tube thickness.

Pressure sensor replaces bellows with flexible bladder

A novel high-sensitivity, shock-resistant device for measuring rapid changes in atmospheric pressure, developed at the AEC Los Alamos Laboratory, is now available for nonexclusive, royalty-free licensing.

Instead of using the conventional metal bellows, it has a flexible bladder immersed in an incompressible fluid.

The bladder is freely supported in one chamber (see diagram), and is vented to the atmosphere; while the other chamber is held at a preset pressure of an airtight housing. When the atmospheric pressure is equal to or greater than the force exerted by the fluid, the bladder expands, making an electrical connection between two contacts mounted inside its cylindrical supporting member (see cross-section).

A movable metal diaphragm separates the two chambers. Its convoluted portion is made of an alloy such as Elgiloy or Ni-Span-C, so designed that there is no change in spring constant with continuous loading.

The bladder itself may be a flexible plastic on which a conductive strip can be electrodeposited, or it may be made of gold foil. The fluid in which it is immersed may be a silicone or other material chosen for the expected operating temperature range.

The inventor of the device, K. E. Pope, of Los Alamos, says the unit shows a large displacement with a small change in pressure, is not sensitive to noise, operates on a small volume of incoming air.

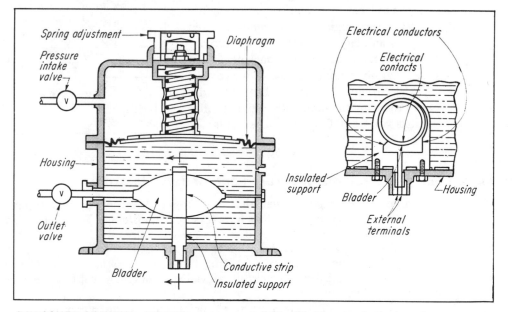

PRESSURE-SENSING DEVICE uses expandable bladder to indicate when pressure rises above preset level. Cross-section through bladder's insulated support shows electrical contacts and conductors that connect to external terminals.

To measure the thickness of transparent films on reflective substrates, IBM researchers have a new optical system that involves simply rotating the sample and observing the reflected light at various angles. W. A. Pliskin and E. E. Conrad of IBM call it the VAMFO system (Variable Angle Monochromatic Fringe Observation). The sample is placed on the rotating stage and, as it rotates, the maxima (bright) and minima (dark)

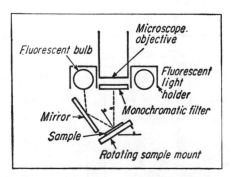

fringes are observed through the microscope, and the angular positions of the sample coinciding with the maxima and minima are read on a calibrated dial attached to the shaft of the rotating stage. The film thickness can then be calculated as a function of the film's refractive index, the wave length of the light, and the angle of refraction at the specific fringe for which the measurement is made.

To measure dimensional changes at a distance, British atomic engineers have devised a micrometer that operates by fluid pressure. It's a dial-indicator movement equipped with a position transmitter and a small turbine wheel, operated by a gas jet, to advance and hold the plunger of the gage against the object being measured.

Either a synchro or a rotary potentiometer may be used as the position transmitter. In the latter case (see diagram) the rotary contact arm of the potentiometer is coupled to the indicator spindle and arranged so that the contact arm of the potentiometer is normally out of contact with the potentiometer winding being brought into engagement for reading.

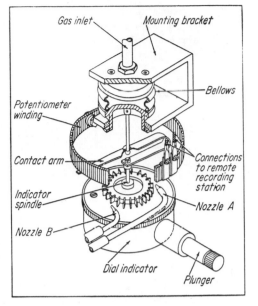

In operation, the plunger is advanced to meet the object being measured, by a jet of gas from the nozzle (A) which acts against the turbine wheel to hold the plunger in position. Then, as the object changes in dimension, the spindle rotates, and with it, the contact arm. When a reading is to be taken, the bellows is evacuated through the gas pipe, pulling the arm into contact with the winding. The second nozzle (B) retracts the plunger. United Kingdom Atomic Energy Authority holds a patent on the device (BP 881,620).

An "electrical spring," a contactless selector, and a position transducer for very small displacements are among the Hall-effect devices being developed by Ultra Electronics Ltd. of England. All make use of Hall generators—strips of semiconductor material placed in a transverse magnetic field, with an axial current flowing through them so an electrical gradient is set up across the strip. In such Hall-effect devices, the voltage gradient eventually reaches a point at which the transverse electrical force balances the deflecting magnetic force. Any change in either the driving current or the flux of the magnetic field induces a change in the voltage which can be monitored and measured.

In the "electrical spring" which is, perhaps, the most interesting and sophisticated of the devices, a Hall-effect transducer system is designed for use in connection with a solenoid such as might be used in fuel flow control. The Hall generator, moving inside a magnetic bridge, is mounted on the solenoid. The generator output, suitably amplified, is fed into a winding operating on the magnetic circuit of the solenoid so it produces a force opposing the excitation current controlling the solenoid. In this way, the Hall generator contributes a displacement-dependent component of the balancing force which is equivalent to a mechanical spring of the required stiffness.

The diagram shows one possible arrangement, described by Ultra engineers at a recent British IRE meeting, in which the Hall output and the control signal form the combined input of a high-gain amplifier, the output feeding a conventional solenoid with only one winding. To adjust the degree of feedback, it is necessary only to vary the drive current.

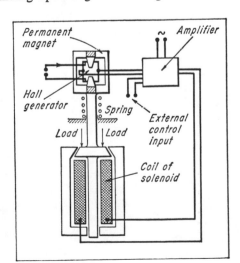

INDEX